Instructor's Resource Manual

for

Kotz & Treichel's

Chemistry and Chemical Reactivity

Fifth Edition

Susan M. Young
Hartwick College

THOMSON
™
BROOKS/COLE

Australia • Canada • Mexico • Singapore • Spain • United Kingdom • United States

Printed in the United States of America

1 2 3 4 5 6 7   05 04 03 02

ISBN 0-03-034954-0

For more information about our products, contact us at:
Thomson Learning Academic Resource Center
1-800-423-0563

For permission to use material from this text, contact us by:
Phone: 1-800-730-2214
Fax: 1-800-731-2215
Web: www.thomsonrights.com

Asia
Thomson Learning
5 Shenton Way, #01-01
UIC Building
Singapore 068808

Australia
Nelson Thomson Learning
102 Dodds Street
South Street
South Melbourne, Victoria 3205
Australia

Canada
Nelson Thomson Learning
1120 Birchmount Road
Toronto, Ontario M1K 5G4
Canada

Europe/Middle East/South Africa
Thomson Learning
High Holborn House
50/51 Bedford Row
London WC1R 4LR
United Kingdom

Latin America
Thomson Learning
Seneca, 53
Colonia Polanco
11560 Mexico D.F.
Mexico

Spain
Paraninfo Thomson Learning
Calle/Magallanes, 25
28015 Madrid, Spain

Table of Contents

PREFACE

In this *Instructor's Resource Manual* for the fifth edition of *Chemistry and Chemical Reactivity*, we continue our attempts to help instructors make general chemistry courses more interesting, challenging, and relevant for their students. This edition of the *Resource Manual* therefore continues to emphasize the organization of the course as well as the important topic of lecture demonstrations. Also, since the authors of the textbook and this manual frequently use multimedia in the classroom, there are many references to appropriate videodisc segments, computer programs, and portions of the *General Chemistry Interactive CD-ROM*, Version 3.0.

Answers to Study Questions

For the first time, this *Instructor's Resource Manual* includes a complete set of solutions to all of the Study Questions in the fifth edition of *Chemistry & Chemical Reactivity*. The solutions, whenever possible, were written in a style that matches the format of the solved Example problems in the textbook. The answers were written assuming they would be used by faculty and posted for students. For this reason, the solutions are not as detailed as the answers to the blue, bold-faced numbered questions in the *Student Solutions Manual*, prepared by Alton Banks.

Instructor's Notes

In each chapter we have described the number of lectures roughly allocated to each topic and have noted where the topics in the text may be placed as an alternate to the order in which they are presented in the text.

Lecture Demonstrations

It is our hope that the textbook conveys a clear and organized view of chemistry as an interesting and useful subject. In order to further emphasize this representation, we believe that demonstrations are especially important. Therefore, in each chapter of this *Manual* we have provided information on the demonstrations often used in our lectures. Some of these demonstrations are pictured in the text since they are too dangerous to be done in the classroom.

Many of the photos in the book and the demonstrations we do are taken from the excellent series of books by Bassam Shakhashiri, *Chemical Demonstrations: A Handbook for Teachers of Chemistry*.

Another excellent source of demonstrations and experiments is the *Journal of Chemical Education*. The journal can be searched on the web at http://jchemed.chem.wisc.edu. There are two excellent computer indexes that are a great help in looking for demonstrations in *JCE* and elsewhere: *The Computerized Index to Journal of Chemical Education* (Paul F. Schatz) and the *Demo-Deck* (Fred Juergens) are both available through *JCE: Software*.

Multimedia

The *Periodic Table Videodisc*, the *Periodic Table Live!* CD-ROM, and the *Redox Videodisc* have been distributed by *JCE: Software*.

Acknowledgments

I could not have completed this manual without the help of Gary Riley, St. Louis College of Pharmacy, and Steve Landers , Columbia College, who worked all the study questions in the fifth edition of the textbook, and Karen Wichelman, University of Louisiana at Lafayette, who accuracy reviewed the study question answers. Also, the advance copy of the *Student Solutions Manual* by Alton Banks, North Carolina State University, and the Appendix answers written by Jack Kotz were invaluable when checking the accuracy of the answers to the bold-faced numbered questions.

Any errors that remain in this *Manual* are the responsibility of the author of this *Manual*, and you should contact me if you have corrections or comments.

This *Manual* was prepared using a G4 PowerBook and printed on a HP LaserJet 4050. Text was prepared using Microsoft Word 2001, plots were created in Microsoft Excel 2001, equations were built using the Equation Editor, and the figures were drawn with CSC ChemDraw.

As a final note, I would like to thank my husband John and the many friends whose support and patience helped make this project possible.

Susan M. Young

youngs@hartwick.edu

July 2002

Chapter 1
Matter and Measurement

INSTRUCTOR'S NOTES

On beginning the course we find the majority of material in Sections 1.1-1.5 can be assigned as reading and then discussed further in a recitation class. One to two lecture periods are devoted to a review of units, handling numbers, and significant figures.

SUGGESTED DEMONSTRATIONS

1.   Density

- Kolb, K. E.; Kolb, D. K. "Method for Separating or Identifying Plastics," *Journal of Chemical Education* **1991**, *68*, 348.

- Franz, D. A. "Densities and Miscibilities of Liquids and Liquid Mixtures," *Journal of Chemical Education* **1991**, *68*, 594.

- Checkai, G.; Whitsett, J. "Density Demonstration Using Diet Soft Drinks," *Journal of Chemical Education* **1986**, *63*, 515.

- Shakhashiri, B. Z. "Density and Miscibility of Liquids," *Chemical Demonstrations: A Handbook for Teachers of Chemistry;* University of Wisconsin Press, 1989; Vol. 3, pp. 229–233.

2.   Properties of Elements

- Pictures of the elements and their uses can be found on the *Periodic Table Videodisc* and on the *Periodic Table Live!* CD-ROM available from JCE Software.

3.   Illustration of "Physical Change"

- Liquid nitrogen is always a favorite of students. We freeze a banana, a hot dog, a flower, or similar object.

4.   Illustration of "Chemical Change"

- The first lecture in the course is often begun with a "bang" by setting off several hydrogen-filled balloons in a darkened lecture room. The demonstration is described in *Chemical Demonstrations: A Handbook for Teachers of Chemistry;* University of Wisconsin Press, 1983; Vol. 1, pp. 106–112. The reaction is also shown on the *General Chemistry Interactive CD-ROM*, the *Periodic Table Videodisc* and the *Periodic Table Live!* CD-ROM.

- Other reactions could be done as well, depending on the facilities available. Possibilities include placing small pieces of potassium in water, the thermite reaction (Shakhashiri, Volume 1, page 85), or the reaction of zinc and ammonium nitrate (Shakhashiri, Volume 1, page 51). The latter reaction gives off a large amount of ZnO dust and other irritating fumes. It is not suitable for a room without good ventilation.

- For fun, and to give some color, as well as talking about our future study of acid-base reactions, we add aqueous NH_3 to separate flasks containing (i) very dilute acid with phenolphthalein, (ii) $Al(NO_3)_3$, and (iii) dilute $CuSO_4$.

- We often have a student contribute a penny to put into concentrated HNO_3. The reaction brings up a brief discussion of oxidation–reduction processes. The NO_2 gas generated prompts a discussion of air pollution problems, as well as the fuels used in the Lunar Lander and in the Space Shuttle. (CAUTION: NO_2 is a very corrosive gas. Use only in a well ventilated room. We do the reaction by putting the penny in a few milliliters of acid in a 2-L Erlenmeyer flask that is lightly stoppered. This effectively contains the gas.)

- The *Periodic Table Videodisc* and the *Periodic Table Live!* CD-ROM can be used to explore reactions of the elements with air, water, acids, and bases. Examples include the reaction of potassium with water and the reaction of cobalt with HCl and HNO_3.

5.   Energy

- We have often noted that chemistry deals with energy and so some demonstrations in the first lecture are a thermite reaction or the use of light sticks.

6.   Units of Measurement

- Add a few drop of bromcresol green to a 2-L flask before the lecture. On filling with water during lecture, the water becomes blue. When the flask is almost full, it is topped off with dilute HCl, and the solution turns yellow. Next, the water is poured into an ordinary 1-L flask or beaker that already contains some dilute base, and the solution turns blue again. This is then poured into a graduated cylinder containing some phenolphthalein. We use this sequence to comment on the relative accuracies of the different types of glassware. We take some containers such as soda cans so students can connect metric units with familiar objects.

- A weighed piece of fruit or some other solid gives some meaning to mass expressed in grams.

7.   Demonstrations Using Significant Figures

- Kirksey, H. G. "Significant Figures: A Classroom Demonstration," *Journal of Chemical Education* **1992**, *69*, 497.

- Abel, K. B.; Hemmerlin, W. M. "Significant Figures," *Journal of Chemical Education* **1990**, *67*, 213.

Solutions to Study Questions

1.1   Calcium: Ca   Fluorine: F

The shape of the fluorite crystals can be described as interwoven cubes.

The overall shape of the crystals indicates that the ions in the solid matrix arrange themselves with alternating calcium and fluoride ions to produce the crystal appearance.

1.2   The states of matter are solid, liquid and gas. See Section 1.5 for descriptions of the three states of matter.

1.3   The non-uniform appearance of the mixture indicates that samples taken from different regions of that mixture would be different—a characteristic of a heterogeneous mixture. Recalling that iron is attracted to a magnetic field, while sand is generally not attracted in this way suggests that passing a magnet through the mixture would separate the sand and iron.

1.4   A chemical compound is a pure substance composed of two or more different elements. A molecule is the smallest, discrete unit that retains the composition and chemical characteristics of the compound. The compound water consists of molecules each with the chemical formula H_2O.

1.5   (a) physical property

(b) chemical property

(c) chemical property

(d) physical property

(e) physical property

(f) physical property

1.6   (a) chemical change

(b) physical change

(c) chemical change

(d) physical change

1.7   Liquids: mercury and water   Solid: copper

Of the substances shown, mercury is most dense and water is least dense.

1.8   (a) 5 significant figures

(b) 3 significant figures

(c) 3 significant figures

(d) 4 significant figures

1.9   (a) Aluminum: Al   Silicon: Si   Oxygen: O

        (b) Oxygen is a gas, while aluminum, silicon, and aquamarine are solids at room temperature. Oxygen is colorless, while aluminum and silicon are gray. The gemstone is a bluish color.

1.10   Qualitative observations: blue-green color, solid physical state

        Quantitative observations: density of 2.65 g/cm^3, mass of 2.5 g, length of 4.6 cm

        Mass and length are extensive properties, color, physical state, and density are intensive properties

1.11   The large colorless block of salt represents the macroscopic view. The spheres represent the microscopic or particulate view. If one can imagine producing multiple "copies" of the particulate view, the macroscopic view will result.

1.12   (a) C   Carbon   (c) Cl   Chlorine   (e) Mg   Magnesium

        (b) K   Potassium   (d) P   Phosphorus   (f) Ni   Nickel

1.13   (a) Mn   Manganese   (c) Na   Sodium   (e) Xe   Xenon

        (b) Cu   Copper   (d) Br   Bromine   (f) Fe   Iron

1.14   (a) Barium   Ba   (d) Lead   Pb

        (b) Titanium   Ti   (e) Arsenic   As

        (c) Chromium   Cr   (f) Zinc   Zn

1.15   (a) Silver   Ag   (d) Tin   Sn

        (b) Aluminum   Al   (e) Technetium   Tc

        (c) Plutonium   Pu   (f) Krypton   Kr

1.16   (a) NaCl is a compound; sodium is an element

        (b) Sugar is a compound; carbon is an element.

        (c) Gold chloride is a compound; gold is an element.

1.17   (a) $Pt(NH_3)_2Cl_2$ is a compound; Pt is an element

        (b) Copper is an element; copper(II) oxide is a compound

        (c) Silicon is an element; sand is a compound

1.18   (a) Physical properties: color (colorless), physical state (liquid)

             Chemical property: reactivity (burns in air)

        (b) Physical properties: color (shiny metal, orange), physical state (liquid)

             Chemical property: reactivity (aluminum reacts readily with bromine)

1.19   (a) Physical properties: color (white), physical state (solid), density ($2.71\ g/cm^3$)

Chemical properties: reactivity towards acid (reacts to produce gaseous carbon dioxide)

(b) Physical property: color (gray zinc, purple iodine, white compound)

Chemical property: reactivity (zinc and iodine react to give a white compound)

1.20 $500.\ mL \cdot \dfrac{1\ cm^3}{1\ mL} \cdot \dfrac{1.11\ g}{1\ cm^3} = 555\ g$

1.21 $2.365\ g \cdot \dfrac{1\ cm^3}{10.5\ g} = 0.225\ cm^3$

1.22 $2.00\ g \cdot \dfrac{1\ cm^3}{0.718\ g} \cdot \dfrac{1\ mL}{1\ cm^3} = 2.79\ mL$

1.23 $1\ cup \cdot \dfrac{237\ mL}{1\ cup} \cdot \dfrac{1\ cm^3}{1\ mL} = 237\ cm^3$ $\dfrac{205\ g}{237\ cm^3} = 0.865\ g/cm^3$

1.24 $\dfrac{37.5\ g}{(20.2 - 6.9)\ mL} \cdot \dfrac{1\ mL}{1\ cm^3} = 2.82\ g/cm^3$

The sample's density matches that of aluminum.

1.25 $\dfrac{23.5\ g}{(52.2 - 47.5)\ mL} \cdot \dfrac{1\ mL}{1\ cm^3} = 5.0\ g/cm^3$

The sample's density matches that of fool's gold.

1.26 $(25\ ^\circ C + 273.15\ ^\circ C)\dfrac{1\ K}{1\ ^\circ C} = 298\ K$

1.27 $(5.5 \times 10^3\ ^\circ C + 273.15\ ^\circ C)\dfrac{1\ K}{1\ ^\circ C} = 5.8 \times 10^3\ K$

1.28   (a) 289 K   (b) 97 °C   (c) 310 K

1.29   (a) −196 °C   (b) 336 K   (c) 1180 °C

1.30 $40.0\ km \cdot \dfrac{1000\ m}{1\ km} = 4.00 \times 10^4\ m$

$40.0\ km \cdot \dfrac{0.62137\ miles}{1\ km} = 24.9\ miles$

1.31 $19\ cm \cdot \dfrac{10\ mm}{1\ cm} = 190\ mm$

$19\ cm \cdot \dfrac{1\ m}{100\ cm} = 0.19\ m$

1.32 $2.5 \text{ cm} \times 2.1 \text{ cm} = 5.3 \text{ cm}^2$

$5.3 \text{ cm}^2 \cdot \left(\dfrac{1 \text{ m}}{100 \text{ cm}}\right)^2 = 5.3 \times 10^{-4} \text{ m}^2$

1.33 $\text{Area} = \pi \, r^2 = \pi \left(\dfrac{11.8 \text{ cm}}{2}\right)^2 = 109 \text{ cm}^2$

$109 \text{ cm}^2 \cdot \left(\dfrac{1 \text{ m}}{100 \text{ cm}}\right)^2 = 1.09 \times 10^{-2} \text{ m}^2$

1.34 $250 \text{ mL} \cdot \dfrac{1 \text{ cm}^3}{1 \text{ mL}} = 250 \text{ cm}^3$

$250 \text{ mL} \cdot \dfrac{1 \text{ L}}{10^3 \text{ mL}} = 0.25 \text{ L}$

$250 \text{ mL} \cdot \dfrac{1 \text{ cm}^3}{1 \text{ mL}} \cdot \left(\dfrac{1 \text{ m}}{100 \text{ cm}}\right)^3 = 2.5 \times 10^{-4} \text{ m}^3$

$250 \text{ mL} \cdot \dfrac{1 \text{ L}}{10^3 \text{ mL}} \cdot \dfrac{1 \text{ dm}^3}{1 \text{ L}} = 0.25 \text{ dm}^3$

1.35 $1.5 \text{ L} \cdot \dfrac{10^3 \text{ mL}}{1 \text{ L}} = 1.5 \times 10^3 \text{ mL}$

$1.5 \text{ L} \cdot \dfrac{10^3 \text{ mL}}{1 \text{ L}} \cdot \dfrac{1 \text{ cm}^3}{1 \text{ mL}} = 1.5 \times 10^3 \text{ cm}^3$

$1.5 \times 10^3 \text{ cm}^3 \cdot \left(\dfrac{1 \text{ dm}}{10 \text{ cm}}\right)^3 = 1.5 \text{ dm}^3$

1.36 $2.52 \text{ kg} \cdot \dfrac{10^3 \text{ g}}{1 \text{ kg}} = 2.52 \times 10^3 \text{ g}$

1.37 $2.265 \text{ g} \cdot \dfrac{1 \text{ kg}}{10^3 \text{ g}} = 2.265 \times 10^{-3} \text{ kg}$

$2.265 \text{ g} \cdot \dfrac{10^3 \text{ mg}}{1 \text{ g}} = 2.265 \times 10^3 \text{ mg}$

1.38

	Method A	Deviation	Method B	Deviation
	2.2	0.2	2.703	0.777
	2.3	0.1	2.701	0.779
	2.7	0.3	2.705	0.775
	2.4	0.0	5.811	2.331
(a) Average:	2.4	0.2	3.480	1.166

For method B the reading of 5.811 can be excluded because it is more than twice as large as all other readings. Using only the first three readings, average = 2.703 g/cm^3 and average deviation = 0.001 g/cm^3.

(b) Method A: Error = –0.3   Method B: Error = 0.001 (omitting data point)

(c) Before excluding a data point for B, method A is more accurate and more precise. After excluding data for B, this method gives a more accurate and more precise result.

1.39

	Student A	Deviation	Student B	Deviation
	134 °C	1 °C	138 °C	0 °C
	136 °C	1 °C	137 °C	1 °C
	133 °C	2 °C	138 °C	0 °C
	138 °C	3 °C	138 °C	0 °C
(a) Average:	135 °C	2 °C	138 °C	0.3 °C

(b) Student A: Error = 0   Student B: Error = –3

(c) Student B is more precise; Student A is more accurate

1.40 (a) 3 significant figures   (c) 5 significant figure

(b) 3 significant figures   (d) 4 significant figures

1.41 (a) 3 significant figures   (c) 4 significant figures

(b) 2 significant figures   (d) 3 significant figures

1.42 0.122 (3 significant figures allowed)

1.43 0.0286 (three significant figures allowed)

1.44 $1.50 \text{ carat} \cdot \dfrac{0.200 \text{ g}}{1 \text{ carat}} \cdot \dfrac{1 \text{ cm}^3}{3.513 \text{ g}} = 0.0854 \text{ cm}^3$

1.45 (a) Volume = $(0.563 \text{ nm})^3 = 0.178 \text{ nm}^3$

$0.178 \text{ nm}^3 \cdot \left(\dfrac{10^{-9} \text{ m}}{1 \text{ nm}}\right)^3 \cdot \left(\dfrac{100 \text{ cm}}{1 \text{ m}}\right)^3 = 1.78 \times 10^{-22} \text{ cm}^3$

(b) $\dfrac{2.17 \text{ g}}{1 \text{ cm}^3} \cdot 1.78 \times 10^{-22} \text{ cm}^3 = 3.86 \times 10^{-22} \text{ g}$

(c) $\dfrac{3.86 \times 10^{-22} \text{ g}}{4 \text{ NaCl formula units}} = 9.65 \times 10^{-23} \text{ g/formula unit}$

1.46 Volume = $(\pi)(\text{radius})^2(\text{thickness}) = (\pi)(2.2 \text{ cm/2})^2(0.30 \text{ cm}) = 1.1 \text{ cm}^3$

$1.1 \text{ cm}^3 \cdot \dfrac{19.3 \text{ g}}{1 \text{ cm}^3} = 22 \text{ g}$

1.47 $57 \text{ kg} \cdot \dfrac{10^3 \text{ g}}{1 \text{ kg}} \cdot \dfrac{1 \text{ cm}^3}{8.94 \text{ g}} = 6.4 \times 10^3 \text{ cm}^3 \text{ copper}$

length of wire $= \dfrac{\text{volume}}{(\pi)(\text{radius})^2} = \dfrac{6.4 \times 10^3 \text{ cm}^3}{(\pi)(0.950/2 \text{ cm})^2} = 9.0 \times 10^3 \text{ cm}$

$9.0 \times 10^3 \text{ cm} \cdot \dfrac{1 \text{ m}}{100 \text{ cm}} = 90. \text{ m}$

1.48 $\dfrac{1.77 \text{ lb}}{1 \text{ L}} \cdot \dfrac{453.6 \text{ g}}{1 \text{ lb}} \cdot \dfrac{1 \text{ kg}}{10^3 \text{ g}} = 0.803 \text{ kg/L (the correct conversion factor)}$

$\dfrac{0.803 \text{ kg}}{1 \text{ L}} \cdot 7682 \text{ L} = 6170 \text{ kg}$

$22{,}300 \text{ kg} - 6170 \text{ kg} = 16{,}130 \text{ kg additional fuel needed}$

$16{,}130 \text{ kg} \cdot \dfrac{1 \text{ L}}{0.803 \text{ kg}} = 20{,}100 \text{ L fuel needed}$

1.49   (a) $\dfrac{(0.125 - 0.106) \text{ g}}{0.125 \text{ g}} \cdot 100\% = 15\% \text{ of mass lost on popping}$

(b) $1 \text{ lb popcorn} \cdot \dfrac{453.6 \text{ g}}{1 \text{ lb}} \cdot \dfrac{1 \text{ kernel}}{0.125 \text{ g}} = 3630 \text{ kernels}$

1.50   The normally accepted value for a human temperature is 98.6° F. On the Celsius scale, this corresponds to 37 °C. Since gallium's melting point is 29.8 °C, the solid should melt in your hand.

1.51 $(-248.6 \text{ °C} + 273.15 \text{ °C}) \dfrac{1 \text{ K}}{1 \text{ °C}} = 24.6 \text{ K}$

$(-246.1 \text{ °C} + 273.15 \text{ °C}) \dfrac{1 \text{ K}}{1 \text{ °C}} = 27.1 \text{ K}$

1.52 $1.97 \text{ Å} \cdot \dfrac{10^{-10} \text{ m}}{1 \text{ Å}} \cdot \dfrac{1 \text{ nm}}{10^{-9} \text{ m}} = 0.197 \text{ nm}$

$1.97 \text{ Å} \cdot \dfrac{10^{-10} \text{ m}}{1 \text{ Å}} \cdot \dfrac{1 \text{ pm}}{10^{-12} \text{ m}} = 197 \text{ pm}$

1.53   (a) $0.154 \text{ nm} \cdot \dfrac{10^{-9} \text{ m}}{1 \text{ nm}} = 1.54 \times 10^{-10} \text{ m}$

(b) $1.54 \times 10^{-10} \text{ m} \cdot \dfrac{1 \text{ Å}}{10^{-10} \text{ m}} = 1.54 \text{ Å}$

1.54   (a)   At 25 °C, $250. \text{ mL} \cdot \dfrac{1 \text{ cm}^3}{1 \text{ mL}} \cdot \dfrac{0.997 \text{ g}}{1 \text{ cm}^3} = 249 \text{ g water} (= 249 \text{ g ice when cooled})$

$249 \text{ g ice} \cdot \dfrac{1 \text{ cm}^3}{0.917 \text{ g}} \cdot \dfrac{1 \text{ mL}}{1 \text{ cm}^3} = 272 \text{ mL ice}$

(b)   The ice cannot be contained in the can.

1.55 $density = \dfrac{2.361 \text{ g}}{(2.35 \text{ cm} \times 1.34 \text{ cm} \times 0.105 \text{ cm})} = 7.14 \text{ g/cm}^3$

The metal is (c) Zinc

1.56 $600 \text{ g H}_2\text{O} \cdot \dfrac{1 \text{ cm}^3}{0.995 \text{ g}} = 600 \text{ cm}^3$

$600 \text{ g Pb} \cdot \dfrac{1 \text{ cm}^3}{11.34 \text{ g}} = 50 \text{ cm}^3$

Given equal masses the less dense substance (water) will have a greater volume.

1.57 $154 \text{ g} \cdot \dfrac{1 \text{ cm}^3}{8.56 \text{ g}} \cdot \dfrac{1 \text{ mL}}{1 \text{ cm}^3} = 18.0 \text{ mL}$

The water will rise 18.0 mL to a final volume of 68.0 mL.

1.58   The lab partner is on the right track in estimating the density to lie between that at 15 °C and that at 25 °C. If one assumes is it halfway between those densities, a better estimate would be 0.99810 g/cm³. A more accurate analysis, however, shows that the decrease in density with increasing temperature is not linear. A more careful analysis would lead to a value of perhaps 0.99820 g/cm³ (not far from the actual value of 0.99840 g/cm³)

1.59   (a) $7.5 \text{ μm} \cdot \dfrac{10^{-6} \text{ m}}{1 \text{ μm}} = 7.5 \times 10^{-6} \text{ m}$

(b) $7.5 \times 10^{-6} \text{ m} \cdot \dfrac{1 \text{ nm}}{10^{-9} \text{ m}} = 7.5 \times 10^3 \text{ nm}$

(c) $7.5 \times 10^{-6} \text{ m} \cdot \dfrac{1 \text{ Å}}{10^{-10} \text{ m}} = 7.5 \times 10^4 \text{ Å}$

1.60   The plastic (with a much lower density than CCl_4) will float. The aluminum (which is more dense than CCl_4) will sink.

1.61 $1.53 \text{ g cisplatin} \cdot \dfrac{65.0 \text{ g Pt}}{100.0 \text{ g cisplatin}} = 0.995 \text{ g Pt}$

1.62 $250 \text{ g solder} \cdot \dfrac{67 \text{ g Pb}}{100 \text{ g solder}} = 170 \text{ g Pb}$

1.63 $0.50 \text{ mL} \cdot \dfrac{10. \text{ g procaine hydrochloride}}{100 \text{ mL solution}} \cdot \dfrac{10^3 \text{ mg}}{1 \text{ g}} = 50. \text{ mg procaine hydrochloride}$

1.64   (a) solid iron   (b) liquid water   (c) water vapor

        (d) water vapor, helium   (e) liquid water, solid aluminum   (f) brass

1.65   The sample's density and melting point could be compared with that of silver to prove whether or not the sample is silver.

1.66   One could check for an odor, check the boiling or freezing point, or determine the density. If the density is approximately 1 g/cm^3 at room temperature, the liquid could be water. If it boils at about 100 °C and freezes about 0 °C, that would be consistent with water. To check for the presence of salt, boil the liquid away. If a substance remains, it could be salt, but further testing would be required.

1.67   The mass of the object is determined and then the volume is determined by submersion in a known volume of liquid. The increase in volume would be equal to the volume of the irregularly shaped object. The density could be calculated by dividing its mass by its volume.

1.68
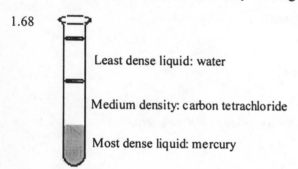
Least dense liquid: water

Medium density: carbon tetrachloride

Most dense liquid: mercury

1.69   If too much sugar is excreted, the density of urine will increase. If too much water is excreted, the density of urine will decrease.

1.70   A copper-colored metal could be copper, but it may also be an alloy of copper, for example, brass or bronze. Testing the material's density and melting temperature would be one way to find out if it is copper.

1.71   (a) The water could be evaporated by heating the solution, leaving the salt behind.

(b) Use of a magnet would attract the iron filings away from the lead.

(c) Mixing the solids with water would dissolve only the sugar. Filtration would separate the solid sulfur from the solution. Finally, the sugar could be separated from the water by boiling the solution.

1.72   (a) Solid potassium reacts with liquid water to produce gaseous hydrogen and a homogeneous mixture of potassium hydroxide in liquid water.

(b) The reaction is a chemical change.

(c) Potassium and water are reactants, hydrogen and potassium hydroxide are products.

(d) Among the qualitative observations are (i) the reaction is violent; and (ii) heat and light (a purple flame) are produced.

1.73   Any balloon filled with a gas having a density less than 1.12 g/L will float in air. Helium and neon balloons will float.

1.74 $12 \text{ oz.} \cdot \dfrac{28.4 \text{ g}}{1 \text{ oz.}} \cdot \dfrac{1 \text{ cm}^3}{2.70 \text{ g}} = 126 \text{ cm}^3$

$75 \text{ ft}^2 \cdot \left(\dfrac{12 \text{ in}}{1 \text{ ft}}\right)^2 \cdot \left(\dfrac{2.54 \text{ cm}}{1 \text{ in}}\right)^2 = 7.0 \times 10^4 \text{ cm}^2$

$\text{thickness} = \dfrac{\text{volume}}{\text{area}} = \dfrac{126 \text{ cm}^3}{7.0 \times 10^4 \text{ cm}^2} = 1.8 \times 10^{-3} \text{ cm} = 1.8 \times 10^{-2} \text{ mm}$

1.75 $150{,}000 \text{ people} \cdot \dfrac{660 \text{ L water}}{1 \text{ day}} \cdot \dfrac{365 \text{ days}}{1 \text{ year}} \cdot \dfrac{10^3 \text{ mL}}{1 \text{ L}} \cdot \dfrac{1 \text{ cm}^3}{1 \text{ mL}} \cdot \dfrac{1.00 \text{ g}}{1 \text{ cm}^3} \cdot \dfrac{1 \text{ kg}}{10^3 \text{ g}}$

$\cdot \dfrac{1 \text{ kg fluoride}}{10^6 \text{ kg water}} \cdot \dfrac{100.0 \text{ kg NaF}}{45.0 \text{ kg fluoride}} = 8.0 \times 10^4 \text{ kg NaF/year}$

1.76 $0.5 \text{ acre} \cdot \dfrac{1.0 \times 10^4 \text{ m}^2}{2.47 \text{ acres}} \cdot \left(\dfrac{100 \text{ cm}}{1 \text{ m}}\right)^2 = 2 \times 10^7 \text{ cm}^2$

$\text{thickness} = \dfrac{\text{volume}}{\text{area}} = \dfrac{5 \text{ cm}^3}{2 \times 10^7 \text{ cm}^2} = 2 \times 10^{-7} \text{ cm}$

This is likely related to the "length" of oil molecules.

1.77 $500. \text{ mL} \cdot \dfrac{1 \text{ cm}^3}{1 \text{ mL}} \cdot \dfrac{1.285 \text{ g}}{1 \text{ cm}^3} \cdot \dfrac{38.08 \text{ g sulfuric acid}}{100.00 \text{ g solution}} = 245 \text{ g sulfuric acid}$

1.78   One possible method is outlined on Screen 1.18.

Chapter 2
Atoms and Elements

INSTRUCTOR'S NOTES

This chapter requires approximately two lecture periods.

SUGGESTED DEMONSTRATIONS

1.   Properties of Elements
   - Take as many samples of elements as possible to your lecture on the elements and the periodic table.
   - The *Periodic Table Videodisc* is ideal for showing samples of elements, their reactions, and their uses. See the series by Alton Banks in the *Journal of Chemical Education* titled "What's the Use?" This series describes a different element each month and gives references to the videodisc.

2.   Chemical Periodicity
   - Like all the alkali metals, sodium reacts vigorously with halogens. When sodium metal is placed in a flask containing chlorine gas, sodium chloride is produced. During the reaction, a large quantity of heat and light is emitted. This reaction is shown on the *Redox Videodisc* and the *General Chemistry Interactive CD-ROM*, Version 3.0.

3.   The Mole Concept
   - To illustrate the mole, take 1 molar quantities of elements such as Mg, Al, C, Sn, Pb, Fe, and Cu to the classroom.
   - When doing examples in lecture, it is helpful to have a sample of the element available. For example, hold up a pre-weighed sample of magnesium wire and ask how many moles of metal it contains (and then ignite the wire to give a preview of the reaction chemistry described in Chapters 4 and 5.). Or, drop a pre-weighed piece of sodium metal into a dish of water on the overhead projector, and ask how many moles of sodium reacted.

Solutions to Study Questions

2.1   Atoms contain the fundamental particles protons (+1 charge), neutrons (zero charge), and electrons (–1 charge). Protons and neutrons are in the nucleus of an atom. Electrons are the least massive of the three particles.

2.2   One amu is 1/12th of the mass of an atom of carbon with six protons and six neutrons.

2.3   The atomic number equal to the number of protons in the nucleus of an element. The sum of the number of protons and neutrons for an atom is its mass number.

2.4   The discovery of radioactivity showed that atoms must be divisible; that is, atoms must be composed of even smaller, subatomic particles.

2.5   Thomson measured the charge-to-mass ratio of the electron. By combining his work with the results of Millikan's experiments to measure the charge on the electron, the mass of the electron was determined. Rutherford's experiments to test Thomson's model of the atom (a uniform sphere of positively charged matter within which thousands of electrons circulated in coplanar rings) showed that this early model was incorrect. Rutherford's experiments resulted in a new model of the atom in which all the positive charge and most of the mass of the atom is concentrated in the nucleus, and electrons occupy the rest of the space in the atom.

2.6   Exercise 2.1 provides the relative sizes of the nuclear and atomic diameters, with the nuclear radius on the order of 0.001 pm and the atomic radius approximately 100 pm. If the nuclear diameter is 6 cm, then the atomic diameter is 600,000 cm (or 6 km).

2.7   Radon, Rn

2.8

	Symbol	Atomic number	Atomic weight	Group	Period	
Titanium	Ti	22	47.867	4B	4	Metal
Thallium	Tl	81	204.3833	3A	6	Metal

2.9   The atomic mass of lithium is closer to 7 than to 6, so ^{7}Li is 92.5% abundant and ^{6}Li is 7.5% abundant.

2.10   (a) One mole of Na has a mass of approximately 23 g while a mole of Si has a mass of 28 g. So 0.5 mol of Si has a greater mass.

        (b) One-half mol of Na would have a mass of approximately 12.5 g, so 0.50 mol Na has a greater mass.

        (c) The atomic weight of K is approximately 39 while that of Fe is approximately 56. Each atom of Fe has a greater mass than an atom of K., so 10 atoms of Fe have a greater mass.

2.11   Zinc is a gray, solid, metallic element with the atomic number 30 and an atomic mass of 65.39. Zinc is at the end of the first transition series and behaves as a metal. The metal is malleable and conducts electricity. Zinc atoms have 30 electrons and 30 protons. Zinc is used as the outer case in "dry" cell batteries and to coat iron to prevent corrosion.

2.12   Groups are the columns on the Periodic Table, while Periods are the horizontal rows.

2.13   Mendeleev thought that the chemical and physical properties of the elements repeated on a basis of atomic mass. The modern periodic law says that the chemical and physical properties of the elements recur periodically based on the atomic number of the elements.

2.14   (a)

Name	Symbol	Group	Period
Lithium	Li	1A	2
Silver	Ag	1B	5
Lead	Pb	4A	6

        (b)

Carbon	C	4A	2
Phosphorus	P	5A	3
Selenium	Se	6A	4
Iodine	I	7A	5

        (c)

Silicon	Si	4A	3
Arsenic	As	5A	4

2.15   Vanadium, V   The metal is used for producing rust-resistant springs and steels used for making tools. Vanadium foil is used as a bonding agent in biding titanium to steel.

        Chromium, Cr   Used to harden steel, to manufacture stainless steel, and to form alloys. The metal is used in plating to produce a hard, beautiful surface and to prevent corrosion. Chromium is used to give glass an emerald green color. It is responsible for the green color of emeralds and the red color of rubies.

        Manganese, Mn   Used to form many important alloys. In steel, manganese improves the rolling and forging qualities, strength, toughness, stiffness, wear resistance, hardness, and hardenability. With aluminum and antimony, especially with small amounts of copper, it forms highly ferromagnetic alloys. (Information found at www.webelements.com)

2.16   Transition Elements: Mo, Molybdenum, Au, Gold, Cm, Curium

        Halogen: Br, Bromine

        Noble Gas: Ne, Neon

        Alkali Metal: Rb, Rubidium

2.17   Chlorine, Cl: Pale yellow, choking poisonous gas used to chlorinate (purify) municipal water supplies.

Iodine, I: Purple-black solid that sublimes (changes from solid to vapor) easily, used as a mild antiseptic.

2.18   Polonium, Po, atomic number 84

Name origin: Curie's homeland, Poland

2.19   Oxygen exists as two different allotropes, odorless O_2 (diatomic oxygen) and O_3 (ozone), a gas with a characteristic, pungent odor.

Carbon exists as diamond, graphite, and fullerenes (such as buckminsterfullerene, C_{60}). Diamond is a very hard solid with each carbon atom connected to four others. Graphite consists of sheets of carbon atoms that cling only weakly to one another (Figure 2.12).

Sulfur has many allotropes, the most common of which consists of eight-member, crown-shaped rings.

2.20   (a) Mass number = 12 + 15 = 27

(b) Mass number = 22 + 26 = 48

(c) Mass number = 30 + 32 = 62

2.21   (a) Mass number = 28 + 31 = 59

(b) Mass number = 94 + 150 = 244

(c) Mass number = 74 + 110 = 184

2.22   (a) $^{39}_{19}K$ (b) $^{84}_{36}Kr$ (c) $^{60}_{27}Co$

2.23   (a) $^{19}_{9}F$ (b) $^{52}_{24}Cr$ (c) $^{132}_{54}Xe$

2.24

	electrons	protons	neutrons
(a)	12	12	12
(b)	50	50	69
(c)	90	90	142

2.25

	electrons	protons	neutrons
(a)	6	6	7
(b)	29	29	34
(c)	83	83	122

2.26   Number of protons = number of electrons = 43; number of neutrons = 56

2.27   Number of protons = number of electrons = 95; number of neutrons = 146

2.28 $^{57}_{27}Co$ (30 neutrons), $^{58}_{27}Co$ (31 neutrons), and $^{60}_{27}Co$ (33 neutrons)

2.29 $^{19}_{9}X$, $^{20}_{9}X$, and $^{21}_{9}X$ are isotopes of X

2.30   The atomic weight of thallium is 204.3833. The fact that this weight is closer to 205 than 203 indicates that the 205 isotope is the more abundant.

2.31   Strontium has an atomic mass of 87.62 so ^{88}Sr is the most abundant.

2.32   (^{6}Li mass)(% abundance) + (^{7}Li mass)(% abundance) = atomic weight of Li
        (6.015121 amu)(0.0750) + (7.016003 amu)(0.9250) = 6.94 amu

2.33   (^{24}Mg mass)(% abundance) + (^{25}Mg mass)(% abundance) + (^{26}Mg mass)(% abundance)
        = atomic weight of Mg
        (23.985 amu)(0.7899) + (24.986 amu)(0.1000) + (25.983 amu)(0.1101)
        = 24.31 amu

2.34   Let x represent the abundance of ^{69}Ga and $(1 - x)$ represent the abundance of ^{71}Ga.
        69.723 amu = (x)(68.9257 amu) + $(1 - x)$(70.9249 amu)
        x = 0.6012; ^{69}Ga abundance is 60.12%, ^{71}Ga abundance is 39.88%

2.35   Let x represent the abundance of ^{121}Sb and $(1 - x)$ represent the abundance of ^{123}Sb.
        121.760 amu = (x)(120.9038 amu) + $(1 - x)$(122.9042 amu)
        x = 0.5720; ^{121}Sb abundance is 57.20%, ^{123}Sb abundance is 42.80%

2.36   (a) 2.5 mol Al $\cdot$ $\dfrac{27.0 \text{ g Al}}{1 \text{ mol Al}}$ = 68 g Al

        (b) 1.25×10^{-3} mol Fe $\cdot$ $\dfrac{55.85 \text{ g Fe}}{1 \text{ mol Fe}}$ = 0.0698 g Fe

        (c) 0.015 mol Ca $\cdot$ $\dfrac{40.1 \text{ g Ca}}{1 \text{ mol Ca}}$ = 0.60 g Ca

        (d) 653 mol Ne $\cdot$ $\dfrac{20.18 \text{ g Ne}}{1 \text{ mol Ne}}$ = 1.32×10^{4} g Ne

2.37   (a) 4.24 mol Au $\cdot$ $\dfrac{197.0 \text{ g Au}}{1 \text{ mol Au}}$ = 835 g Au

        (b) 15.6 mol He $\cdot$ $\dfrac{4.003 \text{ g He}}{1 \text{ mol He}}$ = 62.4 g He

        (c) 0.063 mol Pt $\cdot$ $\dfrac{195 \text{ g Pt}}{1 \text{ mol Pt}}$ = 12 g Pt

        (d) 3.63×10^{-4} mol Pu $\cdot$ $\dfrac{244.7 \text{ g Pu}}{1 \text{ mol Pu}}$ = 0.0888 g Pu

2.38   (a) $127.08 \text{ g Cu} \cdot \dfrac{1 \text{ mol Cu}}{63.546 \text{ g Cu}} = 1.9998 \text{ mol Cu}$

(b) $0.012 \text{ g Li} \cdot \dfrac{1 \text{ mol Li}}{6.94 \text{ g Li}} = 1.7 \times 10^{-3} \text{ mol Li}$

(c) $5.0 \text{ mg Am} \cdot \dfrac{1 \text{ g}}{10^3 \text{ mg}} \cdot \dfrac{1 \text{ mol Am}}{243 \text{ g Am}} = 2.1 \times 10^{-5} \text{ mol Am}$

(d) $6.75 \text{ g Al} \cdot \dfrac{1 \text{ mol Al}}{26.98 \text{ g Al}} = 0.250 \text{ mol Al}$

2.39   (a) $16.0 \text{ g Na} \cdot \dfrac{1 \text{ mol Na}}{22.99 \text{ g Na}} = 0.696 \text{ mol Na}$

(b) $0.876 \text{ g Sn} \cdot \dfrac{1 \text{ mol Sn}}{118.7 \text{ g Sn}} = 7.38 \times 10^{-3} \text{ mol Sn}$

(c) $0.0034 \text{ g Pt} \cdot \dfrac{1 \text{ mol Pt}}{195 \text{ g Pt}} = 1.7 \times 10^{-5} \text{ mol Pt}$

(d) $0.983 \text{ g Xe} \cdot \dfrac{1 \text{ mol Xe}}{131.3 \text{ g Xe}} = 7.49 \times 10^{-3} \text{ mol Xe}$

2.40 $\dfrac{63.546 \text{ g Cu}}{1 \text{ mol Cu}} \cdot \dfrac{1 \text{ mol Cu}}{6.02214 \times 10^{23} \text{ atoms}} = 1.0552 \times 10^{-22} \text{ g/atom}$

2.41 $\dfrac{47.867 \text{ g Ti}}{1 \text{ mol Ti}} \cdot \dfrac{1 \text{ mol Ti}}{6.02214 \times 10^{23} \text{ atoms}} = 7.9485 \times 10^{-23} \text{ g/atom}$

2.42   Group 5A contains 5 elements.

Metal: Bi, Bismuth

Metalloids: As, Arsenic; Sb, Antimony

Nonmetals: N, Nitrogen; P, Phosphorus

2.43   The fourth period contains 18 elements.

Metals: K, Potassium; Ca, Calcium; Sc, Scandium; Ti, Titanium; V, Vanadium; Cr, Chromium;

Mn, Manganese; Fe, Iron; Co, Cobalt; Ni, Nickel; Cu, Copper; Zn, Zinc; Ga, Gallium

Metalloids: Ge, Germanium; As, Arsenic

Nonmetals: Se, Selenium; Br, Bromine; Kr, Krypton

2.44   Periods 2 and 3 have 8 elements, Periods 4 and 5 have 18 elements, and Period 6 has 32 elements.

2.45   There are 26 elements in the seventh period, the majority of them are called the Actinides, and many of them are man-made elements.

2.46	Symbol	^{58}Ni	^{33}S	^{20}Ne	^{55}Mn
	Number of protons	28	16	10	25
	Number of neutrons	30	17	10	30
	Number of electrons	28	16	10	25
	Name of element	nickel	sulfur	neon	manganese

2.47	Symbol	^{65}Cu	^{86}Kr	^{195}Pt	^{81}Br
	Number of protons	29	36	78	35
	Number of neutrons	36	50	117	46
	Number of electrons	29	36	78	35
	Name of element	copper	krypton	platinum	bromine

2.48   The atomic mass for potassium is 39.0983 amu, so the lighter isotope, ^{39}K is more abundant than ^{41}K.

2.49   *Crossword Puzzle*

S	N
B	I

2.50   (a) Mg and Fe are the most abundant metals. (Very similar abundance values)

(b) H is the most abundant nonmetal.

(c) Si is the most abundant metalloid.

(d) Fe is the most abundant transition element.

(e) F, Cl, and Br are the halogens included and of these Cl is the most abundant.

2.51   Element abundance generally decreases with increasing atomic number (with exceptions at Li–B and Sc–Fe). Elements with an even atomic number appear to be slightly more abundant than those with an odd atomic number.

2.52   (d) 3.43×10^{-27} mol S_8 is impossible. This amount is less than one molecule of S_8.

2.53   Barium would be even more reactive than calcium, so a more vigorous evolution of hydrogen would occur (it might even ignite). Mg, Ca, and Ba are in periods 3, 4, and 6, respectively. Reactivity increases on going down a group in the periodic table.

2.54   (a) Cobalt, nickel, and copper have the highest density. The density of all three metals is approximately 9 g/cm^3.

(b) The element in the second period with the largest density is boron while the element in the third period with the largest density is aluminum. Both of these elements belong to group 3A.

(c) The elements with very low densities are gases. These include hydrogen, helium, nitrogen, oxygen, fluorine, neon, chlorine, argon and krypton.

2.55   The nucleus contains two protons and two neutrons. There are two electrons somewhere outside the nucleus.

2.56   Some possible answers:

(a) Ba, Barium   (f) Mg, Magnesium

(b) Si, Silicon   (g) Kr, Krypton

(c) C, Carbon   (h) S, Sulfur

(d) S, Sulfur   (i) As, Arsenic

(e) I, Iodine

2.57   Some possible answers:

(a) Zn, Zinc   (e) Na, Sodium

(b) Zr, Zirconium   (f) Xe, Xenon

(c) Pb, Lead   (g) Se, Selenium, a nonmetal

(d) Se, Selenium   (h) As, Arsenic

2.58 $0.00789 \text{ g Kr} \cdot \dfrac{1 \text{ mol Kr}}{83.80 \text{ g Kr}} = 9.42 \times 10^{-5} \text{ mol Kr}$

$9.42 \times 10^{-5} \text{ mol Kr} \cdot \dfrac{6.0221 \times 10^{23} \text{ atoms Kr}}{1 \text{ mol Kr}} = 5.67 \times 10^{19} \text{ atoms Kr}$

2.59 $15 \text{ mg} \cdot \dfrac{1 \text{ g}}{10^{3} \text{ mg}} \cdot \dfrac{1 \text{ mol Fe}}{55.85 \text{ g Fe}} = 2.7 \times 10^{-4} \text{ mol Fe}$

$2.7 \times 10^{-4} \text{ mol Fe} \cdot \dfrac{6.02 \times 10^{23} \text{ atoms Fe}}{1 \text{ mol Fe}} = 1.6 \times 10^{20} \text{ atoms Fe}$

2.60 $0.125 \text{ mol Na} \cdot \dfrac{22.99 \text{ g Na}}{1 \text{ mol Na}} \cdot \dfrac{1 \text{ cm}^{3}}{0.971 \text{ g Na}} = 2.96 \text{ cm}^{3}$

$\text{Edge} = \sqrt[3]{2.96 \text{ cm}^{3}} = 1.44 \text{ cm}$

2.61 $256 \ mol \ Li \cdot \dfrac{6.941 \ g \ Li}{1 \ mol \ Li} \cdot \dfrac{1 \ cm^3}{0.534 \ g \ Li} = 3.33 \times 10^3 \ cm^3$

Edge $= \sqrt[3]{3.33 \times 10^3 \ cm^3} = 14.9 \ cm$

2.62   Volume $= (0.015 \ cm)(15.3 \ cm^3) = 0.23 \ cm^3$

$0.23 \ cm^3 \cdot \dfrac{7.19 \ g \ Cr}{1 \ cm^3} \cdot \dfrac{1 \ mol \ Cr}{52.00 \ g \ Cr} \cdot \dfrac{6.022 \times 10^{23} \ atoms \ Cr}{1 \ mol \ Cr} = 1.9 \times 10^{22} \ atoms \ Cr$

2.63   Volume $= (\pi)(4.5 \ cm/2)^2(12.00 \ cm) = 190 \ cm^3$

$190 \ cm^3 \cdot \dfrac{0.971 \ g \ Na}{1 \ cm^3} \cdot \dfrac{1 \ mol \ Na}{22.99 \ g \ Na} \cdot \dfrac{6.022 \times 10^{23} \ atoms \ Na}{1 \ mol \ Na} = 4.9 \times 10^{24} \ atoms \ Na$

2.64   0.744 g phosphorus combined with $(1.704 - 0.744) = 0.960 \ g \ O$

$\dfrac{(0.744/4) \ g \ P}{(0.960/10) \ g \ O} = \dfrac{1.94 \ g \ P}{1 \ g \ O}$

$16.000 \ amu \ O \cdot \dfrac{1.94 \ g \ P}{1 \ g \ O} = 31.0 \ amu \ P$

2.65   (a) mass of nucleus $= 1.06 \times 10^{-22} \ g$ (electron mass is negligible)

nuclear radius $= 4.8 \times 10^{-6} \ nm \cdot \dfrac{10^{-9} \ m}{1 \ nm} \cdot \dfrac{100 \ cm}{1 \ m} = 4.8 \times 10^{-13} \ cm$

volume of nucleus $= (^4/_3)(\pi)(4.8 \times 10^{-13} \ cm)^3 = 4.6 \times 10^{-37} \ cm^3$

density of nucleus $= \dfrac{1.06 \times 10^{-22} \ g}{4.6 \times 10^{-37} \ cm^3} = 2.3 \times 10^{14} \ g/cm^3$

(b) atomic radius $= 0.125 \ nm \cdot \dfrac{10^{-9} \ m}{1 \ nm} \cdot \dfrac{100 \ cm}{1 \ m} = 1.25 \times 10^{-8} \ cm$

volume of Zn atom $= (^4/_3)(\pi)(1.25 \times 10^{-8} \ cm)^3 = 8.18 \times 10^{-24} \ cm^3$

volume of space occupied by electrons $= 8.18 \times 10^{-24} \ cm^3 - 4.6 \times 10^{-37} \ cm^3$

$= 8.18 \times 10^{-24} \ cm^3$

density of space occupied by electrons $= \dfrac{(30)(9.11 \times 10^{-28} \ g)}{8.18 \times 10^{-24} \ cm^3} = 3.34 \times 10^{-3} \ g/cm^3$

(c) The nucleus is much more dense than the space occupied by the electrons.

2.66 $2.0000 \ g \ C \cdot \dfrac{1 \ mol \ C}{12.011 \ g \ C} \cdot \dfrac{6.02214 \times 10^{23} \ atoms \ C}{1 \ mol \ C} = 1.0028 \times 10^{23} \ atoms \ C$

The maximum mass of carbon that could have been on the balance is 2.0001 g, so the maximum number of atoms that could be present is also 1.0028×10^{23} atoms.

2.67   (a) Volume of cube $= (1.000 \ cm)^3 = 1.000 \ cm^3$

$1.000 \ cm^3 \ Pb \cdot \dfrac{11.35 \ g \ Pb}{1 \ cm^3} \cdot \dfrac{1 \ mol \ Pb}{207.2 \ g \ Pb} \cdot \dfrac{6.0221 \times 10^{23} \ atoms \ Pb}{1 \ mol \ Pb} = 3.299 \times 10^{22} \ atoms \ Pb$

(b) Volume of one lead atom = $\dfrac{(0.60)(1.000 \text{ cm}^3)}{3.299 \times 10^{22} \text{ atoms Pb}}$ = 1.819×10^{-23} cm^3

1.819×10^{-23} cm^3 = ($^4/_3$)(π)(Pb radius)^3

Pb radius = 1.631×10^{-8} cm

2.68   1 ton = 10^3 kg = 10^6 g, so 1 ton-mol = 10^6 g-mol

1.0 ton-mol Al $\cdot$ $\dfrac{10^6 \text{ g-mol}}{1 \text{ ton-mol}}$ $\cdot$ $\dfrac{6.022 \times 10^{23} \text{ atoms Al}}{1 \text{ g-mol}}$ = 6.022×10^{29} atoms Al

2.69   See Screen 2.20 for one possible method.

2.70   The simulation indicates that Ca has 5 stable isotopes with 20, 22, 23, 24, and 26 neutrons. (^{48}Ca, with a very low abundance, is also possible.) The ratio of neutrons to protons rapidly becomes greater than 1 as the number of protons increases. An isotope such as ^{108}Xe is not possible, because the neutron/proton ratio is only 1.

2.71   (a) Binding energy increases as the atomic number increases to 20. The elements around iron have the maximum binding energy. Iron is the second most abundant metal in the earth's crust.

(b) ^{4}He

(c) ^{16}O

Chapter 3
Molecules, Ions, and Their Compounds

INSTRUCTOR'S NOTES

The material in Chapters 2-5 is treated as a unit and requires approximately fifteen lectures all together. Chapter 3 itself should be completed in about 2-3 lectures.

Some points on which students have some problems or questions are:

(a) The rule of determining the charges on transition metal cations tells students that they can assume such ions usually have 2+ or 3+ charges (with 2+ charges especially prominent). They are often uneasy about being given this choice. We certainly emphasize that they will see other possibilities (and that even negative charges are possible but that they will not see them in the general chemistry course).

(b) Students have to be convinced that they have no choice but to learn the language of chemistry by memorizing the names and charges of polyatomic ions.

(c) A very common problem students have is recognizing that $MgBr_2$, for example, is composed of Mg^{2+} and two Br^- ions. We have seen such combinations as Mg^{2+} and Br_2^{2-}.

SUGGESTED DEMONSTRATIONS

1.   Elements That Form Molecules in Their Natural States

•   Use samples of H_2, O_2, N_2, and Br_2 to illustrate elements that are molecules.

2.   Molecules and Allotropes

•   Show many molecular models in class, if possible, using the CAChe Visualizer on the *General Chemistry Interactive CD-ROM*.

•   For the formation of polymeric sulfur, see the *General Chemistry Interactive CD-ROM*.

3.   Formation of Compounds from Elements

•   Bring many samples of compounds to your lecture. Ignite H_2 in a balloon or burn Mg in O_2 to show how elements are turned into compounds. Also burn Mg in CO_2 to show CO_2 is made of C and that MgO can be made another way.

•   Use the *Periodic Table Videodisc* to illustrate the formation of compounds by elements reacting with O_2 and with acids and bases.

•   See the *General Chemistry Interactive CD-ROM* for the reaction between phosphorus and bromine.

4.   Decomposition of a Compound into Its Elements

•   For the reaction between sugar and sulfuric acid see the *General Chemistry Interactive CD-ROM*.

5.   Ionic Compounds

•   Bring a number of common, ionic compounds to class.

•   See the *General Chemistry Interactive CD-ROM* for molecular models of a sodium chloride unit cell, an extended lattice, and a space-filling unit cell.

6.   Molar Quantities

- Display molar quantities of NaCl, H_2O, sugar, and common ionic compounds. Especially show some hydrated salts to emphasize the inclusion of H_2O in their molar mass.

- Display a teaspoon of water and ask how many moles, how many molecules, and how many total atoms are contained.

- Display a piece of $CaCO_3$ and ask how many moles are contained in the piece and then how many total atoms.

7.   Weight Percent of Elements

- When talking about weight percent of elements, we used NO_2 as an example and then made NO_2 from Cu and nitric acid.

8.   Determine the Formula of a Hydrated Compound

- Heat samples of hydrated $CoSO_4$ or $CuSO_4$ to illustrate analysis of hydrated compounds and the color change that can occur when water is released and evaporated.

- For the discussion of analysis, we heated a sample of $CoCl_2 \cdot 6\ H_2O$ in a crucible to illustrate how to determine the number of waters of hydration. Also discussed the distinctive color change observed in this process.

Solutions to Study Questions

3.1   Cisplatin, $Pt(NH_3)_2Cl_2$, contains 2 nitrogen atoms (1 in each of two NH_3 groups) and 6 hydrogen atoms (3
       in each of two NH_3 groups).

$$\frac{6 \text{ H atoms}}{1 \text{ cisplatin molecule}} \cdot \frac{6.02 \times 10^{23} \text{ molecules}}{1 \text{ mol cisplatin}} = 3.6 \times 10^{24} \text{ H atoms/1 mol cisplatin}$$

Molar mass of cisplatin = 300.05 g/mol

3.2   The H—C—O—H portion of the molecule lies in the plane of the paper. The other two H
       atoms attached to C are above and below the plane of the paper.

3.3   A strontium atom has 38 electrons. When an atom of strontium forms an ion, it loses
       two electrons, forming an ion having the same number of electrons as the noble gas krypton.

3.4 NH_4^+ ammonium ion   +1 charge

       SO_4^{2-} sulfate ion   −2 charge

       Molar mass of ammonium sulfate = 132.14 g/mol

3.5   (a) 3.0×10^{23} molecules represents $^1\!/_2$ mole of adenine. The molar mass of adenine ($C_5H_5N_5$) is
            135.13 g/mol, so $^1\!/_2$ mole of adenine has a mass of 67.56 g. Forty grams of adenine therefore has less
            mass than $^1\!/_2$ mol of adenine.

       (b) Adenine is one of the four bases found in DNA. The bases all have at least a six-member ring
            consisting of carbon and nitrogen atoms.

3.6   Borate ion BO_3^{3-} The borate ion is an anion.

3.7   Molar mass of $BaCl_2$ = 208.23 g/mol   Molar mass of $SiCl_4$ = 169.90 g/mol

       One mole of $BaCl_2$ has a greater mass, so 0.5 mol of $BaCl_2$ will have a greater mass than 0.5 mol of
       $SiCl_4$.

3.8   An empirical formula gives the simplest possible ratio of atoms in a molecule. The molecular formula
       shows both the ratio of atoms and the total number of atoms in a molecule. The empirical formula of
       ethane is CH_3 and the molecular formula is C_2H_6.

3.9   Water, H_2O $\dfrac{16.00 \text{ g}}{18.02 \text{ g}} \cdot 100\% = 88.79\%$ oxygen

       Methanol, CH_3OH $\dfrac{16.00 \text{ g}}{32.04 \text{ g}} \cdot 100\% = 49.94\%$ oxygen

       Water has a larger weight percentage of oxygen.

3.10   (a) $C_7H_{16}O$ (b) $C_6H_8O_6$ (c) $C_{14}H_{18}N_2O_5$

3.11   (a) C_5H_8 (b) $C_{11}H_{16}O_2$ (c) $C_{10}H_{16}O$

3.12   (a) 1 Ca atom, 2 C atoms, 4 O atoms

      (b) 7 C atoms, 6 H atoms, 1 O atom

      (c) 1 Co atom, 6 N atoms, 15 H atoms, 2 O atoms, 2 Cl atoms

      (d) 4 K atoms, 1 Fe atom, 6 C atoms, 6 N atoms

3.13   (a) 2 Mn atoms, 10 C atoms, 10 O atoms

      (b) 4 C atoms, 6 H atoms, 4 O atoms

      (c) 7 C atoms, 5 H atoms, 3 N atoms, 6 O atoms

3.14   The formula of sulfuric acid is H_2SO_4. The molecule is not flat. The O atoms are arranged around the sulfur at the corners of a tetrahedron. The hydrogen atoms are connected to two of the oxygen atoms.

3.15   The formula of toluene is C_7H_8. The ring portion of the molecule is flat. The structure consists of a six-member ring of carbon atoms. Five of the carbon atoms in the ring are attached to an H atom, the sixth carbon is attached to a —CH_3 group.

3.16   (a) Mg^{2+} (b) Zn^{2+} (c) Ni^{2+} (d) Ga^{3+}

3.17   (a) Se^{2-} (b) F^- (c) Fe^{2+}, Fe^{3+} (d) N^{3-}

3.18   (a) Ba^{2+} (e) S^{2-}

      (b) Ti^{4+} (f) ClO_4^-

      (c) PO_4^{3-} (g) Co^{2+}

      (d) HCO_3^- (h) SO_4^{2-}

3.19   (a) MnO_4^- (d) NH_4^+

      (b) NO_2^- (e) PO_4^{3-}

      (c) $H_2PO_4^-$ (f) SO_3^{2-}

3.20   Potassium loses 1 electron when it becomes a monatomic ion. Argon has the same number of electrons as the K^+ ion.

3.21   They both gain two electrons. O^{2-} has the same number of electrons as Ne and S^{2-} has the same number of electrons as Ar. Both elements form 2– anions and both react to form binary compounds with hydrogen.

3.22 Ba^{2+}, Br^- $BaBr_2$

3.23 Co^{3+}, F^- CoF_3

3.24   (a) 2 K^+ ions, 1 S^{2-} ion   (d) 3 NH_4^+ ions, 1 PO_4^{3-} ion

        (b) 1 Co^{2+} ion, 1 SO_4^{2-} ion   (e) 1 Ca^{2+} ion, 2 ClO^- ions

        (c) 1 K^+ ion, 1 MnO_4^- ion

3.25   (a) 1 Mg^{2+}, 2 $CH_3CO_2^-$ (d) 1 K^+, 1 $H_2PO_4^-$

        (b) 1 Ti^{4+}, 2 SO_4^{2-} (e) 1 Cu^{2+}, 1 CO_3^{2-}

        (c) 1 Al^{3+}, 3 OH^-

3.26 Co^{2+}: CoO Co^{3+} Co_2O_3

3.27   (a) Pt^{2+}: $PtCl_2$ Pt^{4+}: $PtCl_4$

        (b) Pt^{2+}: PtS Pt^{4+}: PtS_2

3.28   (a) incorrect, $AlCl_3$ (b) incorrect, KF   (c) correct   (d) correct

3.29   (a) incorrect, CaO   (b) correct   (c) incorrect, Fe_2O_3 or FeO   (d) correct

3.30   MgO, $Mg_3(PO_4)_2$, Al_2O_3, $AlPO_4$

3.31 $(NH_4)_2CO_3$, $(NH_4)_2SO_4$, $NiCO_3$, $NiSO_4$

3.32   (a) potassium sulfide   (c) ammonium phosphate

        (b) cobalt(II) sulfate   (d) calcium hypochlorite

3.33   (a) calcium acetate   (c) aluminum hydroxide

        (b) nickel(II) phosphate   (d) potassium dihydrogen phosphate

3.34   (a) $(NH_4)_2CO_3$ (d) $AlPO_4$

        (b) CaI_2 (e) $AgCH_3CO_2$

        (c) $CuBr_2$

3.35   (a) $Ca(HCO_3)_2$ (d) K_2HPO_4

        (b) $KMnO_4$ (e) Na_2SO_3

        (c) $Mg(ClO_4)_2$

3.36 Na_2CO_3 sodium carbonate   NaI   sodium iodide

        $BaCO_3$ barium carbonate BaI_2 barium iodide

3.37 $Mg_3(PO_4)_2$ magnesium phosphate $Mg(NO_3)_2$ magnesium nitrate

           $FePO_4$ iron(III) phosphate $Fe(NO_3)_3$ iron(III) nitrate

3.38   The force of attraction is stronger in NaF than in NaI because the distance between ion centers is smaller in NaF (235 pm) than in NaI (322 pm).

3.39   The attractive forces are stronger in CaO because the ion charges are greater (+2/–2 in CaO and +1/–1 in NaCl).

3.40   (a) nitrogen trifluoride   (c) boron triiodide

        (b) hydrogen iodide   (d) phosphorus pentafluoride

3.41   (a) dinitrogen pentaoxide   (c) oxygen difluoride

        (b) tetraphosphorus trisulfide   (d) xenon tetrafluoride

3.42   (a) SCl_2 (b) N_2O_5 (c) $SiCl_4$ (d) B_2O_3

3.43   (a) BrF_3 (d) P_2F_4

        (b) XeF_2 (e) C_4H_{10}

        (c) N_2H_4

3.44   (a) Fe_2O_3 159.69 g/mol

        (b) BCl_3 117.17 g/mol

        (c) $C_6H_8O_6$ 176.13 g/mol

3.45   (a) $Fe(C_6H_{11}O_7)_2$ 446.14 g/mol

        (b) $CH_3CH_2CH_2CH_2SH$ 90.19 g/mol

        (c) $C_{20}H_{24}N_2O_2$ 324.42 g/mol

3.46   (a) $Ni(NO_3)_2 \cdot 6\ H_2O$ 290 79 g/mol

        (b) $CuSO_4 \cdot 5\ H_2O$ 249.69 g/mol

3.47   (a) $H_2C_2O_4 \cdot 2\ H_2O$ 126.07 g/mol

        (b) $MgSO_4 \cdot 7\ H_2O$ 246.48 g/mol

3.48   (a) 1.00 g $C_3H_7OH \cdot \dfrac{1\ mol}{60.10\ g}$ = 0.0166 mol C_3H_7OH

        (b) 1.00 g $C_{11}H_{16}O_2 \cdot \dfrac{1\ mol}{180.2\ g}$ = 5.55 × 10^{-3} mol $C_{11}H_{16}O_2$

        (c) 1.00 g $C_9H_8O_4 \cdot \dfrac{1\ mol}{180.2\ g}$ = 5.55 × 10^{-3} mol $C_9H_8O_4$

3.49 (a) $0.250 \text{ g } C_{14}H_{10}O_4 \cdot \dfrac{1 \text{ mol}}{242.2 \text{ g}} = 1.03 \times 10^{-3} \text{ mol } C_{14}H_{10}O_4$

   (b) $0.250 \text{ Pt(NH}_3)_2Cl_2 \cdot \dfrac{1 \text{ mol}}{300.0 \text{ g}} = 8.33 \times 10^{-4} \text{ mol } Pt(NH_3)_2Cl_2$

3.50 $2.50 \text{ kg } CH_3CN \cdot \dfrac{10^3 \text{ g}}{1 \text{ kg}} \cdot \dfrac{1 \text{ mol}}{41.05 \text{ g}} = 60.9 \text{ mol } CH_3CN$

3.51 $1260 \times 10^6 \text{ kg } (CH_3)_2CO \cdot \dfrac{10^3 \text{ g}}{1 \text{ kg}} \cdot \dfrac{1 \text{ mol}}{58.08 \text{ g}} = 2.17 \times 10^{10} \text{ mol } (CH_3)_2CO$

3.52 $1.00 \text{ kg } SO_3 \cdot \dfrac{10^3 \text{ g}}{1 \text{ kg}} \cdot \dfrac{1 \text{ mol}}{80.06 \text{ g}} = 12.5 \text{ mol } SO_3$

  $12.5 \text{ mol } SO_3 \cdot \dfrac{6.022 \times 10^{23} \text{ molecules}}{1 \text{ mol } SO_3} = 7.52 \times 10^{24} \text{ molecules } SO_3$

  $7.52 \times 10^{24} \text{ molecules } SO_3 \cdot \dfrac{1 \text{ S atom}}{1 \text{ } SO_3 \text{ molecule}} = 7.52 \times 10^{24} \text{ S atoms}$

  $7.52 \times 10^{24} \text{ molecules } SO_3 \cdot \dfrac{3 \text{ O atoms}}{1 \text{ } SO_3 \text{ molecule}} = 2.26 \times 10^{25} \text{ O atoms}$

3.53 (a) $324 \text{ mg } C_9H_8O_4 \cdot \dfrac{1 \text{ g}}{10^3 \text{ mg}} \cdot \dfrac{1 \text{ mol}}{180.2 \text{ g}} = 1.80 \times 10^{-3} \text{ mol } C_9H_8O_4$

    $1904 \text{ mg } NaHCO_3 \cdot \dfrac{1 \text{ g}}{10^3 \text{ mg}} \cdot \dfrac{1 \text{ mol}}{84.007 \text{ g}} = 0.02266 \text{ mol } NaHCO_3$

    $1000. \text{ mg } C_6H_8O_7 \cdot \dfrac{1 \text{ g}}{10^3 \text{ mg}} \cdot \dfrac{1 \text{ mol}}{192.13 \text{ g}} = 5.205 \times 10^{-3} \text{ mol } C_6H_8O_7$

   (b) $5.55 \times 10^{-3} \text{ mol } C_9H_8O_4 \cdot \dfrac{6.022 \times 10^{23} \text{ molecules}}{1 \text{ mol } C_9H_8O_4} = 1.08 \times 10^{21} \text{ molecules } C_9H_8O_4$

3.54 (a) $\dfrac{207.2 \text{ g Pb}}{239.3 \text{ g PbS}} \cdot 100\% = 86.59\% \text{ Pb}$ $\dfrac{32.1 \text{ g S}}{239.3 \text{ g PbS}} \cdot 100\% = 13.41\% \text{ S}$

   (b) $\dfrac{(3)(12.01) \text{ g C}}{44.096 \text{ g } C_3H_8} \cdot 100\% = 81.71\% \text{ C}$ $\dfrac{(8)(1.008) \text{ g H}}{44.096 \text{ g } C_3H_8} \cdot 100\% = 18.29\% \text{ H}$

   (c) $\dfrac{(10)(12.01) \text{ g C}}{150.21 \text{ g } C_{10}H_{14}O} \cdot 100\% = 79.95\% \text{ C}$ $\dfrac{(14)(1.008) \text{ g H}}{150.21 \text{ g } C_{10}H_{14}O} \cdot 100\% = 9.395\% \text{ H}$

    $\dfrac{16.00 \text{ g O}}{150.21 \text{ g } C_{10}H_{14}O} \cdot 100\% = 10.65\% \text{ O}$

3.55 (a) $\dfrac{(8)(12.01) \text{ g C}}{166.18 \text{ g } C_8H_{10}N_2O_2} \cdot 100\% = 57.82\% \text{ C}$ $\dfrac{(10)(1.008) \text{ g H}}{166.18 \text{ g } C_8H_{10}N_2O_2} \cdot 100\% = 6.066\% \text{ H}$

    $\dfrac{(2)(14.01) \text{ g N}}{166.18 \text{ g } C_8H_{10}N_2O_2} \cdot 100\% = 16.86\% \text{ N}$ $\dfrac{(2)(16.00) \text{ g O}}{166.18 \text{ g } C_8H_{10}N_2O_2} \cdot 100\% = 19.26\% \text{ O}$

   (b) $\dfrac{(10)(12.01) \text{ g C}}{156.26 \text{ g } C_{10}H_{20}O} \cdot 100\% = 76.86\% \text{ C}$ $\dfrac{(20)(1.008) \text{ g H}}{156.26 \text{ g } C_{10}H_{20}O} \cdot 100\% = 12.90\% \text{ H}$

    $\dfrac{16.00 \text{ g O}}{156.26 \text{ g } C_{10}H_{20}O} \cdot 100\% = 10.24\% \text{ O}$

(c) $\dfrac{58.93 \text{ g Co}}{237.93 \text{ g CoCl}_2 \cdot 6 \text{ H}_2\text{O}} \cdot 100\% = 24.77\% \text{ Co}$ $\qquad$ $\dfrac{(2)(35.45) \text{ g Cl}}{237.93 \text{ g CoCl}_2 \cdot 6 \text{ H}_2\text{O}} \cdot 100\% = 29.80\% \text{ Cl}$

$\dfrac{(12)(1.008) \text{ g H}}{237.93 \text{ g CoCl}_2 \cdot 6 \text{ H}_2\text{O}} \cdot 100\% = 5.084\% \text{ H}$ $\qquad$ $\dfrac{(6)(16.00) \text{ g O}}{237.93 \text{ g CoCl}_2 \cdot 6 \text{ H}_2\text{O}} \cdot 100\% = 40.35\% \text{ O}$

3.56 $\quad 10.0 \text{ g PbS} \cdot \dfrac{207.2 \text{ g Pb}}{239.3 \text{ g PbS}} = 8.66 \text{ g Pb}$

3.57 $\quad 25.0 \text{ g Fe}_2\text{O}_3 \cdot \dfrac{(2)(55.85) \text{ g Fe}}{159.70 \text{ g Fe}_2\text{O}_3} = 17.5 \text{ g Fe}$

3.58 $\quad 10.0 \text{ g Cu} \cdot \dfrac{95.62 \text{ g CuS}}{63.55 \text{ g Cu}} = 15.0 \text{ g CuS}$

3.59 $\quad 750 \text{ g Ti} \cdot \dfrac{157.72 \text{ g FeTiO}_3}{47.87 \text{ g Ti}} = 2.4 \times 10^3 \text{ g FeTiO}_3$

3.60 $\quad$ Empirical formula mass = 59.04 g/mol $\qquad\qquad \dfrac{118.1 \text{ g/mol}}{59.04 \text{ g/mol}} = 2$

The molecular formula is $(C_2H_3O_2)_2$, or $C_4H_6O_4$

3.61 $\quad$ Empirical formula mass = 58.06 g/mol $\qquad\qquad \dfrac{116.1 \text{ g/mol}}{58.06 \text{ g/mol}} = 2$

The molecular formula is $(C_2H_4NO)_2$, or $C_4H_8N_2O_2$

3.62

	Empirical formula	Molar mass (g/mol)	Molecular formula	
(a)	CH	26.0	26.0/13.0 = 2	C_2H_2
(b)	CHO	116.1	116.1/29.0 = 4	$C_4H_4O_4$
(c)	CH_2	112.2	$(CH_2)_8 =$	C_8H_{16}

3.63

	Empirical formula	Molar mass (g/mol)	Molecular formula	
(a)	$C_2H_3O_3$	150.1	150.1/75.0 = 2	$C_4H_6O_6$
(b)	C_3H_8	44.1	44.1/44.1 = 1	C_3H_8
(c)	B_5H_7	122.2	122.2/61.1 = 2	$B_{10}H_{14}$

3.64 $\quad$ Assume 100.00 g compound.

$92.26 \text{ g C} \cdot \dfrac{1 \text{ mol}}{12.011 \text{ g}} = 7.681 \text{ mol C}$ $\qquad\qquad 7.74 \text{ g H} \cdot \dfrac{1 \text{ mol}}{1.008 \text{ g}} = 7.68 \text{ mol H}$

$\dfrac{7.681 \text{ mol C}}{7.68 \text{ mol H}} = \dfrac{1 \text{ mol C}}{1 \text{ mol H}}$ $\qquad$ The empirical formula is CH

$\dfrac{26.02 \text{ g/mol}}{13.02 \text{ g/mol}} = 2$ $\qquad\qquad$ The molecular formula is C_2H_2

3.65   The compound is 88.5% B and 11.5% H. Assume 100.0 g of compound.

$$88.5 \text{ g B} \cdot \frac{1 \text{ mol}}{10.81 \text{ g}} = 8.19 \text{ mol B} \qquad 11.5 \text{ g H} \cdot \frac{1 \text{ mol}}{1.008 \text{ g}} = 11.4 \text{ mol H}$$

$$\frac{11.4 \text{ mol H}}{8.19 \text{ mol B}} = \frac{1.39 \text{ mol H}}{1 \text{ mol B}} = \frac{7/5 \text{ mol H}}{1 \text{ mol B}} = \frac{7 \text{ mol H}}{5 \text{ mol B}} \qquad \text{The empirical formula is } B_5H_7.$$

3.66   The compound is 89.94% C and 10.06% H. Assume 100.00 g of compound.

$$89.94 \text{ g C} \cdot \frac{1 \text{ mol}}{12.011 \text{ g}} = 7.488 \text{ mol C} \qquad 10.06 \text{ g H} \cdot \frac{1 \text{ mol}}{1.0079 \text{ g}} = 9.981 \text{ mol H}$$

$$\frac{9.981 \text{ mol H}}{7.488 \text{ mol C}} = \frac{1.33 \text{ mol H}}{1 \text{ mol C}} = \frac{4/3 \text{ mol H}}{1 \text{ mol C}} = \frac{4 \text{ mol H}}{3 \text{ mol C}} \qquad \text{The empirical formula is } C_3H_4.$$

$$\frac{120.2 \text{ g/mol}}{40.07 \text{ g/mol}} = 3 \qquad \text{The molecular formula is } C_9H_{12}$$

3.67   The compound is 36.84% N and 63.16% O. Assume 100.00 g of compound.

$$36.84 \text{ g N} \cdot \frac{1 \text{ mol}}{14.007 \text{ g}} = 2.630 \text{ mol N} \qquad 63.16 \text{ g O} \cdot \frac{1 \text{ mol}}{15.999 \text{ g}} = 3.948 \text{ mol O}$$

$$\frac{3.948 \text{ mol O}}{2.630 \text{ mol N}} = \frac{1.5 \text{ mol O}}{1 \text{ mol N}} = \frac{3 \text{ mol O}}{2 \text{ mol N}} \qquad \text{The empirical formula is } N_2O_3$$

3.68   Assume 100.00 g of compound.

$$63.15 \text{ g C} \cdot \frac{1 \text{ mol}}{12.011 \text{ g}} = 5.258 \text{ mol C} \qquad 5.30 \text{ g H} \cdot \frac{1 \text{ mol}}{1.008 \text{ g}} = 5.26 \text{ mol H}$$

$$31.55 \text{ g O} \cdot \frac{1 \text{ mol}}{15.999 \text{ g}} = 1.972 \text{ mol O}$$

$$\frac{5.258 \text{ mol C}}{1.972 \text{ mol O}} = \frac{2.667 \text{ mol C}}{1 \text{ mol O}} = \frac{8 \text{ mol C}}{3 \text{ mol O}} \qquad \frac{5.26 \text{ mol H}}{1.972 \text{ mol O}} = \frac{2.667 \text{ mol H}}{1 \text{ mol O}} = \frac{8 \text{ mol H}}{3 \text{ mol O}}$$

The empirical formula is $C_8H_8O_3$

The molar mass is equal to the empirical formula mass, so the molecular formula is also $C_8H_8O_3$

3.69   Assume 100.0 g of compound.

$$74.0 \text{ g C} \cdot \frac{1 \text{ mol}}{12.01 \text{ g}} = 6.16 \text{ mol C} \qquad 8.65 \text{ g H} \cdot \frac{1 \text{ mol}}{1.008 \text{ g}} = 8.58 \text{ mol H}$$

$$17.35 \text{ g N} \cdot \frac{1 \text{ mol}}{14.007 \text{ g}} = 1.239 \text{ mol N}$$

$$\frac{6.16 \text{ mol C}}{1.239 \text{ mol N}} = \frac{5 \text{ mol C}}{1 \text{ mol N}} \qquad \frac{8.58 \text{ mol H}}{1.239 \text{ mol N}} = \frac{7 \text{ mol H}}{1 \text{ mol N}}$$

The empirical formula is C_5H_7N

$$\frac{162 \text{ g/mol}}{81.1 \text{ g/mol}} = 2 \qquad \text{The molecular formula is } C_{10}H_{14}N_2$$

3.70   1.687 g hydrated compound − 0.824 g $MgSO_4$ = 0.863 g H_2O

$$0.863 \text{ g } H_2O \cdot \frac{1 \text{ mol}}{18.02 \text{ g}} = 0.0479 \text{ mol } H_2O$$

$$0.824 \text{ g } MgSO_4 \cdot \frac{1 \text{ mol}}{120.4 \text{ g}} = 0.00684 \text{ mol } MgSO_4$$

$$\frac{0.0479 \text{ mol } H_2O}{0.00684 \text{ mol } MgSO_4} = \frac{7.00 \text{ mol } H_2O}{1 \text{ mol } MgSO_4}$$ There are 7 water molecules per formula unit of $MgSO_4$

3.71   4.74 g hydrated compound − 2.16 g H_2O = 2.58 g $KAl(SO_4)_2$

$$2.16 \text{ g } H_2O \cdot \frac{1 \text{ mol}}{18.02 \text{ g}} = 0.120 \text{ mol } H_2O \qquad 2.58 \text{ g } KAl(SO_4)_2 \cdot \frac{1 \text{ mol}}{258.2 \text{ g}} = 0.00999 \text{ mol } KAl(SO_4)_2$$

$$\frac{0.120 \text{ mol } H_2O}{0.00999 \text{ mol } KAl(SO_4)_2} = \frac{12.0 \text{ mol } H_2O}{1 \text{ mol } KAl(SO_4)_2}$$

There are 12 water molecules per formula unit of $KAl(SO_4)_2$; $x = 12$

3.72   0.678 g compound − 0.526 g Xe = 0.152 g F

$$0.526 \text{ g Xe} \cdot \frac{1 \text{ mol}}{131.3 \text{ g}} = 0.00401 \text{ mol Xe} \qquad 0.152 \text{ g F} \cdot \frac{1 \text{ mol}}{19.00 \text{ g}} = 0.00800 \text{ mol F}$$

$$\frac{0.00800 \text{ mol F}}{0.00401 \text{ mol Xe}} = \frac{2 \text{ mol F}}{1 \text{ mol Xe}}$$ The empirical formula is XeF_2

3.73   5.722 g compound − 1.256 g S = 4.466 g F

$$1.256 \text{ g S} \cdot \frac{1 \text{ mol}}{32.066 \text{ g}} = 0.03917 \text{ mol S} \qquad 4.466 \text{ g F} \cdot \frac{1 \text{ mol}}{18.998 \text{ g}} = 0.2351 \text{ mol F}$$

$$\frac{0.2351 \text{ mol F}}{0.03917 \text{ mol S}} = \frac{6 \text{ mol F}}{1 \text{ mol S}}$$ The empirical formula is SF_6; $x = 6$

3.74 $$2.50 \text{ g Zn} \cdot \frac{1 \text{ mol}}{65.39 \text{ g}} = 0.0382 \text{ mol Zn} \qquad 9.70 \text{ g I} \cdot \frac{1 \text{ mol}}{126.9 \text{ g}} = 0.0764 \text{ mol I}$$

$$\frac{0.0764 \text{ mol I}}{0.0382 \text{ mol Zn}} = \frac{2 \text{ mol I}}{1 \text{ mol Zn}}$$ The empirical formula is ZnI_2

3.75   3.69 g product − 1.25 g Ge = 2.44 g Cl

$$1.25 \text{ g Ge} \cdot \frac{1 \text{ mol}}{72.61 \text{ g}} = 0.0172 \text{ mol Ge} \qquad 2.44 \text{ g Cl} \cdot \frac{1 \text{ mol}}{35.45 \text{ g}} = 0.0688 \text{ mol Cl}$$

$$\frac{0.0688 \text{ mol Cl}}{0.0172 \text{ mol Ge}} = \frac{4 \text{ mol Cl}}{1 \text{ mol Ge}}$$ The empirical formula is $GeCl_4$

3.76 $$0.05 \text{ mL } H_2O \cdot \frac{1 \text{ cm}^3}{1 \text{ mL}} \cdot \frac{1.00 \text{ g}}{1 \text{ cm}^3} \cdot \frac{1 \text{ mol}}{18.02 \text{ g}} \cdot \frac{6.022 \times 10^{23} \text{ molecules}}{1 \text{ mol}} = 2 \times 10^{21} \text{ molecules } H_2O$$

3.77   (a) Molar mass = 305.42 g/mol

        (b) $$55 \text{ mg capsaicin} \cdot \frac{1 \text{ g}}{10^3 \text{ mg}} \cdot \frac{1 \text{ mol}}{305.42 \text{ g}} = 1.8 \times 10^{-4} \text{ mol capsaicin}$$

(c) $\dfrac{(18)(12.01)\text{ g C}}{305.42\text{ g C}_{18}\text{H}_{27}\text{NO}_3} \cdot 100\% = 70.78\%\text{ C}$ $\dfrac{(27)(1.008)\text{ g H}}{305.42\text{ g C}_{18}\text{H}_{27}\text{NO}_3} \cdot 100\% = 8.911\%\text{ H}$

$\dfrac{14.01\text{ g N}}{305.42\text{ g C}_{18}\text{H}_{27}\text{NO}_3} \cdot 100\% = 4.587\%\text{ N}$ $\dfrac{(3)(16.00)\text{ g O}}{305.42\text{ g C}_{18}\text{H}_{27}\text{NO}_3} \cdot 100\% = 15.72\%\text{ O}$

(d) $55\text{ mg capsaicin} \cdot \dfrac{70.78\text{ mg C}}{100.00\text{ mg C}_{18}\text{H}_{27}\text{NO}_3} = 39\text{ mg C}$

3.78   Molar mass = 245.77 g/mol

$\dfrac{63.55\text{ g Cu}}{245.77\text{ g Cu(NH}_3)_4\text{SO}_4 \cdot \text{H}_2\text{O}} \cdot 100\% = 25.86\%\text{ Cu}$

$\dfrac{(4)(14.01)\text{ g N}}{245.77\text{ g Cu(NH}_3)_4\text{SO}_4 \cdot \text{H}_2\text{O}} \cdot 100\% = 22.80\%\text{ N}$

$\dfrac{(14)(1.008)\text{ g H}}{245.77\text{ g Cu(NH}_3)_4\text{SO}_4 \cdot \text{H}_2\text{O}} \cdot 100\% = 5.742\%\text{ H}$

$\dfrac{32.07\text{ g S}}{245.77\text{ g Cu(NH}_3)_4\text{SO}_4 \cdot \text{H}_2\text{O}} \cdot 100\% = 13.05\%\text{ S}$

$\dfrac{(5)(16.00)\text{ g O}}{245.77\text{ g Cu(NH}_3)_4\text{SO}_4 \cdot \text{H}_2\text{O}} \cdot 100\% = 32.55\%\text{ O}$

$10.5\text{ g Cu(NH}_3)_4\text{SO}_4 \cdot \text{H}_2\text{O} \cdot \dfrac{25.86\text{ g Cu}}{100.00\text{ g Cu(NH}_3)_4\text{SO}_4 \cdot \text{H}_2\text{O}} = 2.72\text{ g Cu}$

$10.5\text{ g Cu(NH}_3)_4\text{SO}_4 \cdot \text{H}_2\text{O} \cdot \dfrac{18.02\text{ g H}_2\text{O}}{245.77\text{ g Cu(NH}_3)_4\text{SO}_4 \cdot \text{H}_2\text{O}} = 0.770\text{ g H}_2\text{O}$

3.79 $15.0\text{ kg P} \cdot \dfrac{310.18\text{ kg Ca}_3(\text{PO}_4)_2}{(2)(30.97)\text{ kg P}} = 75.1\text{ kg Ca}_3(\text{PO}_4)_2$

3.80 $850\text{ kg Cr} \cdot \dfrac{152.00\text{ kg Cr}_2\text{O}_3}{(2)(52.00)\text{ kg Cr}} = 1200\text{ kg Cr}_2\text{O}_3$

3.81   (a) $\text{C}_2\text{H}_6\text{O}_2$ Molar mass = 62.07 g/mol

$\dfrac{(2)(12.01)\text{ g C}}{62.07\text{ g C}_2\text{H}_6\text{O}_2} \cdot 100\% = 38.70\%\text{ C}$ $\dfrac{(2)(16.00)\text{ g O}}{62.07\text{ g C}_2\text{H}_6\text{O}_2} \cdot 100\% = 51.55\%\text{ O}$

(b) $\text{C}_3\text{H}_6\text{O}_3$ Molar mass = 90.08 g/mol

$\dfrac{(3)(12.01)\text{ g C}}{90.08\text{ g C}_3\text{H}_6\text{O}_3} \cdot 100\% = 40.00\%\text{ C}$ $\dfrac{(3)(16.00)\text{ g O}}{90.08\text{ g C}_3\text{H}_6\text{O}_3} \cdot 100\% = 53.29\%\text{ O}$

Dihydroxyacetone has a larger percentage of carbon and of oxygen.

3.82 $\dfrac{1.5\text{ mol H}}{1\text{ mol C}} = \dfrac{3/2\text{ mol H}}{1\text{ mol C}} = \dfrac{3\text{ mol H}}{2\text{ mol C}} = \dfrac{6\text{ mol H}}{4\text{ mol C}}$

$\dfrac{1.25\text{ mol O}}{1\text{ mol C}} = \dfrac{5/4\text{ mol O}}{1\text{ mol C}} = \dfrac{5\text{ mol O}}{4\text{ mol C}}$ The empirical formula is $\text{C}_4\text{H}_6\text{O}_5$.

3.83 $\dfrac{55.85\text{ g Fe}}{151.92\text{ g FeSO}_4} \cdot 100\% = 36.76\%\text{ Fe}$ $\dfrac{55.85\text{ g Fe}}{446.15\text{ g Fe(C}_6\text{H}_{11}\text{O}_7)_2} \cdot 100\% = 12.52\%\text{ Fe}$

The tablet containing FeSO_4 will deliver more atoms of iron.

3.84 $0.109 \text{ g compound} \cdot \dfrac{38.82 \text{ g Fe}}{100.00 \text{ g compound}} \cdot \dfrac{1 \text{ mol}}{55.85 \text{ g}} = 7.58 \times 10^{-4} \text{ mol Fe}$

$0.109 \text{ g compound} \cdot \dfrac{61.18 \text{ g C}_2\text{O}_4{}^{2-}}{100.00 \text{ g compound}} \cdot \dfrac{1 \text{ mol}}{88.02 \text{ g}} = 7.58 \times 10^{-4} \text{ mol C}_2\text{O}_4{}^{2-}$

$\dfrac{7.58 \times 10^{-4} \text{ mol Fe}}{7.58 \times 10^{-4} \text{ mol C}_2\text{O}_4{}^{2-}} = \dfrac{1 \text{ mol Fe}}{1 \text{ mol C}_2\text{O}_4{}^{2-}}$ The empirical formula is FeC_2O_4

3.85   Assume 100.00 g of compound.

$30.70 \text{ g Fe} \cdot \dfrac{1 \text{ mol}}{55.845 \text{ g}} = 0.5497 \text{ mol Fe}$ $69.30 \text{ g CO} \cdot \dfrac{1 \text{ mol}}{28.010 \text{ g}} = 2.474 \text{ mol CO}$

$\dfrac{2.474 \text{ mol CO}}{0.5497 \text{ mol Fe}} = \dfrac{4.5 \text{ mol CO}}{1 \text{ mol Fe}} = \dfrac{9 \text{ mol CO}}{2 \text{ mol Fe}}$ The empirical formula is $Fe_2(CO)_9$

3.86   (a) $C_{10}H_{15}NO$ Molar mass = 165.23 g/mol

(b) $\dfrac{(10)(12.01) \text{ g C}}{165.23 \text{ g C}_{10}\text{H}_{15}\text{NO}} \cdot 100\% = 72.69\% \text{ C}$

(c) $0.125 \text{ g C}_{10}\text{H}_{15}\text{NO} \cdot \dfrac{1 \text{ mol}}{165.23 \text{ g}} = 7.57 \times 10^{-4} \text{ mol C}_{10}\text{H}_{15}\text{NO}$

(d) $7.57 \times 10^{-4} \text{ mol C}_{10}\text{H}_{15}\text{NO} \cdot \dfrac{6.022 \times 10^{23} \text{ molecules}}{1 \text{ mol C}_{10}\text{H}_{15}\text{NO}} = 4.56 \times 10^{20} \text{ molecules}$

$4.56 \times 10^{20} \text{ molecules} \cdot \dfrac{10 \text{ C atoms}}{1 \text{ molecule}} = 4.56 \times 10^{21} \text{ C atoms}$

3.87   (a) $C_7H_5NO_3S$

(b) $125 \text{ mg C}_7\text{H}_5\text{NO}_3\text{S} \cdot \dfrac{1 \text{ g}}{10^3 \text{ mg}} \cdot \dfrac{1 \text{ mol}}{183.19 \text{ g}} = 6.82 \times 10^{-4} \text{ mol C}_7\text{H}_5\text{NO}_3\text{S}$

(c) $125 \text{ mg C}_7\text{H}_5\text{NO}_3\text{S} \cdot \dfrac{32.07 \text{ mg S}}{183.19 \text{ mg C}_7\text{H}_5\text{NO}_3\text{S}} = 21.9 \text{ mg S}$

3.88   Ionic compounds (metal + nonmetal)

(c) Li_2S lithium sulfide

(d) In_2O_3 indium oxide

(g) CaF_2 calcium fluoride

3.89   (a) chlorine trifluoride   (f) phosphorus trichloride

(b) nitrogen trichloride   (g) potassium iodide, ionic

(c) strontium sulfate, ionic   (h) aluminum sulfide, ionic

(d) calcium nitrate, ionic   (i) oxygen difluoride

(e) xenon tetrafluoride   (j) potassium phosphate, ionic

3.90 (a) NaOCl, ionic   (f) $(NH_4)_2SO_3$, ionic

      (b) BI_3 (g) KH_2PO_4, ionic

      (c) $Al(ClO_4)_3$, ionic   (h) S_2Cl_2

      (d) $Ca(CH_3CO_2)_2$, ionic   (i) ClF_3

      (e) $KMnO_4$, ionic   (j) PF_3

3.91

Cation	Anion	Name	Formula
NH_4^+	Br^-	ammonium bromide	NH_4Br
Ba^{2+}	S^{2-}	barium sulfide	BaS
Fe^{2+}	Cl^-	iron(II) chloride	$FeCl_2$
Pb^{2+}	F^-	lead(II) fluoride	PbF_2
Al^{3+}	CO_3^{2-}	aluminum carbonate	$Al_2(CO_3)_3$
Fe^{3+}	O^{2-}	iron(III) oxide	Fe_2O_3
Li^+	ClO_4^-	lithium perchlorate	$LiClO_4$
Al^{3+}	PO_4^{3-}	aluminum phosphate	$AlPO_4$
Li^+	Br^-	lithium bromide	$LiBr$
Ba^{2+}	NO_3^-	barium nitrate	$Ba(NO_3)_2$
Al^{3+}	O^{2-}	aluminum oxide	Al_2O_3
Fe^{3+}	CO_3^{2-}	iron(III) carbonate	$Fe_2(CO_3)_3$

3.92 Assume 100.00 g of compound.

$$93.71 \text{ g C} \cdot \frac{1 \text{ mol}}{12.011 \text{ g}} = 7.802 \text{ mol C} \qquad 6.29 \text{ g H} \cdot \frac{1 \text{ mol}}{1.008 \text{ g}} = 6.24 \text{ mol H}$$

$$\frac{7.802 \text{ mol C}}{6.24 \text{ mol H}} = \frac{1.25 \text{ mol C}}{1 \text{ mol H}} = \frac{5 \text{ mol C}}{4 \text{ mol H}} \qquad \text{The empirical formula is } C_5H_4$$

$$\frac{128.16 \text{ g/mol}}{64.08 \text{ g/mol}} = 2 \qquad \text{The molecular formula is } (C_5H_4)_2 \text{ or } C_{10}H_8$$

3.93 Assume 100.0 g of compound.

$$14.6 \text{ g C} \cdot \frac{1 \text{ mol}}{12.01 \text{ g}} = 1.22 \text{ mol C} \qquad 39.0 \text{ g O} \cdot \frac{1 \text{ mol}}{16.00 \text{ g}} = 2.44 \text{ mol O}$$

$$46.3 \text{ g F} \cdot \frac{1 \text{ mol F}}{19.00 \text{ g}} = 2.44 \text{ mol F}$$

$$\frac{2.44 \text{ mol O}}{1.22 \text{ mol C}} = \frac{2 \text{ mol O}}{1 \text{ mol C}} \qquad \frac{2.44 \text{ mol F}}{1.22 \text{ mol C}} = \frac{2 \text{ mol F}}{1 \text{ mol C}}$$

The empirical formula is CO_2F_2. The empirical formula mass is equal to the molar mass, so the molecular

formula is also CO_2F_2.

3.94   Assume 100.00 g of compound.

$58.77 \text{ g C} \cdot \dfrac{1 \text{ mol}}{12.011 \text{ g}} = 4.893 \text{ mol C}$ $13.81 \text{ g H} \cdot \dfrac{1 \text{ mol}}{1.0079 \text{ g}} = 13.70 \text{ mol H}$

$27.40 \text{ g N} \cdot \dfrac{1 \text{ mol}}{14.007 \text{ g}} = 1.956 \text{ mol N}$

$\dfrac{4.893 \text{ mol C}}{1.956 \text{ mol N}} = \dfrac{2.5 \text{ mol C}}{1 \text{ mol N}} = \dfrac{5 \text{ mol C}}{2 \text{ mol N}}$ $\dfrac{13.70 \text{ mol H}}{1.956 \text{ mol N}} = \dfrac{7 \text{ mol H}}{1 \text{ mol N}} = \dfrac{14 \text{ mol H}}{2 \text{ mol N}}$

The empirical formula is $C_5H_{14}N_2$. The empirical formula mass is equal to the molar mass, so the molecular formula is also $C_5H_{14}N_2$.

3.95   Assume 100.00 g of compound.

$22.88 \text{ g C} \cdot \dfrac{1 \text{ mol}}{12.011 \text{ g}} = 1.905 \text{ mol C}$ $5.76 \text{ g H} \cdot \dfrac{1 \text{ mol}}{1.008 \text{ g}} = 5.71 \text{ mol H}$

$71.36 \text{ g As} \cdot \dfrac{1 \text{ mol}}{74.922 \text{ g}} = 0.9525 \text{ mol As}$

$\dfrac{1.905 \text{ mol C}}{0.9525 \text{ mol As}} = \dfrac{2 \text{ mol C}}{1 \text{ mol As}}$ $\dfrac{5.71 \text{ mol H}}{0.9525 \text{ mol As}} = \dfrac{6 \text{ mol H}}{1 \text{ mol As}}$

The empirical formula is C_2H_6As

$\dfrac{210 \text{ g/mol}}{105.0 \text{ g/mol}} = 2$ The molecular formula is $(C_2H_6As)_2$ or $C_4H_{12}As_2$

3.96   Assume 100.0 g of compound.

$49.5 \text{ g C} \cdot \dfrac{1 \text{ mol}}{12.01 \text{ g}} = 4.12 \text{ mol C}$ $3.2 \text{ g H} \cdot \dfrac{1 \text{ mol}}{1.01 \text{ g}} = 3.2 \text{ mol H}$

$22.0 \text{ g O} \cdot \dfrac{1 \text{ mol}}{16.00 \text{ g}} = 1.38 \text{ mol O}$ $25.2 \text{ g Mn} \cdot \dfrac{1 \text{ mol}}{54.94 \text{ g}} = 0.459 \text{ mol Mn}$

$\dfrac{4.12 \text{ mol C}}{0.459 \text{ mol Mn}} = \dfrac{9 \text{ mol C}}{1 \text{ mol Mn}}$ $\dfrac{3.2 \text{ mol H}}{0.459 \text{ mol Mn}} = \dfrac{7 \text{ mol H}}{1 \text{ mol Mn}}$

$\dfrac{1.38 \text{ mol O}}{0.459 \text{ mol Mn}} = \dfrac{3 \text{ mol O}}{1 \text{ mol Mn}}$ The empirical formula is $C_9H_7MnO_3$

3.97 $0.364 \text{ g Ni(CO)}_x - 0.125 \text{ g Ni} = 0.239 \text{ g CO}$

$0.239 \text{ g CO} \cdot \dfrac{1 \text{ mol}}{28.01 \text{ g}} = 0.00853 \text{ mol CO}$ $0.125 \text{ g Ni} \cdot \dfrac{1 \text{ mol}}{58.69 \text{ g}} = 0.00213 \text{ mol Ni}$

$\dfrac{0.00853 \text{ mol CO}}{0.00213 \text{ mol Ni}} = \dfrac{4 \text{ mol CO}}{1 \text{ mol Ni}}$ The compound formula is $NiCO_4$ ($x = 4$)

3.98 $1.246 \text{ g I}_x\text{Cl}_y - 0.678 \text{ g I} = 0.568 \text{ g Cl}$

$0.678 \text{ g I} \cdot \dfrac{1 \text{ mol}}{126.9 \text{ g}} = 0.00534 \text{ mol I}$ $0.568 \text{ g Cl} \cdot \dfrac{1 \text{ mol}}{35.45 \text{ g}} = 0.0160 \text{ mol Cl}$

$\dfrac{0.0160 \text{ mol Cl}}{0.00534 \text{ mol I}} = \dfrac{3 \text{ mol Cl}}{1 \text{ mol I}}$ The empirical formula is ICl_3

$\dfrac{467 \text{ g/mol}}{233.3 \text{ g/mol}} = 2$ The molecular formula is I_2Cl_6

3.99 $2.04 \text{ g V} \cdot \dfrac{1 \text{ mol}}{50.94 \text{ g}} = 0.0400 \text{ mol V}$ $1.93 \text{ g S} \cdot \dfrac{1 \text{ mol}}{32.07 \text{ g}} = 0.0602 \text{ mol S}$

$\dfrac{0.0602 \text{ mol S}}{0.0400 \text{ mol V}} = \dfrac{1.5 \text{ mol S}}{1 \text{ mol V}} = \dfrac{3 \text{ mol S}}{2 \text{ mol V}}$ The empirical formula is V_2S_3

3.100 $15.8 \text{ kg FeS}_2 \cdot \dfrac{55.85 \text{ kg Fe}}{119.99 \text{ kg FeS}_2} = 7.35 \text{ kg Fe}$

3.101 $1.00 \text{ kg ore} \cdot \dfrac{10^3 \text{ g}}{1 \text{ kg}} \cdot \dfrac{10.6 \text{ g Sb}}{100.0 \text{ g ore}} \cdot \dfrac{339.8 \text{ g Sb}_2S_3}{(2)(121.8 \text{ g}) \text{ Sb}} = 148 \text{ g Sb}_2S_3$

3.102   (a) True. The molar mass of C_8H_{18} is 114.2 g/mol, so 57.1 g is 0.500 mol of octane.

   (b) True. $\dfrac{(8)(12.01) \text{ g C}}{114.2 \text{ g C}_8H_{18}} \cdot 100\% = 84.1\% \text{ C}$

   (c) True.

   (d) False. $57.1 \text{ g C}_8H_{18} \cdot \dfrac{(18)(1.008) \text{ g H}}{114.2 \text{ g C}_8H_{18}} = 9.07 \text{ g H}$

3.103   (d) Na_2MoO_4

3.104 $2 \text{ tablets} \cdot \dfrac{300. \text{ mg}}{1 \text{ tablet}} \cdot \dfrac{1 \text{ g}}{10^3 \text{ mg}} \cdot \dfrac{1 \text{ mol}}{1086 \text{ g}} = 5.52 \times 10^{-4} \text{ mol C}_{21}H_{15}Bi_3O_{12}$

$5.52 \times 10^{-4} \text{ mol C}_{21}H_{15}Bi_3O_{12} \cdot \dfrac{3 \text{ mol Bi}}{1 \text{ mol C}_{21}H_{15}Bi_3O_{12}} \cdot \dfrac{209.0 \text{ g}}{1 \text{ mol}} = 0.346 \text{ g Bi}$

3.105 $\dfrac{74.75 \text{ g Cl}}{100.00 \text{ g MCl}_4} = \dfrac{(4)(35.453) \text{ g Cl}}{\text{molar mass MCl}_4}$ Molar mass $MCl_4 = 189.7 \text{ g}$

   Atomic mass M = 189.7 g − (4)(35.453) g = 47.9 g   M is Ti, titanium

3.106   Molar mass of compound $= \dfrac{385 \text{ g}}{2.50 \text{ mol}} = 154 \text{ g/mol}$

   154 g/mol = (molar mass of E) + [4 × (molar mass of Cl)] = M_E + 4(35.45 g/mol)

   M_E = 12, E is C (carbon).

3.107 $\dfrac{15.2 \text{ g O}}{100 \text{ g MO}_2} = \dfrac{(2)(16.00) \text{ g O}}{\text{molar mass MO}_2}$ Molar mass $MO_2 = 211 \text{ g}$

   Atomic mass M = 211 g − (2)(16.00) g = 179 g   M is Hf, hafnium

3.108 Al^{3+} will be most strongly attracted to water because it has the largest positive charge (+3), and force of attraction is directly related to the magnitude of the ion charge.

3.109   Assume 100.0 g of sample.

$54.0 \text{ g C} \cdot \dfrac{1 \text{ mol}}{12.01 \text{ g}} = 4.50 \text{ mol C}$ $6.00 \text{ g H} \cdot \dfrac{1 \text{ mol}}{1.008 \text{ g}} = 5.95 \text{ mol H}$

$40.0 \text{ g O} \cdot \dfrac{1 \text{ mol}}{16.00 \text{ g}} = 2.50 \text{ mol O}$

$\dfrac{4.50 \text{ mol C}}{2.50 \text{ mol O}} = \dfrac{1.8 \text{ mol C}}{1 \text{ mol O}} = \dfrac{9 \text{ mol C}}{5 \text{ mol O}}$ $\dfrac{5.95 \text{ mol H}}{2.50 \text{ mol O}} = \dfrac{2.38 \text{ mol H}}{1 \text{ mol O}} = \dfrac{12 \text{ mol H}}{5 \text{ mol O}}$

Answer (d) $C_9H_{12}O_5$ is correct. The other students apparently did not correctly calculate the number of moles of material in 100.0 g or they improperly calculated the ratio of those moles in determining their empirical formula.

3.110 $0.832 \text{ g} - 0.739 \text{ g} = 0.093 \text{ g H}_2\text{O}$ $0.093 \text{ g H}_2\text{O} \cdot \dfrac{1 \text{ mol}}{18.02 \text{ g}} = 0.0052 \text{ mol H}_2\text{O}$

$0.739 \text{ g CaCl}_2 \cdot \dfrac{1 \text{ mol}}{111.0 \text{ g}} = 0.00666 \text{ mol CaCl}_2$

$\dfrac{0.0052 \text{ mol H}_2\text{O}}{0.00666 \text{ mol CaCl}_2} = \dfrac{0.78 \text{ mol H}_2\text{O}}{1 \text{ mol CaCl}_2}$

The students should (c) heat the crucible again and then reweigh it.

3.111 $\dfrac{15.9 \text{ g}}{0.15 \text{ mol}} = 106 \text{ g/mol A}_2\text{Z}_3$ $\dfrac{9.3 \text{ g}}{0.15 \text{ mol}} = 62 \text{ g/mol AZ}_2$

For AZ_2:   (atomic mass A) + (2)(atomic mass Z) = 62

For A_2Z_3:   (2)(atomic mass A) + (3)(atomic mass Z) = 106

(2)[62 − (2)(atomic mass Z)] + (3)(atomic mass Z) = 106

atomic mass Z = 18 g/mol

atomic mass A = 26 g/mol

3.112   (a)   volume = $(0.0550 \text{ cm})(1.25 \text{ cm})^2 = 0.0859 \text{ cm}^3 \text{ Ni}$

$0.0859 \text{ cm}^3 \text{ Ni} \cdot \dfrac{8.908 \text{ g}}{1 \text{ cm}^3} = 0.765 \text{ g Ni}$

(b)   1.261 g compound − 0.765 g Ni = 0.496 g F

$0.765 \text{ g Ni} \cdot \dfrac{1 \text{ mol}}{58.69 \text{ g}} =$ 0.0130 mol Ni $0.496 \text{ g F} \cdot \dfrac{1 \text{ mol}}{19.00 \text{ g}} = 0.0261 \text{ mol F}$

$\dfrac{0.0261 \text{ mol F}}{0.0130 \text{ mol Ni}} = \dfrac{2 \text{ mol F}}{1 \text{ mol Ni}}$ The empirical formula is NiF_2

(c) NiF_2, nickel(II) fluoride

3.113   (a) $0.199 \text{ g } U_xO_y - 0.169 \text{ g } U = 0.030 \text{ g } O$

$0.169 \text{ g U} \cdot \dfrac{1 \text{ mol}}{238.0 \text{ g}} = 7.10 \times 10^{-4} \text{ mol U}$ $0.030 \text{ g O} \cdot \dfrac{1 \text{ mol}}{16.0 \text{ g O}} = 1.9 \times 10^{-3} \text{ mol O}$

$\dfrac{1.9 \times 10^{-3} \text{ mol O}}{7.10 \times 10^{-4} \text{ mol U}} = \dfrac{2.68 \text{ mol O}}{1 \text{ mol U}} = \dfrac{8 \text{ mol O}}{3 \text{ mol U}}$

The empirical formula is U_3O_8, a mixture of uranium(IV) oxide and uranium(VI) oxide.

$7.10 \times 10^{-4} \text{ mol U} \cdot \dfrac{1 \text{ mol } U_3O_8}{3 \text{ mol U}} = 2.37 \times 10^{-4} \text{ mol } U_3O_8$

(b)   The atomic mass of U is 238.029 amu, implying that the isotope ^{238}U is the most abundant.

(c) $0.865 \text{ g} - 0.679 \text{ g} = 0.186 \text{ g } H_2O$ lost upon heating

$0.186 \text{ g } H_2O \cdot \dfrac{1 \text{ mol}}{18.02 \text{ g}} = 0.0103 \text{ mol } H_2O$

$0.679 \text{ g } UO_2(NO_3)_2 \cdot \dfrac{1 \text{ mol}}{394.0 \text{ g}} = 0.00172 \text{ mol } UO_2(NO_3)_2$

$\dfrac{0.0103 \text{ mol } H_2O}{0.00172 \text{ mol } UO_2(NO_3)_2} = \dfrac{6 \text{ mol } H_2O}{1 \text{ mol } UO_2(NO_3)_2}$

The formula of the hydrated compound is $UO_2(NO_3)_2 \cdot 6 \text{ } H_2O$

3.114   When words are written with the red, hydrated compound, the words are not visible. However, when heated, the hydrated salt loses water to form anhydrous $CoCl_2$, which is deep blue, and the words are visible.

3.115   Examples of constitutional and stereoisomers are shown on the Screen 3.4 sidebar.

3.116   According to Coulomb's law, the force of attraction between oppositely charged ions increases with the ion charges and with decreasing ion-ion separation.

Chapter 4
Chemical Equations and Stoichiometry

INSTRUCTOR'S NOTES

As indicated in Chapter 3, this chapter is treated as a unit along with Chapters 2, 3 and 5. Together they require approximately fifteen, 50-minute lectures. Chapter 4 requires approximately four lectures.

This edition of the book continues to stress the notion of the *stoichiometric factor* in chemical calculations. We constantly remind our students that everything funnels through this step. The diagram below is one we have used in class to emphasize this point.

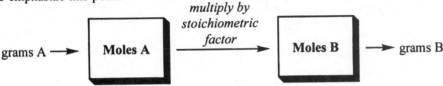

Students have always had difficulties with limiting reagent problems. For this reason we have incorporated a large number of solved examples in the text. Students also have difficulties with chemical analysis of mixtures and combustion analysis. It is well to do as many examples as possible.

SUGGESTED DEMONSTRATIONS

1.   Illustrations of Chemical Reactions and Balancing Equations

   •   Burn sulfur in oxygen.

   •   Make NO_2 from a penny and concentrated HNO_3.

   •   Burn magnesium in air.

   •   Decompose H_2O_2.

   •   React various metals with HCl or H_2O.

2.   Stoichiometry

   •   As an introduction to stoichiometry we have used the decomposition of ammonium nitrate:

   $$NH_4NO_3(s) \rightarrow N_2O(g) + 2\ H_2O(g)$$

   This reaction is part of suggested demonstration found in Shakhashiri (Volume 1, page 51). The overall reaction is spectacular. However, one of the reaction products (ZnO) is irritating, so the reaction must be done in a very well ventilated room.

   •   The reaction of Mg ribbon with O_2 (Figure 4.1, page 123)

   $$2\ Mg(s) + O_2(g) \rightarrow 2\ MgO(s)$$

   is also useful as a demonstration reaction that can be tied to an example of a simple stoichiometry reaction.

- A good classroom example for stoichiometry is the decomposition of H_2O_2:

  $$2\ H_2O_2(\ell) \rightarrow 2\ H_2O(g) + O_2(g)$$

  We use it to power a small "rocket" made as in the following illustration.

  ### THE HYDROGEN PEROXIDE ROCKET

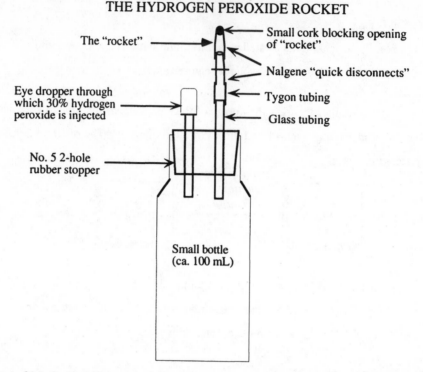

A small quantity of MnO_2 (1-2 g) is placed in the bottle as a catalyst. (We use a 100-mL bottle and find it helps if the bottle is damp.) The top is placed in the bottle, and an eye dropper containing 30% H_2O_2 is placed in the open hole of the 2-hole stopper. All of the H_2O_2 in the dropper is squirted into the bottle. The decomposition reaction is rapid and exothermic, and the steam and O_2 generated provide the thrust for the plastic "rocket." Under the right conditions the "rocket" will fly about 20-30 feet. (CAUTION: Wear rubber gloves when handling the H_2O_2 and wash the residue down the drain with a large amount of water.) The H_2O_2 rocket has proved to be a very useful lecture demonstration. Not only do the students enjoy it, but it can be used to illustrate a redox reaction (Chapter 5), the concept of an exothermic reaction (Chapter 6), and catalysis (Chapter 15).

3.   Limiting Reactants

- One useful demonstration to use when discussing a limiting reagent situation is the production of H_2 from Ca in water.

  $$Ca(s) + 2\ H_2O(\ell) \rightarrow Ca(OH)_2(s) + H_2(g)$$

  This reaction is a good demonstration because both products are visible: bubbles of H_2 and solid $Ca(OH)_2$.

- Add a deficiency, a stoichiometric amount, and an excess of magnesium to three beakers of HCl on an overhead projector to demonstrate limiting reagents.

Solutions to Study Questions

4.1   A balanced chemical equation provides the formulas, physical states, and relative amounts of reactants and products.

4.2 $N_2(g) + 3 H_2(g) \rightarrow 2 NH_3(g)$

4.3   Using the stoichiometric coefficients in the balanced equation, 2000 atoms of Al react with 3000 molecules of Br_2 to produce 1000 molecules of Al_2Br_6.

4.4 $\dfrac{2 \text{ mol } NH_3}{1 \text{ mol } N_2}$

4.5   First convert mass of zinc to moles of zinc using the atomic mass of zinc. Moles of ZnI_2 can be calculated from moles of zinc and the stoichiometric ratio $\dfrac{1 \text{ mol } ZnI_2}{1 \text{ mol } Zn}$. Finally, the molar mass of ZnI_2 can be used to calculate mass of ZnI_2. Percent yield can be calculated from the theoretical yield and the actual amount isolated from the reaction.

4.6 $\dfrac{65 \text{ mol } CO}{25 \text{ mol } Fe_2O_3} = \dfrac{2.6 \text{ mol } CO}{1 \text{ mol } Fe_2O_3}$ The required mole ratio is 3 mol of CO to 1 mol of Fe_2O_3. Less CO is available than required to consume all the Fe_2O_3. CO is the limiting reactant.

$25 \text{ mol } Fe_2O_3 \cdot \dfrac{2 \text{ mol } Fe}{1 \text{ mol } Fe_2O_3} = 50 \text{ mol } Fe$ $\qquad$ $65 \text{ mol } CO \cdot \dfrac{2 \text{ mol } Fe}{3 \text{ mol } CO} = 43 \text{ mol } Fe$

4.7   Determine the mass of a small sample of the mineral. Dissolve the sample in water and add $AgNO_3$ solution until precipitation of chloride ion as $AgCl(s)$ is complete. Collect the $AgCl(s)$ and dry the solid. From the mass of $AgCl(s)$, calculate moles of $AgCl$, convert to moles of NaCl (using the correct stoichiometric ratio), and finally to mass of NaCl. Mass of NaCl divided by mass of the original sample ($\times 100\%$) will give the mass percent of NaCl in the original sample.

4.8   (a) $4 Cr(s) + 3 O_2(g) \rightarrow 2 Cr_2O_3(s)$

(b) $Cu_2S(s) + O_2(g) \rightarrow 2 Cu(s) + SO_2(g)$

(c) $C_6H_5CH_3(\ell) + 9 O_2(g) \rightarrow 4 H_2O(\ell) + 7 CO_2(g)$

4.9   (a) $2 Cr(s) + 3 Cl_2(g) \rightarrow 2 CrCl_3(s)$

(b) $SiO_2(s) + 2 C(s) \rightarrow Si(s) + 2 CO(g)$

(c) $3 Fe(s) + 4 H_2O(g) \rightarrow Fe_3O_4(s) + 4 H_2(g)$

4.10   (a) $Fe_2O_3(s) + 3 Mg(s) \rightarrow 3 MgO(s) + 2 Fe(s)$

iron(II) oxide, magnesium, magnesium oxide, iron

(b) $AlCl_3(s) + 3 H_2O(\ell) \rightarrow Al(OH)_3(s) + 3 HCl(aq)$

   aluminum chloride, water, aluminum hydroxide, hydrogen chloride (hydrochloric acid)

(c) $2 NaNO_3(s) + H_2SO_4(\ell) \rightarrow Na_2SO_4(s) + 2 HNO_3(\ell)$

   sodium nitrate, hydrogen sulfate (sulfuric acid), sodium sulfate, hydrogen nitrate (nitric acid)

(d) $NiCO_3(s) + 2 HNO_3(aq) \rightarrow Ni(NO_3)_2(aq) + CO_2(g) + H_2O(\ell)$

   nickel(II) carbonate, hydrogen nitrate (nitric acid), nickel(II) nitrate, carbon dioxide, water

4.11   (a) $SF_4(g) + 2 H_2O(\ell) \rightarrow SO_2(g) + 4 HF(\ell)$

   sulfur tetrafluoride, water, sulfur dioxide, hydrogen fluoride

(b) $4 NH_3(aq) + 5 O_2(g) \rightarrow 4 NO(g) + 6 H_2O(\ell)$

   ammonia, oxygen, nitrogen monoxide, water

(c) $BF_3(g) + 3 H_2O(\ell) \rightarrow 3 HF(aq) + H_3BO_3(\ell)$

   boron trifluoride, water, hydrogen fluoride, hydrogen borate (boric acid)

4.12 $6.0 \text{ mol Al} \cdot \dfrac{3 \text{ mol O}_2}{4 \text{ mol Al}} = 4.5 \text{ mol O}_2$

   $6.0 \text{ mol Al} \cdot \dfrac{2 \text{ mol Al}_2O_3}{4 \text{ mol Al}} \cdot \dfrac{102 \text{ g}}{1 \text{ mol Al}_2O_3} = 310 \text{ g Al}_2O_3$

4.13 $0.750 \text{ g Al(OH)}_3 \cdot \dfrac{1 \text{ mol Al(OH)}_3}{78.00 \text{ g}} \cdot \dfrac{3 \text{ mol HCl}}{1 \text{ mol Al(OH)}_3} \cdot \dfrac{36.46 \text{ g}}{1 \text{ mol HCl}} = 1.05 \text{ g HCl}$

   $0.750 \text{ g Al(OH)}_3 \cdot \dfrac{1 \text{ mol Al(OH)}_3}{78.00 \text{ g}} \cdot \dfrac{3 \text{ mol H}_2O}{1 \text{ mol Al(OH)}_3} \cdot \dfrac{18.02 \text{ g}}{1 \text{ mol H}_2O} = 0.520 \text{ g H}_2O$

4.14 $2.56 \text{ g Al} \cdot \dfrac{1 \text{ mol Al}}{26.98 \text{ g}} \cdot \dfrac{3 \text{ mol Br}_2}{2 \text{ mol Al}} \cdot \dfrac{159.8 \text{ g}}{1 \text{ mol Br}_2} = 22.7 \text{ g Br}_2$

   $2.56 \text{ g Al} + 22.7 \text{ g Br}_2 = 25.3 \text{ g Al}_2Br_6$

4.15   (a) $454 \text{ g Fe}_2O_3 \cdot \dfrac{1 \text{ mol Fe}_2O_3}{159.7 \text{ g}} \cdot \dfrac{2 \text{ mol Fe}}{1 \text{ mol Fe}_2O_3} \cdot \dfrac{55.85 \text{ g}}{1 \text{ mol Fe}} = 318 \text{ g Fe}$

(b) $454 \text{ g Fe}_2O_3 \cdot \dfrac{1 \text{ mol Fe}_2O_3}{159.7 \text{ g}} \cdot \dfrac{3 \text{ mol CO}}{1 \text{ mol Fe}_2O_3} \cdot \dfrac{28.01 \text{ g}}{1 \text{ mol CO}} = 239 \text{ g CO}$

4.16   (a) $4 Fe(s) + 3 O_2(g) \rightarrow 2 Fe_2O_3(s)$

(b) $2.68 \text{ g Fe} \cdot \dfrac{1 \text{ mol Fe}}{55.85 \text{ g}} \cdot \dfrac{2 \text{ mol Fe}_2O_3}{4 \text{ mol Fe}} \cdot \dfrac{159.7 \text{ g}}{1 \text{ mol Fe}_2O_3} = 3.83 \text{ g Fe}_2O_3$

(c) $3.83 \text{ g Fe}_2O_3 - 2.68 \text{ g Fe} = 1.15 \text{ g O}_2$

4.17   (a) CO_2, carbon dioxide, and H_2O, water

(b) $CH_4(g) + 2 O_2(g) \rightarrow CO_2(g) + 2 H_2O(\ell)$

(c) $25.5 \text{ g CH}_4 \cdot \dfrac{1 \text{ mol CH}_4}{16.04 \text{ g}} \cdot \dfrac{2 \text{ mol O}_2}{1 \text{ mol CH}_4} \cdot \dfrac{32.00 \text{ g}}{1 \text{ mol O}_2} = 102 \text{ g O}_2$

(d) $25.5 \text{ g CH}_4 + 102 \text{ g O}_2 = 128 \text{ g reactants} = 128 \text{ g products}$

4.18 (a) $155 \text{ g SO}_2 \cdot \dfrac{1 \text{ mol SO}_2}{64.06 \text{ g}} \cdot \dfrac{2 \text{ mol CaCO}_3}{2 \text{ mol SO}_2} \cdot \dfrac{100.1 \text{ g}}{1 \text{ mol CaCO}_3} = 242 \text{ g CaCO}_3$

(b) $155 \text{ g SO}_2 \cdot \dfrac{1 \text{ mol SO}_2}{64.06 \text{ g}} \cdot \dfrac{2 \text{ mol CaSO}_4}{2 \text{ mol SO}_2} \cdot \dfrac{136.1 \text{ g}}{1 \text{ mol CaSO}_4} = 329 \text{ g CaSO}_4$

4.19 (a) $BaCl_2(aq) + 2 \, AgNO_3(aq) \rightarrow 2 \, AgCl(s) + Ba(NO_3)_2(aq)$

(b) $0.156 \text{ g BaCl}_2 \cdot \dfrac{1 \text{ mol BaCl}_2}{208.2 \text{ g}} \cdot \dfrac{2 \text{ mol AgNO}_3}{1 \text{ mol BaCl}_2} \cdot \dfrac{169.9 \text{ g}}{1 \text{ mol AgNO}_3} = 0.255 \text{ g AgNO}_3$

$0.156 \text{ g BaCl}_2 \cdot \dfrac{1 \text{ mol BaCl}_2}{208.2 \text{ g}} \cdot \dfrac{2 \text{ mol AgCl}}{1 \text{ mol BaCl}_2} \cdot \dfrac{143.3 \text{ g}}{1 \text{ mol AgCl}} = 0.215 \text{ g AgCl}$

4.20 $\dfrac{35 \text{ mol F}_2}{1.6 \text{ mol S}_8} = \dfrac{22 \text{ mol F}_2}{1 \text{ mol S}_8}$ The required mole ratio is 24 mol F_2 to 1 mol S_8. Less F_2 is available

than required, so F_2 is the limiting reactant.

4.21 $32.0 \text{ g S}_8 \cdot \dfrac{1 \text{ mol S}_8}{256.5 \text{ g}} = 0.125 \text{ mol S}_8$ $71.0 \text{ g Cl}_2 \cdot \dfrac{1 \text{ mol Cl}_2}{70.91 \text{ g}} = 1.00 \text{ mol Cl}_2$

$\dfrac{1.00 \text{ mol Cl}_2}{0.125 \text{ mol S}_8} = \dfrac{8.00 \text{ mol Cl}_2}{1 \text{ mol S}_8} > \dfrac{4 \text{ mol Cl}_2}{1 \text{ mol S}_8}$ S_8 is the limiting reactant.

4.22 (a) $995 \text{ g CH}_4 \cdot \dfrac{1 \text{ mol CH}_4}{16.04 \text{ g}} = 62.0 \text{ mol CH}_4$ $2510 \text{ g H}_2\text{O} \cdot \dfrac{1 \text{ mol H}_2\text{O}}{18.02 \text{ g}} = 139 \text{ mol H}_2\text{O}$

$\dfrac{139 \text{ mol H}_2\text{O}}{62.0 \text{ mol CH}_4} = \dfrac{2.24 \text{ mol H}_2\text{O}}{1 \text{ mol CH}_4} > \dfrac{1 \text{ mol H}_2\text{O}}{1 \text{ mol CH}_4}$ CH_4 is the limiting reactant.

(b) $62.0 \text{ mol CH}_4 \cdot \dfrac{3 \text{ mol H}_2}{1 \text{ mol CH}_4} \cdot \dfrac{2.016 \text{ g}}{1 \text{ mol H}_2} = 375 \text{ g H}_2$

(c) Since 1 mol CH_4 reacts with 1 mol H_2O,

139 mol H_2O available – 62.0 mol H_2O used = 77 mol H_2O remains

$77 \text{ mol H}_2\text{O} \cdot \dfrac{18.0 \text{ g}}{1 \text{ mol H}_2\text{O}} = 1400 \text{ g H}_2\text{O}$

4.23 (a) $2.70 \text{ g Al} \cdot \dfrac{1 \text{ mol Al}}{26.98 \text{ g}} = 0.100 \text{ mol Al}$ $4.06 \text{ g Cl}_2 \cdot \dfrac{1 \text{ mol Cl}_2}{70.91 \text{ g}} = 0.0573 \text{ mol Cl}_2$

$\dfrac{0.100 \text{ mol Al}}{0.0573 \text{ mol Cl}_2} = \dfrac{1.75 \text{ mol Al}}{1 \text{ mol Cl}_2}$ The required mole ratio is 2 mol Al to 3 mol Cl_2.

More Al is available than required, so Cl_2 is the limiting reactant.

(b) $0.0573 \text{ mol Cl}_2 \cdot \dfrac{2 \text{ mol AlCl}_3}{3 \text{ mol Cl}_2} \cdot \dfrac{133.3 \text{ g}}{1 \text{ mol AlCl}_3} = 5.09 \text{ g AlCl}_3$

(c) $0.0573 \text{ mol Cl}_2 \cdot \dfrac{2 \text{ mol Al}}{3 \text{ mol Cl}_2} \cdot \dfrac{26.98 \text{ g}}{1 \text{ mol Al}} = 1.03 \text{ g Al used}$

2.70 g Al available – 1.03 g Al used = 1.67 g Al remains

4.24   (a) $112 \text{ g CaO} \cdot \dfrac{1 \text{ mol CaO}}{56.08 \text{ g}} \cdot \dfrac{2 \text{ mol NH}_3}{1 \text{ mol CaO}} \cdot \dfrac{17.03 \text{ g}}{1 \text{ mol NH}_3} = 68.0 \text{ g NH}_3$

          $224 \text{ g NH}_4\text{Cl} \cdot \dfrac{1 \text{ mol NH}_4\text{Cl}}{53.49 \text{ g}} \cdot \dfrac{2 \text{ mol NH}_3}{2 \text{ mol NH}_4\text{Cl}} \cdot \dfrac{17.03 \text{ g}}{1 \text{ mol NH}_3} = 71.3 \text{ g NH}_3$

          The maximum amount that can be produced is 68.0 g NH_3.

        (b) $112 \text{ g CaO} \cdot \dfrac{1 \text{ mol CaO}}{56.08 \text{ g}} \cdot \dfrac{2 \text{ mol NH}_4\text{Cl}}{1 \text{ mol CaO}} \cdot \dfrac{53.49 \text{ g}}{1 \text{ mol NH}_4\text{Cl}} = 214 \text{ g NH}_4\text{Cl used}$

          $224 \text{ g NH}_4\text{Cl available} - 214 \text{ g NH}_4\text{Cl used} = 10. \text{ g NH}_4\text{Cl remains}$

4.25 $100. \text{ g C}_7\text{H}_6\text{O}_3 \cdot \dfrac{1 \text{ mol C}_7\text{H}_6\text{O}_3}{138.1 \text{ g}} \cdot \dfrac{1 \text{ mol C}_9\text{H}_8\text{O}_4}{1 \text{ mol C}_7\text{H}_6\text{O}_3} \cdot \dfrac{180.2 \text{ g}}{1 \text{ mol C}_9\text{H}_8\text{O}_4} = 130. \text{ g aspirin}$

        $100. \text{ g C}_4\text{H}_6\text{O}_3 \cdot \dfrac{1 \text{ mol C}_4\text{H}_6\text{O}_3}{102.1 \text{ g}} \cdot \dfrac{1 \text{ mol C}_9\text{H}_8\text{O}_4}{1 \text{ mol C}_4\text{H}_6\text{O}_3} \cdot \dfrac{180.2 \text{ g}}{1 \text{ mol C}_9\text{H}_8\text{O}_4} = 176 \text{ g aspirin}$

        The maximum amount that can be produced is 130. g aspirin.

4.26 $\dfrac{332 \text{ g}}{407 \text{ g}} \cdot 100\% = 81.6\% \text{ yield}$

4.27 $\dfrac{16.3 \text{ g}}{68.0 \text{ g}} \cdot 100\% = 24.0\% \text{ yield}$

4.28   (a) $10.0 \text{ g CuSO}_4 \cdot \dfrac{1 \text{ mol CuSO}_4}{159.6 \text{ g}} \cdot \dfrac{1 \text{ mol Cu(NH}_3)_4\text{SO}_4}{1 \text{ mol CuSO}_4} \cdot \dfrac{227.7 \text{ g}}{1 \text{ mol Cu(NH}_3)_4\text{SO}_4} = 14.3 \text{ g Cu(NH}_3)_4\text{SO}_4$

        (b) $\dfrac{12.6 \text{ g}}{14.3 \text{ g}} \cdot 100\% = 88.3\% \text{ yield}$

4.29   (a) $10.0 \text{ g CH}_3\text{SH} \cdot \dfrac{1 \text{ mol CH}_3\text{SH}}{48.11 \text{ g}} \cdot \dfrac{1 \text{ mol CH}_3\text{COSCH}_3}{2 \text{ mol CH}_3\text{SH}} \cdot \dfrac{90.15 \text{ g}}{1 \text{ mol CH}_3\text{COSCH}_3} = 9.37 \text{ g CH}_3\text{COSCH}_3$

        (b) $\dfrac{8.65 \text{ g}}{9.37 \text{ g}} \cdot 100\% = 92.3\% \text{ yield}$

4.30   1.245 g mixture − 0.832 g after heating = 0.413 g H_2O lost

        $0.413 \text{ g H}_2\text{O} \cdot \dfrac{1 \text{ mol H}_2\text{O}}{18.02 \text{ g}} \cdot \dfrac{1 \text{ mol CuSO}_4 \cdot 5 \text{ H}_2\text{O}}{5 \text{ mol H}_2\text{O}} \cdot \dfrac{249.7 \text{ g}}{1 \text{ mol CuSO}_4 \cdot 5 \text{ H}_2\text{O}} = 1.14 \text{ g CuSO}_4 \cdot 5 \text{ H}_2\text{O}$

        $\dfrac{1.14 \text{ g CuSO}_4 \cdot 5 \text{ H}_2\text{O}}{1.245 \text{ g mixture}} \cdot 100\% = 91.9\% \text{ CuSO}_4 \cdot 5 \text{ H}_2\text{O}$

4.31   2.634 g mixture − 2.125 g after heating = 0.509 g H_2O lost

        $0.509 \text{ g H}_2\text{O} \cdot \dfrac{1 \text{ mol H}_2\text{O}}{18.02 \text{ g}} \cdot \dfrac{1 \text{ mol CuCl}_2 \cdot 2 \text{ H}_2\text{O}}{2 \text{ mol H}_2\text{O}} \cdot \dfrac{170.5 \text{ g}}{1 \text{ mol CuCl}_2 \cdot 2 \text{ H}_2\text{O}} = 2.41 \text{ g CuCl}_2 \cdot 2 \text{ H}_2\text{O}$

        $\dfrac{2.41 \text{ g CuCl}_2 \cdot 2 \text{ H}_2\text{O}}{2.634 \text{ g mixture}} \cdot 100\% = 91.4\% \text{ CuCl}_2 \cdot 2 \text{ H}_2\text{O}$

4.32 $0.558 \text{ g } CO_2 \cdot \dfrac{1 \text{ mol } CO_2}{44.01 \text{ g}} \cdot \dfrac{1 \text{ mol } CaCO_3}{1 \text{ mol } CO_2} \cdot \dfrac{100.1 \text{ g}}{1 \text{ mol } CaCO_3} = 1.27 \text{ g } CaCO_3$

$\dfrac{1.27 \text{ g}}{1.506 \text{ g}} \cdot 100\% = 84.3\% \text{ } CaCO_3$

4.33   **NOTE:** Problem should read "Heating a 1.7184-g sample of impure $NaHCO_3$ …"

$0.4724 \text{ g } Na_2CO_3 \cdot \dfrac{1 \text{ mol } Na_2CO_3}{105.99 \text{ g}} \cdot \dfrac{2 \text{ mol } NaHCO_3}{1 \text{ mol } Na_2CO_3} \cdot \dfrac{84.007 \text{ g}}{1 \text{ mol } NaHCO_3} = 0.7488 \text{ g } NaHCO_3$

$\dfrac{0.7488 \text{ g}}{1.7184 \text{ g}} \cdot 100\% = 43.58\% \text{ } NaHCO_3$

4.34 $0.1964 \text{ g } TlI \cdot \dfrac{1 \text{ mol } TlI}{331.29 \text{ g}} \cdot \dfrac{1 \text{ mol } Tl_2SO_4}{2 \text{ mol } TlI} \cdot \dfrac{504.83 \text{ g}}{1 \text{ mol } Tl_2SO_4} = 0.1496 \text{ g } Tl_2SO_4$

$\dfrac{0.1496 \text{ g}}{10.20 \text{ g}} \cdot 100\% = 1.467\% \text{ } Tl_2SO_4$

4.35 $0.127 \text{ g } Al_2O_3 \cdot \dfrac{1 \text{ mol } Al_2O_3}{102.0 \text{ g}} \cdot \dfrac{2 \text{ mol } Al}{1 \text{ mol } Al_2O_3} \cdot \dfrac{26.98 \text{ g}}{1 \text{ mol } Al} = 0.0672 \text{ g } Al$

$\dfrac{0.0672 \text{ g}}{0.764 \text{ g}} \cdot 100\% = 8.79\% \text{ } Al$

4.36 $1.481 \text{ g } CO_2 \cdot \dfrac{1 \text{ mol } CO_2}{44.010 \text{ g}} \cdot \dfrac{1 \text{ mol } C}{1 \text{ mol } CO_2} = 0.03365 \text{ mol } C$

$0.303 \text{ g } H_2O \cdot \dfrac{1 \text{ mol } H_2O}{18.02 \text{ g}} \cdot \dfrac{2 \text{ mol } H}{1 \text{ mol } H_2O} = 0.0336 \text{ mol } H$

$\dfrac{0.03365 \text{ mol } C}{0.0336 \text{ mol } H} = \dfrac{1 \text{ mol } C}{1 \text{ mol } H}$ The empirical formula is CH

4.37 $0.379 \text{ g } CO_2 \cdot \dfrac{1 \text{ mol } CO_2}{44.01 \text{ g}} \cdot \dfrac{1 \text{ mol } C}{1 \text{ mol } CO_2} = 0.00861 \text{ mol } C$

$0.1035 \text{ g } H_2O \cdot \dfrac{1 \text{ mol } H_2O}{18.015 \text{ g}} \cdot \dfrac{2 \text{ mol } H}{1 \text{ mol } H_2O} = 0.01149 \text{ mol } H$

$\dfrac{0.01149 \text{ mol } H}{0.00861 \text{ mol } C} = \dfrac{1.33 \text{ mol } H}{1 \text{ mol } C} = \dfrac{4/3 \text{ mol } H}{1 \text{ mol } C} = \dfrac{4 \text{ mol } H}{3 \text{ mol } C}$

The empirical formula is C_3H_4

4.38   (a) $0.300 \text{ g } CO_2 \cdot \dfrac{1 \text{ mol } CO_2}{44.01 \text{ g}} \cdot \dfrac{1 \text{ mol } C}{1 \text{ mol } CO_2} = 0.00682 \text{ mol } C$

$0.123 \text{ g } H_2O \cdot \dfrac{1 \text{ mol } H_2O}{18.02 \text{ g}} \cdot \dfrac{2 \text{ mol } H}{1 \text{ mol } H_2O} = 0.0137 \text{ mol } H$

$\dfrac{0.0137 \text{ mol } H}{0.00682 \text{ mol } C} = \dfrac{2 \text{ mol } H}{1 \text{ mol } C}$

The empirical formula is CH_2

(b) $\dfrac{70.1 \text{ g/mol}}{14.0 \text{ g/mol}} = 5$ The molecular formula is $(CH_2)_5$ or C_5H_{10}

4.39   (a) $0.364 \text{ g CO}_2 \cdot \dfrac{1 \text{ mol CO}_2}{44.01 \text{ g}} \cdot \dfrac{1 \text{ mol C}}{1 \text{ mol CO}_2} = 0.00827 \text{ mol C}$

$0.0596 \text{ g H}_2\text{O} \cdot \dfrac{1 \text{ mol H}_2\text{O}}{18.02 \text{ g}} \cdot \dfrac{2 \text{ mol H}}{1 \text{ mol H}_2\text{O}} = 0.00661 \text{ mol H}$

$\dfrac{0.00827 \text{ mol C}}{0.00661 \text{ mol H}} = \dfrac{1.25 \text{ mol C}}{1 \text{ mol H}} = \dfrac{5/4 \text{ mol C}}{1 \text{ mol H}} = \dfrac{5 \text{ mol C}}{4 \text{ mol H}}$

The empirical formula is C_5H_4

(b) $\dfrac{128.2 \text{ g/mol}}{64.09 \text{ g/mol}} = 2$ The molecular formula is $(C_5H_4)_2$ or $C_{10}H_8$

4.40 $0.328 \text{ g oxide} - 0.233 \text{ g K} = 0.095 \text{ g oxygen}$

$0.233 \text{ g K} \cdot \dfrac{1 \text{ mol K}}{39.10 \text{ g}} = 0.00596 \text{ mol K}$ $0.095 \text{ O} \cdot \dfrac{1 \text{ mol O}}{16.0 \text{ g}} = 0.0059 \text{ mol O}$

$\dfrac{0.00596 \text{ mol K}}{0.0059 \text{ mol O}} = \dfrac{1 \text{ mol K}}{1 \text{ mol O}}$ The empirical formula is KO

4.41 $0.263 \text{ g compound} - 0.125 \text{ g S} = 0.138 \text{ g Cl}$

$0.125 \text{ g S} \cdot \dfrac{1 \text{ mol S}}{32.07 \text{ g}} = 0.00390 \text{ mol S}$ $0.138 \text{ g Cl} \cdot \dfrac{1 \text{ mol Cl}}{35.45 \text{ g}} = 0.00389 \text{ mol Cl}$

$\dfrac{0.00390 \text{ mol S}}{0.00389 \text{ mol Cl}} = \dfrac{1 \text{ mol S}}{1 \text{ mol Cl}}$ The empirical formula is SCl

$\dfrac{135.0 \text{ g/mol}}{67.52 \text{ g/mol}} = 2$ The molecular formula is $(SCl)_2$ or S_2Cl_2

4.42 $0.0426 \text{ g NiO} \cdot \dfrac{1 \text{ mol NiO}}{74.69 \text{ g}} \cdot \dfrac{1 \text{ mol Ni}}{1 \text{ mol NiO}} = 5.70 \times 10^{-4} \text{ mol Ni}$

$0.100 \text{ g CO}_2 \cdot \dfrac{1 \text{ mol CO}_2}{44.01 \text{ g}} \cdot \dfrac{1 \text{ mol CO}}{1 \text{ mol CO}_2} = 2.27 \times 10^{-3} \text{ mol CO}$

$\dfrac{2.27 \times 10^{-3} \text{ mol CO}}{5.70 \times 10^{-4} \text{ mol Ni}} = \dfrac{4 \text{ mol CO}}{1 \text{ mol Ni}}$ The empirical formula is $Ni(CO)_4$

4.43 $0.799 \text{ g Fe}_2\text{O}_3 \cdot \dfrac{1 \text{ mol Fe}_2\text{O}_3}{159.7 \text{ g}} \cdot \dfrac{2 \text{ mol Fe}}{1 \text{ mol Fe}_2\text{O}_3} = 0.0100 \text{ mol Fe}$

$2.200 \text{ g CO}_2 \cdot \dfrac{1 \text{ mol CO}_2}{44.010 \text{ g}} \cdot \dfrac{1 \text{ mol CO}}{1 \text{ mol CO}_2} = 0.04999 \text{ mol CO}$

$\dfrac{0.04999 \text{ mol CO}}{0.0100 \text{ mol Fe}} = \dfrac{5 \text{ mol CO}}{1 \text{ mol Fe}}$ The empirical formula is $Fe(CO)_5$.

4.44   (a) $CO_2(g) + 2 \text{ NH}_3(g) \rightarrow NH_2CONH_2(s) + H_2O(\ell)$

(b) $UO_2(s) + 4 \text{ HF}(aq) \rightarrow UF_4(s) + 2 \text{ H}_2\text{O}(\ell)$

$UF_4(s) + F_2(g) \rightarrow UF_6(s)$

(c) $TiO_2(s) + 2 \text{ Cl}_2(g) + 2 \text{ C}(s) \rightarrow TiCl_4(\ell) + 2 \text{ CO}(g)$

$TiCl_4(\ell) + 2 \text{ Mg}(s) \rightarrow Ti(s) + 2 \text{ MgCl}_2(s)$

4.45   (a) $Ca_3(PO_4)_2(s) + 2 H_2SO_4(aq) \rightarrow Ca(H_2PO_4)_2(aq) + 2 CaSO_4(s)$

        (b) $2 NaBH_4(s) + H_2SO_4(aq) \rightarrow B_2H_6(g) + 2 H_2(g) + Na_2SO_4(aq)$

        (c) $WO_3(s) + 3 H_2(g) \rightarrow W(s) + 3 H_2O(\ell)$

        (d) $(NH_4)_2Cr_2O_7(s) \rightarrow N_2(g) + 4 H_2O(\ell) + Cr_2O_3(s)$

4.46   (a) CO_2, carbon dioxide, and H_2O, water

        (b) $CH_4(g) + 2 O_2(g) \rightarrow CO_2(g) + 2 H_2O(\ell)$

        (c) $16.04 \text{ g } CH_4 \cdot \dfrac{1 \text{ mol } CH_4}{16.043 \text{ g}} \cdot \dfrac{2 \text{ mol } O_2}{1 \text{ mol } CH_4} \cdot \dfrac{31.999 \text{ g}}{1 \text{ mol } O_2} = 63.99 \text{ g } O_2$

        (d) $16.04 \text{ g } CH_4 + 63.99 \text{ g } O_2 = 80.03 \text{ g products}$

4.47 $C(s) + O_2(g) \rightarrow CO_2(g)$

        If stoichiometric amounts are used, the mass of product (CO_2) is equal to the total mass of reactants:

        Mass $CO_2 = 10.0 \text{ g} + 26.6 \text{ g} = 36.6 \text{ g } CO_2$

4.48 $125 \text{ mg acetoacetic acid} \cdot \dfrac{1 \text{ g}}{10^3 \text{ mg}} \cdot \dfrac{1 \text{ mol acetoacetic acid}}{102.1 \text{ g}} \cdot \dfrac{1 \text{ mol acetone}}{1 \text{ mol acetoacetic acid}} \cdot \dfrac{58.08 \text{ g}}{1 \text{ mol acetone}}$

$$= 0.0711 \text{ g acetone}$$

4.49 $95 \text{ mg urea} \cdot \dfrac{1 \text{ g}}{10^3 \text{ mg}} \cdot \dfrac{1 \text{ mol urea}}{60.1 \text{ g}} \cdot \dfrac{1 \text{ mol arginine}}{1 \text{ mol urea}} \cdot \dfrac{174 \text{ g}}{1 \text{ mol arginine}} = 0.28 \text{ g arginine}$

        $95 \text{ mg urea} \cdot \dfrac{1 \text{ g}}{10^3 \text{ mg}} \cdot \dfrac{1 \text{ mol urea}}{60.1 \text{ g}} \cdot \dfrac{1 \text{ mol ornithine}}{1 \text{ mol urea}} \cdot \dfrac{132 \text{ g}}{1 \text{ mol ornithine}} = 0.21 \text{ g ornithine}$

4.50   (a) $2 Fe(s) + 3 Cl_2(g) \rightarrow 2 FeCl_3(s)$

        (b) $10.0 \text{ g Fe} \cdot \dfrac{1 \text{ mol Fe}}{55.85 \text{ g}} \cdot \dfrac{3 \text{ mol } Cl_2}{2 \text{ mol Fe}} \cdot \dfrac{70.91 \text{ g}}{1 \text{ mol } Cl_2} = 19.0 \text{ g } Cl_2$

             $10.0 \text{ g Fe} \cdot \dfrac{1 \text{ mol Fe}}{55.85 \text{ g}} \cdot \dfrac{2 \text{ mol } FeCl_3}{2 \text{ mol Fe}} \cdot \dfrac{162.2 \text{ g}}{1 \text{ mol } FeCl_3} = 29.0 \text{ g } FeCl_3$

        (c) $\dfrac{18.5 \text{ g}}{29.0 \text{ g}} \cdot 100\% = 63.7\% \text{ yield}$

4.51   (a) titanium(IV) chloride, water, titanium(IV) oxide, hydrogen chloride

        (b) $14.0 \text{ mL } TiCl_4 \cdot \dfrac{1.73 \text{ g}}{1 \text{ mL}} \cdot \dfrac{1 \text{ mol } TiCl_4}{189.7 \text{ g}} \cdot \dfrac{2 \text{ mol } H_2O}{1 \text{ mol } TiCl_4} \cdot \dfrac{18.02 \text{ g}}{1 \text{ mol } H_2O} = 4.60 \text{ g } H_2O$

        (c) $14.0 \text{ mL } TiCl_4 \cdot \dfrac{1.73 \text{ g}}{1 \text{ mL}} \cdot \dfrac{1 \text{ mol } TiCl_4}{189.7 \text{ g}} \cdot \dfrac{1 \text{ mol } TiO_2}{1 \text{ mol } TiCl_4} \cdot \dfrac{79.87 \text{ g}}{1 \text{ mol } TiO_2} = 10.2 \text{ g } TiO_2$

             $14.0 \text{ mL } TiCl_4 \cdot \dfrac{1.73 \text{ g}}{1 \text{ mL}} \cdot \dfrac{1 \text{ mol } TiCl_4}{189.7 \text{ g}} \cdot \dfrac{4 \text{ mol } HCl}{1 \text{ mol } TiCl_4} \cdot \dfrac{36.46 \text{ g}}{1 \text{ mol } HCl} = 18.6 \text{ g } HCl$

4.52   (a)   According to the text (p. 129), O_2 is the limiting reactant

$$750. \text{ g } O_2 \cdot \frac{1 \text{ mol } O_2}{32.00 \text{ g}} \cdot \frac{6 \text{ mol } H_2O}{5 \text{ mol } O_2} \cdot \frac{18.02 \text{ g}}{1 \text{ mol } H_2O} = 507 \text{ g } H_2O$$

(b) $750. \text{ g } NH_3 \cdot \dfrac{1 \text{ mol } NH_3}{17.03 \text{ g}} \cdot \dfrac{5 \text{ mol } O_2}{4 \text{ mol } NH_3} \cdot \dfrac{32.00 \text{ g}}{1 \text{ mol } O_2} = 1760 \text{ g } O_2$

4.53 $0.2070 \text{ g } BaSO_4 \cdot \dfrac{1 \text{ mol } BaSO_4}{233.39 \text{ g}} \cdot \dfrac{1 \text{ mol } S}{1 \text{ mol } BaSO_4} \cdot \dfrac{1 \text{ mol saccharin}}{1 \text{ mol } S} \cdot \dfrac{183.19 \text{ g}}{1 \text{ mol saccharin}}$

$$= 0.1625 \text{ g saccharin}$$

$$\frac{0.1625 \text{ g}}{0.2140 \text{ g}} \cdot 100\% = 75.92\% \text{ saccharin}$$

4.54 $0.422 \text{ g } B_2O_3 \cdot \dfrac{1 \text{ mol } B_2O_3}{69.62 \text{ g}} \cdot \dfrac{2 \text{ mol } B}{1 \text{ mol } B_2O_3} \cdot \dfrac{10.81 \text{ g}}{1 \text{ mol } B} = 0.131 \text{ g } B$

$0.148 \text{ g } B_xH_y - 0.131 \text{ g } B = 0.017 \text{ g } H$

$0.131 \text{ g } B \cdot \dfrac{1 \text{ mol } B}{10.81 \text{ g}} = 0.0121 \text{ mol } B$ $0.017 \text{ g } H \cdot \dfrac{1 \text{ mol } H}{1.01 \text{ g}} = 0.017 \text{ mol } H$

$\dfrac{0.017 \text{ mol } H}{0.0121 \text{ mol } B} = \dfrac{1.4 \text{ mol } H}{1 \text{ mol } B} = \dfrac{7 \text{ mol } H}{5 \text{ mol } B}$ The empirical formula is B_5H_7

4.55 $11.64 \text{ g } SiO_2 \cdot \dfrac{1 \text{ mol } SiO_2}{60.084 \text{ g}} \cdot \dfrac{1 \text{ mol } Si}{1 \text{ mol } SiO_2} = 0.1937 \text{ mol } Si$

$6.980 \text{ g } H_2O \cdot \dfrac{1 \text{ mol } H_2O}{18.015 \text{ g}} \cdot \dfrac{2 \text{ mol } H}{1 \text{ mol } H_2O} = 0.7749 \text{ mol } H$

$\dfrac{0.7749 \text{ mol } H}{0.1937 \text{ mol } Si} = \dfrac{4 \text{ mol } H}{1 \text{ mol } Si}$ The empirical formula is SiH_4

4.56 $269 \text{ mg } CO_2 \cdot \dfrac{1 \text{ g}}{10^3 \text{ mg}} \cdot \dfrac{1 \text{ mol } CO_2}{44.01 \text{ g}} \cdot \dfrac{1 \text{ mol } C}{1 \text{ mol } CO_2} = 0.00611 \text{ mol } C$

$0.00611 \text{ mol } C \cdot \dfrac{12.01 \text{ g}}{1 \text{ mol } C} = 0.0734 \text{ g } C$

$110 \text{ mg } H_2O \cdot \dfrac{1 \text{ g}}{10^3 \text{ mg}} \cdot \dfrac{1 \text{ mol } H_2O}{18.0 \text{ g}} \cdot \dfrac{2 \text{ mol } H}{1 \text{ mol } H_2O} = 0.012 \text{ mol } H$

$0.012 \text{ mol } H \cdot \dfrac{1.01 \text{ g}}{1 \text{ mol } H} = 0.012 \text{ g } H$

mass of O   = sample mass − mass of C − mass of H

$$= (95.6 \text{ mg} \cdot \frac{1 \text{ g}}{10^3 \text{ mg}}) - 0.0734 \text{ g} - 0.012 \text{ g}$$

$$= 0.010 \text{ g } O$$

$0.010 \text{ g } O \cdot \dfrac{1 \text{ mol } O}{16.0 \text{ g}} = 0.00063 \text{ mol } O$

$\dfrac{0.00611 \text{ mol } C}{0.00063 \text{ mol } O} = \dfrac{10 \text{ mol } C}{1 \text{ mol } O}$ $\dfrac{0.012 \text{ mol } H}{0.00063 \text{ mol } O} = \dfrac{20 \text{ mol } H}{1 \text{ mol } O}$

The empirical formula is $C_{10}H_{20}O$

4.57 $0.257 \text{ g } CO_2 \cdot \dfrac{1 \text{ mol } CO_2}{44.01 \text{ g}} \cdot \dfrac{1 \text{ mol C}}{1 \text{ mol } CO_2} = 0.00584 \text{ mol C}$

$0.00584 \text{ mol C} \cdot \dfrac{12.01 \text{ g}}{1 \text{ mol C}} = 0.0701 \text{ g C}$

$0.0350 \text{ g } H_2O \cdot \dfrac{1 \text{ mol } H_2O}{18.0 \text{ g}} \cdot \dfrac{2 \text{ mol H}}{1 \text{ mol } H_2O} = 0.00388 \text{ mol H}$

$0.00388 \text{ mol H} \cdot \dfrac{1.008 \text{ g}}{1 \text{ mol H}} = 0.00391 \text{ g H}$

mass of O = sample mass − mass of C − mass of H

$= 0.105 \text{ g} - 0.0701 - 0.00391$

$= 0.031 \text{ g O}$

$0.031 \text{ g O} \cdot \dfrac{1 \text{ mol O}}{16.0 \text{ g}} = 0.0019 \text{ mol O}$

$\dfrac{0.00584 \text{ mol C}}{0.0019 \text{ mol O}} = \dfrac{3 \text{ mol C}}{1 \text{ mol O}}$ $\qquad\qquad$ $\dfrac{0.00388 \text{ mol H}}{0.0019 \text{ mol O}} = \dfrac{2 \text{ mol H}}{1 \text{ mol O}}$

The empirical formula is C_3H_2O

4.58 $0.376 \text{ g } CO_2 \cdot \dfrac{1 \text{ mol } CO_2}{44.01 \text{ g}} \cdot \dfrac{1 \text{ mol } MCO_3}{1 \text{ mol } CO_2} = 0.00854 \text{ mol } MCO_3$

$\dfrac{1.056 \text{ g}}{0.00854 \text{ mol}} = 124 \text{ g/mol}$

124 g/mol (MCO_3) − 60 g/mol (CO_3) = 64 g/mol   The metal is copper, Cu.

4.59 $M(s) + O_2(g) \rightarrow MO_2(s)$

$(0.452 - 0.356) \text{ g } O_2 \cdot \dfrac{1 \text{ mol } O_2}{32.00 \text{ g}} \cdot \dfrac{1 \text{ mol M}}{1 \text{ mol } O_2} = 0.0030 \text{ mol M}$

$\dfrac{0.356 \text{ g}}{0.0030 \text{ mol}} = 120 \text{ g/mol (119 g/mol with three significant figures)}$

The metal is probably Sn (118.67 g/mol).

4.60 $1.598 \text{ g } TiO_2 \cdot \dfrac{1 \text{ mol } TiO_2}{79.866 \text{ g}} \cdot \dfrac{1 \text{ mol Ti}}{1 \text{ mol } TiO_2} = 0.02001 \text{ mol Ti}$

$1.438 \text{ g } Ti_xO_y - (0.02001 \text{ mol Ti} \cdot \dfrac{47.867 \text{ g}}{1 \text{ mol Ti}}) = 0.480 \text{ g O}$

$0.480 \text{ g O} \cdot \dfrac{1 \text{ mol O}}{16.00 \text{ g}} = 0.0300 \text{ mol O}$

$\dfrac{0.0300 \text{ mol O}}{0.02001 \text{ mol Ti}} = \dfrac{1.5 \text{ mol O}}{1 \text{ mol Ti}} = \dfrac{3 \text{ mol O}}{2 \text{ mol Ti}}$ $\qquad$ The empirical formula is Ti_2O_3

4.61 $8.63 \text{ g Ag} \cdot \dfrac{1 \text{ mol Ag}}{107.9 \text{ g}} \cdot \dfrac{1 \text{ mol Ag}_2\text{MoS}_4}{2 \text{ mol Ag}} \cdot \dfrac{439.9 \text{ g}}{1 \text{ mol Ag}_2\text{MoS}_4} = 17.6 \text{ g Ag}_2\text{MoS}_4$

$3.36 \text{ g Mo} \cdot \dfrac{1 \text{ mol Mo}}{95.94 \text{ g}} \cdot \dfrac{1 \text{ mol Ag}_2\text{MoS}_4}{1 \text{ mol Mo}} \cdot \dfrac{439.9 \text{ g}}{1 \text{ mol Ag}_2\text{MoS}_4} = 15.4 \text{ g Ag}_2\text{MoS}_4$

$4.81 \text{ g S} \cdot \dfrac{1 \text{ mol S}}{32.07 \text{ g}} \cdot \dfrac{1 \text{ mol Ag}_2\text{MoS}_4}{4 \text{ mol S}} \cdot \dfrac{439.9 \text{ g}}{1 \text{ mol Ag}_2\text{MoS}_4} = 16.5 \text{ g Ag}_2\text{MoS}_4$

The maximum mass that can be obtained is 15.4 g Ag$_2$MoS$_4$.

4.62 $0.301 \text{ g BaSO}_4 \cdot \dfrac{1 \text{ mol BaSO}_4}{233.4 \text{ g}} \cdot \dfrac{1 \text{ mol S}}{1 \text{ mol BaSO}_4} \cdot \dfrac{1 \text{ mol thioridazine}}{2 \text{ mol S}} \cdot \dfrac{370.6 \text{ g}}{1 \text{ mol thioridazine}} \cdot \dfrac{10^3 \text{ mg}}{1 \text{ g}}$

$= 239 \text{ mg thioridazine}$

$\dfrac{239 \text{ mg}}{12 \text{ tablets}} = 19.9 \text{ mg thioridazine per tablet}$

4.63 $0.1840 \text{ g AgCl} \cdot \dfrac{1 \text{ mol AgCl}}{143.32 \text{ g}} \cdot \dfrac{1 \text{ mol Cl}}{1 \text{ mol AgCl}} \cdot \dfrac{1 \text{ mol } 2,4\text{-D}}{2 \text{ mol Cl}} \cdot \dfrac{221.04 \text{ g}}{1 \text{ mol } 2,4\text{-D}} = 0.1419 \text{ g } 2,4\text{-D}$

$\dfrac{0.1419 \text{ g}}{1.236 \text{ g}} \cdot 100\% = 11.48\% \ 2,4\text{-D}$

4.64   (a) 10.8 g product – 2.0 g Fe = 8.8 g Br$_2$

(b) $2.0 \text{ g Fe} \cdot \dfrac{1 \text{ mol Fe}}{55.8 \text{ g}} = 0.036 \text{ mol Fe}$ $8.8 \text{ g Br}_2 \cdot \dfrac{1 \text{ mol Br}_2}{160. \text{ g}} \cdot \dfrac{2 \text{ mol Br}}{1 \text{ mol Br}_2} = 0.11 \text{ mol Br}$

$\dfrac{0.11 \text{ mol Br}}{0.036 \text{ mol Fe}} = \dfrac{3 \text{ mol Br}}{1 \text{ mol Fe}}$

(c) FeBr$_3$

(d) 2 Fe(s) + 3 Br$_2$(ℓ) → 2 FeBr$_3$

(e) Iron(III) bromide

(f) (i) When 1.00 g of Fe is added to the Br$_2$, Fe is the limiting reagent.

4.65   **NOTE:** problem should read "A 0.7184-g sample of impure NaHCO$_3$ …"

0.7184 g sample – 0.4724 g residue = 0.2460 g gas lost

Treating the gas lost as the compound H$_2$CO$_3$,

$0.2460 \text{ g H}_2\text{CO}_3 \cdot \dfrac{1 \text{ mol H}_2\text{CO}_3}{62.025 \text{ g}} \cdot \dfrac{2 \text{ mol NaHCO}_3}{1 \text{ mol H}_2\text{CO}_3} \cdot \dfrac{84.007 \text{ g}}{1 \text{ mol NaHCO}_3} = 0.6664 \text{ g NaHCO}_3$

$\dfrac{0.6664 \text{ g}}{0.7184 \text{ g}} \cdot 100\% = 92.76\% \text{ NaHCO}_3$

4.66   See Screen 4.8 for an explanation and calculations that support these results.

Chapter 5
Reactions in Aqueous Solution

INSTRUCTOR'S NOTES

Chapter 5 requires approximately five, 50-minute lectures.

Chapter 5 is focused on chemical reactions in solution, including electrolytes, types of reactions, concentration, and solution stoichiometry. Chapter 5 also includes a heavy emphasis on chemistry at the molecular level. The images representing electrolytic behavior and chemical reactions at the molecular level are intended to help students visualize molecules instead of chemical formulas. New in this edition is the introduction of pH in this chapter as a way to describe the H^+ concentration in acidic and basic solutions.

We consider Chapter 5 an important early chapter in the book. We cover this material early in our course because our students use the concepts the laboratory. However, *we emphasize that it is not crucial that this material be covered at this time in the course*. In particular, *it would be easy to cover the subject of redox reactions at some other point in the year,* such as when covering electrochemistry later in the year.

Chapter 5 introduces the properties of ionic compounds in aqueous solution and general guidelines to predict the aqueous solubility of simple ionic compounds. Although one can readily find many exceptions to the guidelines in Figure 5.1, we do find them useful for students in a beginning course. We hope that the many photos of soluble and insoluble compounds in this chapter will help students remember some of these guidelines.

The section on net ionic equations beginning on page 155 can be a difficult one for our students. We admit it does take time and effort to help the students come to grips with this concept. However, it is a useful one, since (1) many reactions are best seen in this fashion and (2) balancing reactions is made easier. Students can generally write balanced equations for exchange reactions, but they sometimes have a difficult time turning them into net ionic equations. Time and effort on everyone's part is needed here.

The introduction to acids and bases beginning on page 156 is somewhat brief at this stage, but it does enable one to use common acids and bases in examples and in the laboratory with the knowledge that students have some familiarity with them and with the pH scale. Oxidation numbers have been introduced *only* as a way of telling if a redox reaction has occurred.

SUGGESTED DEMONSTRATIONS

1.   Electrolytes
   *   We always illustrate the conductivity, and the difference between strong and weak electrolytes, using an apparatus such as that in the Chapter Focus. We use solutions such as $CuSO_4$, Na_2CO_3, vinegar, and pure water. It is interesting to compare the behavior of these solutions with the conductivity of soda or juice.

2.   Solubility of Ionic Compounds

- It is very important to illustrate the solubility of salts. Our most recent demonstrations are outlined below. Throughout the demonstrations the solubility guidelines are projected onto the screen in the lecture room. *Note: Precipitation reactions **cannot** be illustrated on an overhead projector. The precipitate is seen only as a dark blob. However, even in a large lecture room, students can see the reaction if it is done in a large flask (1-2 L).*

   (a) A gram or so of KI is dissolved in a few hundred milliliters of water in one flask, and $Pb(NO_3)_2$ is dissolved in water in another flask. The students can clearly see the salts dissolve. On mixing the solutions, though, a bright yellow precipitate of PbI_2 appears, clearly demonstrating one of the exceptions to the general rule that halide salts are water-soluble.

   (b) A solution of $(NH_4)_2S$ is mixed with a solution of $Cd(NO_3)_2$ to show that metal sulfides (bright yellow CdS in this case) are generally not soluble.

   (c) $BaCl_2$ is dissolved in water while discussing halide solubility and mixed with a solution of $CuSO_4$ (which shows the usual solubility of sulfates). Precipitation of $BaSO_4$ on mixing the solutions then demonstrates the exceptions to the guideline regarding sulfates.

   (d) Our attempt at dissolving a piece of blackboard chalk fails, clearly showing that many carbonates are not soluble.

- Other solubility demonstrations include:

   (a) Dissolve NaCl in water and then precipitate AgCl with $AgNO_3$.

   (b) Dissolve Na_2CO_3 and compare this with chalk.

   (c) Show a sample of fool's gold (iron pyrite) to illustrate the insolubility of metal sulfides.

   (d) Add NaOH to solutions of $Fe(NO_3)_3$ and $CuSO_4$ to get insoluble hydroxides.

   (e) Shakhashiri, B. Z. *Chemical Demonstrations: A Handbook for Teachers of Chemistry*; University of Wisconsin Press, 1983; Vol. 1, pp. 307-313.

3.   Acid-Base Reaction

- Although is it easy for students to see precipitation reactions done in large flasks, we find that acid-base reactions are difficult to demonstrate, since common ones are not spectacular. However, a suggested demonstration would be to dissolve a precipitate of $Ca(OH)_2$. At least the solid would be seen to dissolve on adding acid.

- Bring a pH meter to class to demonstrate the pH scale using common acids and bases.

4.   Oxides

- Show samples of metal oxides, especially those of iron, aluminum, boron, lead, and magnesium. Show a sample of anodized aluminum (kitchen ware is effective) or aluminum oxide sandpaper.

- Show samples of silica sand and quartz crystals.

- Take a sample of dry ice and discuss some of the chemistry of CO_2.

- React hot sulfur with pure O_2 (Shakhashiri, Vol. 2, pp. 184-189). This is especially effective in a very dark room. (Fill the bottle with pure O_2 before lecture and tightly stopper.)

- Make NO_2 from copper (a penny) and concentrated HNO_3. (Place a penny in about 15 mL of concentrated HNO_3 in a 2-L flask and stopper lightly with a rubber stopper. Although a little NO_2 comes out of the flask, in a large lecture room it is not noticeable.

5.   Combustion Reaction

- A very simple demonstration of combustion reactions is the "plastic soda bottle rocket." Insert large nails on opposite sides of a plastic soda bottle near the bottom. Place a few milliliters of methanol in the bottle and shake to saturate the atmosphere in the bottle with alcohol. Place a cork in the top of the bottle (it will take some experimenting to see how firmly to seat the cork), and then touch one of the nails with a Tesla coil. The cork will fly out of the bottle with a loud bang.

6.   Oxidation-Reduction Chemistry

- After introducing the ideas of redox and the concept of oxidation numbers, we do a demonstration on the oxidation states of vanadium.

  Directions: Dissolve 1 g of ammonium vanadate in 200 mL of water. (Warm to dissolve completely.)

  (a)   Add 3 M H_2SO_4 (20-50 mL), and the solution turns yellow owing to an acid-base reaction

  $$VO_3^- + 2\,H^+ \rightarrow VO_2^+ + H_2O$$

  (b)   Add a handful of zinc chips. These reduce the V(V) to V(IV).

  $$2\,VO_2^+ + Zn + 4\,H^+ \rightarrow 2\,VO^{2+} \text{ (vanadyl, blue)} + 2\,H_2O + Zn^{2+}$$

  (c)   The solution will slowly turn emerald green owing to another reduction step.

  $$2\,VO^{2+} \text{ (blue)} + Zn + 4\,H^+ \rightarrow 2\,V^{3+} \text{ (green)} + 2\,H_2O + Zn^{2+}$$

  (d)   The solution will finally turn violet. We allow the reaction to continue throughout the lecture with a stopper on the flask. This excludes air well enough that the violet, aqueous vanadium(II) ion can form. (The vanadium(II) ion is readily oxidized by oxygen in air to V^{3+}. Therefore, to see the violet color air must be excluded.)

7.   Solution Stoichiometry

- One of the biggest problems in teaching stoichiometry is to get the students to connect the words on paper with actual operations in the laboratory. To help in making this connection, we have included photos in the text of (a) the preparation of a solution starting with a solid compound (Figure 5.15), preparing a solution by dilution of a more concentrated one (Figure 5.16), and acid–base and redox titrations (Figure 5.20 and Example 5.15, respectively). We find it very helpful to demonstrate these processes in class as well.

Solutions to Study Questions

5.1   The solvent is the medium in which another substance, the solute, is dissolved in a solution. The solvent
        is usually the component present in the largest amount.

5.2   Acid-base reaction: $HCl(aq) + NaOH(aq) \rightarrow H_2O(\ell) + NaCl(aq)$

        An acid, hydrochloric acid, reacts with a base, sodium hydroxide, to produce a salt, sodium chloride,
        and water

        Precipitation reaction: $AgNO_3(aq) + KCl(aq) \rightarrow AgCl(s) + KNO_3(aq)$

        Two soluble salts, silver nitrate and potassium chloride, react to form an insoluble salt, silver
        chloride, and a soluble salt, potassium nitrate

        Gas-forming reaction: $Na_2S(aq) + 2\ HCl(aq) \rightarrow 2\ NaCl(aq) + H_2S(g)$

        A metal sulfide, sodium sulfide, and acid, hydrochloric acid, react to form a salt, sodium chloride, and
        a gas, hydrogen sulfide

        Oxidation-reduction reaction: $2\ Na(s) + Cl_2(g) \rightarrow 2\ NaCl(s)$

        An oxidizing agent, chlorine, reacts with a reducing agent, sodium, to form sodium chloride

5.3   Electrolytes are compounds whose aqueous solutions conduct electricity. Substances whose solutions are
        good electrical conductors are strong electrolytes (such as sodium chloride), poor electrical conductors are
        weak electrolytes (such as acetic acid).

5.4   Hydrochloric acid and nitric acid are strong electrolytes. Acetic acid is a weak electrolyte. Sodium
        hydroxide and potassium hydroxide are strong electrolytes. Calcium hydroxide is a weak electrolyte.

5.5 $Cu(NO_3)_2$ and $CuCl_2$ are soluble in water, $CuCO_3$ and $Cu_3(PO_4)_2$ are insoluble in water

5.6   The anions NO_3^-, ClO_3^-, ClO_4^-, $CH_3CO_2^-$, Cl^-, Br^-, I^-, F^-, and SO_4^{2-} form soluble salts with Al^{3+}.

5.7   Nitrate ions are spectator ions in this acid-base reaction
        $2\ H^+(aq) + Mg(OH)_2(s) \rightarrow 2\ H_2O(\ell) + Mg^{2+}(aq)$

5.8   (a) $CuS(s)$ copper(II) sulfide

        (b) $CaCO_3(s)$ calcium carbonate

        (c) $AgI(s)$ silver iodide

5.9 Cl_2, chlorine, has been reduced and is the oxidizing agent

        NaBr, sodium bromide, has been oxidized and is the reducing agent

5.10   For example, consider the reaction $2\ Na + Cl_2 \rightarrow 2\ NaCl$

      (a) Oxidation is the loss of electrons ($Na \rightarrow Na^+ + e^-$), reduction is the gain of electrons

          ($Cl_2 + 2\ e^- \rightarrow 2\ Cl^-$).

      (b) An oxidizing agent is reduced in a reaction (Cl_2), a reducing agent is oxidized in a reaction (Na).

5.11   Oxidizing agents: HNO_3, Cl_2, O_2, $KMnO_4$ Reducing agent: Na

5.12 $NiCO_3(s) + H_2SO_4(aq) \rightarrow NiSO_4(aq) + H_2O(\ell) + CO_2(g)$

      nickel(II) carbonate, sulfuric acid, nickel(II) sulfate, water, carbon dioxide

5.13 $1\ L \cdot \dfrac{0.1\ mol\ NaCl}{1\ L} \cdot \dfrac{58\ g}{1\ mol\ NaCl} = 6\ g\ NaCl$

      $1\ L \cdot \dfrac{0.06\ mol\ Na_2CO_3}{1\ L} \cdot \dfrac{106\ g}{1\ mol\ Na_2CO_3} = 6\ g\ Na_2CO_3$

      Limited to one significant figure, the solutions contain the same amount of solute.

5.14 $0.20\ M\ BaCl_2 \cdot \dfrac{3\ mol\ ions}{1\ mol\ BaCl_2} = 0.60\ M\ ions$

      $0.25\ M\ NaCl \cdot \dfrac{2\ mol\ ions}{1\ mol\ NaCl} = 0.50\ M\ ions$

      $0.20\ M\ BaCl_2$ has a larger concentration of ions.

5.15   (a) reactant favored

      (b) product favored

5.16 $500.0\ mL \cdot \dfrac{1\ L}{10^3\ mL} \cdot \dfrac{0.20\ mol\ Na_2CO_3}{1\ L} \cdot \dfrac{106\ g}{1\ mol\ Na_2CO_3} = 11\ g\ Na_2CO_3$

      Weigh out 11 g of Na_2CO_3 and place it in the 500.0 mL flask. Add a small amount of distilled water and

      mix until the solute dissolves. Add water until the meniscus of the solution rests at the calibrated mark on

      the neck of the volumetric flask. Cap the flask and swirl to ensure adequate mixing.

5.17 $250.\ mL \cdot \dfrac{1\ L}{10^3\ mL} \cdot \dfrac{0.500\ mol\ KCl}{1\ L} = 0.125\ mol\ KCl$

      Take one-fourth of the KCl, place it in the volumetric flask, and a small amount of distilled water and mix

      until the solute dissolves. Add water until the meniscus of the solution rests at the calibrated mark on the

      neck of the volumetric flask. Cap the flask and swirl to ensure adequate mixing.

5.18   In 0.015 M HCl, $[H^+] = 0.015\ M$

      In pH 1.2 solution, $[H^+] = 10^{-pH} = 10^{-1.2} = 0.06\ M$

      The pH 1.2 solution has a higher hydrogen ion concentration.

5.19   The equivalence point in a titration is when a stoichiometric or equivalent amount of one reactant has been added to the second reactant in a chemical process. The function of an indicator is to change color when a very slight excess of one reactant is present.

5.20   (a) $CuCl_2$

(b) $AgNO_3$

(c) K_2CO_3, KI, $KMnO_4$

5.21   (a) $Ba(NO_3)_2$

(b) Na_2SO_4, $NaClO_4$, and $NaCH_3CO_2$

(c) KBr and Al_2Br_6

5.22   (a) K^+ and OH^- ions   (c) Li^+ and NO_3^- ions

(b) K^+ and SO_4^{2-} ions   (d) NH_4^+ and SO_4^{2-} ions

5.23   (a) K^+ and I^- ions   (c) K^+ and HPO_4^{2-} ions

(b) Mg^{2+} and $CH_3CO_2^-$ ions   (d) Na^+ and CN^- ions

5.24   (a) soluble; Na^+ and CO_3^{2-} ions   (c) insoluble

(b) soluble; Cu^{2+} and SO_4^{2-} ions   (d) soluble; Ba^{2+} and Br^- ions

5.25   (a) soluble; Ni^{2+} and Cl^- ions   (c) soluble; Pb^{2+} and NO_3^- ions

(b) soluble; Cr^{2+} and NO_3^- ions   (d) insoluble

5.26 $CdCl_2(aq) + 2\ NaOH(aq) \rightarrow Cd(OH)_2(s) + 2\ NaCl(aq)$

$Cd^{2+}(aq) + 2\ OH^-(aq) \rightarrow Cd(OH)_2(s)$

5.27 $Ni(NO_3)_2(aq) + Na_2CO_3(aq) \rightarrow NiCO_3(s) + 2\ NaNO_3(aq)$

$Ni^{2+}(aq) + CO_3^{2-}(aq) \rightarrow NiCO_3(s)$

5.28   (a) $NiCl_2(aq) + (NH_4)_2S(aq) \rightarrow NiS(s) + 2\ NH_4Cl(aq)$

(b) $3\ Mn(NO_3)_2(aq) + 2\ Na_3PO_4(aq) \rightarrow Mn_3(PO_4)_2(s) + 6\ NaNO_3(aq)$

5.29   (a) $Pb(NO_3)_2(aq) + 2\ KBr(aq) \rightarrow PbBr_2(s) + 2\ KNO_3(aq)$

(b) $Ca(NO_3)_2(aq) + 2\ KF(aq) \rightarrow CaF_2(s) + 2\ KNO_3(aq)$

(c) $Ca(NO_3)_2(aq) + Na_2C_2O_4(aq) \rightarrow CaC_2O_4(s) + 2\ NaNO_3(aq)$

5.30   (a) $(NH_4)_2CO_3(aq) + Cu(NO_3)_2 \rightarrow CuCO_3(s) + 2\ NH_4NO_3(aq)$

$CO_3^{2-}(aq) + Cu^{2+}(aq) \rightarrow CuCO_3(s)$

(b) $Pb(OH)_2(s) + 2 HCl(aq) \rightarrow PbCl_2(s) + 2 H_2O(\ell)$

   $Pb(OH)_2(s) + 2 H^+(aq) + 2 Cl^-(aq) \rightarrow PbCl_2(s) + 2 H_2O(\ell)$

(c) $BaCO_3(s) + 2 HCl(aq) \rightarrow BaCl_2(aq) + H_2O(\ell) + CO_2(g)$

   $BaCO_3(s) + 2 H^+(aq) \rightarrow Ba^{2+}(aq) + H_2O(\ell) + CO_2(g)$

5.31 (a) $Zn(s) + 2 HCl(aq) \rightarrow H_2(g) + ZnCl_2(aq)$

    $Zn(s) + 2 H^+(aq) \rightarrow H_2(g) + Zn^{2+}(aq)$

   (b) $Mg(OH)_2(s) + 2 HCl(aq) \rightarrow MgCl_2(aq) + 2 H_2O(\ell)$

    $Mg(OH)_2(s) + 2 H^+(aq) \rightarrow Mg^{2+}(aq) + 2 H_2O(\ell)$

   (c) $2 HNO_3(aq) + CaCO_3(s) \rightarrow Ca(NO_3)_2(aq) + H_2O(\ell) + CO_2(g)$

    $2 H^+(aq) + CaCO_3(s) \rightarrow Ca^{2+}(aq) + H_2O(\ell) + CO_2(g)$

5.32 (a) $AgNO_3(aq) + KI(aq) \rightarrow AgI(s) + KNO_3(aq)$

    $Ag^+(aq) + I^-(aq) \rightarrow AgI(s)$

   (b) $Ba(OH)_2(aq) + 2 HNO_3(aq) \rightarrow Ba(NO_3)_2(aq) + 2 H_2O(\ell)$

    $OH^-(aq) + H^+(aq) \rightarrow H_2O(\ell)$

   (c) $2 Na_3PO_4(aq) + 3 Ni(NO_3)_2(aq) \rightarrow Ni_3(PO_4)_2(s) + 6 NaNO_3(aq)$

    $2 PO_4^{3-}(aq) + 3 Ni^{2+}(aq) \rightarrow Ni_3(PO_4)_2(s)$

5.33 (a) $2 NaOH(aq) + FeCl_2(aq) \rightarrow Fe(OH)_2(s) + 2 NaCl(aq)$

    $2 OH^-(aq) + Fe^{2+}(aq) \rightarrow Fe(OH)_2(s)$

   (b) $BaCl_2(aq) + Na_2CO_3(aq) \rightarrow BaCO_3(s) + 2 NaCl(aq)$

    $Ba^{2+}(aq) + CO_3^{2-}(aq) \rightarrow BaCO_3(s)$

5.34 $HNO_3(aq) \rightarrow H^+(aq) + NO_3^-(aq)$

5.35 $HClO_4(aq) \rightarrow H^+(aq) + ClO_4^-(aq)$

5.36 $H_2C_2O_4(aq) \rightarrow H^+(aq) + HC_2O_4^-(aq)$

   $HC_2O_4^-(aq) \rightarrow H^+(aq) + C_2O_4^{2-}(aq)$

5.37 $H_3PO_4(aq) \rightarrow H^+(aq) + H_2PO_4^-(aq)$

   $H_2PO_4^-(aq) \rightarrow H^+(aq) + HPO_4^{2-}(aq)$

   $HPO_4^{2-}(aq) \rightarrow H^+(aq) + PO_4^{3-}(aq)$

5.38 $MgO(s) + H_2O(\ell) \rightarrow Mg(OH)_2(s)$

5.39 $SO_3(g) + H_2O(\ell) \rightarrow H_2SO_4(aq)$

5.40   (a) $2 CH_3CO_2H(aq) + Mg(OH)_2(s) \rightarrow Mg(CH_3CO_2)_2(aq) + 2 H_2O(\ell)$

             acetic acid, magnesium hydroxide, magnesium acetate, water

       (b) $HClO_4(aq) + NH_3(aq) \rightarrow NH_4ClO_4(aq)$

             perchloric acid, ammonia, ammonium perchlorate

5.41   (a) $H_3PO_4(aq) + 3 KOH(aq) \rightarrow K_3PO_4(aq) + 3 H_2O(\ell)$

             phosphoric acid, potassium hydroxide, potassium phosphate, water

       (b) $H_2C_2O_4(aq) + Ca(OH)_2(s) \rightarrow CaC_2O_4(s) + 2 H_2O(\ell)$

             oxalic acid, calcium hydroxide, calcium oxalate, water

5.42 $Ba(OH)_2(s) + 2 HNO_3(aq) \rightarrow Ba(NO_3)_2(aq) + 2 H_2O(\ell)$

5.43 $2 Al(OH)_3(s) + 3 H_2SO_4(aq) \rightarrow Al_2(SO_4)_3(aq) + 6 H_2O(\ell)$

5.44 $FeCO_3(s) + 2 HNO_3(aq) \rightarrow Fe(NO_3)_2(aq) + CO_2(g) + H_2O(\ell)$

       iron(II) carbonate, nitric acid, iron(II) nitrate, carbon dioxide, water

5.45 $MnCO_3(s) + 2 HCl(aq) \rightarrow MnCl_2(aq) + CO_2(g) + H_2O(\ell)$

       manganese(II) carbonate, hydrochloric acid, manganese(II) chloride, carbon dioxide, water

5.46   (a) $Ba(OH)_2(s) + 2 HCl(aq) \rightarrow BaCl_2(aq) + 2 H_2O(\ell)$

             acid-base reaction

       (b) $2 HNO_3(aq) + CoCO_3(s) \rightarrow Co(NO_3)_2(aq) + H_2O(\ell) + CO_2(g)$

             gas-forming reaction

       (c) $2 Na_3PO_4(aq) + 3 Cu(NO_3)_2(aq) \rightarrow Cu_3(PO_4)_2(s) + 6 NaNO_3(aq)$

             precipitation reaction

5.47   (a) $K_2CO_3(aq) + Cu(NO_3)_2(aq) \rightarrow CuCO_3(s) + 2 KNO_3(aq)$

             precipitation reaction

       (b) $Pb(NO_3)_2(aq) + 2 HCl(aq) \rightarrow PbCl_2(s) + 2 HNO_3(aq)$

             precipitation reaction

       (c) $MgCO_3(s) + 2 HCl(aq) \rightarrow MgCl_2(aq) + CO_2(g) + H_2O(\ell)$

             gas-forming reaction

5.48   (a) $MnCl_2(aq) + Na_2S(aq) \rightarrow MnS(s) + 2 NaCl(aq)$

             precipitation reaction

             $Mn^{2+}(aq) + S^{2-}(aq) \rightarrow MnS(s)$

(b) $K_2CO_3(aq) + ZnCl_2(aq) \rightarrow ZnCO_3(s) + 2\ KCl(aq)$

precipitation reaction

$CO_3^{2-}(aq) + Zn^{2+}(aq) \rightarrow ZnCO_3(s)$

5.49   (a) $Fe(OH)_3(s) + 3\ HNO_3(aq) \rightarrow Fe(NO_3)_3(aq) + 3\ H_2O(\ell)$

Acid-base reaction

$Fe(OH)_3(s) + 3\ H^+(aq) \rightarrow Fe^{3+}(aq) + 3\ H_2O(\ell)$

(b) $FeCO_3(s) + 2\ HNO_3(aq) \rightarrow Fe(NO_3)_2(aq) + CO_2(g) + H_2O(\ell)$

Gas-forming reaction

$FeCO_3(s) + 2\ H^+(aq) \rightarrow Fe^{2+}(aq) + CO_2(g) + H_2O(\ell)$

5.50   (a) The formation of a solid, CuS

(b) The formation of a liquid, H_2O

5.51   (a) is a product-favored reaction

5.52   (a) Br is +5 and O is –2   (d) Ca is +2 and H is –1

(b) C is +3 and O is –2   (e) H is +1, Si is +4, and O is –2

(c) F is –1   (f) H is +1, S is +6, and O is –2

5.53   (a) P is +5 and F is –1   (d) N is +5 and O is –2

(b) H is +1, As is +5, and O is –2   (e) P is +5, O is –2, and Cl is –1

(c) U is +4 and O is –2   (f) Xe is +6 and O is –2

5.54   (a) oxidation-reduction reaction

Oxidation number of Zn changes from 0 to +2, while that of N changes from +5 to +4

(b) acid-base reaction

(c) oxidation-reduction reaction

Oxidation number of Ca changes from 0 to +2, while that of H changes from +1 to 0

5.55   (a) precipitation reaction

(b) oxidation-reduction reaction

Oxidation number of Ca changes from 0 to +2, while that of O changes from 0 to –2

(c) oxidation-reduction reaction

Oxidation number of Fe changes from +2 to +3, while that of O changes from 0 to –2

5.56   (a) C_2H_4 is oxidized and is the reducing agent; O_2 is reduced and is the oxidizing agent

(b) Si is oxidized and is the reducing agent; Cl_2 is reduced and is the oxidizing agent

5.57   (a) $Cr_2O_7^{2-}$ is reduced and is the oxidizing agent; Sn^{2+} is oxidized and is the reducing agent.

      (c) FeS is oxidized and is the reducing agent; NO_3^- is reduced and is the oxidizing agent.

5.58 $6.73 \text{ g } Na_2CO_3 \cdot \dfrac{1 \text{ mol}}{106.0 \text{ g}} = 0.0635 \text{ mol } Na_2CO_3$ $\dfrac{0.0635 \text{ mol}}{0.250 \text{ L}} = 0.254 \text{ M } Na_2CO_3$

      $[Na^+] = 2 \times [Na_2CO_3] = 0.508 \text{ M } Na^+$ $[CO_3^{2-}] = [Na_2CO_3] = 0.254 \text{ M } CO_3^{2-}$

5.59 $2.335 \text{ g } K_2Cr_2O_7 \cdot \dfrac{1 \text{ mol } K_2Cr_2O_7}{294.18 \text{ g}} = 0.007937 \text{ mol } K_2Cr_2O_7$

      $\dfrac{0.007937 \text{ mol}}{0.500 \text{ L}} = 0.0159 \text{ M } K_2Cr_2O_7$

      $[K^+] = 2 \times [K_2Cr_2O_7] = 0.0318 \text{ M}$ $[Cr_2O_7^{2-}] = [K_2Cr_2O_7] = 0.0159 \text{ M}$

5.60 $0.250 \text{ L} \cdot \dfrac{0.0125 \text{ mol } KMnO_4}{1 \text{ L}} \cdot \dfrac{158.0 \text{ g}}{1 \text{ mol } KMnO_4} = 0.494 \text{ g } KMnO_4$

5.61 $0.125 \text{ L} \cdot \dfrac{1.023 \times 10^{-3} \text{ mol } Na_3PO_4}{1 \text{ L}} \cdot \dfrac{163.9 \text{ g}}{1 \text{ mol } Na_3PO_4} = 0.0210 \text{ g } Na_3PO_4$

      $[Na^+] = 3 \times [Na_3PO_4] = 3.069 \times 10^{-3} \text{ M}$ $[PO_4^{3-}] = [Na_3PO_4] = 1.023 \times 10^{-3} \text{ M}$

5.62 $25.0 \text{ g } NaOH \cdot \dfrac{1 \text{ mol } NaOH}{40.00 \text{ g}} \cdot \dfrac{1 \text{ L}}{0.123 \text{ mol } NaOH} \cdot \dfrac{10^3 \text{ mL}}{1 \text{ L}} = 5080 \text{ mL solution}$

5.63 $322 \text{ g } KMnO_4 \cdot \dfrac{1 \text{ mol } KMnO_4}{158.0 \text{ g}} \cdot \dfrac{1 \text{ L}}{2.06 \text{ mol } KMnO_4} = 0.989 \text{ L solution}$

5.64   (a) $0.50 \text{ M } NH_4^+$; $0.25 \text{ M } SO_4^{2-}$

      (b) $0.246 \text{ M } Na^+$; $0.123 \text{ M } CO_3^{2-}$

      (c) $0.056 \text{ M } H^+$; $0.056 \text{ M } NO_3^-$

5.65   (a) $0.12 \text{ M } Ba^{2+}$; $0.24 \text{ M } Cl^-$

      (b) $0.0125 \text{ M } Cu^{2+}$; $0.0125 \text{ M } SO_4^{2-}$

      (c) $1.000 \text{ M } K^+$; $0.500 \text{ M } Cr_2O_7^{2-}$

5.66 $500.0 \text{ mL} \cdot \dfrac{1 \text{ L}}{10^3 \text{ mL}} \cdot \dfrac{0.0200 \text{ mol } Na_2CO_3}{1 \text{ L}} \cdot \dfrac{105.99 \text{ g}}{1 \text{ mol } Na_2CO_3} = 1.06 \text{ g } Na_2CO_3$

      Weigh out 1.06 g of Na_2CO_3 and place it in the 500.0 mL flask. Add a small amount of distilled water and mix until the solute dissolves. Add water until the meniscus of the solution rests at the calibrated mark on the neck of the volumetric flask. Cap the flask and swirl to ensure adequate mixing.

5.67 $0.250 \text{ L} \cdot \dfrac{0.15 \text{ mol } H_2C_2O_4}{1 \text{ L}} \cdot \dfrac{90.04 \text{ g}}{1 \text{ mol } H_2C_2O_4} = 3.4 \text{ g } H_2C_2O_4$

5.68 $c_d = c_c \cdot \dfrac{V_c}{V_d} = 1.50 \text{ M} \cdot \dfrac{25.0 \text{ mL}}{500. \text{ mL}} = 0.0750 \text{ M HCl}$

5.69 $c_d = c_c \cdot \dfrac{V_c}{V_d} = 0.0250 \text{ M} \cdot \dfrac{4.00 \text{ mL}}{10.0 \text{ mL}} = 0.0100 \text{ M CuSO}_4$

5.70   (a) $c_d = c_c \cdot \dfrac{V_c}{V_d} = 6.00 \text{ M} \cdot \dfrac{0.0208 \text{ L}}{1.00 \text{ L}} = 0.125 \text{ M H}_2\text{SO}_4$ Correct method

       (b) $c_d = c_c \cdot \dfrac{V_c}{V_d} = 3.00 \text{ M} \cdot \dfrac{0.0500 \text{ L}}{1.00 \text{ L}} = 0.150 \text{ M H}_2\text{SO}_4$

5.71   (a) $c_d = c_c \cdot \dfrac{V_c}{V_d} = 1.50 \text{ M} \cdot \dfrac{30.0 \text{ mL}}{300. \text{ mL}} = 0.150 \text{ M K}_2\text{Cr}_2\text{O}_7$

       (b) $c_d = c_c \cdot \dfrac{V_c}{V_d} = 0.600 \text{ M} \cdot \dfrac{250. \text{ mL}}{300. \text{ mL}} = 0.500 \text{ M K}_2\text{Cr}_2\text{O}_7$ Correct method

5.72 $[\text{H}^+] = 10^{-\text{pH}} = 10^{-3.40} = 4.0 \times 10^{-4} \text{ M}$ The solution is acidic (pH < 7)

5.73 $[\text{H}^+] = 10^{-\text{pH}} = 10^{-10.5} = 3 \times 10^{-11} \text{ M}$ The solution is basic (pH > 7)

5.74 $[\text{H}^+] = [\text{HNO}_3] = 0.0013 \text{ M}$ $\text{pH} = -\log[\text{H}^+] = -\log(0.0013) = 2.89$

5.75 $[\text{H}^+] = [\text{HClO}_4] = 1.2 \times 10^{-4} \text{ M}$ $\text{pH} = -\log[\text{H}^+] = -\log(1.2 \times 10^{-4}) = 3.92$

5.76

	pH	$[\text{H}^+]$	
(a)	1.00	0.10 M	acidic
(b)	10.50	3.2×10^{-11} M	basic
(c)	4.89	1.3×10^{-5} M	acidic
(d)	7.64	2.3×10^{-8} M	basic

5.77

	pH	$[\text{H}^+]$	
(a)	9.17	6.7×10^{-10} M	basic
(b)	5.66	2.2×10^{-6} M	acidic
(c)	5.25	5.6×10^{-6} M	acidic
(d)	1.60	2.5×10^{-2} M	acidic

5.78 $2.50 \text{ g Ba(OH)}_2 \cdot \dfrac{1 \text{ mol Ba(OH)}_2}{171.3 \text{ g}} \cdot \dfrac{2 \text{ mol HNO}_3}{1 \text{ mol Ba(OH)}_2} \cdot \dfrac{1 \text{ L}}{0.109 \text{ mol HNO}_3} \cdot \dfrac{10^3 \text{ mL}}{1 \text{ L}} = 268 \text{ mL solution}$

5.79 $50.0 \text{ mL} \cdot \dfrac{1 \text{ L}}{10^3 \text{ mL}} \cdot \dfrac{0.125 \text{ mol HNO}_3}{1 \text{ L}} \cdot \dfrac{1 \text{ mol Na}_2\text{CO}_3}{2 \text{ mol HNO}_3} \cdot \dfrac{106.0 \text{ g}}{1 \text{ mol Na}_2\text{CO}_3} = 0.331 \text{ g Na}_2\text{CO}_3$

5.80 $15.0 \text{ L} \cdot \dfrac{0.35 \text{ mol NaCl}}{1 \text{ L}} \cdot \dfrac{2 \text{ mol NaOH}}{2 \text{ mol NaCl}} \cdot \dfrac{40.00 \text{ g}}{1 \text{ mol NaOH}} = 210 \text{ g NaOH}$

$15.0 \text{ L} \cdot \dfrac{0.35 \text{ mol NaCl}}{1 \text{ L}} \cdot \dfrac{1 \text{ mol Cl}_2}{2 \text{ mol NaCl}} \cdot \dfrac{70.91 \text{ g}}{1 \text{ mol Cl}_2} = 190 \text{ g Cl}_2$

5.81 $250. \text{ mL} \cdot \dfrac{1 \text{ L}}{10^3 \text{ mL}} \cdot \dfrac{0.146 \text{ mol H}_2\text{SO}_4}{1 \text{ L}} \cdot \dfrac{2 \text{ mol N}_2\text{H}_4}{1 \text{ mol H}_2\text{SO}_4} \cdot \dfrac{32.05 \text{ g}}{1 \text{ mol N}_2\text{H}_4} = 2.34 \text{ g N}_2\text{H}_4$

5.82 $0.225 \text{ g AgBr} \cdot \dfrac{1 \text{ mol AgBr}}{187.8 \text{ g}} \cdot \dfrac{2 \text{ mol Na}_2\text{S}_2\text{O}_3}{1 \text{ mol AgBr}} \cdot \dfrac{1 \text{ L}}{0.0138 \text{ mol Na}_2\text{S}_2\text{O}_3} \cdot \dfrac{10^3 \text{ mL}}{1 \text{ L}} = 174 \text{ mL solution}$

5.83 $2.05 \text{ g Al} \cdot \dfrac{1 \text{ mol Al}}{26.98 \text{ g}} \cdot \dfrac{2 \text{ mol KAl(OH)}_4}{2 \text{ mol Al}} \cdot \dfrac{134.1 \text{ g}}{1 \text{ mol KAl(OH)}_4} = 10.2 \text{ g KAl(OH)}_4$

$0.185 \text{ L} \cdot \dfrac{1.35 \text{ mol KOH}}{1 \text{ L}} \cdot \dfrac{2 \text{ mol KAl(OH)}_4}{2 \text{ mol KOH}} \cdot \dfrac{134.1 \text{ g}}{1 \text{ mol KAl(OH)}_4} = 33.5 \text{ g KAl(OH)}_4$

Al is the limiting reactant, so none will remain. 10.2 g KAl(OH)$_4$ is produced in the reaction.

5.84 $1.00 \text{ L} \cdot \dfrac{2.25 \text{ mol NaCl}}{1 \text{ L}} \cdot \dfrac{1 \text{ mol Pb(NO}_3)_2}{2 \text{ mol NaCl}} \cdot \dfrac{1 \text{ L}}{0.750 \text{ mol Pb(NO}_3)_2} \cdot \dfrac{10^3 \text{ mL}}{1 \text{ L}} = 1.50 \times 10^3 \text{ mL solution}$

5.85 $0.0352 \text{ L} \cdot \dfrac{0.546 \text{ mol NaOH}}{1 \text{ L}} \cdot \dfrac{1 \text{ mol H}_2\text{C}_2\text{O}_4}{2 \text{ mol NaOH}} \cdot \dfrac{1 \text{ L}}{0.125 \text{ mol H}_2\text{C}_2\text{O}_4} = 0.0769 \text{ L} \ (76.9 \text{ mL})$

5.86 $1.45 \text{ g NaOH} \cdot \dfrac{1 \text{ mol NaOH}}{40.00 \text{ g}} \cdot \dfrac{1 \text{ mol HCl}}{1 \text{ mol NaOH}} \cdot \dfrac{1 \text{ L}}{0.812 \text{ mol HCl}} \cdot \dfrac{10^3 \text{ mL}}{1 \text{ L}} = 44.6 \text{ mL}$

5.87 $2.152 \text{ g Na}_2\text{CO}_3 \cdot \dfrac{1 \text{ mol Na}_2\text{CO}_3}{105.99 \text{ g}} \cdot \dfrac{2 \text{ mol HCl}}{1 \text{ mol Na}_2\text{CO}_3} \cdot \dfrac{1 \text{ L}}{0.955 \text{ mol HCl}} \cdot \dfrac{10^3 \text{ mL}}{1 \text{ L}} = 42.5 \text{ mL}$

5.88 $2.150 \text{ g Na}_2\text{CO}_3 \cdot \dfrac{1 \text{ mol Na}_2\text{CO}_3}{105.99 \text{ g}} \cdot \dfrac{2 \text{ mol HCl}}{1 \text{ mol Na}_2\text{CO}_3} \cdot \dfrac{1}{0.03855 \text{ L}} = 1.052 \text{ M HCl}$

5.89 $0.902 \text{ g KHC}_8\text{H}_4\text{O}_4 \cdot \dfrac{1 \text{ mol KHC}_8\text{H}_4\text{O}_4}{204.22 \text{ g}} \cdot \dfrac{1 \text{ mol NaOH}}{1 \text{ mol KHC}_8\text{H}_4\text{O}_4} \cdot \dfrac{1}{0.02645 \text{ L}} = 0.167 \text{ M NaOH}$

5.90 $36.04 \text{ mL} \cdot \dfrac{1 \text{ L}}{10^3 \text{ mL}} \cdot \dfrac{0.509 \text{ mol NaOH}}{1 \text{ L}} \cdot \dfrac{1 \text{ mol H}_2\text{A}}{2 \text{ mol NaOH}} = 0.00917 \text{ mol H}_2\text{A}$

$\dfrac{0.954 \text{ g}}{0.00917 \text{ mol}} = 104 \text{ g/mol}$

5.91 $29.1 \text{ mL} \cdot \dfrac{1 \text{ L}}{10^3 \text{ mL}} \cdot \dfrac{0.513 \text{ mol NaOH}}{1 \text{ L}} = 0.0149 \text{ mol NaOH}$

$0.0149 \text{ mol NaOH} \cdot \dfrac{1 \text{ mol citric acid}}{3 \text{ mol NaOH}} = 0.00498 \text{ mol acid}$ $\qquad$ $\dfrac{0.956 \text{ g}}{0.00498 \text{ mol}} = 192 \text{ g/mol}$

$0.0149 \text{ mol NaOH} \cdot \dfrac{1 \text{ mol tartaric acid}}{2 \text{ mol NaOH}} = 0.00746 \text{ mol acid}$ $\qquad$ $\dfrac{0.956 \text{ g}}{0.00746 \text{ mol}} = 128 \text{ g/mol}$

The calculated molar mass matches that of citric acid (192 g/mol) but not that of tartaric acid (150. g/mol), so the unknown acid is citric acid.

5.92 $22.25 \text{ mL} \cdot \dfrac{1 \text{ L}}{10^3 \text{ mL}} \cdot \dfrac{0.0123 \text{ mol KMnO}_4}{1 \text{ L}} \cdot \dfrac{5 \text{ mol Fe}^{2+}}{1 \text{ mol KMnO}_4} \cdot \dfrac{55.85 \text{ g}}{1 \text{ mol Fe}^{2+}} = 0.0764 \text{ g Fe}$

$\dfrac{0.0764 \text{ g Fe}}{0.598 \text{ g sample}} \cdot 100\% = 12.8\% \text{ Fe}$

5.93 $27.85 \text{ mL} \cdot \dfrac{1 \text{ L}}{10^3 \text{ mL}} \cdot \dfrac{0.102 \text{ mol Br}_2}{1 \text{ L}} \cdot \dfrac{1 \text{ mol C}_6\text{H}_8\text{O}_6}{1 \text{ mol Br}_2} \cdot \dfrac{176.13 \text{ g}}{1 \text{ mol C}_6\text{H}_8\text{O}_6} = 0.500 \text{ g C}_6\text{H}_8\text{O}_6$

5.94 $2 \text{ KOH(aq)} + \text{H}_2\text{SO}_4\text{(aq)} \rightarrow \text{K}_2\text{SO}_4\text{(aq)} + 2 \text{ H}_2\text{O}(\ell)$

$1.56 \text{ g KOH} \cdot \dfrac{1 \text{ mol KOH}}{56.11 \text{ g}} \cdot \dfrac{1 \text{ mol H}_2\text{SO}_4}{2 \text{ mol KOH}} \cdot \dfrac{1 \text{ L}}{0.054 \text{ mol H}_2\text{SO}_4} = 0.26 \text{ L } (260 \text{ mL})$

5.95 $\text{MgCO}_3\text{(s)} + 2 \text{ H}^+\text{(aq)} \rightarrow \text{CO}_2\text{(g)} + \text{Mg}^{2+}\text{(aq)} + \text{H}_2\text{O}(\ell)$

spectator ions: Cl^- $\qquad$ gas-forming reaction

5.96   (a) $\text{Mg(s)} + 4 \text{ HNO}_3\text{(aq)} \rightarrow \text{Mg(NO}_3)_2\text{(aq)} + 2 \text{ NO}_2\text{(g)} + 2 \text{ H}_2\text{O}(\ell)$

(b) magnesium, nitric acid, magnesium nitrate, nitrogen dioxide, water

(c) $\text{Mg(s)} + 4 \text{ H}^+\text{(aq)} + 2 \text{ NO}_3^-\text{(aq)} \rightarrow \text{Mg}^{2+}\text{(aq)} + 2 \text{ NO}_2\text{(g)} + 2 \text{ H}_2\text{O}(\ell)$

(d) Mg is the reducing agent and HNO_3 is the oxidizing agent

5.97   (a) $(\text{NH}_4)_2\text{S(aq)} + \text{Hg(NO}_3)_2\text{(aq)} \rightarrow \text{HgS(s)} + 2 \text{ NH}_4\text{NO}_3\text{(aq)}$

(b) ammonium sulfide, mercury(II) nitrate, mercury(II) sulfide, ammonium nitrate

(c) precipitation reaction

5.98   (a) H_2O, NH_3, NH_4^+, and OH^- (and a trace of H^+)

(b) H_2O, $\text{CH}_3\text{CO}_2\text{H}$, CH_3CO_2^-, and H^+ (and a trace of OH^-)

(c) H_2O, Na^+, and OH^- (and a trace of H^+)

(d) H_2O, H^+, and Br^- (and a trace of OH^-)

5.99 $\text{H}_3\text{C}_6\text{H}_5\text{O}_7\text{(aq)} + 3 \text{ NaHCO}_3\text{(aq)} \rightarrow 3 \text{ H}_2\text{O}(\ell) + 3 \text{ CO}_2\text{(g)} + \text{Na}_3\text{C}_6\text{H}_5\text{O}_7\text{(aq)}$

$0.100 \text{ g H}_3\text{C}_6\text{H}_5\text{O}_7 \cdot \dfrac{1 \text{ mol H}_3\text{C}_6\text{H}_5\text{O}_7}{192.1 \text{ g}} \cdot \dfrac{3 \text{ mol NaHCO}_3}{1 \text{ mol H}_3\text{C}_6\text{H}_5\text{O}_7} \cdot \dfrac{84.01 \text{ g}}{1 \text{ mol NaHCO}_3} = 0.131 \text{ g}$

5.100 $0.125 \text{ L} \cdot \dfrac{0.15 \text{ mol CH}_3\text{CO}_2\text{H}}{1 \text{ L}} \cdot \dfrac{1 \text{ mol NaHCO}_3}{1 \text{ mol CH}_3\text{CO}_2\text{H}} \cdot \dfrac{84.01 \text{ g}}{1 \text{ mol NaHCO}_3} = 1.58 \text{ g NaHCO}_3$

15.0 g $NaHCO_3$ is available, so CH_3CO_2H is the limiting reactant

5.101 $0.03351 \text{ L} \cdot \dfrac{0.0102 \text{ mol NaOH}}{1 \text{ L}} \cdot \dfrac{1 \text{ mol H}_3\text{C}_6\text{H}_5\text{O}_7}{3 \text{ mol NaOH}} \cdot \dfrac{192.13 \text{ g}}{1 \text{ mol H}_3\text{C}_6\text{H}_5\text{O}_7} = 0.219 \text{ g}$

5.102 $0.02958 \text{ L} \cdot \dfrac{0.550 \text{ mol NaOH}}{1 \text{ L}} \cdot \dfrac{1 \text{ mol H}_2\text{C}_2\text{O}_4}{2 \text{ mol NaOH}} \cdot \dfrac{90.035 \text{ g}}{1 \text{ mol H}_2\text{C}_2\text{O}_4} = 0.732 \text{ g H}_2\text{C}_2\text{O}_4$

$\dfrac{0.732 \text{ g}}{4.554 \text{ g}} \cdot 100\% = 16.1\%$

5.103 $0.04021 \text{ L} \cdot \dfrac{0.246 \text{ mol I}_2}{1 \text{ L}} \cdot \dfrac{2 \text{ mol Na}_2\text{S}_2\text{O}_3}{1 \text{ mol I}_2} \cdot \dfrac{158.11 \text{ g}}{1 \text{ mol Na}_2\text{S}_2\text{O}_3} = 3.13 \text{ g Na}_2\text{S}_2\text{O}_3$

$\dfrac{3.13 \text{ g}}{3.232 \text{ g}} \cdot 100\% = 96.8\%$

5.104   (a) $CuCl_2$, copper(II) chloride $Cu(NO_3)_2$, copper(II) nitrate

$CuCO_3$, copper(II) carbonate CuS, copper(II) sulfide

(b) $BaBr_2$, barium bromide $Ba(CH_3CO_2)_2$, barium acetate

$BaSO_4$, barium sulfate $BaCrO_4$, barium chromate

5.105   (a) $Pb(NO_3)_2(aq) + 2 \text{ KOH}(aq) \rightarrow Pb(OH)_2(s) + 2 \text{ KNO}_3(aq)$

(b) lead(II) nitrate, potassium hydroxide, lead(II) hydroxide, potassium nitrate

(c) $Pb^{2+}(aq) + 2 \text{ OH}^-(aq) \rightarrow Pb(OH)_2(s)$

5.106   (a) $K_2CO_3(aq) + 2 \text{ HClO}_4(aq) \rightarrow 2 \text{ KClO}_4(aq) + CO_2(g) + H_2O(\ell)$

gas-forming reaction

$CO_3^{2-}(aq) + 2 \text{ H}^+(aq) \rightarrow CO_2(g) + H_2O(\ell)$

(b) $FeCl_2(aq) + (NH_4)_2S(aq) \rightarrow FeS(s) + 2 \text{ NH}_4Cl(aq)$

precipitation reaction

$Fe^{2+}(aq) + S^{2-} \rightarrow FeS(s)$

(c) $Fe(NO_3)_2(aq) + Na_2CO_3(aq) \rightarrow FeCO_3(s) + 2 \text{ NaNO}_3(aq)$

precipitation reaction

$Fe^{2+}(aq) + CO_3^{2-}(aq) \rightarrow FeCO_3(s)$

5.107   (a) $Cu(NO_3)_2(aq) + Na_2CO_3(aq) \rightarrow CuCO_3(s) + 2 \text{ NaNO}_3(aq)$

(b) copper(II) nitrate, sodium carbonate, copper(II) carbonate, sodium nitrate

(c) $Cu^{2+}(aq) + CO_3^{2-}(aq) \rightarrow CuCO_3(s)$

5.108   (a) $pH = -\log[H^+] = -\log(0.105) = 0.979$

   (b) $[H^+] = 10^{-pH} = 10^{-2.56} = 0.0028$ M   The solution is acidic

   (c) $[H^+] = 10^{-pH} = 10^{-9.67} = 2.1 \times 10^{-10}$ M   The solution is basic

5.109   (a) $c_d = c_c \cdot \dfrac{V_c}{V_d} = 2.56 \text{ M} \cdot \dfrac{10.0 \text{ mL}}{250. \text{ mL}} = 0.102$ M

   (b) $pH = -\log[H^+] = -\log(0.102) = 0.990$

5.110 $0.500 \text{ L} \cdot \dfrac{2.50 \text{ mol HCl}}{1 \text{ L}} + 0.250 \text{ L} \cdot \dfrac{3.75 \text{ mol HCl}}{1 \text{ L}} = 2.19$ mol HCl

   $\dfrac{2.19 \text{ mol HCl}}{0.750 \text{ L}} = 2.92$ M HCl

   $pH = -\log[H^+] = -\log(2.92) = -0.465$

5.111   Net ionic equation: $H^+(aq) + HCO_3^-(aq) \rightarrow H_2O(\ell) + CO_2(g)$

   $[H^+] = 10^{-pH} = 10^{-2.56} = 0.0028$ M H^+

   $0.125 \text{ L} \cdot \dfrac{0.0028 \text{ mol } H^+}{1 \text{ L}} \cdot \dfrac{1 \text{ mol NaHCO}_3}{1 \text{ mol } H^+} \cdot \dfrac{84.01 \text{ g}}{1 \text{ mol NaHCO}_3} = 0.029$ g $NaHCO_3$

5.112 $HCl(aq) + NaOH(aq) \rightarrow NaCl(aq) + H_2O(\ell)$

   $[H^+] = 10^{-1.92} = 0.012$ M H^+ = 0.012 M HCl $0.250 \text{ L} \cdot \dfrac{0.012 \text{ mol}}{1 \text{ L}} = 0.0030$ mol HCl

   $0.250 \text{ L} \cdot \dfrac{0.0105 \text{ mol NaOH}}{1 \text{ L}} \cdot \dfrac{1 \text{ mol HCl}}{1 \text{ mol NaOH}} = 0.00263$ mol HCl reacted

   $0.0030 \text{ mol} - 0.00263 \text{ mol} = 0.0004$ mol HCl remains

   $pH = -\log\left(\dfrac{0.0004 \text{ mol}}{0.500 \text{ L}}\right) = 3.1$

5.113 $c_d = c_c \cdot \dfrac{V_c}{V_d} = 0.110 \text{ M} \cdot \dfrac{25.0 \text{ mL}}{100.0 \text{ mL}} = 0.0275$ M

   $0.0275 \text{ M} \cdot \dfrac{10.0 \text{ mL}}{250. \text{ mL}} = 0.00110$ M Na_2CO_3

5.114   (a) Reactants: Na (+1), I (−1), H (+1), S (+6), O (−2), Mn (+4)

      Products: Na (+1), S (+6), O (−2), Mn (+2), I (0), H (+1)

   (b) Oxidizing agent MnO_2, NaI was oxidized; Reducing agent NaI, MnO_2 was reduced

   (c) $20.0 \text{ g NaI} \cdot \dfrac{1 \text{ mol NaI}}{149.9 \text{ g}} \cdot \dfrac{1 \text{ mol } I_2}{2 \text{ mol NaI}} \cdot \dfrac{253.8 \text{ g}}{1 \text{ mol } I_2} = 16.9$ g I_2

      $10.0 \text{ g MnO}_2 \cdot \dfrac{1 \text{ mol MnO}_2}{86.94 \text{ g}} \cdot \dfrac{1 \text{ mol } I_2}{1 \text{ mol MnO}_2} \cdot \dfrac{253.8 \text{ g}}{1 \text{ mol } I_2} = 29.2$ g I_2

   NaI is the limiting reactant; 16.9 g I_2 is produced

5.115 $0.250 \text{ L} \cdot \dfrac{0.125 \text{ mol HCl}}{1 \text{ L}} \cdot \dfrac{1 \text{ mol CaCO}_3}{2 \text{ mol HCl}} \cdot \dfrac{100.1 \text{ g}}{1 \text{ mol CaCO}_3} = 1.56 \text{ g CaCO}_3 \text{ required}$

2.56 g available − 1.56 g required = 1.00 g $CaCO_3$ remains

$0.250 \text{ L} \cdot \dfrac{0.125 \text{ mol HCl}}{1 \text{ L}} \cdot \dfrac{1 \text{ mol CaCl}_2}{2 \text{ mol HCl}} \cdot \dfrac{111.0 \text{ g}}{1 \text{ mol CaCl}_2} = 1.73 \text{ g CaCl}_2$

5.116 precipitation reaction: $BaCl_2(aq) + Na_2SO_4(aq) \rightarrow BaSO_4(s) + 2 \text{ NaCl}(aq)$

gas-forming reaction: $BaCO_3(s) + H_2SO_4(aq) \rightarrow BaSO_4(s) + CO_2(g) + H_2O(\ell)$

5.117 $Ba(OH)_2(s) + 2 \text{ HCl}(aq) \rightarrow BaCl_2(aq) + 2 H_2O(\ell)$

5.118 (a) $Zn(OH)_2(s) + 2 \text{ HCl}(aq) \rightarrow ZnCl_2(aq) + 2 H_2O(\ell)$

(b) $ZnCO_3(s) + 2 \text{ HCl}(aq) \rightarrow ZnCl_2(aq) + H_2O(\ell) + CO_2(g)$

(c) $Zn(s) + Cl_2(g) \rightarrow ZnCl_2(s)$

5.119 $0.03450 \text{ L} \cdot \dfrac{0.108 \text{ mol KMnO}_4}{1 \text{ L}} \cdot \dfrac{5 \text{ mol C}_2\text{O}_4{}^{2-}}{2 \text{ mol KMnO}_4} = 0.00932 \text{ mol C}_2\text{O}_4{}^{2-}$

Use mol $C_2O_4{}^{2-}$ to determine which formula is correct:

$0.00932 \text{ mol C}_2\text{O}_4{}^{2-} \cdot \dfrac{1 \text{ mol K[Fe(C}_2\text{O}_4)_2(\text{H}_2\text{O})_2]}{2 \text{ mol C}_2\text{O}_4{}^{2-}} \cdot \dfrac{307.0 \text{ g}}{1 \text{ mol K[Fe(C}_2\text{O}_4)_2(\text{H}_2\text{O})_2]} = 1.43 \text{ g compound}$

$0.00932 \text{ mol C}_2\text{O}_4{}^{2-} \cdot \dfrac{1 \text{ mol K}_3[\text{Fe(C}_2\text{O}_4)_3]}{3 \text{ mol C}_2\text{O}_4{}^{2-}} \cdot \dfrac{437.2 \text{ g}}{1 \text{ mol K}_3[\text{Fe(C}_2\text{O}_4)_3]} = 1.36 \text{ g compound}$

The correct formula is $K_3[Fe(C_2O_4)_3]$

5.120 If both students base their calculations on the amount of HCl solution pipetted into the flask (20 mL), then the second student's result will be (e) the same as the first student's. However, if the HCl concentration is calculated using the diluted solution volume, student 1 will use a volume of 40 mL and student 2 will use a volume of 80 mL in the calculation. The second student's result will be (c) two times less than the first student's.

5.121 $1.0 \text{ g methylene blue} \cdot \dfrac{1 \text{ mol}}{320. \text{ g}} \cdot \dfrac{1}{0.0500 \text{ L}} = 0.063 \text{ M methylene blue}$

$V_d = \dfrac{c_c}{c_d} \cdot V_c = \dfrac{0.063 \text{ M}}{4.1 \times 10^{-8} \text{ M}} \cdot 0.0500 \text{ L} = 7.6 \times 10^4 \text{ L}$

5.122 (a) Au, gold, has been oxidized and is the reducing agent

O_2, oxygen, has been reduced and is the oxidizing agent

(b) $10^3 \text{ kg ore} \cdot \dfrac{10^3 \text{ g}}{1 \text{ kg}} \cdot \dfrac{0.019 \text{ g Au}}{100. \text{ g ore}} \cdot \dfrac{1 \text{ mol Au}}{197 \text{ g}} \cdot \dfrac{8 \text{ mol NaCN}}{4 \text{ mol Au}} \cdot \dfrac{1 \text{ L}}{0.075 \text{ mol NaCN}} = 26 \text{ L solution}$

5.123 $FeCl_3(aq) + 3\ NaOH(aq) \rightarrow Fe(OH)_3(s) + 3\ NaCl(aq)$

(a) $0.0250\ L \cdot \dfrac{0.234\ mol\ FeCl_3}{1\ L} \cdot \dfrac{1\ mol\ Fe(OH)_3}{1\ mol\ FeCl_3} \cdot \dfrac{106.9\ g}{1\ mol\ Fe(OH)_3} = 0.625\ g\ Fe(OH)_3$

$0.0425\ L \cdot \dfrac{0.453\ mol\ NaOH}{1\ L} \cdot \dfrac{1\ mol\ Fe(OH)_3}{3\ mol\ NaOH} \cdot \dfrac{106.9\ g}{1\ mol\ Fe(OH)_3} = 0.686\ g\ Fe(OH)_3$

NaOH is the excess reactant

(b)   0.625 g $Fe(OH)_3$ precipitates

(c) $0.0250\ L \cdot \dfrac{0.234\ mol\ FeCl_3}{1\ L} \cdot \dfrac{3\ mol\ NaOH}{1\ mol\ FeCl_3} = 0.0176\ mol\ NaOH$ required

$0.0425\ L \cdot \dfrac{0.453\ mol\ NaOH}{1\ L} - 0.0176\ mol\ NaOH = 0.0017\ mol\ NaOH$ remains

$\dfrac{0.0017\ mol}{0.0675\ L} = 0.025\ M\ NaOH$

5.124 $0.02632\ L \cdot \dfrac{0.101\ mol\ Na_2S_2O_3}{1\ L} \cdot \dfrac{1\ mol\ I_3^-}{2\ mol\ Na_2S_2O_3} = 0.00133\ mol\ I_3^-$

$0.00133\ mol\ I_3^- \cdot \dfrac{2\ mol\ Cu^{2+}}{1\ mol\ I_3^-} \cdot \dfrac{63.55\ g}{1\ mol\ Cu^{2+}} = 0.169\ g\ Cu$

$\dfrac{0.169\ g}{0.251\ g} \cdot 100\% = 67.3\%$

5.125 $0.02426\ L \cdot \dfrac{1.500\ mol\ HCl}{1\ L} \cdot \dfrac{1\ mol\ NH_4^+}{1\ mol\ HCl} \cdot \dfrac{1\ mol\ NH_3}{1\ mol\ NH_4^+} = 0.03639\ mol\ NH_3$

$0.03639\ mol\ NH_3 \cdot \dfrac{17.030\ g}{1\ mol\ NH_3} = 0.6197\ g\ NH_3$

1.580 g compound $-$ 0.6197 g NH_3 = 0.960 g $CrCl_3$

$0.960\ g\ CrCl_3 \cdot \dfrac{1\ mol}{158.4\ g} = 0.00606\ mol\ CrCl_3$ $x = \dfrac{0.03639\ mol\ NH_3}{0.00606\ mol\ CrCl_3} = 6$

5.126   (a) $(NH_4)_2PtCl_4 + 2\ NH_3 \rightarrow Pt(NH_3)_2Cl_2 + 2\ NH_4Cl$

(b) $12.50\ g\ Pt(NH_3)_2Cl_2 \cdot \dfrac{1\ mol\ Pt(NH_3)_2Cl_2}{300.05\ g} \cdot \dfrac{1\ mol\ (NH_4)_2PtCl_4}{1\ mol\ Pt(NH_3)_2Cl_2} \cdot \dfrac{372.97\ g}{1\ mol\ (NH_4)_2PtCl_4}$

$= 15.54\ g\ (NH_4)_2PtCl_4$

$12.50\ g\ Pt(NH_3)_2Cl_2 \cdot \dfrac{1\ mol\ Pt(NH_3)_2Cl_2}{300.05\ g} \cdot \dfrac{2\ mol\ NH_3}{1\ mol\ Pt(NH_3)_2Cl_2} \cdot \dfrac{1\ L}{0.125\ mol\ NH_3}$

$= 0.667\ L\ solution$

(c) $0.0370 \text{ L} \cdot \dfrac{0.475 \text{ mol HCl}}{1 \text{ L}} \cdot \dfrac{1 \text{ mol } C_5H_5N}{1 \text{ mol HCl}} = 0.0176 \text{ mol } C_5H_5N \text{ unused by titration}$

$1.50 \text{ mL} \cdot \dfrac{0.979 \text{ g}}{1 \text{ mL}} \cdot \dfrac{1 \text{ mol } C_5H_5N}{79.10 \text{ g}} = 0.0186 \text{ mol } C_5H_5N \text{ originally added}$

$0.0186 \text{ mol} - 0.0176 \text{ mol} = 0.0010 \text{ mol } C_5H_5N \text{ reacted with cisplatin}$

$0.150 \text{ g Pt(NH}_3)_2Cl_2 \cdot \dfrac{1 \text{ mol Pt(NH}_3)_2Cl_2}{300.0 \text{ g}} = 5.00 \times 10^{-4} \text{ mol Pt(NH}_3)_2Cl_2$

$\dfrac{0.0010 \text{ mol } C_5H_5N}{5.00 \times 10^{-4} \text{ mol Pt(NH}_3)_2Cl_2} = \dfrac{2 \text{ mol } C_5H_5N}{1 \text{ mol Pt(NH}_3)_2Cl_2}$

The compound formula is $Pt(NH_3)_2Cl_2(C_5H_5N)_2$

5.127 $0.200 \text{ L} \cdot \dfrac{50.0 \text{ g CH}_3CO_2H}{1 \text{ L vinegar}} \cdot \dfrac{1 \text{ mol CH}_3CO_2H}{60.05 \text{ g}} \cdot \dfrac{1 \text{ mol NaHCO}_3}{1 \text{ mol CH}_3CO_2H} \cdot \dfrac{84.01 \text{ g}}{1 \text{ mol NaHCO}_3} \cdot \dfrac{1 \text{ spoonful}}{3.8 \text{ g}}$

$= 3.7 \text{ spoonfuls of baking soda}$

Four spoonfuls of baking soda are required to consume the acetic acid.

5.128   100 mL of 0.10 M HCl contains 0.010 mol of HCl. This requires 0.0050 mol of Zn or 3.27 g for

complete reaction. Thus, in flask 2 the reaction just uses all of the Zn and produces 0.0050 mol H_2 gas.

In flask 1, containing 7.00 g of Zn, some Zn remains after the HCl has been consumed; 0.005 mol H_2 gas

is produced. In flask 3, there is insufficient Zn, so less hydrogen is produced.

Chapter 6
Principles of Reactivity: Energy and Chemical Reactions

INSTRUCTOR'S NOTES

This topic is normally covered in three to four, 50-minute lectures. Our experience is that students will have some difficulty with thermochemistry, primarily because they have problems with the concept of energy. Some demonstrations, described below, can help them.

This chapter need not be covered at this point in the course. However, we have used the notion of energy changes in our discussions of atomic properties and in the discussion of bond energies in the first chapter on bonding (Chapter 9).

SUGGESTED DEMONSTRATIONS

1.   Introduction to the Chapter
   - In spite of their experience, some students do not have a good "feeling" for heat and energy. Therefore, demonstrations are quite useful here. In particular, we open the lecture on heat transfer, thermometers, and heat capacity with the demonstration in Figure 6.5.

2.   Product-Favored Reactions
   - See the *General Chemistry Interactive CD-ROM* for the Gummy Bear decomposition and the aluminum/bromine reaction.
   - Many product-favored reaction demonstrations were described in Chapter 5. For some excellent examples see Shakhashiri, B. Z. *Chemical Demonstrations: A Handbook for Teachers of Chemistry*; University of Wisconsin Press, 1983; Vol. 1.

3.   Reactant-Favored Reactions
   - Bring mineral samples into lecture to demonstrate reactant-favored reactions.

4.   Energy Conversion
   - See the *General Chemistry Interactive CD-ROM* for a screen showing examples of energy conversion.
   - See the *General Chemistry Interactive CD-ROM* for an animation of the law of energy conservation.

5.   Heat Transfer
   - Heat a metal block in a Bunsen burner and plunge it into water to demonstrate heat transfer. See the *General Chemistry Interactive CD-ROM* for a Quicktime movie of this process.
   - See the *General Chemistry Interactive CD-ROM* for an animation of heat transfer.

6.   Exothermic Reactions
   - McAfee, L. V.; Jumper, C. F. "The Reusable Heat Pack," *Journal of Chemical Education* **1991**, *68*, 780.
   - Shakhashiri, B. Z. "The Nonburning Towel," *Chemical Demonstrations: A Handbook for Teachers of Chemistry*; University of Wisconsin Press, 1983; Vol. 1, pp. 13-14.

- Shakhashiri, B. Z. "Reaction of Calcium Oxide and Water (Slaking of Lime)," *Chemical Demonstrations: A Handbook for Teachers of Chemistry*; University of Wisconsin Press, 1983; Vol. 1, pp. 19-20.

- We often do the peroxide rocket again (Chapter 4 in this *Manual*) and blow up a hydrogen balloon.

7.   Endothermic Reactions

- Shakhashiri, B. Z. "Chemical Cold Pack," *Chemical Demonstrations: A Handbook for Teachers of Chemistry*; University of Wisconsin Press, 1983; Vol. 1, pp. 8-9.

- Shakhashiri, B. Z. "Barium Hydroxide and Ammonium Salts," *Chemical Demonstrations: A Handbook for Teachers of Chemistry*; University of Wisconsin Press, 1983; Vol. 1, pp. 10-12.

- The demonstration with the plastic bag and dry ice in Figure 6.13 is very effective and very easy to do.

8.   Changes of State

- Burgstahler, A. W.; Bricker, C. E. "Measuring the Heat of Sublimation of Dry Ice with a Polystyrene Foam Cup Calorimeter," *Journal of Chemical Education* **1991**, *68*, 332.

- Vemulapalli, G. K. "A Discourse on the Drinking Bird," *Journal of Chemical Education* **1990**, *67*, 457.

- Place some Dry Ice in a plastic bag and seal it (Figure 6.13). This process can also be used to demonstrate the First Law of Thermodynamics.

9.   State Functions

- Use a balloon to demonstrate state functions.

10.   Calorimetry

- When discussing calorimetry, we always take a laboratory calorimeter to the lecture so the students can see the various parts and get a better notion of how they work in practice.

Solutions to Study Questions

6.1   (a) Exothermic: a process in which heat is transferred from a system to the surroundings

             (the combustion of methane gives off heat)

             Endothermic: a process in which heat is transferred from surroundings to the system

             (ice melting absorbs heat)

        (b) System: the object, or collection of objects, being studied (a chemical reaction taking place inside a

             calorimeter)

             Surroundings: everything outside the system that can exchange energy with the system (the calorimeter

             and everything else outside the calorimeter)

        (c) Specific heat capacity: the quantity of heat required to raise the temperature of 1 gram of a substance

             one kelvin (the specific heat capacity of water is 4.184 J/g·K)

        (d) State function: a quantity that is characterized by changes that do not depend on which path is chosen

             in going from the initial state to the final state (enthalpy and internal energy)

        (e) Standard state: the most stable form of a substance in the physical state that exists at a pressure of 1

             bar and at a specified temperature (the standard state of carbon at 25 °C is graphite)

        (f) Enthalpy change, ΔH: the difference between the final and initial heat content of a substance at

             constant pressure (the enthalpy change for melting ice at 0 °C is 6.00 kJ/mol)

        (g) Standard enthalpy of formation: the enthalpy change for the formation of 1 mol of a compound

             directly from its component elements in their standard states (ΔH_f° for liquid H_2O is −285.83 kJ/mol)

6.2   (a) exothermic

        (b) exothermic

        (c) exothermic

        (d) endothermic

6.3   (a) system: reaction between methane and oxygen

             surroundings: the furnace and the rest of the universe

             heat flows from system to surroundings

        (b) system: water

             surroundings: skin and the rest of the universe

             heat flows from surroundings to the system

        (c) system: water

             surroundings: freezer and the rest of the universe

             heat flows from system to surroundings

(d) system: reaction between aluminum and iron(III) oxide

   surroundings: flask, laboratory bench, and the rest of the universe

   heat flows from system to surroundings

6.4   (a), (c), and (d) are state functions

6.5 $\Delta E = q + w$ ΔE is the change in energy content, q is heat transferred to or from the system, and

        w is work transferred to or from the system

6.6   Yes, the first law is a version of the general principle of conservation of energy applied specifically to the

        system. See Section 6.4.

6.7   People who make perpetual motion machines claim they produce more energy than is supplied to the

        machines. According to the law of conservation of energy, this is impossible.

6.8   Standard state is the most stable form of a substance in the physical state that exists at a pressure of 1 bar

        and at a specified temperature. H_2O (liquid), NaCl (solid), Hg (liquid), CH_4 (gas)

6.9 ΔH_f° O(g) = 249.170 kJ/mol ΔH_f° O_2(g) = 0 kJ/mol ΔH_f° O_3(g) = 142.67 kJ/mol

        The standard state of oxygen is O_2(g)

        O_2(g) → 2 O(g) ΔH° = 2 mol · 249.170 kJ/mol – 0 kJ/mol = 498.34 kJ   (endothermic)

        $^3/_2$ O_2(g) → O_3(g) ΔH° = 1 mol · 142.67 kJ/mol – 0 kJ/mol = 142.67 kJ

6.10   Product-favored reactions are those in which reactants are largely converted to products and generally have

        negative values of ΔH°_{rxn}. The reverse is true for reactant-favored reactions.

6.11   (a) product-favored   (b) reactant-favored

6.12   1200 Cal · $\dfrac{10^3 \text{ cal}}{1 \text{ Cal}}$ · $\dfrac{4.184 \text{ J}}{1 \text{ cal}}$ = 5.0×10^6 J

6.13   1670 kJ · $\dfrac{10^3 \text{ J}}{1 \text{ kJ}}$ · $\dfrac{1 \text{ cal}}{4.184 \text{ J}}$ · $\dfrac{1 \text{ Cal}}{10^3 \text{ cal}}$ = 399 Cal

6.14 $\dfrac{28.1 \text{ J}}{\text{mol·K}}$ · $\dfrac{1 \text{ mol Hg}}{200.6 \text{ g}}$ = 0.140 J/g·K

6.15 $\dfrac{1.74 \text{ J}}{\text{g·K}}$ · $\dfrac{78.11 \text{ g}}{1 \text{ mol } C_6H_6}$ = 136 J/mol·K

6.16 q = 168 g · 0.385 J/g·K · (298.8 K – 261.0 K) = 2440 J

6.17 $q = (50.00 \text{ mL} \cdot \dfrac{0.997 \text{ g}}{1 \text{ mL}}) \cdot 4.184 \text{ J/g·K} \cdot (301.90 \text{ K} - 298.67 \text{ K}) = 674 \text{ J}$

6.18 $2.25 \times 10^3 \text{ J} = 344 \text{ g} \cdot 0.449 \text{ J/g·K} \cdot (T_f - 291.4 \text{ K})$

$T_f = 306.0 \text{ K} \ (32.8 \text{ °C})$

6.19 $1.850 \times 10^3 \text{ J} = 500. \text{ g} \cdot 0.385 \text{ J/g·K} \cdot (310. \text{ K} - T_i)$

$T_i = 300. \text{ K} \ (27 \text{ °C})$

6.20 $0 = q_{metal} + q_{water}$

$0 = [45.5 \text{ g} \cdot 0.385 \text{ J/g·K} \cdot (T_f - 373.0 \text{ K})] + [152 \text{ g} \cdot 4.184 \text{ J/g·K} \cdot (T_f - 291.7 \text{ K})]$

$T_f = 294 \text{ K} \ (21 \text{ °C})$

6.21 $0 = q_{metal} + q_{water}$

$0 = [182 \text{ g} \cdot 0.128 \text{ J/g·K} \cdot (300.7 \text{ K} - T_i)] + [22.1 \text{ g} \cdot 4.184 \text{ J/g·K} \cdot (300.7 \text{ K} - 298.2 \text{ K})]$

$T_i = 311 \text{ K} \ (37 \text{ °C})$

6.22 $0 = q_{cool \ water} + q_{warm \ water}$

$0 = [156 \text{ g} \cdot 4.184 \text{ J/g·K} \cdot (T_f - 295 \text{ K})] + [85.2 \text{ g} \cdot 4.184 \text{ J/g·K} \cdot (T_f - 368 \text{ K})]$

$T_f = 321 \text{ K} \ (48 \text{ °C})$

6.23   Since the final temperature is greater than 22.5 °C, the 65.1-g sample of water must be warmer than the 108-g sample.

$0 = q_{cool \ water} + q_{warm \ water}$

$0 = [108 \text{ g} \cdot 4.184 \text{ J/g·K} \cdot (321.1 - 295.7 \text{ K})] + [65.1 \text{ g} \cdot 4.184 \text{ J/g·K} \cdot (321.1 \text{ K} - T_i)]$

$T_i = 363 \text{ K} \ (90. \text{ °C})$

6.24 $0 = q_{metal} + q_{water}$

$0 = [13.8 \text{ g} \cdot C_{Zn} \cdot (300.3 \text{ K} - 372.0 \text{ K})] + [45.0 \text{ g} \cdot 4.184 \text{ J/g·K} \cdot (300.3 \text{ K} - 298.2 \text{ K})]$

$C_{Zn} = 0.40 \text{ J/g·K}$

6.25 $0 = q_{metal} + q_{water}$

$0 = [237 \text{ g} \cdot C_{Mo} \cdot (288.5 \text{ K} - 373.2 \text{ K})] + [244 \text{ g} \cdot 4.184 \text{ J/g·K} \cdot (288.5 \text{ K} - 283.2 \text{ K})]$

$C_{Mo} = 0.27 \text{ J/g·K}$

6.26 $1.0 \times 10^3 \text{ mL H}_2\text{O} \cdot \dfrac{1.00 \text{ g}}{1 \text{ mL}} \cdot 333 \text{ J/g} = 3.3 \times 10^5 \text{ J}$

6.27 $16 \text{ cubes} \cdot \dfrac{62.0 \text{ g}}{1 \text{ cube}} \cdot 333 \text{ J/g} = 3.30 \times 10^5 \text{ J}$

6.28 $125 \text{ g} \cdot \dfrac{1 \text{ mol } C_6H_6}{78.11 \text{ g}} \cdot \dfrac{30.8 \text{ kJ}}{1 \text{ mol } C_6H_6} = 49.3 \text{ kJ}$

6.29 $92.5 \text{ g} \cdot \dfrac{1 \text{ mol } CH_3Cl}{50.49 \text{ g}} \cdot \dfrac{21.40 \text{ kJ}}{1 \text{ mol } CH_3Cl} = 39.2 \text{ kJ}$

6.30 $1.00 \text{ mL} \cdot \dfrac{1 \text{ cm}^3}{1 \text{ mL}} \cdot \dfrac{13.6 \text{ g}}{1 \text{ cm}^3} = 13.6 \text{ g Hg}$

q_{total} = energy to cool liquid + energy to change phase from liquid to solid

$q_{cool \ liquid} = 13.6 \text{ g} \cdot 0.140 \text{ J/g·K} \cdot (234.4 \text{ K} - 296.2 \text{ K}) = -118 \text{ J}$

$q_{phase \ change} = -(13.6 \text{ g} \cdot 11.4 \text{ J/g}) = -155 \text{ J}$

$q_{total} = -118 \text{ J} + (-155 \text{ J}) = -273 \text{ J}$ (273 J released to the surroundings)

6.31 q_{total} = energy to heat metal + energy to change phase from solid to liquid

$q_{heat \ metal} = 454 \text{ g} \cdot 0.227 \text{ J/g·K} \cdot (505.1 \text{ K} - 298.2 \text{ K}) = 2.13 \times 10^4 \text{ J}$

$q_{phase \ change} = 454 \text{ g} \cdot 59.2 \text{ J/g} = 2.69 \times 10^4 \text{ J}$

$q_{total} = 2.13 \times 10^4 \text{ J} + 2.69 \times 10^4 = 4.82 \times 10^4 \text{ J}$

6.32 q = energy to heat liquid + energy to change phase from liquid to vapor

$q_{heat \ liquid} = 1.00 \times 10^3 \text{ g} \cdot 2.44 \text{ J/g·K} \cdot (351.44 \text{ K} - 293.2 \text{ K}) = 1.42 \times 10^5 \text{ J}$

$q_{phase \ change} = 1.00 \times 10^3 \text{ g} \cdot 855 \text{ J/g} = 8.55 \times 10^5 \text{ J}$

$q_{total} = 1.42 \times 10^5 \text{ J} + 8.55 \times 10^5 \text{ J} = 9.97 \times 10^5 \text{ J}$

6.33 $25.0 \text{ mL} \cdot \dfrac{0.80 \text{ g}}{1 \text{ mL}} = 20. \text{ g } C_6H_6$

q_{total} = energy to cool liquid + energy to change phase from liquid to solid

$q_{cool \ liquid} = 20. \text{ g} \cdot 1.74 \text{ J/g·K} \cdot (278.7 \text{ K} - 293.1 \text{ K}) = -5.0 \times 10^2 \text{ J}$

$q_{phase \ change} = -(20. \text{ g} \cdot 127 \text{ J/g}) = -2500 \text{ J}$

$q_{total} = -5.0 \times 10^2 \text{ J} + (-2500 \text{ J}) = -3.0 \times 10^3 \text{ J}$ (3.0 × 10³ J released to the surroundings)

6.34   exothermic

$1.25 \text{ g NO} \cdot \dfrac{1 \text{ mol NO}}{30.01 \text{ g}} \cdot \dfrac{114.1 \text{ kJ}}{2 \text{ mol NO}} = 2.38 \text{ kJ heat evolved}$

6.35   exothermic

$10.0 \text{ g CaO} \cdot \dfrac{1 \text{ mol CaO}}{56.08 \text{ g}} \cdot \dfrac{464.8 \text{ kJ}}{1 \text{ mol CaO}} = 82.9 \text{ kJ heat evolved}$

6.36 $1.00 \times 10^3 \text{ mL} \cdot \dfrac{0.69 \text{ g}}{1 \text{ mL}} \cdot \dfrac{1 \text{ mol } C_8H_{18}}{114.2 \text{ g}} \cdot \dfrac{10,922 \text{ kJ}}{2 \text{ mol } C_8H_{18}} = 3.3 \times 10^4 \text{ kJ heat evolved}$

6.37 $1.00 \times 10^3 \text{ mL} \cdot \dfrac{1.044 \text{ g}}{1 \text{ mL}} \cdot \dfrac{1 \text{ mol CH}_3\text{CO}_2\text{H}}{60.05 \text{ g}} \cdot \dfrac{355.9 \text{ kJ}}{1 \text{ mol CH}_3\text{CO}_2\text{H}} = 6.19 \times 10^3 \text{ kJ heat evolved}$

6.38 $q = (100.0 \text{ mL} + 50.0 \text{ mL}) \cdot \dfrac{1.00 \text{ g}}{1 \text{ mL}} \cdot 4.2 \text{ J/g·K} \cdot (297.43 \text{ K} - 295.65 \text{ K}) = 1100 \text{ J}$

$0.1000 \text{ L} \cdot \dfrac{0.200 \text{ mol CsOH}}{1 \text{ L}} = 0.0200 \text{ mol CsOH}$

$\dfrac{1100 \text{ J}}{0.0200 \text{ mol CsOH}} \cdot \dfrac{1 \text{ kJ}}{10^3 \text{ J}} = 56 \text{ kJ/mol CsOH}$

6.39 $q = (125 \text{ mL} + 50.0 \text{ mL}) \cdot \dfrac{1.00 \text{ g}}{1 \text{ mL}} \cdot 4.2 \text{ J/g·K} \cdot (297.55 \text{ K} - 294.65 \text{ K}) = 2100 \text{ J}$

$0.125 \text{ L} \cdot \dfrac{0.250 \text{ mol CsOH}}{1 \text{ L}} = 0.0313 \text{ mol CsOH}$

$\dfrac{2100 \text{ J}}{0.0313 \text{ mol CsOH}} \cdot \dfrac{1 \text{ kJ}}{10^3 \text{ J}} = 68 \text{ kJ/mol CsOH}$

6.40 $0 = q_{\text{metal}} + q_{\text{water}}$

$0 = [20.8 \text{ g} \cdot C_{\text{Ti}} \cdot (297.5 \text{ K} - 372.7 \text{ K})] + [75 \text{ g} \cdot 4.184 \text{ J/g·K} \cdot (297.5 \text{ K} - 294.9 \text{ K})]$

$C_{\text{Ti}} = 0.52 \text{ J/g·K}$

6.41 $0 = q_{\text{metal}} + q_{\text{water}}$

$0 = [24.26 \text{ g} \cdot C_{\text{Cr}} \cdot (298.8 \text{ K} - 371.5 \text{ K})] + [82.3 \text{ g} \cdot 4.184 \text{ J/g·K} \cdot (298.8 \text{ K} - 296.5 \text{ K})]$

$C_{\text{Cr}} = 0.45 \text{ J/g·K}$

6.42 $q_{\text{solution}} = 155.4 \text{ g} \cdot 4.2 \text{ J/g·K} \cdot (289.4 \text{ K} - 291.8 \text{ K}) = -1600 \text{ J}$

$5.44 \text{ g NH}_4\text{NO}_3 \cdot \dfrac{1 \text{ mol NH}_4\text{NO}_3}{80.04 \text{ g}} = 0.0680 \text{ mol NH}_4\text{NO}_3$

$q_{\text{dissolving}} = -q_{\text{solution}} = -\dfrac{-1600 \text{ J}}{0.0680 \text{ mol NH}_4\text{NO}_3} \cdot \dfrac{1 \text{ kJ}}{10^3 \text{ J}} = 23 \text{ kJ/mol NH}_4\text{NO}_3$

6.43   Assume $C_{\text{solution}} = 4.2 \text{ J/g·K}$

$q_{\text{solution}} = 140.2 \text{ g} \cdot 4.2 \text{ J/g·K} \cdot (302.0 \text{ K} - 293.4 \text{ K}) = 5100 \text{ J}$

$5.2 \text{ g H}_2\text{SO}_4 \cdot \dfrac{1 \text{ mol H}_2\text{SO}_4}{98.1 \text{ g}} = 0.053 \text{ mol H}_2\text{SO}_4$

$q_{\text{dissolving}} = -q_{\text{solution}} = -\dfrac{5100 \text{ J}}{0.053 \text{ mol H}_2\text{SO}_4} \cdot \dfrac{1 \text{ kJ}}{10^3 \text{ J}} = -96 \text{ kJ/mol H}_2\text{SO}_4$

6.44 $q = q_{water} + q_{calorimeter}$

$q = [815 \text{ g} \cdot 4.184 \text{ J/g·K} \cdot (299.87 \text{ K} - 294.40 \text{ K})] + [923 \text{ J/K} \cdot (299.87 \text{ K} - 294.40 \text{ K})]$

$q = 2.37 \times 10^4 \text{ J}$

$2.56 \text{ g S}_8 \cdot \dfrac{1 \text{ mol S}_8}{256.5 \text{ g}} \cdot \dfrac{8 \text{ mol SO}_2}{1 \text{ mol S}_8} = 0.0798 \text{ mol SO}_2$

$\dfrac{2.37 \times 10^4 \text{ J}}{0.0798 \text{ mol SO}_2} \cdot \dfrac{1 \text{ kJ}}{10^3 \text{ J}} = 297 \text{ kJ/mol SO}_2$

6.45 $q = q_{water} + q_{calorimeter}$

$q = [775 \text{ g} \cdot 4.184 \text{ J/g·K} \cdot (300.53 \text{ K} - 298.15 \text{ K})] + [893 \text{ J/K} \cdot (300.53 \text{ K} - 298.15 \text{ K})]$

$q = 9840 \text{ J}$

$0.300 \text{ g C} \cdot \dfrac{1 \text{ mol C}}{12.01 \text{ g}} = 0.0250 \text{ mol C}$

$\dfrac{9840 \text{ J}}{0.0250 \text{ mol C}} \cdot \dfrac{1 \text{ kJ}}{10^3 \text{ J}} = 394 \text{ kJ/mol C}$

6.46 $q = q_{water} + q_{calorimeter}$

$q = [775 \text{ g} \cdot 4.184 \text{ J/g·K} \cdot (304.84 \text{ K} - 295.65 \text{ K})] + [893 \text{ J/K} \cdot (304.84 \text{ K} - 295.65 \text{ K})]$

$q = 3.80 \times 10^4 \text{ J}$

$1.500 \text{ g C}_6\text{H}_5\text{CO}_2\text{H} \cdot \dfrac{1 \text{ mol C}_6\text{H}_5\text{CO}_2\text{H}}{122.12 \text{ g}} = 0.01228 \text{ mol C}_6\text{H}_5\text{CO}_2\text{H}$

$\dfrac{3.80 \times 10^4 \text{ J}}{0.01228 \text{ mol C}_6\text{H}_5\text{CO}_2\text{H}} \cdot \dfrac{1 \text{ kJ}}{10^3 \text{ J}} = 3090 \text{ kJ/mol C}_6\text{H}_5\text{CO}_2\text{H}$

6.47 $q = q_{water} + q_{calorimeter}$

$q = [575 \text{ g} \cdot 4.184 \text{ J/g·K} \cdot (298.37 \text{ K} - 294.85 \text{ K})] + [650 \text{ J/K} \cdot (298.37 \text{ K} - 294.85 \text{ K})]$

$q = 1.1 \times 10^4 \text{ J}$

$0.692 \text{ g C}_6\text{H}_{12}\text{O}_6 \cdot \dfrac{1 \text{ mol C}_6\text{H}_{12}\text{O}_6}{180.2 \text{ g}} = 0.00384 \text{ mol C}_6\text{H}_{12}\text{O}_6$

$\dfrac{1.1 \times 10^4 \text{ J}}{0.00384 \text{ mol C}_6\text{H}_{12}\text{O}_6} \cdot \dfrac{1 \text{ kJ}}{10^3 \text{ J}} = 2800 \text{ kJ/mol C}_6\text{H}_{12}\text{O}_6$

6.48 $0 = q_{Ag} + q_{ice}$

$0 = [50.0 \text{ g} \cdot C_{Ag} \cdot (273.2 \text{ K} - 373.0 \text{ K})] + [3.54 \text{ g} \cdot 333 \text{ J/g}]$

$C_{Ag} = 0.236 \text{ J/g·K}$

6.49 $0 = q_{Pt} + q_{ice}$

$0 = [9.36 \text{ g} \cdot C_{Pt} \cdot (273.2 \text{ K} - 371.8 \text{ K})] + [0.37 \text{ g} \cdot 333 \text{ J/g}]$

$C_{Pt} = 0.13 \text{ J/g·K}$

6.50 (a) $CH_4(g) + 2\,O_2(g) \rightarrow CO_2(g) + 2\,H_2O(g)$ $\Delta H^\circ = -802.4$ kJ

$CO_2(g) + 2\,H_2O(g) \rightarrow CH_3OH(g) + {}^3/_2\,O_2(g)$ $\Delta H^\circ = -(-676$ kJ$)$

$CH_4(g) + {}^1/_2\,O_2(g) \rightarrow CH_3OH(g)$ $\Delta H^\circ = -126$ kJ

(b)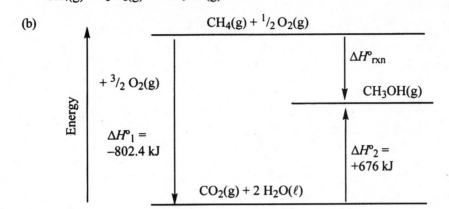

6.51 (a) $C_2H_4(g) + 3\,O_2(g) \rightarrow 2\,CO_2(g) + 2\,H_2O(\ell)$ $\Delta H^\circ = -1411.1$ kJ

$2\,CO_2(g) + 3\,H_2O(\ell) \rightarrow C_2H_5OH(\ell) + 3\,O_2(g)$ $\Delta H^\circ = -(-1367.5$ kJ$)$

$C_2H_4(g) + H_2O(\ell) \rightarrow C_2H_5OH(\ell)$ $\Delta H^\circ = -43.6$ kJ

(b)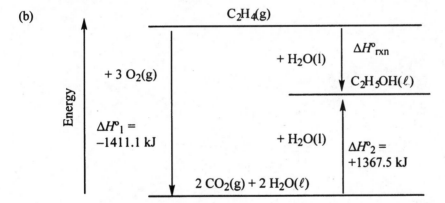

6.52 ${}^1/_2\,N_2(g) + {}^3/_2\,H_2(g) \rightarrow NH_3(g)$ $\Delta H^\circ = (-91.8$ kJ$)/2$

$NH_3(g) + {}^5/_4\,O_2(g) \rightarrow NO(g) + {}^3/_2\,H_2O(g)$ $\Delta H^\circ = (-906.2$ kJ$)/4$

${}^3/_2\,H_2O(g) \rightarrow {}^3/_2\,H_2(g) + {}^3/_4\,O_2(g)$ $\Delta H^\circ = -(-241.8$ kJ$) \times {}^3/_2$

${}^1/_2\,N_2(g) + {}^1/_2\,O_2(g) \rightarrow NO(g)$ $\Delta H^\circ = 90.3$ kJ

6.53 $P_4(s) + 10\,Cl_2(g) \rightarrow 4\,PCl_5(s)$ $\Delta H^\circ = -1774.0$ kJ

$4\,PCl_5(s) \rightarrow 4\,PCl_3(\ell) + 4\,Cl_2(g)$ $\Delta H^\circ = -(-123.8$ kJ$) \times 4$

$P_4(s) + 6\,Cl_2(g) \rightarrow 4\,PCl_3(\ell)$ $\Delta H^\circ = -1278.8$ kJ

1.00 mol $PCl_3 \cdot \dfrac{-1278.8 \text{ kJ}}{4 \text{ mol } PCl_3} = -320.$ kJ/mol PCl_3

6.54 $C(s) + {}^1/_2\, O_2(g) + 2\, H_2(g) \rightarrow CH_3OH(\ell)$ $\Delta H_f^\circ = -238.4$ kJ

6.55 $Ca(s) + C(s) + {}^3/_2\, O_2(g) \rightarrow CaCO_3(s)$ $\Delta H_f^\circ = -1207.6$ kJ

6.56   (a) $2\, Cr(s) + {}^3/_2\, O_2(g) \rightarrow Cr_2O_3(s)$ $\Delta H_f^\circ = -1134.7$ kJ

  (b) $2.4\text{ g Cr} \cdot \dfrac{1\text{ mol Cr}}{52.0\text{ g}} \cdot \dfrac{1\text{ mol Cr}_2O_3}{2\text{ mol Cr}} \cdot \dfrac{-1134.7\text{ kJ}}{1\text{ mol Cr}_2O_3} = -26$ kJ

6.57   (a) $Mg(s) + {}^1/_2\, O_2(g) \rightarrow MgO(s)$ $\Delta H_f^\circ = -601.24$ kJ

  (b) $2.5\text{ mol Mg} \cdot \dfrac{1\text{ mol MgO}}{1\text{ mol Mg}} \cdot \dfrac{-601.24\text{ kJ}}{1\text{ mol MgO}} = -1500$ kJ

6.58   (a) $1.0\text{ g P} \cdot \dfrac{1\text{ mol P}}{31.0\text{ g}} \cdot \dfrac{1\text{ mol P}_4O_{10}}{4\text{ mol P}} \cdot \dfrac{-2984.0\text{ kJ}}{1\text{ mol P}_4O_{10}} = -24$ kJ

  (b) $0.20\text{ mol NO} \cdot \dfrac{-90.29\text{ kJ}}{1\text{ mol NO}} = -18$ kJ

  (c) $2.40\text{ g NaCl} \cdot \dfrac{1\text{ mol NaCl}}{58.44\text{ g}} \cdot \dfrac{-411.12\text{ kJ}}{1\text{ mol NaCl}} = -16.9$ kJ

  (d) $250\text{ g Fe} \cdot \dfrac{1\text{ mol Fe}}{55.8\text{ g}} \cdot \dfrac{1\text{ mol Fe}_2O_3}{2\text{ mol Fe}} \cdot \dfrac{-824.2\text{ kJ}}{1\text{ mol Fe}_2O_3} = -1800$ kJ

6.59   (a) $0.054\text{ g S} \cdot \dfrac{1\text{ mol S}}{32.1\text{ g}} \cdot \dfrac{1\text{ mol SO}_2}{1\text{ mol S}} \cdot \dfrac{-296.84\text{ kJ}}{1\text{ mol SO}_2} = -0.50$ kJ

  (b) $0.20\text{ mol HgO} \cdot \dfrac{90.83\text{ kJ}}{1\text{ mol HgO}} = 18$ kJ

  (c) $2.40\text{ g NH}_3 \cdot \dfrac{1\text{ mol NH}_3}{17.03\text{ g}} \cdot \dfrac{-45.90\text{ kJ}}{1\text{ mol NH}_3} = -6.47$ kJ

  (d) $1.05 \times 10^{-2}\text{ mol C} \cdot \dfrac{1\text{ mol CO}_2}{1\text{ mol C}} \cdot \dfrac{-393.509\text{ kJ}}{1\text{ mol CO}_2} = -4.13$ kJ

6.60   (a) $\Delta H_f^\circ[O_2(g)] = 0$ kJ/mol

  $\Delta H^\circ{}_{rxn} = \Delta H_f^\circ[NO(g)] + \Delta H_f^\circ[H_2O(g)] - \Delta H_f^\circ[NH_3(g)]$

  $\Delta H^\circ{}_{rxn} = 4\text{ mol} \cdot 90.29\text{ kJ/mol} + 6\text{ mol} \cdot (-241.83\text{ kJ/mol}) - 4\text{ mol} \cdot (-45.90\text{ kJ/mol})$

  $\Delta H^\circ{}_{rxn} = -906.22$ kJ

  (b) $10.0\text{ g NH}_3 \cdot \dfrac{1\text{ mol NH}_3}{17.03\text{ g}} \cdot \dfrac{-906.22\text{ kJ}}{4\text{ mol NH}_3} = -133$ kJ (133 kJ evolved)

6.61   (a) $\Delta H^\circ{}_{rxn} = \Delta H_f^\circ[CaCO_3(s)] + \Delta H_f^\circ[H_2O(g)] - (\Delta H_f^\circ[Ca(OH)_2(s)] + \Delta H_f^\circ[CO_2(g)])$

  $\Delta H^\circ{}_{rxn} = 1\text{ mol} \cdot (-1207.6\text{ kJ/mol}) + 1\text{ mol} \cdot (-241.83\text{ kJ/mol})$

  $- [1\text{ mol} \cdot (-986.09\text{ kJ/mol}) + 1\text{ mol} \cdot (-393.509\text{ kJ/mol})]$

  $\Delta H^\circ{}_{rxn} = -69.8$ kJ

  (b) $1.00 \times 10^3\text{ g Ca(OH)}_2 \cdot \dfrac{1\text{ mol Ca(OH)}_2}{74.09\text{ g}} \cdot \dfrac{-69.8\text{ kJ}}{1\text{ mol Ca(OH)}_2} = -942$ kJ (942 kJ evolved)

6.62   (a) $\Delta H_f^\circ[O_2(g)] = 0$ kJ/mol

$\Delta H^\circ_{rxn} = \Delta H_f^\circ[BaO(s)] - \Delta H_f^\circ[BaO_2(s)]$

$\Delta H^\circ_{rxn} = 1$ mol $\cdot$ (-553.5 kJ/mol) $-$ 1 mol $\cdot$ (-634.3 kJ/mol)

$\Delta H^\circ_{rxn} = 80.8$ kJ   The reaction is endothermic

(b)

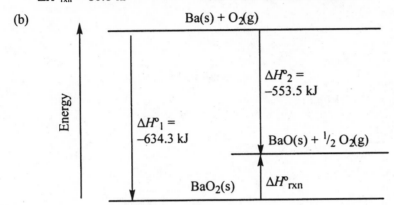

6.63   (a) $\Delta H_f^\circ[O_2(g)] = 0$ kJ/mol

$\Delta H^\circ_{rxn} = \Delta H_f^\circ[SO_3(g)] - \Delta H_f^\circ[SO_2(g)]$

$\Delta H^\circ_{rxn} = 1$ mol $\cdot$ (-395.77 kJ/mol) $-$ 1 mol $\cdot$ (-296.84 kJ/mol)

$\Delta H^\circ_{rxn} = -98.93$ kJ   The reaction is exothermic

(b)

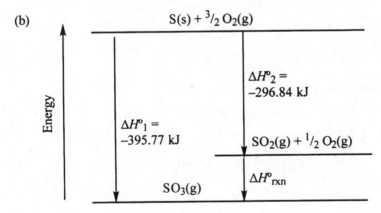

6.64 $\Delta H_f^\circ[O_2(g)] = 0$ kJ/mol

$\Delta H^\circ_{rxn} = \Delta H_f^\circ[CO_2(g)] + \Delta H_f^\circ[H_2O(\ell)] - \Delta H_f^\circ[C_{10}H_8(s)]$

-5156.1 kJ $= 10$ mol $\cdot$ (-393.509 kJ/mol) $+$ 4 mol $\cdot$ (-285.83 kJ/mol) $- \Delta H_f^\circ[C_{10}H_8(s)]$

$\Delta H_f^\circ[C_{10}H_8(s)] = 77.7$ kJ/mol

6.65 $\Delta H_f^\circ[O_2(g)] = 0$ kJ/mol

$\Delta H^\circ_{rxn} = \Delta H_f^\circ[CO_2(g)] + \Delta H_f^\circ[H_2O(\ell)] - \Delta H_f^\circ[C_8H_8(\ell)]$

-4395.0 kJ $= 8$ mol $\cdot$ (-393.509 kJ/mol) $+$ 4 mol $\cdot$ (-285.83 kJ/mol) $- \Delta H_f^\circ[C_8H_8(\ell)]$

$\Delta H_f^\circ[C_8H_8(\ell)] = 103.6$ kJ/mol

6.66   (a)   Al(s) + $^3/_2$ Cl$_2$(g) → AlCl$_3$(s)   product-favored

$\Delta H^\circ_{rxn} = \Delta H_f^\circ[\text{AlCl}_3(s)] = -705.63$ kJ/mol

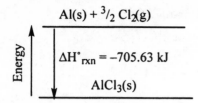

(b)   HgO(s) → Hg(ℓ) + O$_2$(g)   reactant-favored

$\Delta H^\circ_{rxn} = -\Delta H_f^\circ[\text{HgO}(s)] = 90.83$ kJ/mol

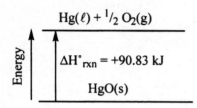

6.67   (a)   O$_2$(g) + O(g) → O$_3$(g)   product-favored

$\Delta H^\circ_{rxn} = \Delta H_f^\circ[\text{O}_3(g)] - \Delta H_f^\circ[\text{O}(g)] = 1$ mol · 142.67 kJ/mol − 1 mol · 249.170 kJ/mol

$\Delta H^\circ_{rxn} = -106.50$ kJ

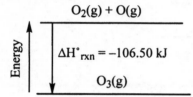

(b)   NaOH(s) → NaOH(aq)   product-favored

$\Delta H^\circ_{rxn} = \Delta H_f^\circ[\text{NaOH}(aq)] - \Delta H_f^\circ[\text{NaOH}(aq)]$

$\Delta H^\circ_{rxn} = 1$ mol · (−469.15 kJ/mol) − 1 mol · (−425.93 kJ/mol)

$\Delta H^\circ_{rxn} = -43.22$ kJ

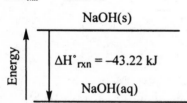

(c) $MgCO_3(s) \rightarrow MgO(s) + CO_2(g)$ reactant-favored

$\Delta H^{\circ}_{rxn} = \Delta H_f^{\circ}[MgO(s)] + \Delta H_f^{\circ}[CO_2(g)] - \Delta H_f^{\circ}[MgCO_3(s)]$

$\Delta H^{\circ}_{rxn} = 1 \text{ mol} \cdot (-601.24 \text{ kJ/mol}) + 1 \text{ mol} \cdot (-393.509 \text{ kJ/mol}) - 1 \text{ mol} \cdot (-1111.69 \text{ kJ/mol})$

$\Delta H^{\circ}_{rxn} = 116.94 \text{ kJ}$

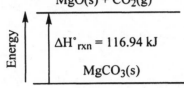

6.68 $0 = q_{metal} + q_{water}$

$0 = [27.3 \text{ g} \cdot C_{Pb} \cdot (299.47 \text{ K} - 372.05 \text{ K})] + [15.0 \text{ g} \cdot 4.184 \text{ J/g·K} \cdot (299.47 \text{ K} - 295.65 \text{ K})]$

$C_{Pb} = 0.121 \text{ J/g·K}$

6.69 $q_{water} = 50.0 \text{ g} \cdot 4.184 \text{ J/g·K} \cdot (-40 \text{ K}) = -8400 \text{ J}$

$q_{ethanol} = 100. \text{ g} \cdot 2.46 \text{ J/g·K} \cdot (-40 \text{ K}) = -9800 \text{ J}$ Ethanol gives up more heat

6.70 $0 = q_{Cu} + q_{water}$

$0 = [192 \text{ g} \cdot 0.385 \text{ J/g·K} (T_f - 373.2 \text{ K})] + [751 \text{ g} \cdot 4.184 \text{ J/g·K} \cdot (T_f - 277.2 \text{ K})]$

$T_f = 279 \text{ K} (6.2 \text{ °C})$

6.71 $187 \text{ J} = 93.45 \text{ g} \cdot C_{silver} \cdot (300.2 \text{ K} - 291.7 \text{ K})$

$C_{silver} = 0.24 \text{ J/g·K}$

6.72 q = energy to melt ice + energy to heat liquid + energy to vaporize liquid

$q_{melt ice} = 60.1 \text{ g} \cdot 333 \text{ J/g} = 2.00 \times 10^4 \text{ J}$

$q_{heat liquid} = 60.1 \text{ g} \cdot 4.184 \text{ J/g·K} \cdot (373.2 \text{ K} - 273.2 \text{ K}) = 2.51 \times 10^4 \text{ J}$

$q_{vaporize liquid} = 60.1 \text{ g} \cdot 2260 \text{ J/g} = 1.36 \times 10^5 \text{ J}$

$q_{total} = 2.00 \times 10^4 \text{ J} + 2.51 \times 10^4 \text{ J} + 1.36 \times 10^5 \text{ J} = 1.8 \times 10^5 \text{ J}$

6.73 $0 = q_{water} + q_{ice}$

$0 = [100.0 \text{ g} \cdot 4.184 \text{ J/g·K} \cdot (273.2 \text{ K} - 333.2 \text{ K})] + [m_{ice melted} \cdot 333 \text{ J/g}]$

$m_{ice melted} = 75.4 \text{ g}$

6.74   Assume the density of the tea is 1.00 g/mL

$0 = q_{tea} + q_{ice}$

$0 = [5.00 \times 10^2 \text{ g} \cdot 4.184 \text{ J/g·K} \cdot (273.2 \text{ K} - 293.2 \text{ K})] + [m_{ice melted} \cdot 333 \text{ J/g}]$

$m_{ice melted} = 126 \text{ g}$

$(3 \times 45 \text{ g}) - 126 \text{ g} = 9 \text{ g ice remaining}$

6.75   Assume the density of the tea is 1.00 g/mL and specific heat capacity is 4.184 J/g·K

$0 = q_{tea} + q_{melt\ ice} + q_{warm\ ice}$

$0 = [5.00 \times 10^2\ g \cdot 4.184\ J/g\cdot K \cdot (T_f - 293.2\ K)] + [90.\ g \cdot 333\ J/g]$

$+ [90.\ g \cdot 4.184\ J/g\cdot K \cdot (T_f - 273.2\ K)]$

$T_f = 278\ K\ (4.8\ ^\circ C)$

6.76   Assume the density of the cola is 1.00 g/mL and specific heat capacity is 4.184 J/g·K

Energy required to cool cola to 0 °C:

$q_{cola} = 240\ g \cdot 4.184\ J/g\cdot K \cdot (273.2\ K - 283.7\ K) = -1.1 \times 10^4\ J$

Energy supplied by melting one ice cube:

$q_{ice} = 45\ g \cdot 333\ J/g = 1.5 \times 10^4\ J$

(a)   The temperature is 0 °C and some ice remains

$0 = q_{cola} + q_{melt\ ice}$

$0 = -1.1 \times 10^4\ J + [m_{ice\ melted} \cdot 333\ J/g]$

$m_{ice\ melted} = 32\ g$

$45\ g - 32\ g = 13\ g$ ice remaining

6.77   "Kooler" specific heat capacity $= 0.10 \cdot 850\ J/g + 0.90 \cdot 2260\ J/g = 2120\ J/g$

$3.6 \times 10^3\ J = m_{Kooler} \cdot 2120\ J/g$

$m_{Kooler} = 1.7\ g$

6.78 $q_{solution} = (250.\ g + 125\ g) \cdot 4.2\ J/g\cdot K \cdot (296.05\ K - 294.30\ K)$

$q_{solution} = 2.8 \times 10^3\ J$

$q_{rxn} = -q_{solution} = -2.8 \times 10^3\ J$

Reactants are present in equimolar amounts

$0.250\ L \cdot \dfrac{0.18\ mol\ AgNO_3}{1\ L} \cdot \dfrac{1\ mol\ AgCl}{1\ mol\ AgNO_3} = 0.045\ mol\ AgCl$

$\dfrac{-2.8 \times 10^3\ J}{0.045\ mol} \cdot \dfrac{1\ kJ}{10^3\ J} = -61\ kJ/mol\ AgCl$

6.79 $q_{solution} = (200.\ g + 200.\ g) \cdot 4.2\ J/g\cdot K \cdot (2.44\ K)$

$q_{solution} = 4.1 \times 10^3\ J$

$q_{rxn} = -q_{solution} = -4.1 \times 10^3\ J$

Reactants are present in equimolar amounts

$0.200\ L \cdot \dfrac{0.75\ mol\ Pb(NO_3)_2}{1\ L} \cdot \dfrac{1\ mol\ PbBr_2}{1\ mol\ Pb(NO_3)_2} = 0.15\ mol\ AgCl$

$\dfrac{-4.1 \times 10^3\ J}{0.15\ mol} \cdot \dfrac{1\ kJ}{10^3\ J} = -27\ kJ/mol\ AgCl$

6.80 $q = q_{water} + q_{calorimeter}$

$q = [415 \text{ g} \cdot 4.184 \text{ J/g·K} \cdot (293.87 \text{ K} - 292.05 \text{ K})] + [155 \text{ J/K} \cdot (293.87 \text{ K} - 292.05 \text{ K})]$

$q = 3.44 \times 10^3 \text{ J}$

$7.647 \text{ g NH}_4\text{NO}_3 \cdot \dfrac{1 \text{ mol NH}_4\text{NO}_3}{80.043 \text{ g}} = 0.09554 \text{ mol NH}_4\text{NO}_3$

$\dfrac{3.44 \times 10^3 \text{ J}}{0.09554 \text{ mol}} \cdot \dfrac{1 \text{ kJ}}{10^3 \text{ J}} = 36.0 \text{ kJ/mol NH}_4\text{NO}_3 \text{ evolved}$

6.81 $q = q_{water} + q_{calorimeter}$

$q = [650 \text{ g} \cdot 4.184 \text{ J/g·K} \cdot (295.5 \text{ K} - 291.7 \text{ K})] + [550 \text{ J/K} \cdot (295.5 \text{ K} - 291.7 \text{ K})]$

$q = 1.2 \times 10^4 \text{ J}$

$4.20 \text{ g C}_2\text{H}_5\text{OH} \cdot \dfrac{1 \text{ mol C}_2\text{H}_5\text{OH}}{46.07 \text{ g}} = 0.0912 \text{ mol C}_2\text{H}_5\text{OH}$

$\dfrac{1.2 \times 10^4 \text{ J}}{0.0912 \text{ mol}} \cdot \dfrac{1 \text{ kJ}}{10^3 \text{ J}} = 140 \text{ kJ/mol C}_2\text{H}_5\text{OH}$

$\Delta H_{combustion} = -q = -140 \text{ kJ/mol}$

6.82   (a) $2 \text{ B(s)} + {}^3/_2 \text{ O}_2\text{(g)} \rightarrow \text{B}_2\text{O}_3\text{(s)}$ $\Delta H^{\circ}{}_{rxn} = (-2543.8 \text{ kJ})/2$

$3 \text{ H}_2\text{(g)} + {}^3/_2 \text{ O}_2\text{(g)} \rightarrow 3 \text{ H}_2\text{O(g)}$ $\Delta H^{\circ}{}_{rxn} = (-241.8 \text{ kJ}) \times 3$

$\text{B}_2\text{O}_3\text{(s)} + 3 \text{ H}_2\text{O(g)} \rightarrow \text{B}_2\text{H}_6\text{(g)} + 3 \text{ O}_2\text{(g)}$ $\Delta H^{\circ}{}_{rxn} = -(-2032.9 \text{ kJ})$

$2 \text{ B(s)} + 3 \text{ H}_2\text{(g)} \rightarrow \text{B}_2\text{H}_6\text{(g)}$ $\Delta H^{\circ}{}_{rxn} = 35.6 \text{ kJ}$

(b) $\Delta H_f^{\circ} = 35.6 \text{ kJ/mol}$

(c)

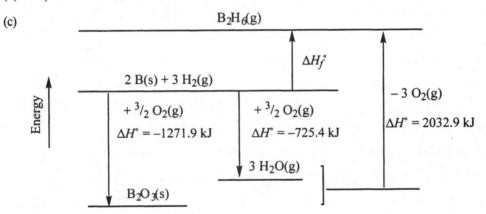

(d)   reactant-favored

6.83   (a) $\text{C(s)} + \text{O}_2\text{(g)} \rightarrow \text{CO}_2\text{(g)}$ $\Delta H^{\circ}{}_{rxn} = -393.5 \text{ kJ}$

$2 \text{ S(s)} + 2 \text{ O}_2\text{(g)} \rightarrow 2 \text{ SO}_2\text{(g)}$ $\Delta H^{\circ}{}_{rxn} = (-296.8 \text{ kJ}) \times 2$

$\text{CO}_2\text{(g)} + 2 \text{ SO}_2\text{(g)} \rightarrow \text{CS}_2\text{(g)} + 3 \text{ O}_2\text{(g)}$ $\Delta H^{\circ}{}_{rxn} = -(-1103.9 \text{ kJ})$

$\text{C(s)} + 2 \text{ S(s)} \rightarrow \text{CS}_2\text{(g)}$ $\Delta H^{\circ}{}_{rxn} = 116.8 \text{ kJ}$

(b) $\Delta H_f^\circ = 116.8$ kJ/mol

(c)

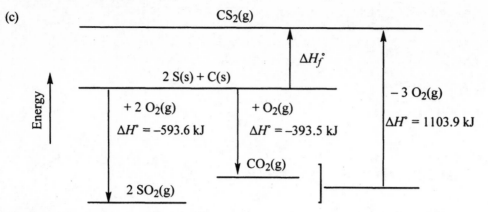

(d)   reactant-favored

6.84 $\Delta H_f^\circ[\text{Mg(s)}] = \Delta H_f^\circ[\text{H}_2\text{(g)}] = 0$ kJ/mol

$\Delta H^\circ_{rxn} = \Delta H_f^\circ[\text{Mg(OH)}_2\text{(s)}] - \Delta H_f^\circ[\text{H}_2\text{O}(\ell)]$

$\Delta H^\circ_{rxn} = 1 \text{ mol} \cdot (-924.54 \text{ kJ/mol}) - 2 \text{ mol} \cdot (-285.83 \text{ kJ/mol})$

$\Delta H^\circ_{rxn} = -352.88 \text{ kJ} = -3.5288 \times 10^5 \text{ J}$

$q_{water} = 250 \text{ g} \cdot 4.184 \text{ J/g·K} \cdot (358 \text{ K} - 298 \text{ K}) = 6.3 \times 10^4 \text{ J}$

$6.3 \times 10^4 \text{ J} \cdot \dfrac{1 \text{ mol Mg}}{3.5288 \times 10^5 \text{ J}} \cdot \dfrac{24.3 \text{ g}}{1 \text{ mol Mg}} = 4.3 \text{ g Mg}$

6.85   (a)   product-favored

        (b) $\Delta H_f^\circ[\text{O}_2\text{(g)}] = \Delta H_f^\circ[\text{N}_2\text{(g)}] = 0$ kJ/mol

            $\Delta H^\circ_{rxn} = \Delta H_f^\circ[\text{H}_2\text{O(g)}] - \Delta H_f^\circ[\text{N}_2\text{H}_4(\ell)]$

            $-534.3 \text{ kJ} = 2 \text{ mol} \cdot (-241.83 \text{ kJ}) - \Delta H_f^\circ[\text{N}_2\text{H}_4(\ell)]$

            $\Delta H_f^\circ[\text{N}_2\text{H}_4(\ell)] = 50.6$ kJ/mol

6.86   (a) $\Delta H_f^\circ[\text{C(s)}] = \Delta H_f^\circ[\text{H}_2\text{(g)}] = 0$ kJ/mol

            $\Delta H^\circ_{rxn} = \Delta H_f^\circ[\text{CO(g)}] - \Delta H_f^\circ[\text{H}_2\text{O(g)}]$

            $\Delta H^\circ_{rxn} = 1 \text{ mol} \cdot (-110.525 \text{ kJ/mol}) - 1 \text{ mol} \cdot (-241.83 \text{ kJ/mol})$

            $\Delta H^\circ_{rxn} = 131.31$ kJ

        (b)   reactant-favored

        (c) $1000.0 \text{ kg} \cdot \dfrac{10^3 \text{ g}}{1 \text{ kg}} \cdot \dfrac{1 \text{ mol C}}{12.011 \text{ g}} \cdot \dfrac{131.31 \text{ kJ}}{1 \text{ mol C}} = 1.0932 \times 10^7 \text{ kJ}$

6.87   This problem was solved assuming $\text{H}_2\text{O}(\ell)$ is a product in the combustion reactions, but also could be correctly solved using $\text{H}_2\text{O(g)}$ as a product.

        Propane: $\text{C}_3\text{H}_8\text{(g)} + 5 \text{ O}_2\text{(g)} \rightarrow 3 \text{ CO}_2\text{(g)} + 4 \text{ H}_2\text{O}(\ell)$

$\Delta H_f^\circ[O_2(g)] = 0$ kJ/mol

$\Delta H^\circ_{rxn} = \Delta H_f^\circ[CO_2(g)] + \Delta H_f^\circ[H_2O(\ell)] - \Delta H_f^\circ[C_3H_8(g)]$

$\Delta H^\circ_{rxn} = 3$ mol $\cdot$ (-393.509 kJ/mol) $+ 4$ mol $\cdot$ (-285.83 kJ/mol) $- 1$ mol $\cdot$ (-104.7 kJ/mol)

$\Delta H^\circ_{rxn} = -2219.1$ kJ

$\dfrac{-2219.1 \text{ kJ}}{1 \text{ mol C}_3\text{H}_8} \cdot \dfrac{1 \text{ mol C}_3\text{H}_8}{44.096 \text{ g}} = -50.325$ kJ/g

Butane: $\qquad\qquad\qquad C_4H_{10}(g) + {}^{13}/_2\, O_2(g) \rightarrow 4\, CO_2(g) + 5\, H_2O(\ell)$

$\Delta H_f^\circ[O_2(g)] = 0$ kJ/mol

$\Delta H^\circ_{rxn} = \Delta H_f^\circ[CO_2(g)] + \Delta H_f^\circ[H_2O(\ell)] - \Delta H_f^\circ[C_4H_{10}(g)]$

$\Delta H^\circ_{rxn} = 4$ mol $\cdot$ (-393.509 kJ/mol) $+ 5$ mol $\cdot$ (-285.83 kJ/mol) $- 1$ mol $\cdot$ (-127.1 kJ/mol)

$\Delta H^\circ_{rxn} = -2876.1$ kJ

$\dfrac{-2876.1 \text{ kJ}}{1 \text{ mol C}_4\text{H}_{10}} \cdot \dfrac{1 \text{ mol C}_4\text{H}_{10}}{58.123 \text{ g}} = -49.482$ kJ/g

Gasoline: $\qquad\qquad\qquad C_8H_{18}(\ell) + {}^{25}/_2\, O_2(g) \rightarrow 8\, CO_2(g) + 9\, H_2O(\ell)$

$\Delta H_f^\circ[O_2(g)] = 0$ kJ/mol

$\Delta H^\circ_{rxn} = \Delta H_f^\circ[CO_2(g)] + \Delta H_f^\circ[H_2O(\ell)] - \Delta H_f^\circ[C_8H_{18}(\ell)]$

$\Delta H^\circ_{rxn} = 8$ mol $\cdot$ (-393.509 kJ/mol) $+ 9$ mol $\cdot$ (-285.83 kJ/mol) $- 1$ mol $\cdot$ (-259.2 kJ/mol)

$\Delta H^\circ_{rxn} = -5261.3$ kJ

$\dfrac{-5261.3 \text{ kJ}}{1 \text{ mol C}_8\text{H}_{18}} \cdot \dfrac{1 \text{ mol C}_8\text{H}_{18}}{114.230 \text{ g}} = -47.810$ kJ/g

Ethanol: $\qquad\qquad\qquad C_2H_5OH(\ell) + 3\, O_2(g) \rightarrow 2\, CO_2(g) + 3\, H_2O(\ell)$

$\Delta H_f^\circ[O_2(g)] = 0$ kJ/mol

$\Delta H^\circ_{rxn} = \Delta H_f^\circ[CO_2(g)] + \Delta H_f^\circ[H_2O(\ell)] - \Delta H_f^\circ[C_2H_5OH(\ell)]$

$\Delta H^\circ_{rxn} = 2$ mol $\cdot$ (-393.509 kJ/mol) $+ 3$ mol $\cdot$ (-285.83 kJ/mol) $- 1$ mol (-277.0 kJ/mol)

$\Delta H^\circ_{rxn} = -1367.5$ kJ

$\dfrac{-1367.5 \text{ kJ}}{1 \text{ mol C}_2\text{H}_5\text{OH}} \cdot \dfrac{1 \text{ mol C}_2\text{H}_5\text{OH}}{46.069 \text{ g}} = -29.684$ kJ/g

The hydrocarbons give off more heat per gram than the ethanol. Of the hydrocarbons, the smaller ones give off more heat than the larger ones. More C—C and C—H bonds are broken in combustion per gram of fuel, meaning that more energy is released per gram in the smaller hydrocarbons.

6.88   Methanol: $\qquad\qquad\qquad 2\, CH_3OH(\ell) + 3\, O_2(g) \rightarrow 2\, CO_2(g) + 4\, H_2O(\ell)$

$\Delta H_f^\circ[O_2(g)] = 0$ kJ/mol

$\Delta H^\circ_{rxn} = \Delta H_f^\circ[CO_2(g)] + \Delta H_f^\circ[H_2O(\ell)] - \Delta H_f^\circ[CH_3OH(\ell)]$

$\Delta H^\circ_{rxn} = 2$ mol $\cdot$ (-393.509 kJ/mol) $+ 4$ mol $\cdot$ (-285.83 kJ/mol) $- 2$ mol $\cdot$ (-238.4 kJ/mol)

$\Delta H^\circ_{rxn} = -1453.5$ kJ

$\dfrac{-1453.5 \text{ kJ}}{2 \text{ mol CH}_3\text{OH}} \cdot \dfrac{1 \text{ mol CH}_3\text{OH}}{32.042 \text{ g}} = -22.68$ kJ/g

Gasoline: $C_8H_{18}(\ell) + {}^{25}/_2 O_2(g) \rightarrow 8\ CO_2(g) + 9\ H_2O(\ell)$

$\Delta H_f^\circ[O_2(g)] = 0\ kJ/mol$

$\Delta H^\circ_{rxn} = \Delta H_f^\circ[CO_2(g)] + \Delta H_f^\circ[H_2O(\ell)] - \Delta H_f^\circ[C_8H_{18}(\ell)]$

$\Delta H^\circ_{rxn} = 8\ mol \cdot (-393.509\ kJ/mol) + 9\ mol \cdot (-285.83\ kJ/mol) - 1\ mol \cdot (-259.2\ kJ/mol)$

$\Delta H^\circ_{rxn} = -5461.3\ kJ$

$$\frac{-5461.3\ kJ}{1\ mol\ C_8H_{18}} \cdot \frac{1\ mol\ C_8H_{18}}{114.230\ g} = -47.810\ kJ/g$$

6.89 $\Delta H_f^\circ[O_2(g)] = \Delta H_f^\circ[N_2(g)] = 0\ kJ/mol$

Hydrazine:

$\Delta H^\circ_{rxn} = \Delta H_f^\circ[H_2O(g)] - \Delta H_f^\circ[N_2H_4(\ell)]$

$\Delta H^\circ_{rxn} = 2\ mol \cdot (-241.83\ kJ/mol) - 1\ mol \cdot (50.6\ kJ/mol)$

$\Delta H^\circ_{rxn} = -534.3\ kJ$

$$\frac{-534.3\ kJ}{1\ mol\ N_2H_4} \cdot \frac{1\ mol\ N_2H_4}{32.045\ g} = -16.67\ kJ/g\ N_2H_4$$

1,1-Dimethylhydrazine:

$\Delta H^\circ_{rxn} = \Delta H_f^\circ[CO_2(g)] + \Delta H_f^\circ[H_2O(g)] - \Delta H_f^\circ[N_2H_2(CH_3)_2(\ell)]$

$\Delta H^\circ_{rxn} = 2\ mol \cdot (-393.509\ kJ/mol) + 4\ mol \cdot (-241.83\ kJ/mol) - 1\ mol \cdot (48.9\ kJ/mol)$

$\Delta H^\circ_{rxn} = -1803.2\ kJ$

$$\frac{-1803.2\ kJ}{1\ mol\ N_2H_2(CH_3)_2} \cdot \frac{1\ mol\ N_2H_2(CH_3)_2}{60.099\ g} = -30.004\ kJ/g\ N_2H_2(CH_3)_2$$

1,1-Dimethylhydrazine gives more heat per gram when reacting with oxygen

6.90   Al: $\dfrac{0.897\ J}{g \cdot K} \cdot \dfrac{26.98\ g}{1\ mol\ Al} = 24.2\ J/mol \cdot K$

Fe: $\dfrac{0.449\ J}{g \cdot K} \cdot \dfrac{55.85\ g}{1\ mol\ Fe} = 25.1\ J/mol \cdot K$

Cu: $\dfrac{0.385\ J}{g \cdot K} \cdot \dfrac{63.55\ g}{1\ mol\ Cu} = 24.5\ J/mol \cdot K$

Au: $\dfrac{0.129\ J}{g \cdot K} \cdot \dfrac{197.0\ g}{1\ mol\ Au} = 25.4\ J/mol \cdot K$

The molar heat capacity values for the four metals are quite similar, with an average of 24.8 J/mol·K.

Ag: $\dfrac{24.8\ J}{mol \cdot K} \cdot \dfrac{1\ mol\ Ag}{107.9\ g\ Au} = 0.230\ J/g \cdot K$ close to the correct value of 0.236 J/g·K

6.91   There is a rough non-linear correspondence, which shows that the specific heat increases with decreasing atomic weight. Using the relationship $C_{metal} \propto 1/\text{atomic weight}$, or $C_{metal} \times \text{atomic weight} = \text{constant} \approx 26$, $C_{Pt} \approx 26/195 \approx 0.130$ J/g·K. This is in good agreement with the literature value (0.133 J/g·K).

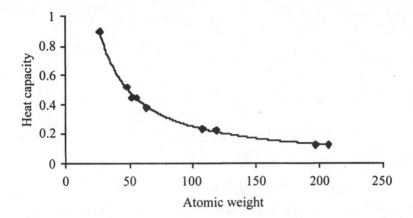

6.92   To extract heat from the inside of the refrigerator, work has to be done. That work (by the condenser and motor) releases heat to the environment (your room). So while the temporary relief of cool air from the inside of the refrigerator is pleasant, the motor has to do work—and heats your room.

6.93   **NOTE**: $\Delta H°_{rxn}$ should be −402.7 kJ, not −502.7 kJ

      Reaction 1: $Ca(s) + \frac{1}{2}O_2(g) \rightarrow CaO(s)$ $\Delta H(1)$

      Reaction 2: $S_8(s) + 12\ O_2(g) \rightarrow 8\ SO_3(g)$ $\Delta H(2)$

      Reaction 3: $CaO(s) + SO_3(g) \rightarrow CaSO_4(s)$ $\Delta H(3)$

      Combine reactions to produce desired overall reaction:

      $Ca(s) + \frac{1}{2}O_2(g) \rightarrow CaO(s)$ $\Delta H(1)$

      $\frac{1}{8} S_8(s) + \frac{3}{2} O_2(g) \rightarrow SO_3(g)$ $\frac{1}{8} \times \Delta H(2)$

      $CaO(s) + SO_3(g) \rightarrow CaSO_4(s)$ $\Delta H(3)$

      $Ca(s) + \frac{1}{8} S_8(s) + 2\ O_2(g) \rightarrow CaSO_4(s)$ $\Delta H = \Delta H(1) + [\frac{1}{8} \times \Delta H(2)] + \Delta H(3)$

      The enthalpy values for reactions 1, 2, and 3 could be determined experimentally using calorimetry.

      For Reaction 3: $CaO(s) + SO_3(g) \rightarrow CaSO_4(s)$

      $\Delta H°_{rxn} = \Delta H_f°[CaSO_4(s)] - (\Delta H_f°[CaO(s)] + \Delta H_f°[SO_3(g)])$

      $-402.7\ kJ = \Delta H_f°[CaSO_4(s)] - [1\ mol \cdot (-635.09\ kJ/mol) + 1\ mol \cdot (-395.77\ kJ/mol)]$

      $\Delta H_f°[CaSO_4(s)] = -1433.6\ kJ/mol$

6.94   (a) $q_{soda} = 350\ g \cdot 4.184\ J/g·K \cdot (310.\ K - 278\ K) = 4.7 \times 10^4\ J$

           $q_{body} = -q_{soda} = -4.7 \times 10^4\ J$ (or $4.7 \times 10^4\ J$ expended by your body)

(b) -4.7×10^4 J $\cdot \dfrac{1 \text{ cal}}{4.184 \text{ J}} \cdot \dfrac{1 \text{ Cal}}{10^3 \text{ cal}} = -11$ Cal (or 11 Cal expended by your body)

      net energy change = 1 Cal $-$ (-11 Cal) = -10. (or 10 Cal expended by your body)

6.95 -4.7×10^4 J $\cdot \dfrac{1 \text{ cal}}{4.184 \text{ J}} \cdot \dfrac{1 \text{ Cal}}{10^3 \text{ cal}} = -11$ Cal (or 11 Cal expended by your body)

net energy change = 240 Cal -11 Cal = 229 Cal absorbed by your body

6.96   275 m^2 $\cdot$ 2.50 m $\cdot \dfrac{1 \text{ L}}{10^{-3} \text{ m}^3} \cdot \dfrac{1.22 \text{ g}}{1 \text{ L}} \cdot \dfrac{1 \text{ mol air}}{28.9 \text{ g}} = 2.90 \times 10^4$ mol air

$q_{\text{air}} = 2.90 \times 10^4$ mol $\cdot$ 29.1 J/mol·K $\cdot$ (295.2 K $-$ 288.2 K) = 5.9×10^6 J = 5.9×10^3 kJ

$CH_4(g) + 2 O_2(g) \rightarrow CO_2(g) + 2 H_2O(g)$

$\Delta H^\circ_{\text{comb}} = \Delta H_f^\circ[CO_2(g)] + \Delta H_f^\circ[H_2O(g)] - \Delta H_f^\circ[CH_4(g)]$

$\Delta H^\circ_{\text{comb}} = 1$ mol $\cdot$ (-393.509 kJ/mol) + 2 mol $\cdot$ (-241.83 kJ/mol) $-$ 1 mol $\cdot$ (-74.87 kJ/mol)

$\Delta H^\circ_{\text{comb}} = -802.30$ kJ

5.9×10^3 kJ $\cdot \dfrac{1 \text{ mol CH}_4}{-802.30 \text{ kJ}} \cdot \dfrac{16.04 \text{ g}}{1 \text{ mol CH}_4} = 120$ g CH$_4$

6.97   **NOTE:** enthalpy change for second reaction should be labeled $\Delta H^\circ_{\text{rxn}}$ not ΔH_f°

    (a) $Sr(s) + \frac{1}{2} O_2(g) \rightarrow SrO(s)$ $\Delta H_f^\circ = -592$ kJ

          $SrO(s) + CO_2(g) \rightarrow SrCO_3(s)$ $\Delta H^\circ_{\text{rxn}} = -234$ kJ

          $C(\text{graphite}) + O_2(g) \rightarrow CO_2(g)$ $\Delta H_f^\circ = -394$ kJ

          $Sr(s) + C(\text{graphite}) + \frac{3}{2} O_2(g) \rightarrow SrCO_3(s)$ $\Delta H^\circ = -1220$. kJ

    (b)

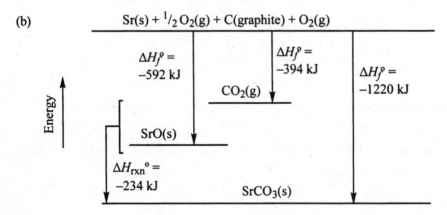

6.98

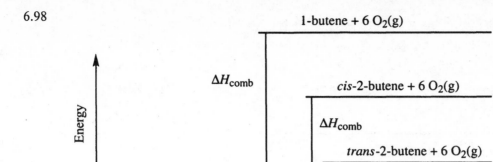

1-butene + 6 $O_2(g)$

ΔH_{comb}

cis-2-butene + 6 $O_2(g)$

ΔH_{comb}

trans-2-butene + 6 $O_2(g)$

ΔH_{comb}

Energy

4 $CO_2(g)$ + 4 $H_2O(\ell)$

6.99 $C_4H_8(g) + 6\ O_2(g) \rightarrow 4\ CO_2(g) + 4\ H_2O(\ell)$

$\Delta H_{combustion} = \Delta H_f^\circ[CO_2(g)] + \Delta H_f^\circ[H_2O(g)] - \Delta H_f^\circ[C_4H_8(g)]$

(a) *cis*-2-butene

-2687.5 kJ $= 4$ mol $\cdot$ $(-393.509$ kJ/mol$)$ $+ 4$ mol $\cdot$ $(-285.83$ kJ/mol$)$ $- \Delta H_f^\circ[C_4H_8(g)]$

$\Delta H_f^\circ[C_4H_8(g)] = -29.9$ kJ/mol

trans-2-butene

-2684.2 kJ $= 4$ mol $\cdot$ $(-393.509$ kJ/mol$)$ $+ 4$ mol $\cdot$ $(-285.83$ kJ/mol$)$ $- \Delta H_f^\circ[C_4H_8(g)]$

$\Delta H_f^\circ[C_4H_8(g)] = -33.2$ kJ/mol

1-butene

-2696.7 kJ $= 4$ mol $\cdot$ $(-393.509$ kJ/mol$)$ $+ 4$ mol $\cdot$ $(-285.83$ kJ/mol$)$ $- \Delta H_f^\circ[C_4H_8(g)]$

$\Delta H_f^\circ[C_4H_8(g)] = -20.7$ kJ/mol

(b)

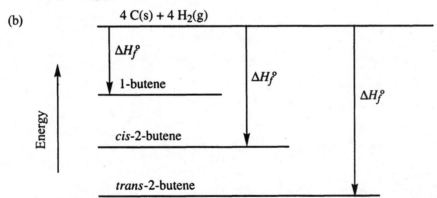

4 C(s) + 4 $H_2(g)$

ΔH_f°

1-butene

ΔH_f°

cis-2-butene

ΔH_f°

Energy

trans-2-butene

(c) $\Delta H_f^\circ[\textit{trans}\text{-2-butene}] - \Delta H_f^\circ[\textit{cis}\text{-2-butene}] = -33.2$ kJ $- (-29.9$ kJ$) = -3.3$ kJ/mol

6.100 $C(graphite) + \frac{1}{2} H_2(g) + \frac{3}{2} Cl_2(g) \rightarrow CHCl_3(g)$ $\Delta H_f^{\circ} = -103.1$ kJ

           $CH_4(g) + 2\, O_2(g) \rightarrow 2\, H_2O(\ell) + CO_2(g)$ $\Delta H^{\circ}_{rxn} = -890.3$ kJ

           $\frac{3}{2} Cl_2(g) + \frac{3}{2} H_2(g) \rightarrow 3\, HCl(g)$ $\Delta H^{\circ}_{rxn} = -(+184.6 \text{ kJ}) \times \frac{3}{2}$

           $CO_2(g) \rightarrow C(graphite) + O_2(g)$ $\Delta H^{\circ}_{rxn} = -(-393.5 \text{ kJ})$

           $2\, H_2O(\ell) \rightarrow 2\, H_2(g) + O_2(g)$ $\Delta H^{\circ}_{rxn} = -(-285.8 \text{ kJ}) \times 2$

           $CH_4(g) + 3\, Cl_2(g) \rightarrow 3\, HCl(g) + CHCl_3(g)$ $\Delta H^{\circ}_{rxn} = -305.2$ kJ

6.101 $q = 6.6 \times 10^{10} \text{ g} \cdot \dfrac{1 \text{ mol } H_2O}{18.0 \text{ g}} \cdot \dfrac{44.0 \text{ kJ}}{1 \text{ mol } H_2O} = 1.6 \times 10^{11}$ kJ released to surroundings

           Equivalent to 1.6×10^{11} kJ $\cdot \dfrac{1 \text{ ton dynamite}}{4.2 \times 10^{6} \text{ kJ}} = 3.8 \times 10^{4}$ tons of dynamite exploding

6.102 $325 \text{ m} \cdot 50.0 \text{ m} \cdot \dfrac{2.6 \times 10^{7} \text{ J}}{m^2} = 4.2 \times 10^{11}$ J/day

6.103 $1 \text{ day} \cdot \dfrac{24 \text{ h}}{1 \text{ day}} \cdot \dfrac{1.0 \times 10^{6} \text{ J}}{1 \text{ h}} \cdot \dfrac{1 \text{ kJ}}{10^{3} \text{ J}} = 2.4 \times 10^{4}$ kJ/day

           2.4×10^{4} kJ/day $\cdot \dfrac{10^{3} \text{ J}}{1 \text{ kJ}} \cdot \dfrac{1 \text{ kwh}}{3.60 \times 10^{6} \text{ J}} = 6.7$ kwh/day

6.104   See Screen 6.19 for the answer to this problem.

6.105   Thermodynamics is the study of the transformation of energy. Kinetics is the study of rates of chemical reactions. Sand is not thermodynamically favored to turn into elemental Si and O_2.

6.106   Electrical and thermal

6.107   (a)   The temperature of the colder object increases, and its particles move faster. The temperature of the warmer object decreases, and its particles move slower.

           (b)   The two objects have the same temperature.

6.108 $T_f = 31.0 \,^{\circ}C$

           $0 = q_{metal} + q_{water}$

           $0 = [10.0 \text{ g} \cdot C_{Al} \cdot (304.2 \text{ K} - 353.2 \text{ K})] + [10.0 \text{ g} \cdot 4.184 \text{ J/g·K} \cdot (304.2 \text{ K} - 293.2 \text{ K})]$

           $C_{Al} = 0.939$ J/g·K

6.109   73.8 kJ

Chapter 7
Atomic Structure

INSTRUCTOR'S NOTES

We consider this chapter and the next one (Chapter 8) to be of some importance in giving the students a firm foundation for understanding of the theories of chemistry. Therefore, we devote a total of about nine lectures to these chapters, most of that time devoted to electron configurations—particularly of ions—and to periodic properties.

SUGGESTED DEMONSTRATIONS

1.   Line Spectra

  • One place where our students have some difficulty is in understanding the ideas of "line spectra." This subject is not so important when discussed in terms of the Bohr model as it is in understanding the general idea of the absorption and emission of energy by atoms or molecules. To help students understand line spectra, we give each of them a small diffraction grating. (Large sheets from a scientific supply house are cut into small pieces, and each piece is mounted in cardboard and held with a staple.) Using these gratings, students can view the spectra of light from discharge tubes in the classroom.

  • Hughes, E. Jr.; George, A. "Suitable Light Sources and Spectroscopes for Student Observation of Emission Spectra in Lecture Halls," *Journal of Chemical Education*, **1984**, *61*, 908.

2.   Properties of Waves

  • If you have access to a laser pointer, the Optical Transform Kit available from the Institute for Chemical Education (Department of Chemistry, University of Wisconsin, 1101 University Avenue, Madison, WI 53706) can be used to project diffraction patterns on the wall of a lecture room.

3.   Atomic Orbitals

  • To illustrate the shapes of atomic orbitals, we use a set of wooden orbital models. These are currently obtainable from Klinger Educational Products Corp., 112-9 14th Road, College Point, New York, 11356.

Solutions to Study Questions

7.1   Determination of the charge-to-mass ratio of the electron (Thomson), determination of the charge of the electron (Millikan), and the experiments with alpha particles and metal foil that resulted in the nuclear model of the atom (Rutherford).

7.2   (a) $c = \lambda v$

      (b) $E = hv$

      (c) $E = \dfrac{Rhc}{n^2}$

7.3   The energy of a photon, a massless particle of radiation, is proportional to its frequency.
$E = hv$

7.4   violet, indigo, blue, green, yellow, orange, red

7.5   Wavelength is the distance between two corresponding points of a wave (two peaks, for example). Amplitude is the maximum height of a wave. Nodes are points of zero amplitude.

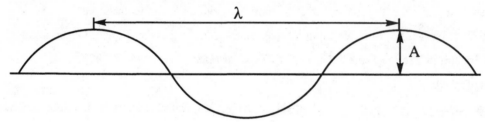

7.6   (a) correct

      (b) incorrect; the intensity of a light beam is independent of frequency and is related to the number of photons of light with a certain energy.

      (c) correct

7.7   A photon is a massless "particle," a packet of energy. To displace a particle such as an electron requires collision with another particle. Since light shining on certain metals causes electrons to be released, light must be composed of "particles," or packets of energy called photons.

7.8   An electron orbiting the nucleus could occupy only certain orbits or energy levels in which it is stable. An electron in an atom will remain in its lowest energy level unless disturbed.

7.9   The Lyman series is found in the ultraviolet region and the Balmer series is in the visible region.

7.10   (c)   Electrons moving from a given level to one of lower n results in the emission of energy, which is observed as light.

7.11   Fixed circular orbits implies that both the exact position and energy of the electron can be known precisely.

7.12   It is impossible to fix both the position of an electron in an atom and its energy with any degree of certainty if the electron is described as a wave. As a result of this viewpoint, modern atomic theory describes regions around an atom's nucleus in which there is the highest probability of finding a given electron.

7.13 ψ^2 (1/volume) is related to the probability of finding the electron within a given region of space.

7.14 n, principle quantum number, describes the size of an orbital, $= 1, 2, 3, \ldots$

ℓ, angular momentum quantum number, describes different orbital subshells and their shapes

$= 0, 1, 2, 3, \ldots, n - 1$

m_ℓ, magnetic quantum number, specifies to which orbital within a subshell the electron is assigned

$= 0, \pm 1, \pm 2, \pm 3, \ldots \pm \ell$

7.15 s 0 nodal surface

p 1 nodal surface

d 2 nodal surfaces

f 3 nodal surfaces

7.16

orbital	maximum number in a given shell
s	1
p	3
d	5
f	7

7.17

ℓ value	orbital type
3	f
0	s
1	p
2	d

7.18   *s* orbital   *p*x orbital

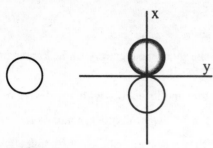

7.19   orbital type   number of orbitals in a given subshell   number of nodal surfaces

s	1	0
p	3	1
d	5	2
f	7	3

7.20   (a) microwaves

(b) red light

(c) infrared light

7.21   (a) red, orange, yellow

(b) blue

(c) blue

7.22   (a) green

(b) $595 \text{ nm} \cdot \dfrac{10^{-9} \text{ m}}{1 \text{ nm}} = 5.95 \times 10^{-7} \text{ m}$ $\nu = \dfrac{c}{\lambda} = \dfrac{2.998 \times 10^{8} \text{ m·s}^{-1}}{5.95 \times 10^{-7} \text{ m}} = 5.04 \times 10^{14} \text{ s}^{-1}$

7.23   (a) $\lambda = \dfrac{c}{\nu} = \dfrac{2.998 \times 10^{8} \text{ m·s}^{-1}}{1150 \times 10^{3} \text{ s}^{-1}} = 261 \text{ m}$ $225 \text{ m} \cdot \dfrac{1 \text{ wavelength}}{261 \text{ m}} = 0.863 \text{ wavelengths}$

(b) $\lambda = \dfrac{c}{\nu} = \dfrac{2.998 \times 10^{8} \text{ m·s}^{-1}}{98.1 \times 10^{6} \text{ s}^{-1}} = 3.06 \text{ m}$ $225 \text{ m} \cdot \dfrac{1 \text{ wavelength}}{3.06 \text{ m}} = 73.6 \text{ wavelengths}$

7.24 $5.0 \times 10^{2} \text{ nm} \cdot \dfrac{10^{-9} \text{ m}}{1 \text{ nm}} = 5.0 \times 10^{-7} \text{ m}$

$E = \dfrac{hc}{\lambda} = \dfrac{(6.626 \times 10^{-34} \text{ J·s})(2.998 \times 10^{8} \text{ m·s}^{-1})}{5.0 \times 10^{-7} \text{ m}} = 4.0 \times 10^{-19} \text{ J/photon}$

$4.0 \times 10^{-19} \text{ J/photon} \cdot \dfrac{6.02 \times 10^{23} \text{ photons}}{1 \text{ mol}} = 2.4 \times 10^{5} \text{ J/mol photons}$

7.25 $410 \text{ nm} \cdot \dfrac{10^{-9} \text{ m}}{1 \text{ nm}} = 4.1 \times 10^{-7} \text{ m}$ $\nu = \dfrac{c}{\lambda} = \dfrac{2.998 \times 10^{8} \text{ m·s}^{-1}}{4.1 \times 10^{-7} \text{ m}} = 7.3 \times 10^{14} \text{ s}^{-1}$

$E = h\nu = (6.626 \times 10^{-34} \text{ J·s})(7.3 \times 10^{14} \text{ s}^{-1}) = 4.8 \times 10^{-19} \text{ J/photon}$

$$4.8 \times 10^{-19} \text{ J/photon} \cdot \frac{6.02 \times 10^{23} \text{ photons}}{1 \text{ mol}} = 2.9 \times 10^5 \text{ J/mol photons}$$

According to the text, red light has an energy of 1.75×10^5 J/mol

$$\frac{2.9 \times 10^5 \text{ J}}{1.75 \times 10^5 \text{ J}} = 1.7 \qquad\qquad \text{Violet light is 1.7 times more energetic than red light.}$$

7.26 $396.15 \text{ nm} \cdot \dfrac{10^{-9} \text{ m}}{1 \text{ nm}} = 3.9615 \times 10^{-7} \text{ m}$

$$\nu = \frac{c}{\lambda} = \frac{2.99792 \times 10^8 \text{ m·s}^{-1}}{3.9615 \times 10^{-7} \text{ m}} = 7.5676 \times 10^{14} \text{ s}^{-1}$$

$$E = h\nu = (6.62607 \times 10^{-34} \text{ J·s})(7.5676 \times 10^{14} \text{ s}^{-1}) = 5.0144 \times 10^{-19} \text{ J/photon}$$

$$5.0144 \times 10^{-19} \text{ J/photon} \cdot \frac{6.02214 \times 10^{23} \text{ photons}}{1.00 \text{ mol}} = 3.02 \times 10^5 \text{ J/mol photons}$$

7.27   285.2 nm is in the ultraviolet region, 383.8 nm is just at the edge of the visible region, and 518.4 nm is in the visible region. The most energetic line has the shortest wavelength, 285.2 nm.

$$285.2 \text{ nm} \cdot \frac{10^{-9} \text{ m}}{1 \text{ nm}} = 2.852 \times 10^{-7} \text{ m}$$

$$E = \frac{hc}{\lambda} = \frac{(6.6261 \times 10^{-34} \text{ J·s})(2.9979 \times 10^8 \text{ m·s}^{-1})}{2.852 \times 10^{-7} \text{ m}} \cdot \frac{6.0221 \times 10^{23} \text{ photons}}{1 \text{ mol}} = 4.194 \times 10^5 \text{ J/mol}$$

7.28   (d) FM radiowaves   (c) microwaves   (a) yellow light   (b) X-rays

—increasing energy per photon→

7.29   (a) radar   (b) microwaves   (d) red light   (e) ultraviolet radiation   (c) γ-rays

—increasing energy per photon→

7.30 $2.0 \times 10^2 \text{ kJ/mol} \cdot \dfrac{1 \text{ mol}}{6.02 \times 10^{23} \text{ photons}} \cdot \dfrac{10^3 \text{ J}}{1 \text{ kJ}} = 3.3 \times 10^{-19} \text{ J/photon}$

$$\lambda = \frac{hc}{E} = \frac{(6.626 \times 10^{-34} \text{ J·s})(2.998 \times 10^8 \text{ m·s}^{-1})}{3.3 \times 10^{-19} \text{ J}} = 6.0 \times 10^{-7} \text{ m (visible region)}$$

7.31 $540 \text{ nm} \cdot \dfrac{10^{-9} \text{ m}}{1 \text{ nm}} = 5.4 \times 10^{-7} \text{ m}$

$$E = \frac{hc}{\lambda} = \frac{(6.626 \times 10^{-34} \text{ J·s})(2.998 \times 10^8 \text{ m·s}^{-1})}{5.4 \times 10^{-7} \text{ m}} = 3.7 \times 10^{-19} \text{ J/photon}$$

This radiation does not have enough energy to activate the switch. This is also true for radiation with wavelengths greater than 540 nm.

7.32   (a)   The most energetic line has the shortest wavelength, 253.652 nm.

(b) $253.652 \text{ nm} \cdot \dfrac{10^{-9} \text{ m}}{1 \text{ nm}} = 2.53652 \times 10^{-7} \text{ m}$

$\nu = \dfrac{c}{\lambda} = \dfrac{2.997925 \times 10^8 \text{ m·s}^{-1}}{2.53652 \times 10^{-7} \text{ m}} = 1.18190 \times 10^{15} \text{ s}^{-1}$

$E = h\nu = (6.626069 \times 10^{-34} \text{ J·s})(1.18190 \times 10^{15} \text{ s}^{-1}) = 7.83135 \times 10^{-19}$ J/photon

(c)   The 404.656 nm line is violet, while the 435.833 nm line is blue.

7.33   (a)   The infrared region

(b)   None of the lines mentioned are in the spectrum shown in Figure 7.9. None of the lines listed are in the visible region.

(c)   The most energetic line has the shortest wavelength, 837.761 nm.

(d) $865.438 \text{ nm} \cdot \dfrac{10^{-9} \text{ m}}{1 \text{ nm}} = 8.65438 \times 10^{-7} \text{ m}$

$\nu = \dfrac{c}{\lambda} = \dfrac{2.997925 \times 10^8 \text{ m·s}^{-1}}{8.65438 \times 10^{-7} \text{ m}} = 3.46406 \times 10^{14} \text{ s}^{-1}$

$E = h\nu = (6.626069 \times 10^{-34} \text{ J·s})(3.46406 \times 10^{14} \text{ s}^{-1}) = 2.29531 \times 10^{-19}$ J/photon

7.34   Violet; $n_{initial} = 6$ and $n_{final} = 2$

7.35 $\lambda = 91.2 \text{ nm } (9.12 \times 10^{-8} \text{ m})$ $\nu = \dfrac{c}{\lambda} = \dfrac{2.998 \times 10^8 \text{ m·s}^{-1}}{9.12 \times 10^{-8} \text{ m}} = 3.29 \times 10^{15} \text{ s}^{-1}$

$n_{initial} = \infty$ and $n_{final} = 1$

7.36   (a) $n = 3$ to $n = 2$

(b) $n = 4$ to $n = 1$ The energy levels are progressively closer at higher levels, so the energy difference from $n = 4$ to $n = 1$ is greater than from $n = 5$ to $n = 2$.

7.37   (a) $n = 2$ to $n = 4$ and (d) $n = 3$ to $n = 5$

7.38   (a)   From $n = 4$ to $n = 3, 2,$ or 1   = 3 lines

From $n = 3$ to $n = 2$ or 1   = 2 lines

From $n = 2$ to $n = 1$ = 1 line

Total   = 6 lines possible

(b)   Lowest energy $n = 4$ to $n = 3$

(c)   Shortest wavelength (highest energy) $n = 4$ to $n = 1$

7.39   (a)   From $n = 5$ to $n = 4, 3, 2,$ or 1 = 4 lines

       From $n = 4$ to $n = 3, 2,$ or 1 = 3 lines

       From $n = 3$ to $n = 2$ or 1 = 2 lines

       From $n = 2$ to $n = 1$ = 1 line

       Total   = 10 lines possible

       (b)   Highest frequency (highest energy) $n = 5$ to $n = 1$

       (c)   Longest wavelength (lowest energy) $n = 5$ to $n = 4$

7.40 $\Delta E = -Rhc\left(\dfrac{1}{n_{final}^2} - \dfrac{1}{n_{initial}^2}\right) = -1312 \text{ kJ/mol}\left(\dfrac{1}{1^2} - \dfrac{1}{3^2}\right) = -1166 \text{ kJ/mol}$

       $1166 \text{ kJ/mol} \cdot \dfrac{1 \text{ mol}}{6.0221 \times 10^{23} \text{ photons}} \cdot \dfrac{10^3 \text{ J}}{1 \text{ kJ}} = 1.936 \times 10^{-18} \text{ J/photon}$

       $\nu = \dfrac{E}{h} = \dfrac{1.936 \times 10^{-18} \text{ J}}{6.6261 \times 10^{-34} \text{ J·s}} = 2.922 \times 10^{15} \text{ s}^{-1}$

       $\lambda = \dfrac{c}{\nu} = \dfrac{2.9979 \times 10^8 \text{ m·s}^{-1}}{2.922 \times 10^{15} \text{ s}^{-1}} = 1.026 \times 10^{-7} \text{ m (ultraviolet region)}$

7.41 $\Delta E = -Rhc\left(\dfrac{1}{n_{final}^2} - \dfrac{1}{n_{initial}^2}\right) = -1312 \text{ kJ/mol}\left(\dfrac{1}{3^2} - \dfrac{1}{4^2}\right) = -63.78 \text{ kJ/mol}$

       $63.78 \text{ kJ/mol} \cdot \dfrac{1 \text{ mol}}{6.0221 \times 10^{23} \text{ photons}} \cdot \dfrac{10^3 \text{ J}}{1 \text{ kJ}} = 1.059 \times 10^{-19} \text{ J/photon}$

       $\nu = \dfrac{E}{h} = \dfrac{1.059 \times 10^{-19} \text{ J}}{6.6261 \times 10^{-34} \text{ J·s}} = 1.598 \times 10^{14} \text{ s}^{-1}$

       $\lambda = \dfrac{c}{\nu} = \dfrac{2.9979 \times 10^8 \text{ m·s}^{-1}}{1.598 \times 10^{14} \text{ s}^{-1}} = 1.876 \times 10^{-6} \text{ m (infrared region)}$

7.42 $\dfrac{2.5 \times 10^8 \text{ cm}}{1 \text{ s}} \cdot \dfrac{1 \text{ m}}{10^2 \text{ cm}} = 2.5 \times 10^6 \text{ m/s}$

       $\lambda = \dfrac{h}{mv} = \dfrac{6.626 \times 10^{-34} \text{ J·s}}{(9.109 \times 10^{-31} \text{ kg})(2.5 \times 10^6 \text{ m/s})} = 2.9 \times 10^{-10} \text{ m}$

7.43 $\lambda = \dfrac{h}{mv} = \dfrac{6.626 \times 10^{-34} \text{ J·s}}{(9.11 \times 10^{-31} \text{ kg})(1.3 \times 10^8 \text{ m·s}^{-1})} = 5.6 \times 10^{-12} \text{ m}$

7.44 $1.0 \times 10^2 \text{ g} \cdot \dfrac{1 \text{ kg}}{10^3 \text{ g}} = 0.10 \text{ kg}$ $\lambda = \dfrac{h}{mv} = \dfrac{6.626 \times 10^{-34} \text{ J·s}}{(0.10 \text{ kg})(30 \text{ m·s}^{-1})} = 2.2 \times 10^{-34} \text{ m}$

       $5.6 \times 10^{-3} \text{ nm} \cdot \dfrac{1 \text{ m}}{10^9 \text{ nm}} = 5.6 \times 10^{-12} \text{ m}$

       $v = \dfrac{h}{m\lambda} = \dfrac{6.626 \times 10^{-34} \text{ J·s}}{(0.10 \text{ kg})(5.6 \times 10^{-12} \text{ m})} = 1.2 \times 10^{-21} \text{ m·s}^{-1}$

7.45 $$\frac{7.00 \times 10^2 \text{ mile}}{1 \text{ hour}} \cdot \frac{1 \text{ km}}{0.6214 \text{ mile}} \cdot \frac{10^3 \text{ m}}{1 \text{ km}} \cdot \frac{1 \text{ hour}}{3600 \text{ s}} = 313 \text{ m·s}^{-1}$$

$$\lambda = \frac{h}{mv} = \frac{6.626 \times 10^{-34} \text{ J·s}}{(1.50 \times 10^{-3} \text{ kg})(313 \text{ m·s}^{-1})} = 1.41 \times 10^{-33} \text{ m}$$

7.46   (a) ℓ can be 0, 1, 2, 3

(b) m_ℓ can be 0, ±1, ±2

(c) $n = 4$, $\ell = 0$, $m_\ell = 0$

(d) $n = 4$, $\ell = 3$, $m_\ell = 0$, ±1, ±2, ±3

7.47   (a) The orbital type is d. It is a $4d$ orbital.

(b) When $n = 5$, $\ell = 0, 1, 2, 3,$ and 4

$\ell = 0$	1 s orbital
$\ell = 1$	3 p orbitals
$\ell = 2$	5 d orbitals
$\ell = 3$	7 f orbitals
$\ell = 4$	9 g orbitals

There are a total of 5^2 or 25 orbitals in the $n = 5$ electron shell.

(c) In an f subshell there are 7 orbitals. $m_\ell = 0$, ±1, ±2, and ±3

7.48

n	ℓ	m_ℓ
4	1	−1
4	1	0
4	1	1

7.49

n	ℓ	m_ℓ
5	2	−2
5	2	−1
5	2	0
5	2	1
5	2	2

7.50   When $n = 4$, there are four subshells, $4s$, $4p$, $4d$, and $4f$

7.51   When $n = 5$, there are five subshells, $5s$, $5p$, $5d$, $5f$, and $5g$

7.52   (a) When $n = 2$, the maximum value of ℓ is 1

(b) When $\ell = 0$, m_ℓ can only have a value of 0

(c) When $\ell = 0$, m_ℓ can only have a value of 0

7.53   (a) incorrect; when $n = 3$, the maximum value of ℓ is 2

         (d) incorrect; when $\ell = 3$, m_ℓ can only have values of 0, ±1, ±2, or ±3

7.54   (a) none; when $\ell = 0$, m_ℓ can only have a value of 0

         (b) 3 orbitals

         (c) 11 orbitals

         (d) 1 orbital

7.55   (a) 7 orbitals

         (b) None; ℓ cannot have a value equal to n

         (c) 25 orbitals

         (d) 1 orbital

7.56 $2d$ and $3f$ cannot exist. They do not follow the $\ell = 0, 1, 2, ..., n - 1$ rule

7.57 $2f$ and $1p$ are incorrect designations. They do not follow the $\ell = 0, 1, 2, ..., n - 1$ rule

7.58

	n	ℓ	m_ℓ
(a) $2p$	2	1	−1
	2	1	0
	2	1	1
(b) $3d$	3	2	−2
	3	2	−1
	3	2	0
	3	2	1
	3	2	2
(c) $4f$	4	3	−3
	4	3	−2
	4	3	−1
	4	3	0
	4	3	1
	4	3	2
	4	3	3

7.59

	n	ℓ	m_ℓ
(a) 5f	5	3	−3
	5	3	−2
	5	3	−1
	5	3	0
	5	3	1
	5	3	2
	5	3	3
(b) 4d	4	2	−2
	4	2	−1
	4	2	0
	4	2	1
	4	2	2
(c) 2s	2	0	0

7.60   (d) 4d

7.61   (d) s orbital

7.62   The value of ℓ indicates the number of nodal surfaces

(a) 2s: $\ell = 0$, zero nodal surfaces

(b) 5d: $\ell = 2$, two nodal surfaces

(c) 5f: $\ell = 3$, three nodal surfaces

7.63   The value of ℓ indicates the number of nodal surfaces

(a) 4f: $\ell = 3$, three nodal surfaces

(b) 2p: $\ell = 1$, one nodal surface

(c) 6s: $\ell = 0$, zero nodal surfaces

7.64 2.093×10^{-18} J

7.65 $\Delta E = -Rhc\left(\dfrac{1}{n_{final}^2} - \dfrac{1}{n_{initial}^2}\right) = -1312 \text{ kJ/mol}\left(\dfrac{1}{5^2} - \dfrac{1}{6^2}\right) = -16.04 \text{ kJ/mol}$

$16.04 \text{ kJ/mol} \cdot \dfrac{1 \text{ mol}}{6.0221 \times 10^{23} \text{ photons}} \cdot \dfrac{10^3 \text{ J}}{1 \text{ kJ}} = 2.663 \times 10^{-20} \text{ J/photon}$

$\nu = \dfrac{E}{h} = \dfrac{2.663 \times 10^{-20} \text{ J}}{6.6261 \times 10^{-34} \text{ J·s}} = 4.019 \times 10^{13} \text{ s}^{-1}$

$\lambda = \dfrac{c}{\nu} = \dfrac{2.9979 \times 10^8 \text{ m·s}^{-1}}{4.019 \times 10^{13} \text{ s}^{-1}} = 7.460 \times 10^{-6} \text{ m}$

7.66   (a) green light

      (b) Shorter wavelength corresponds to higher energy. Green light has a wavelength of 500 nm and red light has a wavelength of 680 nm.

      (c) green light

7.67 $375 \text{ nm} \cdot \dfrac{10^{-9} \text{ m}}{1 \text{ nm}} = 3.75 \times 10^{-7} \text{ m}$

$$E = \frac{hc}{\lambda} = \frac{(6.626 \times 10^{-34} \text{ J·s})(2.998 \times 10^{8} \text{ m·s}^{-1})}{3.75 \times 10^{-7} \text{ m}} \cdot \frac{6.022 \times 10^{23} \text{ photons}}{1.00 \text{ mol}} \cdot \frac{1 \text{ kJ}}{10^{3} \text{ J}} = 319 \text{ kJ/mol}$$

7.68   (a) $\lambda = \dfrac{c}{\nu} = \dfrac{2.998 \times 10^{8} \text{ m·s}^{-1}}{850 \times 10^{6} \text{ s}^{-1}} = 0.35 \text{ m}$

      (b) $E = h\nu = (6.626 \times 10^{-34} \text{ J·s})(850 \times 10^{6} \text{ s}^{-1}) \cdot \dfrac{6.02 \times 10^{23} \text{ photons}}{1.0 \text{ mol}} = 0.34 \text{ J/mol}$

      (c) $E = \dfrac{hc}{\lambda} = \dfrac{(6.626 \times 10^{-34} \text{ J·s})(2.998 \times 10^{8} \text{ m·s}^{-1})}{4.2 \times 10^{-7} \text{ m}} \cdot \dfrac{6.02 \times 10^{23} \text{ photons}}{1.0 \text{ mol}} = 2.8 \times 10^{5} \text{ J/mol}$

      $\dfrac{2.8 \times 10^{5} \text{ J/mol}}{0.34 \text{ J/mol}} = 84{,}000$

      (d) Blue light is 84,000 times more energetic than the radiation sent from cell phones.

7.69 $E = \dfrac{hc}{\lambda} = \dfrac{(6.626 \times 10^{-34} \text{ J·s})(2.998 \times 10^{8} \text{ m·s}^{-1})}{4.7 \times 10^{-7} \text{ m}} = 4.2 \times 10^{-19} \text{ J/photon}$

      $\dfrac{2.50 \times 10^{-14} \text{ J}}{4.2 \times 10^{-19} \text{ J/photon}} = 5.9 \times 10^{4} \text{ photons}$

7.70 $\Delta E = -Z^{2} Rhc \left(\dfrac{1}{n_{\text{final}}^{2}} - \dfrac{1}{n_{\text{initial}}^{2}} \right) = -(2^{2})(1312 \text{ kJ/mol}) \left(\dfrac{1}{\infty^{2}} - \dfrac{1}{1^{2}} \right) = 5248 \text{ kJ/mol}$

7.71   The shortest wavelength would be the transition from $n = \infty$ to $n = 1$, a wavelength of 91.2 nm (see Figure 7.12).

7.72   (i)   (b) $n = 7$ to $n = 6$

      (ii) (a) $n = 7$ to $n = 1$

      (iii) (a) $n = 7$ to $n = 1$

7.73 $1s, 2s, 2p, 3s, 3p, 3d, 4s$

7.74   (a) 3   (d) 5   (g) 25

      (b) 3   (e) 5   (h) 1

      (c) 1   (f) 7

7.75   Bohr's circular orbit model contradicts the laws of classical physics, and Bohr had to artificially introduce the concept of quantization to explain how these electron orbits could be stable.

7.76   In Bohr's model, at any given instant we would know the precise distance of the electron from the nucleus, as well as its energy. However, according to the uncertainty principle, because we know the energy of the electron with great certainty, we would be very uncertain about its location or distance from the nucleus. So Bohr's concept of fixed orbits violates the uncertainty principle.

7.77   The electron behaves simultaneously as a wave and a particle. The modern view of atomic structure is based on the wave properties of the electron, and describes regions around an atom's nucleus in which there is the highest probability of finding a given electron.

7.78   (b), (e) – (j)

7.79   (a) and (b)

7.80 $N = 1, L = 1, M = -1, 0, +1$ 3 orbitals

$N = 2, L = 2, M = -1, 0, +1$ 3 orbitals

$N = 3, L = 3, M = -1, 0, +1$ 3 orbitals

A total of 9 orbitals in the first three electron shells

7.81   The electron density for a $1s$ orbital of the H atom is not zero at 0.40 nm from the nucleus. While the electron density decreases significantly at greater and greater distances from the nucleus, there is still a finite probability of the electron being there. The only true probability of the electron density being zero would be at a node, but the $1s$ orbital has no nodes.

7.82 $$1.173 \times 10^6 \text{ eV} \cdot \frac{9.6485 \times 10^4 \text{ J/mol}}{1 \text{ eV}} \cdot \frac{1 \text{ mol}}{6.0221 \times 10^{23} \text{ photons}} = 1.879 \times 10^{-13} \text{ J/photon}$$

$$v = \frac{E}{h} = \frac{1.879 \times 10^{-13} \text{ J}}{6.6261 \times 10^{-34} \text{ J·s}} = 2.836 \times 10^{20} \text{ s}^{-1}$$

$$\lambda = \frac{c}{v} = \frac{2.9979 \times 10^8 \text{ m·s}^{-1}}{2.836 \times 10^{20} \text{ s}^{-1}} = 1.057 \times 10^{-12} \text{ m}$$

7.83 $q_{eye} = 11 \text{ g} \cdot 4.0 \text{ J/g·K} \cdot (3.0 \text{ K}) = 130 \text{ J}$

$$E = \frac{hc}{\lambda} = \frac{(6.626 \times 10^{-34} \text{ J·s})(2.998 \times 10^8 \text{ m·s}^{-1})}{0.12 \text{ m}} = 1.7 \times 10^{-24} \text{ J/photon}$$

$$\frac{130 \text{ J}}{1.7 \times 10^{-24} \text{ J/photon}} = 8.0 \times 10^{25} \text{ photons}$$

7.84 $$7.8 \times 10^7 \text{ km} \cdot \frac{10^3 \text{ m}}{1 \text{ km}} \cdot \frac{1 \text{ s}}{2.998 \times 10^8 \text{ m}} = 260 \text{ seconds (4.3 minutes)}$$

7.85   (a) The most energetic line has the shortest wavelength, 357.9 nm

(b) blue-indigo

7.86   (a) size and energy

       (b) ℓ

       (c) more

       (d) 7

       (e) 1

       (f) d, s, p

       (g) 0, 1, 2, 3, 4

       (h) 16

7.87   (a) size and energy; shape

       (b) 0, 1, 2

       (c) f

       (d) 4; 2; −2

       (e)

letter	p	d
ℓ value	1	2
nodal planes	1	2

       (f) f

       (g) $2d, 3f$

       (h) $n = 2$, $\ell = 1$, $m_\ell = 2$ is not valid

       (i) (i)   3

           (ii) 9

           (iii) none

           (iv) 1

7.88   (a) Group VII B, period 5

       (b) $n = 5$, $\ell = 0$, $m_\ell = 0$

       (c) $0.141 \times 10^6 \text{ eV} \cdot \dfrac{9.6485 \times 10^4 \text{ J/mol}}{1 \text{ eV}} \cdot \dfrac{1 \text{ mol}}{6.0221 \times 10^{23} \text{ photons}} = 2.26 \times 10^{-14} \text{ J/photon}$

$$\nu = \frac{E}{h} = \frac{2.26 \times 10^{-14} \text{ J}}{6.626 \times 10^{-34} \text{ J·s}} = 3.41 \times 10^{19} \text{ s}^{-1}$$

$$\lambda = \frac{c}{\nu} = \frac{2.998 \times 10^8 \text{ m·s}^{-1}}{3.41 \times 10^{19} \text{ s}^{-1}} = 8.79 \times 10^{-12} \text{ m}$$

       (d) (i) $HTcO_4(aq) + NaOH(aq) \rightarrow NaTcO_4(aq) + H_2O(\ell)$

           (ii) $4.5 \times 10^{-3} \text{ g} \cdot \dfrac{1 \text{ mol Tc}}{97.9 \text{ g}} \cdot \dfrac{1 \text{ mol NaTcO}_4}{1 \text{ mol Tc}} \cdot \dfrac{185 \text{ g}}{1 \text{ mol NaTcO}_4} = 8.5 \times 10^{-3} \text{ g NaTcO}_4$

$$4.5 \times 10^{-3} \text{ g} \cdot \frac{1 \text{ mol Tc}}{97.9 \text{ g}} \cdot \frac{1 \text{ mol HTcO}_4}{1 \text{ mol Tc}} \cdot \frac{1 \text{ mol NaOH}}{1 \text{ mol HTcO}_4} \cdot \frac{40.0 \text{ g}}{1 \text{ mol NaOH}} = 1.8 \times 10^{-3} \text{ g NaOH}$$

7.89   The light is emitted from atoms or ions in excited states as they decay from an excited electronic state to a lower energy state. In the "neon" light, the electric current provides the energy needed to excite the gaseous atoms. In the flame, the ions in the salt are excited by the thermal energy of the flame.

7.90   The pickle glows since the materials in the pickle are being excited by the addition of the energy (electric current). Since the pickle has been soaked in brine (NaCl), the electrons in the sodium atom are excited and release energy as they return to lower energy states, providing yellow light. The same kind of light is visible in many street lamps.

Chapter 8
Atomic Electron Configurations and Chemical Periodicity

INSTRUCTOR'S NOTES

As noted in the previous chapter, about 9 lectures are devoted to the material in Chapters 7 and 8.

Tables of ionization energy values and electron affinity values have been moved to Appendix F. The definition of electron affinity in this edition is the energy involved when an atom in the gas phase aquires an electron (the ionization energy of a neutral atom). Therefore, the electron affinity for F is –328 kJ/mol, for example. In class, we emphasize that the affinity for an electron increases (becomes more negative) moving across a period.

SUGGESTED DEMONSTRATIONS

1.   Paramagnetism of Oxygen

- Shakhashiri, B. Z. "Preparation and Properties of Liquid Oxygen," *Chemical Demonstrations: A Handbook for Teachers of Chemistry*; University of Wisconsin Press, 1985; Vol. 2, pp. 147-152.

- Shimada, H.; Yasuoda, T.; Mitsuzawa, S. "Observation of the Paramagnetic Property of Oxygen by Simple Method," *Journal of Chemical Education* **1990**, *67*, 63.

- See the *General Chemistry Interactive CD-ROM* for a demonstration of paramagnetic liquid oxygen.

2.   Periodic Properties of the Elements

- The *Periodic Table Videodisc* and the *Periodic Table Live!* CD-ROM from *JCE: Software* are most valuable with this chapter. See the information in the Preface to this *Manual* and the following article: Kotz, J. *Journal of Chemical Education* **1989**, *66*, 750. The *Periodic Table Videodisc* and the *Periodic Table Live!* CD-ROM can be used to illustrate periodic trends in reactions. The videodisc is an image data base that contains images of the elements reacting with air, water, acids, and a base. In addition, it has information on the uses of the elements. We use it, for example, to illustrate the trend in reactivity of the alkali and alkaline earth metals with air and water. In addition, we carry out the reactions of some of the alkali and alkaline earth metals with water in petri dishes on the overhead projector.

Solutions to Study Questions

8.1 n, principle quantum number, describes the size of an orbital, = 1, 2, 3, ...

       ℓ, angular momentum quantum number, describes different orbital subshells and their shapes,

           = 0, 1, 2, 3, ... $n - 1$

       m_ℓ, magnetic quantum number, specifies to which orbital within a subshell the electron is

           assigned, = 0, ±1, ±2, ±3, ... ±ℓ

       m_s, electron spin quantum number, specifies electron spin orientation, ±$\frac{1}{2}$

8.2   No two electrons in an atom can have the same set of four quantum numbers.

8.3   Li $1s^2 2s^1$

          1s   2s

8.4   The most stable arrangement of electrons is that with the maximum number of unpaired electrons, all with the same spin direction.

       Carbon has the configuration   not

                         1s   2s   2p   1s   2s   2p

8.5   Noble gas notation is using a noble gas symbol in brackets to represent completed electron shells.

       Li [He]

                  2s

8.6   Boron, B, is in Group 3A. The group designation tells you that there are three electrons in the outer shell of boron.

8.7   Manganese, Mn, is in Group 7B. The group designation indicates that there are seven electrons in the outer shell of manganese.

8.8   The element in the fourth period in Group 4A is germanium, Ge. The location indicates that (a) the outermost electrons are in the fourth shell, with a total of 4 electrons in the outer shell.

8.9   Atomic size decreases when proceeding across a period and increases down a group. Ionization energy and electron affinity both increase when proceeding across a period and decrease down a group.

8.10   P $1s^2 2s^2 2p^6 3s^2 3p^3$

                   1s   2s   2p   3s   3p

       Phosphorus is in Group 5A and has five electrons in its outer shell.

Cl $1s^2 2s^2 2p^6 3s^2 3p^5$

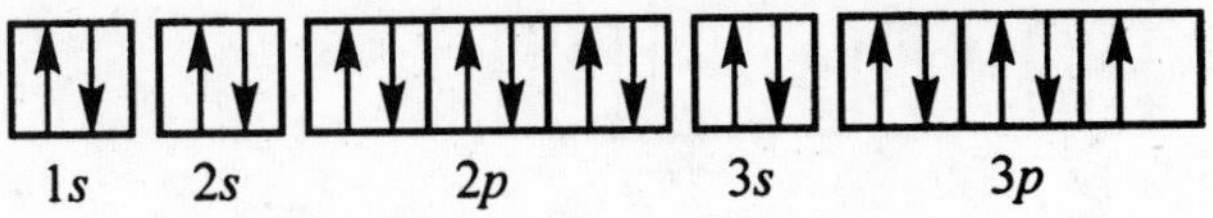

Chlorine is in Group 7A and has seven electrons in its outer shell.

8.11 Mg $1s^2 2s^2 2p^6 3s^2$

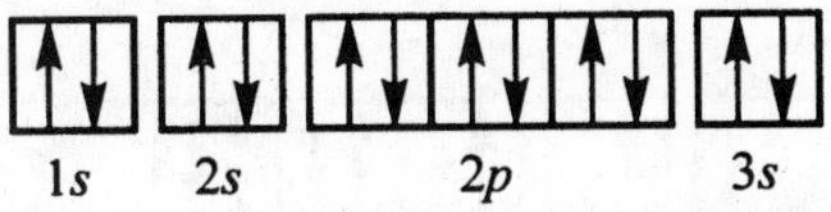

Magnesium is in group 2A and has two electrons in its outer shell.

Ar $1s^2 2s^2 2p^6 3s^2 3p^6$

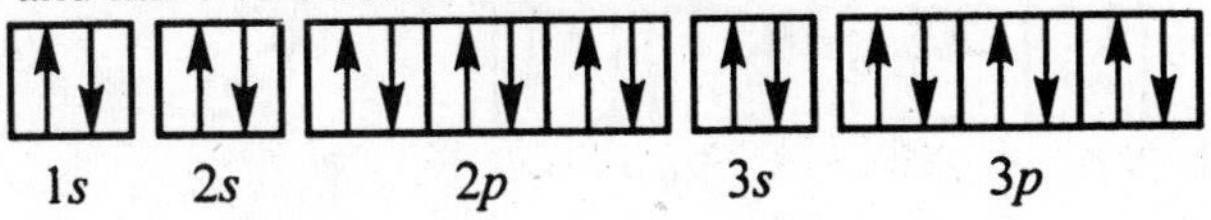

Argon is in group 8A and has eight electrons in its outer shell.

8.12 Cr $1s^2 2s^2 2p^6 3s^2 3p^6 3d^5 4s^1$

Fe $1s^2 2s^2 2p^6 3s^2 3p^6 3d^6 4s^2$

8.13 V $1s^2 2s^2 2p^6 3s^2 3p^6 3d^3 4s^2$

8.14 (a) As $[Ar]3d^{10}4s^2 4p^3$

(b) Kr $[Ar]3d^{10}4s^2 4p^6$

8.15 (a) Sr $[Kr]5s^2$

(b) Zr $[Kr]4d^2 5s^2$

(c) Rh $[Kr]4d^7 5s^2$ (actual configuration $[Kr]4d^8 5s^1$)

(d) Sn $[Kr]4d^{10}5s^2 5p^2$

8.16 (a) Ta $[Xe]4f^{14}5d^3 6s^2$

(b) Pt $[Xe]4f^{14}5d^8 6s^2$ (actual configuration $[Xe]4f^{14}5d^9 6s^1$)

8.17 (a) Sm $[Xe]4f^5 5d^1 6s^2$ (actual configuration $[Xe]4f^6 6s^2$)

(b) Yb $[Xe]4f^{13}5d^1 6s^2$ (actual configuration $[Xe]4f^{14}6s^2$)

8.18 Am $[Rn]5f^7 7s^2$

8.19 (a) Pu $[Rn]5f^5 6d^1 7s^2$ (actual configuration $[Rn]5f^6 7s^2$)

(b) Cm $[Rn]5f^7 6d^1 7s^2$

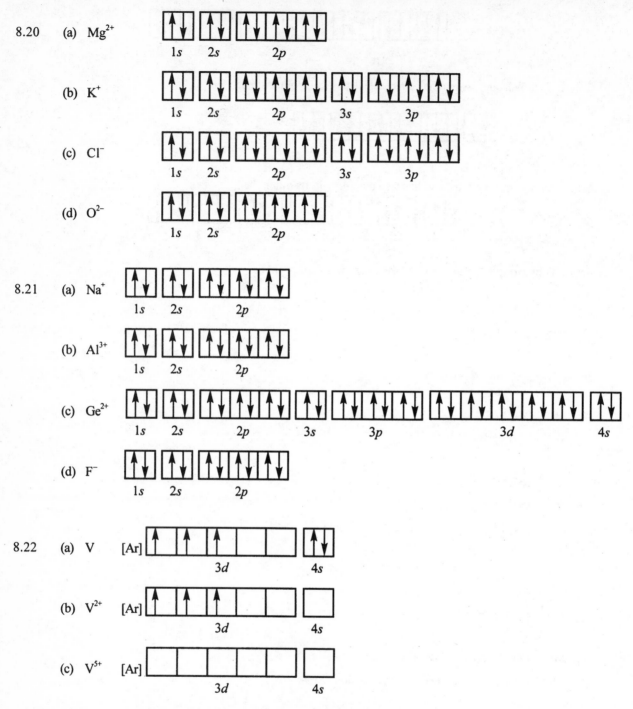

8.20 (a) Mg²⁺
      (b) K⁺
      (c) Cl⁻
      (d) O²⁻

8.21 (a) Na⁺
      (b) Al³⁺
      (c) Ge²⁺
      (d) F⁻

8.22 (a) V   [Ar]
      (b) V²⁺ [Ar]
      (c) V⁵⁺ [Ar]

The V²⁺ ion is paramagnetic with three unpaired electrons

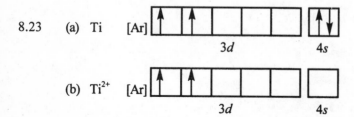

8.23 (a) Ti   [Ar]
      (b) Ti²⁺ [Ar]

(c) Ti^{4+} [Ar]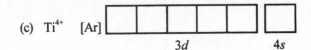
3d   4s

The Ti^{2+} ion is paramagnetic with two unpaired electrons.

8.24   (a) Mn   [Ar]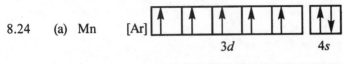
3d   4s

(b) Mn^{2+} [Ar]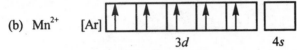
3d   4s

(c) Yes, the +2 ion is paramagnetic.

(d) The ion has five unpaired electrons.

8.25   Cu$^+$ [Ar] ↑↓ ↑↓ ↑↓ ↑↓ ↑↓ [ ]   Not paramagnetic
3d   4s

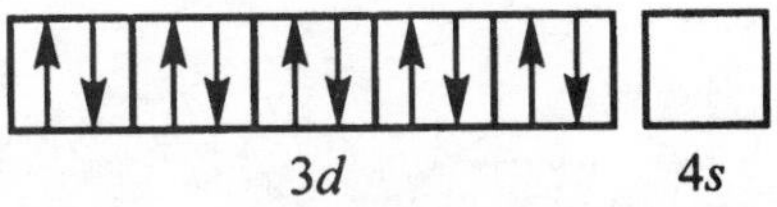

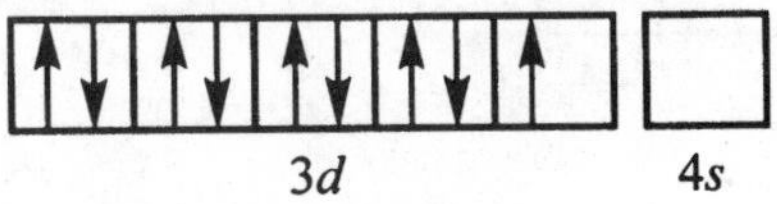

Cu^{2+} [Ar] ↑↓ ↑↓ ↑↓ ↑↓ ↑ [ ]   Paramagnetic
3d   4s

8.26   (a) m_s can only have values of $\pm^1/_2$ $m_s = +^1/_2$

(b) when $\ell = 1$, m_ℓ can only have values of 0, ± 1 $m_\ell = 0$

(c) the maximum value of ℓ is $(n - 1)$ $\ell = 2$

8.27   (a) the maximum value of ℓ is $(n - 1)$ $\ell = 1$

(b) m_s can only have values of $\pm^1/_2$ $m_s = +^1/_2$

(c) when $\ell = 1$, m_ℓ can only have values of 0, ± 1 $m_\ell = 0$

8.28   (a) 14 electrons

(b) 2 electrons

(c) none; the maximum value of ℓ is $(n - 1)$

8.29   (a) 18 electrons

(b) 10 electrons

(c) 1 electron

(d) none; when $\ell = 0$, m_ℓ can only have a value of 0

8.30   Mg   [Ne] ⊞ ↑↓
                     3s

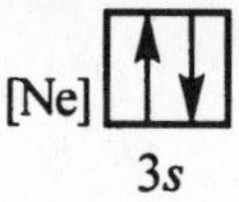

$n = 3$, $\ell = 0$, $m_\ell = 0$, $m_s = +\frac{1}{2}$
$n = 3$, $\ell = 0$, $m_\ell = 0$, $m_s = -\frac{1}{2}$

8.31   P   [Ne] ↑↓ | ↑ | ↑ | ↑
                     3s   3p

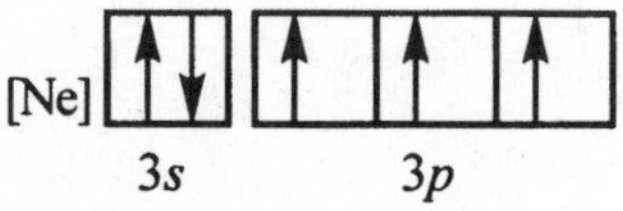

$n = 3$, $\ell = 0$, $m_\ell = 0$, $m_s = +\frac{1}{2}$
$n = 3$, $\ell = 0$, $m_\ell = 0$, $m_s = -\frac{1}{2}$
$n = 3$, $\ell = 1$, $m_\ell = -1$, $m_s = +\frac{1}{2}$
$n = 3$, $\ell = 1$, $m_\ell = 0$, $m_s = +\frac{1}{2}$
$n = 3$, $\ell = 1$, $m_\ell = +1$, $m_s = +\frac{1}{2}$

8.32   Ga   [Ar]
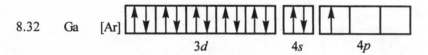
            3d   4s   4p

$n = 4$, $\ell = 1$, $m_\ell = 0$, $m_s = +\frac{1}{2}$

8.33   ↑ | ↑ | | | | ↑↓
            3d   4s

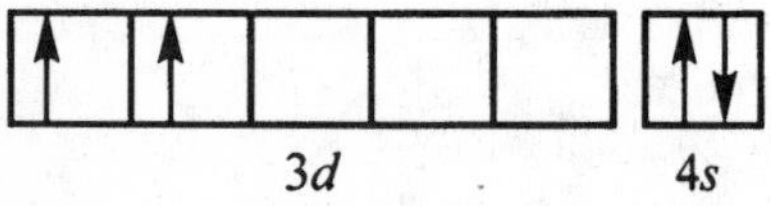

$n = 3$, $\ell = 2$, $m_\ell = 2$, $m_s = +\frac{1}{2}$
$n = 3$, $\ell = 2$, $m_\ell = 1$, $m_s = +\frac{1}{2}$
$n = 4$, $\ell = 0$, $m_\ell = 0$, $m_s = +\frac{1}{2}$
$n = 4$, $\ell = 0$, $m_\ell = 0$, $m_s = -\frac{1}{2}$

8.34   C < B < Al < Na < K

8.35   P < Ge < Ca < Sr < Rb

8.36   (a) $Cl^- > Cl$ (b) Al > O   (c) In > I

8.37   (a) Cs > Rb   (b) $O^{2-} > O$ (c) As > Br

8.38   (c) Li < Si < C < Ne

8.39   K < Li < C < N

8.40   (a) Na   (b) O   (c) Na < Mg < P < O

8.41   (a) Al   (b) Al

       (c) C (based on periodic trends) Si (according to experimental data)

       (d) Al < B < C

8.42   (a) S < O < F   The trend is to increase to the right and decrease down the periodic table.

       (b) O   The trend is to decrease down the periodic table.

       (c) Cl   The trend is to be more negative to the right and less negative down the periodic

             table

       (d) O^{2-} Ions are larger than neutral atoms. O^{2-} and F^- are isoelectronic, but the O^{2-} ion

             has only 8 protons in its nucleus to attract the 10 electrons whereas the F^- ion

             has 9.

8.43   (a) F < O < S   The trend is to increase to the left and down the periodic table.

       (b) Based on a knowledge of first-order periodic trends, we would predict that S should have the largest

             IE of the group P, Si, S, and Se. However, recall that the O atom IE is smaller than that of N, so it is

             not surprising that the same effect carries over into the third period. That is, the order of ionization

             energies is Si < Se < S < P.

       (c) $F^- < O^{2-} < N^{3-}$ These ions are isoelectronic and size increases as the number of protons in the

             nucleus available to attract the electrons decreases.

       (d) Cs < Ba < Sr   The trend is to increase to the right and decrease down the periodic table.

8.44   Rf $[Rn]5f^{14}6d^27s^2$

8.45   U   [Rn]

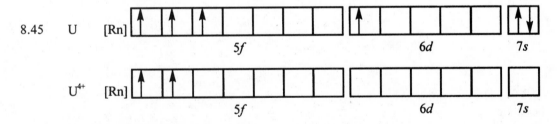

       U^{4+} [Rn]

       Both uranium and the uranium(IV) ion are paramagnetic.

8.46   (a) Ce   [Xe]

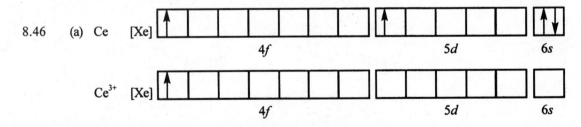

       Ce^{3+} [Xe]

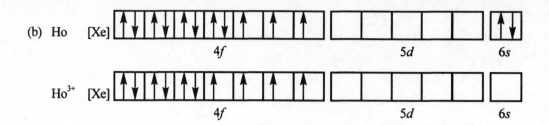

(b) Ho   [Xe]   4f   5d   6s

Ho^{3+} [Xe]   4f   5d   6s

8.47   (a)   atomic number = (2 + 8 + 8 + 2) = 20

      (b)   total number of s electrons = (2 + 2 + 2 + 2) = 8

      (c)   total number of p electrons = (6 + 6) = 12

      (d)   total number of d electrons = 0

      (e)   The element is Ca, calcium, a metal

8.48   Element 109, Mt [Rn]$5f^{14}6d^{7}7s^{2}$ Co, Rh, Ir

8.49   (b)   the maximum value of ℓ is $(n - 1)$

8.50 $n = 4, \ell = 1, m_\ell = -1, m_s = +\frac{1}{2}$

      $n = 4, \ell = 1, m_\ell = -1, m_s = -\frac{1}{2}$

      $n = 4, \ell = 1, m_\ell = 0, m_s = +\frac{1}{2}$

      $n = 4, \ell = 1, m_\ell = 0, m_s = -\frac{1}{2}$

      $n = 4, \ell = 1, m_\ell = +1, m_s = +\frac{1}{2}$

      $n = 4, \ell = 1, m_\ell = +1, m_s = -\frac{1}{2}$

8.51   (a)   4

      (b)   3

8.52   (a)   P, phosphorus

      (b)   Be, beryllium

      (c)   N, nitrogen

      (d)   Tc, technetium

      (e)   Cl, chlorine

      (f)   Zn, zinc

8.53   K < Ca < Si < As

8.54 $Cl^- < Cl < Ca^{2+}$

Ca^{2+} and Cl^- are isoelectronic. Ca^{2+} has a larger IE than Cl^- because the calcium ion has a 2+ charge and removing another electron from that ion would take more energy. Removing an electron from the chloride ion would require less energy than the removal of an electron from the Cl atom due to electron repulsion forces.

8.55   (a) metal

(b) B

(c) B

(d) A

8.56   (a) alkaline earth metal

(b) nonmetal (halogen)

(c) B

(d) B

8.57 In^{4+} Indium has three outer shell electrons, so it is unlikely to form a 4+ ion

Fe^{6+} Ions with charges greater than +3 or +4 are unlikely to form

Sn^{5+} Tin has four outer shell electrons, so it is unlikely to form a 5+ ion

8.58 $S^{2-} > Cl^- > K^+ > Ca^{2+}$

8.59   (a) Se

(b) Br^-

(c) Na

(d) N

(e) N^{3-}

8.60   (a) $Ca^{2+} < K^+ < Cl^-$

(b) $Cl^- < K^+ < Ca^{2+}$

(c) $Cl^- < K^+ < Ca^{2+}$

8.61   (a) Na

(b) C

(c) Na < Al < B < C

8.62   Tc and Rh

8.63   Ionization energy increases across the periodic table and decreases down the periodic table. The decrease down a group occurs because the electron removed is farther and farther from the nucleus, thus reducing the nucleus–electron attractive force.

8.64   (a) Co, cobalt

         (b) paramagnetic (three unpaired electrons)

         (c) The 3+ ion would be formed by the loss of both $4s$ electrons and one d electron leaving four unpaired electrons

8.65   (a) V, vanadium

         (b) Group 5B, Period 4

         (c) Transition element

         (d) Paramagnetic, three unpaired electrons

         (e) $n = 3$, $\ell = 2$, $m_\ell = -2$, $m_s = +\frac{1}{2}$

              $n = 3$, $\ell = 2$, $m_\ell = -1$, $m_s = +\frac{1}{2}$

              $n = 3$, $\ell = 2$, $m_\ell = 0$, $m_s = +\frac{1}{2}$

              $n = 4$, $\ell = 0$, $m_\ell = 0$, $m_s = +\frac{1}{2}$

              $n = 4$, $\ell = 0$, $m_\ell = 0$, $m_s = -\frac{1}{2}$

         (f) V^{2+} $[Ar]3d^3$ The two $4s$ electrons are removed and the resulting ion is paramagnetic

8.66   (a) In going from one element to the next across a period, the effective nuclear charge increases slightly and the attraction between the nucleus and electrons increases.

         (b) The slight decrease in atomic radius of the transition metals is a result of increased repulsions of $(n-1)d$ electrons for ns electrons. This repulsion reduces the effects of the increasing nuclear charge across a period.

8.67 $[Ne]3s^23p^64s^1 \rightarrow [Ne]3s^23p^6 + e^-$

         $K \rightarrow K^+$

         $[Ne]3s^23p^6 \rightarrow [Ne]3s^23p^5 + e^-$

         $K^+ \rightarrow K^{2+}$

         The second ionization energy requires removing an electron from the filled $3p$ orbitals, which are at a much lower energy than the $4s$ electron removed in the first ionization.

8.68   Li, lithium Of the four elements shown, only Li is in Group 1A. The loss of the first electron results in an ion with a filled outer shell. Removal of a second electron (from a filled electron shell) would require a much larger amount of energy.

8.69   For Li^+, there is one less electron to be attracted by the same nuclear charge, but the outer electrons are in the $n = 1$ shell, closer to the nucleus. For F^-, there is one additional electron in the $2p$ orbital. This adds additional electron–electron repulsions while the nuclear charge remains the same.

8.70 K^{2+} Potassium has one outer shell electron, so it is unlikely to form a 2+ ion

        Al^{4+} Aluminum has three outer shell electrons, so it is unlikely to form a 4+ ion

        F^{2-} Fluorine has seven outer shell electrons, so adding one electron forms an anion with the same number of electrons as the nearest noble gas. Adding a second electron would increase electron–electron repulsions and require a great amount of energy.

8.71   There are many arguments for an Mg/O compound being composed of Mg^{2+} and O^{2-} ions. A few are:

        (1)   The groups characteristically form ions with noble gas configurations; Group 2A loses two electrons and Group 6A gains two electrons.

        (2)   Look at other ionic compounds from the same groups; MgS and CaO.

        (3)   Calculate and compare ΔH_f^o values for the two compounds Mg^+/O^- and Mg^{2+}/O^{2-}. The Mg^{2+}/O^{2-} combination is more favorable thermodynamically.

        Some possible experiments:

        (1)   Determine the first and second ionization energy values for Mg and the first and second electron affinity values for O.

        (2)   Determine the melting point of MgO and compare it to the +1/–1 compound NaF (990 °C) and the +2/–2 compound CaO (2580 °C).

8.72   Ca is smaller than K, so we would expect the first IE of Ca to be greater than that of K. Once K has lost one electron, it has a noble gas (Ar) configuration. Removal of a second electron (from a filled electron shell) requires much additional energy. Ca, on the other hand, can lose a "second" electron to obtain a noble gas configuration with a much smaller amount of energy (smaller IE).

8.73   In the Group 4A elements, an added electron is assigned to a previously unoccupied orbital. In contrast, in Group 5A elements the added electron is assigned an orbital already occupied by an electron. Electron-electron repulsions cause the EA to be less negative than expected.

8.74   To form CaF_3, calcium would have to form a 3+ cation. Since calcium (in Group 2A) normally forms 2+ cations (with noble gas configuration), the formation of the 3+ cation is highly unlikely.

8.75   While lithium has a low ionization energy, the electron affinity for argon is predicted to be small because additional electrons would be added to a higher energy level. The addition of an electron to form Ar^- would require a large amount of energy.

8.76   Atomic radius decreases from potassium to vanadium. Because the mass of these elements increases from K to V as the radius decreases, the density is expected to increase.

8.77 Co^{2+} [Ar]$3d^7$ 3 unpaired electrons

        Co^{3+} [Ar]$3d^6$ 4 unpaired electrons

        The two ions have different numbers of unpaired electrons, so $Co(NO_3)_2$ would be more paramagnetic than $CoCl_2$. The magnetic moment of the reaction product could be measured to determine the identity of the product.

8.78   Generally the increasing effective nuclear charge across a period causes ionization energy to also increase. For boron, however, the $2p$ electron is slightly higher in energy than the $2s$ electron of Be, and is therefore somewhat easier to remove.

8.79   Generally the increasing effective nuclear charge across a period causes ionization energy to also increase. For sulfur, however, two of its four $2p$ electrons are paired in the same orbital. The greater repulsion experienced by these electrons makes it easier to remove one of them, and the ionization energy of sulfur is lower than expected.

8.80 | Element | Atomic radius |
        | --- | --- |
        | On | 90 |
        | M | 120 |
        | E | 140 |
        | Ch | 180 |

8.81   (a) S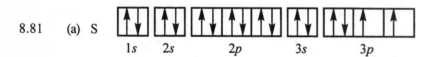

        (b) $n = 3$, $\ell = 1$, $m_\ell = 1$, $m_s = -\frac{1}{2}$

        (c) smallest ionization energy: S   smallest radius: O

        (d) $S < S^{2-}$

8.82   (a) The reducing agent is Na. The low ionization energy of sodium plays a major role in making it a good reducing agent.

        (b) The oxidizing agent is Cl_2. Among other properties, the element has a high electron affinity.

        (c) Na_2Cl would have a Cl^{2-} ion. Adding a second electron to Cl^- means placing an electron in a higher energy electron shell. Conversely, $NaCl_2$ would have a Na^{2+} ion. Here one would have to remove the second electron from the atom's core. See page 314.

8.83   It is easier to remove an electron from B than from Be because B's outermost electron is in a $2p$ orbital, whereas that in Be is in a $2s$ orbital, which is lower in energy.

8.84   (a) Z* is a modified nuclear charge, modified by the screening of inner electrons. Only in the case of H would Z and Z* be the same.

(b) Effective nuclear charge increases across the periodic table.

(c) The effective nuclear charge drops on going from Ne to Na. It is difficult to ionize Ne, whereas Na readily forms a +1 ion.

8.85   (a) The energy if the $2s$ orbital decreases moving across the second period.

(b) The highest occupied orbital increases in energy on moving down a group of elements.

8.86   (a) Mg has a higher ionization energy than Al for the same reason IE(Be) is greater than IE(B). See Question 8.78.

(b) The orbital energies drop, thus raising the element ionization energies.

8.87

Atom distance	Calculated (pm)	Measured (pm)
B—F	157	131
P—F	182	178
C—H	114	104
C—O	150	150

Chapter 9
Bonding and Molecular Structure: Fundamental Concepts

INSTRUCTOR'S NOTES

About five to six lectures are devoted to this chapter. We pay particular attention to the following topics:

(a) drawing electron dot structures for main group elements.

(b) resonance structures for simple molecules.

(c) bond properties (order, length, energy, polarity).

(d) VSEPR theory.

(e) molecular polarity.

With regard to VSEPR theory, we use the term "electron-pair geometry" to designate the positions of the stereochemically active pairs. We find our students then differentiate between the geometry of the electron pairs (electron-pair geometry) and the positions of the atoms in the molecule or ion (molecular geometry). However, there is still some problem getting students to see that, while the electron-pair geometry determines the positions of the atoms, the word description given the molecular geometry reflects only the atom positions.

SUGGESTED DEMONSTRATIONS

1.   Electron-Pair and Molecular Geometry

   • The most useful demonstrations here are models of electron-pair and molecular geometries. We find it useful to illustrate the former with balloons as indicated in Figure 9.11. Purchase a bag of round "party balloons" at a stationery or drug store. After blowing them up, tie them together in pairs; additionally, make at least one set of three tied together. All of the models in Figure 9.11 can be assembled easily in class as you discuss various geometries. The students are always impressed that these are the natural geometries assumed.

   • Molecular models of ionic and covalent compounds can be found on the *General Chemistry Interactive CD-ROM*

   • Large scale molecular models are very useful. Styrofoam orbital models can be purchased from Aldrich Chemical Company. Smaller models can be purchased from Allyn and Bacon, Inc.

Solutions to Study Questions

9.1   Li   1 valence electron

        Ti   4 valence electrons

        Zn   2 valence electrons

        Si   4 valence electrons

        Cl   7 valence electrons

9.2 $\cdot$ K $\cdot$ Mg $\cdot$ $: \overset{\cdot\cdot}{\underset{\cdot}{S}} \cdot$ $: \overset{\cdot\cdot}{\underset{\cdot\cdot}{Ar}} :$

9.3 $\cdot$ K + $: \overset{\cdot\cdot}{\underset{\cdot\cdot}{F}} \cdot$ $\rightarrow$ [K$^+$ $: \overset{\cdot\cdot}{\underset{\cdot\cdot}{F}} :$]   The bonding in KF is ionic.

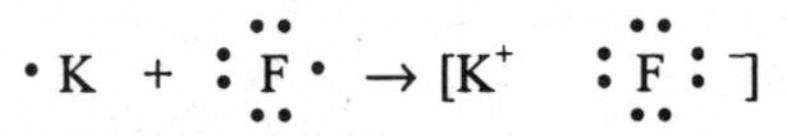

9.4   Ionic: KI and MgS   Covalent: CS_2 and P_4O_{10}

9.5   Lattice energy is the energy of formation of one mole of a solid crystalline ionic compound when ions in the gas phase combine. The lithium ion is smaller than the cesium ion, so the LiF lattice energy should be more negative than the CsF lattice energy.

9.6 $CaCl_4$ is not likely to exist. Calcium has two outer shell electrons so it is unlikely to form a Ca^{4+} ion. Removal of two more electrons from Ca^{2+} (with a filled electron shell) would require a large amount of energy.

9.7   (a) NH_2^- has two lone pairs and two bond pairs

             HF has three lone pairs and one bond pair

        (b) N_2H_4 has five single bonds and no double bonds

             C_2H_4 has four single bonds and one double bond

9.8

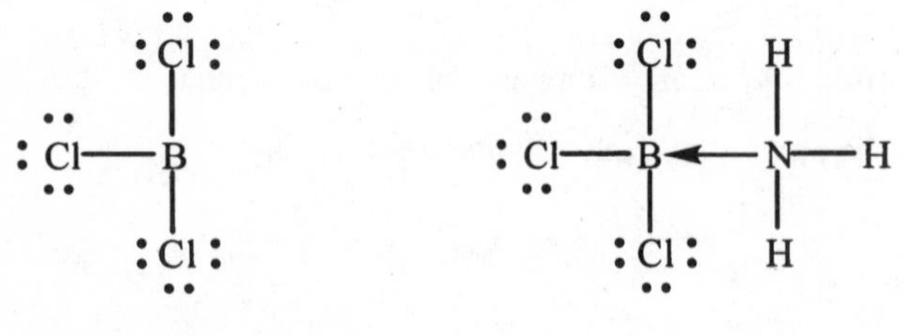

9.9 SeF_4, BrF_4^-, XeF_4

9.10 NH_3 and SO_3 follow the octet rule

        NO_2 and O_2^- are odd-electron molecules/ions

9.11   Benzene has two possible resonance structures that differ only in double bond placement.

9.12   Acetylene has two C—H bonds with a bond order of 1 and a CC triple bond with a bond order of 3.

Phosgene has two C—Cl single bonds with a bond order of 1 and a CO double bond with a bond order of

2.

9.13   bond order = (3 pairs linking CO)/(2 CO links) = $^3/_2$

9.14 NO_3^-

$$\left[\begin{array}{c} :\overset{..}{O}: \\ \parallel \\ :\overset{..}{\underset{..}{O}}\!\!-\!\!N\!\!-\!\!\overset{..}{\underset{..}{O}}: \end{array} \right]^-$$

bond order = (4 pairs linking NO)/(3 NO links) = $^4/_3$

9.15   C—F < C—O < C—N < C—C < C—B

9.16   Bond dissociation energy is the energy required to break a bond in a molecule with the reactants and

products (in the gas phase) under standard conditions. Bond-breaking reactions always require the input of

energy, and so always have a positive sign.

9.17   The higher the bond order, the shorter the bond length and the larger the bond energy.

9.18   Bond energy values needed: O=O, O—H, and H—H

$\Delta H°_{rxn} = 1 \text{ mol} \cdot D_{O=O} + 2 \text{ mol} \cdot D_{H-H} - 4 \text{ mol} \cdot D_{O-H}$

$\Delta H°_{rxn} = 1 \text{ mol} \cdot 498 \text{ kJ/mol} + 2 \text{ mol} \cdot 436 \text{ kJ/mol} - 4 \text{ mol} \cdot 463 \text{ kJ/mol}$

$\Delta H°_{rxn} = -482 \text{ kJ}$

9.19   A polar covalent bond such as the bond in H—Cl has a positive end and a negative end. An example of a

nonpolar bond is the bond in H—H.

9.20   Electronegativity is the ability of an atom in a molecule to attract electrons to itself while electron affinity

is the energy change when an atom of an element (in the gas phase) gains an electron.

9.21   Electronegativities generally increase from left to right across a period and decrease down a group.

9.22   The electroneutrality principle states that the electrons in a molecule are distributed in such a way that the

charges on the atoms are as close to zero as possible and that when a negative charge occurs it should be

placed on the most electronegative atom. Similarly, a positive charge should be on the least

electronegative atom.

9.23   VSEPR theory, a model that provides a reliable method for predicting the shapes of covalent molecules
        and polyatomic ions, is based on the idea that bond and lone electron pairs in the valence shell of an
        element repel each other and seek to be as far apart as possible.

9.24   In water there are four electron pairs around the O atom. The electron-pair geometry is the geometry
        adopted by these four pairs. The molecular geometry is the geometry described by the atoms of the
        molecule. In water the electron-pair geometry is tetrahedral, whereas the molecular geometry is bent.

9.25   Bent, H—X—H is slightly less than 109°
        Trigonal pyramid, H—X—H is slightly less than 109°
        Tetrahedral, H—X—H is approximately 109.5°

9.26   Four electron pairs form a pyramidal molecule if one of the electron pairs is a lone electron pair. A bent
        molecule is obtained if two electron pairs are lone electron pairs. In either case, the bond angle is
        approximately 109°.

9.27

        The molecule has a net dipole moment and the negative end of the dipole points toward the oxygen end of
        the molecule

9.28   (a) O   Group 6A   6 valence electrons
        (b) B   Group 3A   3 valence electrons
        (c) Na   Group 1A   1 valence electron
        (d) Mg   Group 2A   2 valence electrons
        (e) F   Group 7A   7 valence electrons
        (f) S   Group 6A   6 valence electrons

9.29   (a) C   Group 4A   4 valence electrons
        (b) Cl   Group 7A   7 valence electrons
        (c) Ne   Group 8A   8 valence electrons
        (d) Si   Group 4A   4 valence electrons
        (e) Se   Group 6A   6 valence electrons
        (f) Al   Group 3A   3 valence electrons

9.30   Group 3A   3 bonds

                Group 4A   4 bonds

                Group 5A   3 bonds

                Group 6A   2 bonds

                Group 7A   1 bond

9.31   P, Cl, Se, and Sn can accommodate more than four valence electron pairs.

9.32   Most negative: MgS

            Least negative: NaCl

9.33   MgCl (Mg typically forms Mg^{2+} ions)

            BaF_3 (Ba typically forms Ba^{2+} ions)

            CsKr (Kr is not likely to form a Kr^- ion)

9.34   RbI < LiI < LiF < CaO

9.35

$Li(s) \rightarrow Li(g)$	$\Delta H_f^\circ = +159.37$ kJ/mol
$Li(g) \rightarrow Li^+(g) + e^-$	IE = +520. kJ/mol
$\frac{1}{2} F_2(g) \rightarrow F(g)$	$\Delta H_f^\circ = +78.99$ kJ/mol
$F(g) + e^- \rightarrow F^-(g)$	EA = −328.0 kJ/mol
$Li^+(g) + F^-(g) \rightarrow LiF(s)$	$\Delta H_{lattice} = -1037$ kJ/mol

        $Li(s) + \frac{1}{2} F_2(g) \rightarrow LiF(s)$ $\Delta H_f^\circ = -607$ kJ/mol

9.36   As the ion-ion distance decreases, the force of attraction between the ions increases. This should make the lattice more stable, and more energy should be required to melt the compound.

9.37   (a) NaCl   (b) MgO   (c) MgS

9.38   (a) 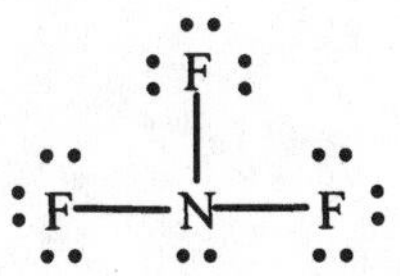   (c)

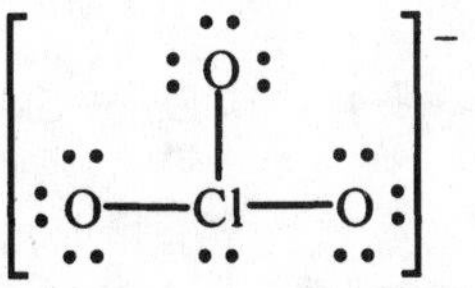

          (b) 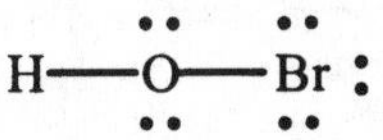   (d)

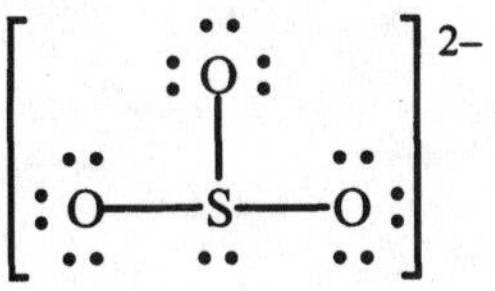

9.39 (a) 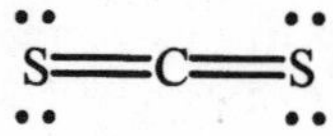

(b) 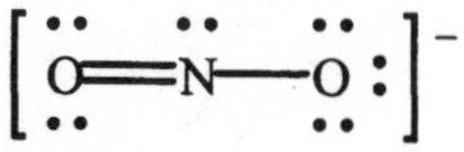

(c) 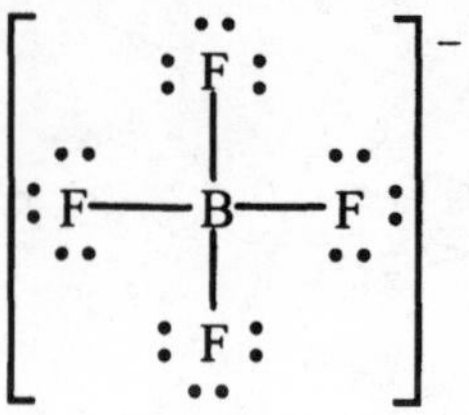

(d) 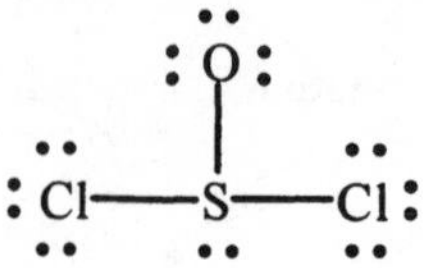

9.40 (a) 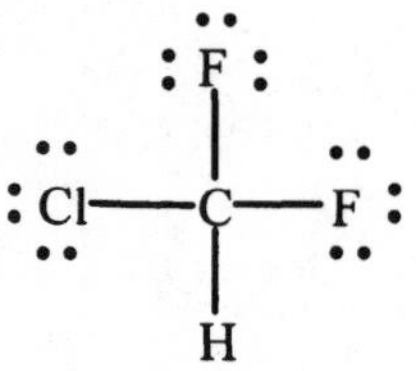

(b) 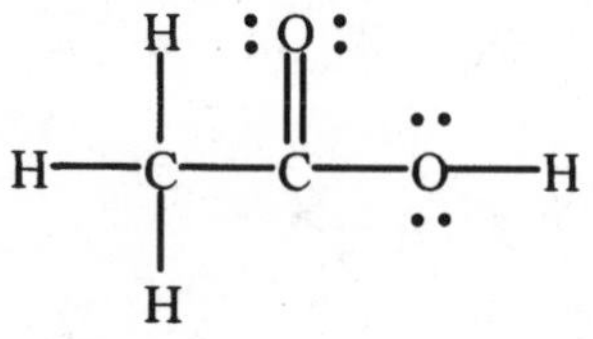

(c) 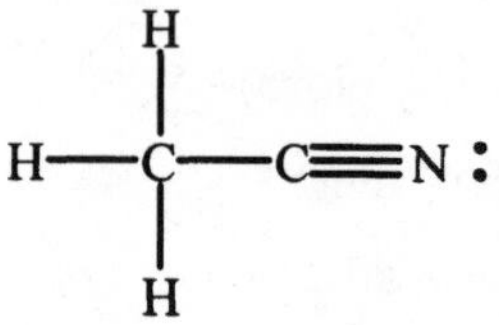

(d) 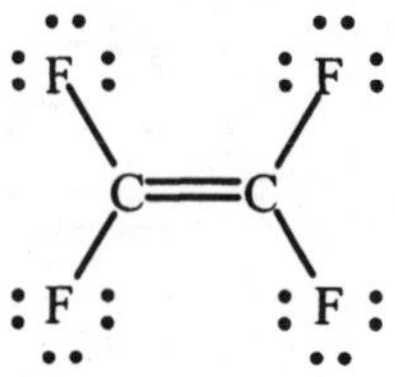

9.41 (a) 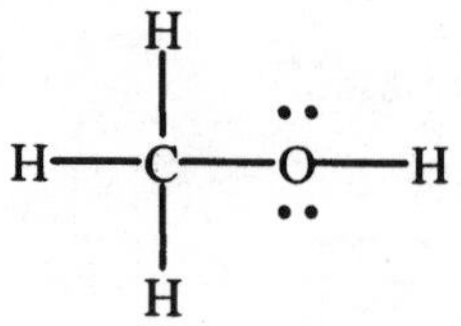

(b) 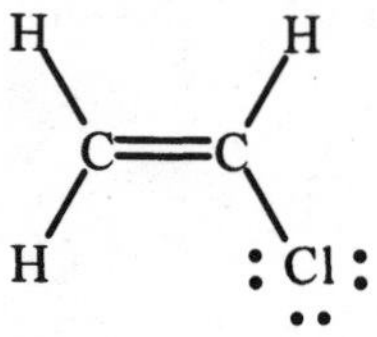

(c) 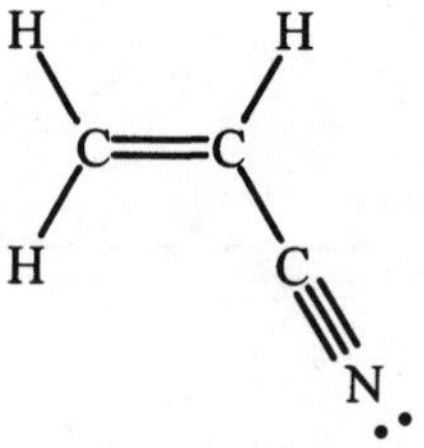

9.42 (a) 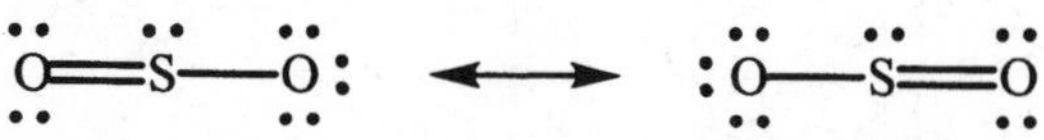

(b) 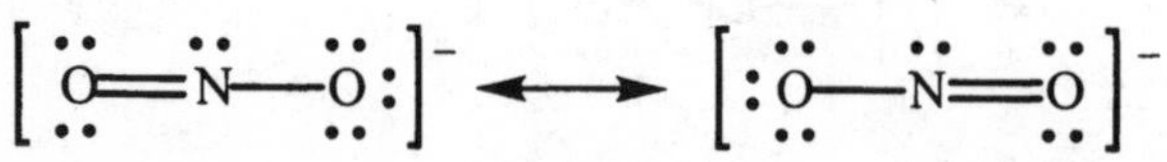

(c) 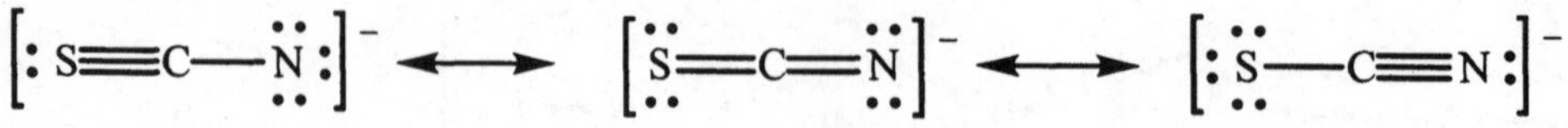

9.43 (a)

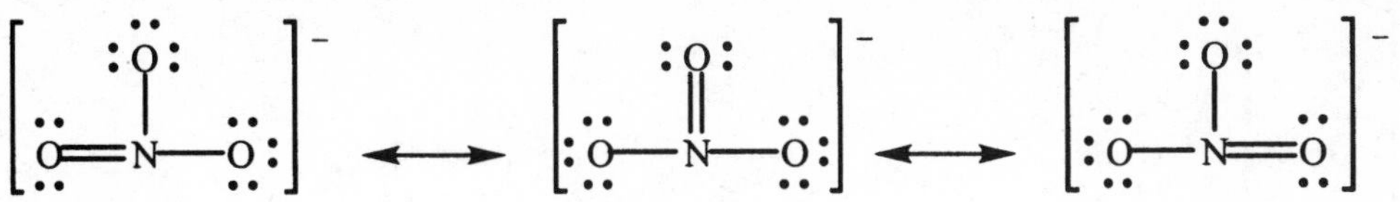

(b)

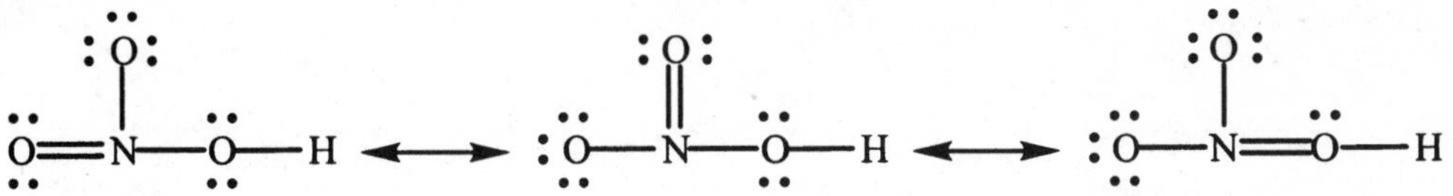

(c)

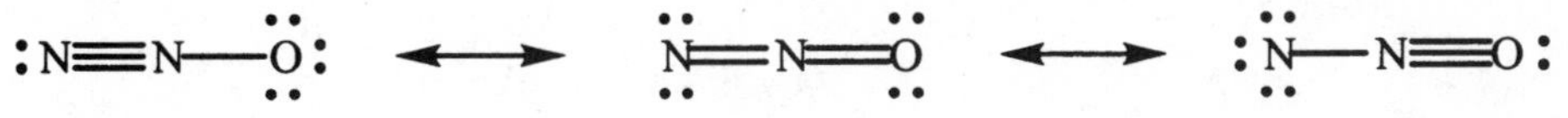

9.44 (a)

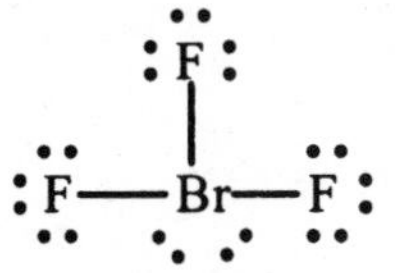

(c)

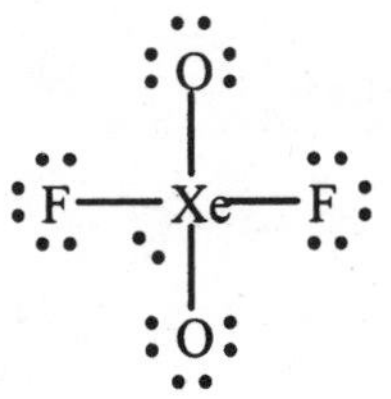

(b)

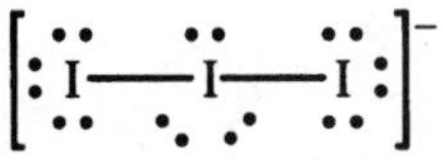

(d)

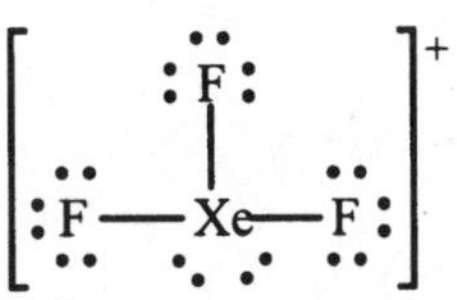

9.45 (a)

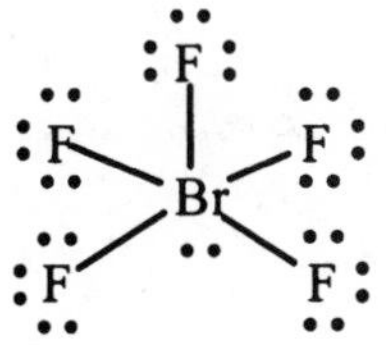

(c)

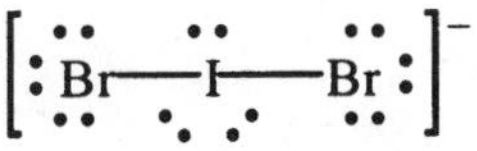

(b)

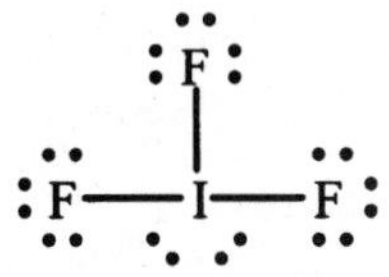

(d)

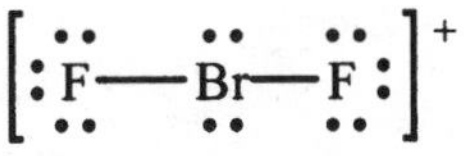

9.46 (a)

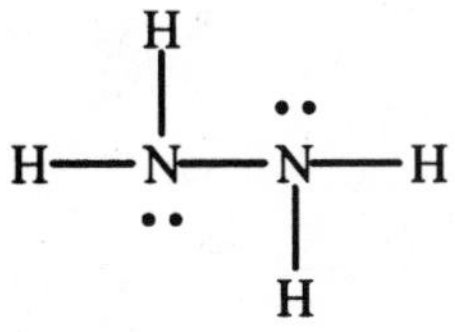

(c)

$H = 1 - 0 - \frac{1}{2}(2) = 0$

$N = 5 - 2 - \frac{1}{2}(6) = 0$

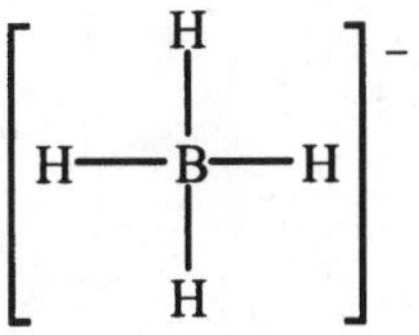

$H = 1 - 0 - \frac{1}{2}(2) = 0$

$B = 3 - 0 - \frac{1}{2}(8) = -1$

(b)

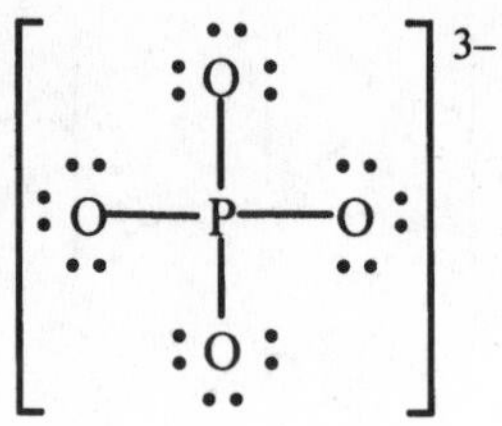

$O = 6 - 6 - \frac{1}{2}(2) = -1$

$P = 5 - 0 - \frac{1}{2}(8) = 1$

(d)

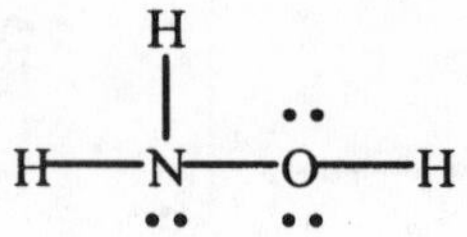

$H = 1 - 0 - \frac{1}{2}(2) = 0$

$N = 5 - 2 - \frac{1}{2}(6) = 0$

$O = 6 - 4 - \frac{1}{2}(4) = 0$

9.47   (a)

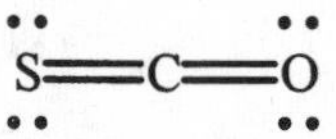

$S = 6 - 4 - \frac{1}{2}(4) = 0$

$C = 4 - 0 - \frac{1}{2}(8) = 0$

$O = 6 - 4 - \frac{1}{2}(4) = 0$

(c)

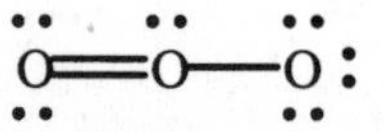

$O = 6 - 4 - \frac{1}{2}(4) = 0$

$O = 6 - 2 - \frac{1}{2}(6) = 1$

$O = 6 - 6 - \frac{1}{2}(2) = -1$

(b)

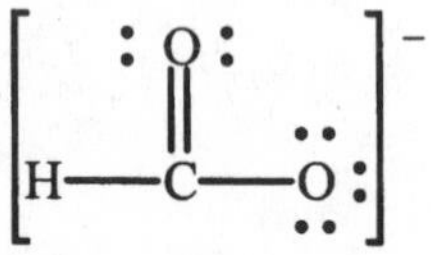

$H = 1 - 0 - \frac{1}{2}(2) = 0$

$C = 4 - 0 - \frac{1}{2}(8) = 0$

$O = 6 - 4 - \frac{1}{2}(4) = 0$

$O = 6 - 6 - \frac{1}{2}(2) = -1$

(d)

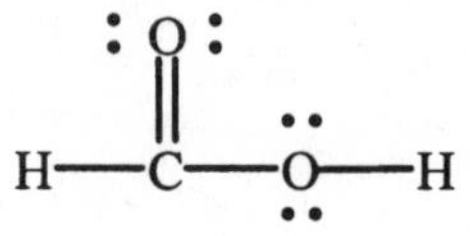

$H = 1 - 0 - \frac{1}{2}(2) = 0$

$C = 4 - 0 - \frac{1}{2}(8) = 0$

$O = 6 - 4 - \frac{1}{2}(4) = 0$

$O = 6 - 4 - \frac{1}{2}(4) = 0$

$H = 1 - 0 - \frac{1}{2}(2) = 0$

9.48   (a)

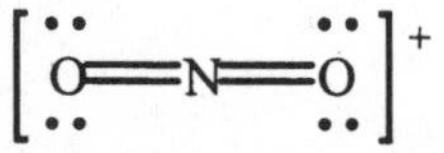

$O = 6 - 4 - \frac{1}{2}(4) = 0$

$N = 5 - 0 - \frac{1}{2}(8) = 1$

(c)

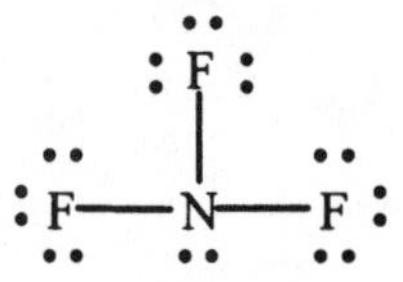

$F = 7 - 6 - \frac{1}{2}(2) = 0$

$N = 5 - 2 - \frac{1}{2}(6) = 0$

(b)

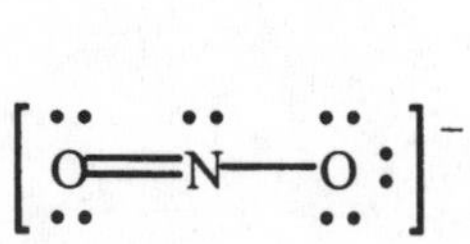

$O = 6 - 4 - \frac{1}{2}(4) = 0$

$N = 5 - 2 - \frac{1}{2}(6) = 0$

$O = 6 - 6 - \frac{1}{2}(2) = -1$

(d)

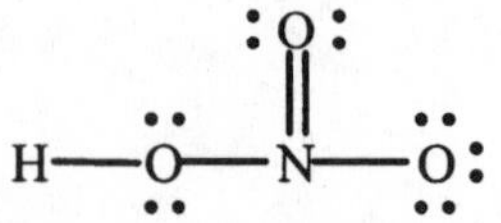

$H = 1 - 0 - \frac{1}{2}(2) = 0$

$O = 6 - 4 - \frac{1}{2}(4) = 0$

$N = 5 - 0 - \frac{1}{2}(8) = 1$

$O = 6 - 4 - \frac{1}{2}(4) = 0$

$O = 6 - 6 - \frac{1}{2}(2) = -1$

9.49   (a)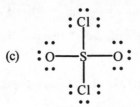

O = 6 – 6 – $\frac{1}{2}$(2) = –1

S = 6 – 2 – $\frac{1}{2}$(6) = 1

O = 6 – 4 – $\frac{1}{2}$(4) = 0

(c)

O = 6 – 6 – $\frac{1}{2}$(2) = –1

S = 6 – 0 – $\frac{1}{2}$(8) = 2

Cl = 7 – 6 – $\frac{1}{2}$(2) = 0

(b)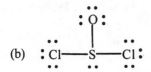

Cl = 7 – 6 – $\frac{1}{2}$(2) = 0

S = 6 – 2 – $\frac{1}{2}$(6) = 1

O = 6 – 6 – $\frac{1}{2}$(2) = –1

(d)

O = 6 – 6 – $\frac{1}{2}$(2) = –1

S = 6 – 0 – $\frac{1}{2}$(8) = 2

F = 7 – 6 – $\frac{1}{2}$(2) = 0

9.50   Arrow points toward the negative end of the bond dipole

(a) C—O   (c) B—O

⟶   ⟶

(b) P—Cl   (d) B—F

⟶   ⟶

9.51   Bond   Atom more negatively charged

(a) C—N   N

(b) C—H   C

(c) C—Br   Br

(d) S—O   O

9.52   (a) The C—H and C=O bonds are polar; the C—C and C=C bonds are nonpolar

(b) The C=O bond is the most polar bond; the O atom is the more negative atom

9.53   (a) All of the bonds in urea are polar.

(b) The C=O bond is the most polar bond; the O atom is the negative end of the dipole.

9.54   (a) Even though the formal charge on B is 1 and on F is 0, F is much more electronegative. The four F

atoms therefore likely bear the –1 charge of the ion, and the bonds are polar with the F atom the

negative end.

(b) Even though the formal charge on B is 1 and on H is 0, H is slightly more electronegative. The four H atoms therefore likely bear the –1 charge of the ion. The B—H bonds are polar with the H atom the negative end.

(c) The formal charge on O is –1 and on H it is 0. This conforms with the relative electronegativities. The bond is polar with O the negative end.

(d) The C—H and CO bonds are polar. The negative charge of the CO bonds lies on the O atoms.

9.55 (a) Even though the formal charge on O is 1 and on H is 0, H is less electronegative. The three H atoms therefore likely bear the +1 charge of the ion. The O—H bonds are polar with the H atom the positive end.

(b) Even though the formal charge on N is 1 and on H is 0, H is less electronegative. The three H atoms therefore likely bear the +1 charge of the ion. The N—H bonds are polar with the H atom the positive end.

(c) The formal charge on N is +1 and on O it is 0. This conforms with the relative electronegativities. The bonds are polar with N the positive end.

(d) The formal charge on N is +1 and on F it is 0. This conforms with the relative electronegativities. The bonds are polar with N the positive end.

9.56 (a) $:N{\equiv}N{-}\overset{..}{\underset{..}{O}}: \longleftrightarrow \overset{..}{N}{=}N{=}\overset{..}{O} \longleftrightarrow :\overset{..}{\underset{..}{N}}{-}N{\equiv}O:$

(b)
$N = 5 - 2 - \frac{1}{2}(6) = 0$ $N = 5 - 4 - \frac{1}{2}(4) = -1$ $N = 5 - 6 - \frac{1}{2}(2) = -2$

$N = 5 - 0 - \frac{1}{2}(8) = 1$ $N = 5 - 0 - \frac{1}{2}(8) = 1$ $N = 5 - 0 - \frac{1}{2}(8) = 1$

$O = 6 - 6 - \frac{1}{2}(2) = -1$ $O = 6 - 4 - \frac{1}{2}(4) = 0$ $O = 6 - 2 - \frac{1}{2}(6) = 1$

(c) The first resonance structure is most reasonable (the most electronegative element, oxygen, has a negative formal charge).

9.57 (a) Yes, both ions contain 24 valence electrons

(b) CO_3^{2-} has three reasonable resonance structures and BO_3^{2-} has four

(c)

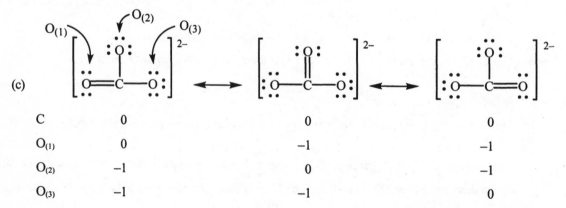

C	0	0	0
$O_{(1)}$	0	–1	–1
$O_{(2)}$	–1	0	–1
$O_{(3)}$	–1	–1	0

$$\left[\begin{array}{c} \ddot{O} \\ | \\ \ddot{O}-B-\ddot{O} \end{array}\right]^{3-} \longleftrightarrow \left[\begin{array}{c} \ddot{O} \\ | \\ O=B-\ddot{O} \end{array}\right]^{3-} \longleftrightarrow \left[\begin{array}{c} \ddot{O} \\ || \\ \ddot{O}-B-\ddot{O} \end{array}\right]^{3-} \longleftrightarrow \left[\begin{array}{c} \ddot{O} \\ | \\ \ddot{O}-B=O \end{array}\right]^{3-}$$

B	0	−1	−1	−1
$O_{(1)}$	−1	0	−1	−1
$O_{(2)}$	−1	−1	0	−1
$O_{(3)}$	−1	−1	−1	0

(d) The H^+ ion would attach to the oxygen atom

9.58 $\left[\ddot{O}=N-\ddot{O}\right]^- \longleftrightarrow \left[\ddot{O}-N=\ddot{O}\right]^-$

$O = 6 - 4 - \frac{1}{2}(4) = 0$ $O = 6 - 6 - \frac{1}{2}(2) = -1$

$N = 5 - 2 - \frac{1}{2}(6) = 0$ $N = 5 - 2 - \frac{1}{2}(6) = 0$

$O = 6 - 6 - \frac{1}{2}(2) = -1$ $O = 6 - 4 - \frac{1}{2}(4) = 0$

The H^+ ion would attach to the oxygen

9.59 $\left[\begin{array}{c} \ddot{O} \\ || \\ H-C-\ddot{O} \end{array}\right]^- \longleftrightarrow \left[\begin{array}{c} \ddot{O} \\ | \\ H-C=O \end{array}\right]^-$

$H = 2 - 0 - \frac{1}{2}(2) = 0$ $H = 2 - 0 - \frac{1}{2}(2) = 0$

$C = 4 - 0 - \frac{1}{2}(8) = 0$ $C = 4 - 0 - \frac{1}{2}(8) = 0$

$O = 6 - 4 - \frac{1}{2}(4) = 0$ $O = 6 - 6 - \frac{1}{2}(2) = -1$

$O = 6 - 6 - \frac{1}{2}(2) = -1$ $O = 6 - 4 - \frac{1}{2}(4) = 0$

The H^+ ion would attach to the oxygen

9.60 (a) H_2CO two carbon-hydrogen single bonds   bond order = 1

                             one carbon-oxygen double bond   bond order = 2

      (b) SO_3^{2-} three sulfur-oxygen single bonds   bond order = 1

      (c) NO_2^+ two nitrogen-oxygen double bonds   bond order = 2

      (d) NOCl   (assume atoms are connected N—O—Cl)

                             one nitrogen-oxygen double bond   bond order = 2

                             one oxygen-chlorine single bond   bond order = 1

9.61 (a) CN^- one carbon-nitrogen triple bond   bond order = 3

      (b) CH_3CN three carbon-hydrogen single bonds   bond order = 1

                             one carbon-carbon single bond   bond order = 1

                             one carbon-nitrogen triple bond   bond order = 3

    (c) SO_3 two sulfur-oxygen single bonds   bond order = 1

                           one sulfur-oxygen double bond   bond order = 2

                           with resonance structures, overall bond order = 1.33

    (d) $CH_3CH{=}CH_2$ six carbon-hydrogen single bonds   bond order = 1

                           one carbon-carbon single bond   bond order = 1

                           one carbon-carbon double bond   bond order = 2

9.62   (a) B—Cl   (c) P—O

       (b) C—O   (d) C=O

9.63   (a) Si—O   (c) C—F

       (b) C—O   (d) C≡N

9.64 NO_2^+ two NO double bonds   NO bond order = 2

       NO_2^- one NO single bond, one NO double bond

                      two resonance structures   NO bond order = $^3/_2$

       NO_3^- two NO single bonds, one NO triple bond

                      three resonance structures   NO bond order = $^4/_3$

       NO_3^- has the longest NO bonds (lowest bond order)

       NO_2^+ has the shortest NO bonds (highest bond order)

9.65 HCO_2^- one CO single bond, one CO double bond

                      two resonance structures   CO bond order = $^3/_2$

       CH_3OH one CO single bond   CO bond order = 1

       CO_3^{2-} two CO single bonds, one CO double bond

                      three resonance structures   CO bond order = $^4/_3$

       CH_3OH has the longest CO bond (lowest bond order)

       HCO_2^- has the shortest CO bonds (highest bond order)

9.66   The carbon-oxygen bond in formaldehyde is a double bond with a bond order of 2. The carbon-oxygen bond in carbon monoxide is a triple bond with a bond order of 3. Carbon monoxide has the shorter CO bond and the stronger CO bond.

9.67   The nitrogen-nitrogen bond in hydrazine is a single bond with a bond order of 1. The nitrogen-nitrogen bond in N_2O has a bond order greater than one, so it has the shorter and stronger nitrogen-nitrogen bond.

9.68   One C=C double bond and one H—H single bond are broken in the reaction

One C—C single bond and two C—H single bonds are formed in the reaction

$\Delta H^\circ_{rxn} = (1\ mol \cdot D_{C=C} + 1\ mol \cdot D_{H-H}) - (1\ mol \cdot D_{C-C} + 2\ mol \cdot D_{C-H})$

$\Delta H^\circ_{rxn} = (1\ mol \cdot 610\ kJ/mol + 1\ mol \cdot 436\ kJ/mol) - (1\ mol \cdot 346\ kJ/mol + 2\ mol \cdot 413\ kJ/mol)$

$\Delta H^\circ_{rxn} = -126\ kJ$

9.69   One C≡O triple bond and one Cl—Cl single bond are broken in the reaction

One C=O double bond and two C—Cl single bonds are formed in the reaction

$\Delta H^\circ_{rxn} = (1\ mol \cdot D_{C\equiv O} + 1\ mol \cdot D_{Cl-Cl}) - (1\ mol \cdot D_{C=O} + 2\ mol \cdot D_{C-Cl})$

$\Delta H^\circ_{rxn} = (1\ mol \cdot 1046\ kJ/mol + 1\ mol \cdot 242\ kJ/mol) - (1\ mol \cdot 745\ kJ/mol + 2\ mol \cdot 339\ kJ/mol)$

$\Delta H^\circ_{rxn} = -135\ kJ$

9.70 $\Delta H^\circ_{rxn} = (2\ mol \cdot D_{O-F} + 2\ mol \cdot D_{O-H}) - (1\ mol \cdot D_{O=O} + 2\ mol \cdot D_{H-F})$

$-318\ kJ = (2\ mol \cdot D_{O-F} + 2\ mol \cdot 463\ kJ/mol) - (1\ mol \cdot 498\ kJ/mol + 2\ mol \cdot 565\ kJ/mol)$

$D_{O-F} = 192\ kJ/mol$

9.71 $\Delta H^\circ_{rxn} = 2\ mol \cdot D_{OO\ in\ ozone} - 2\ mol \cdot D_{O=O}$

$-394\ kJ = 2\ mol \cdot D_{OO\ in\ ozone} - 2\ mol \cdot 498\ kJ/mol$

$D_{OO\ in\ ozone} = 301\ kJ/mol$

$D_{O-O} = 146\ kJ$

$D_{O=O} = 498\ kJ$

The estimate of the oxygen-oxygen bond energy in ozone is between the values for the single and double oxygen-oxygen bond energies. The bond order in ozone is 1.5, which is between the bond order values for a single bond (bond order = 1) and a double bond (bond order = 2). Therefore, the oxygen-oxygen bond energy in ozone does correlate with its bond order.

9.72   (a)

electron pair geometry, tetrahedral

molecular geometry, trigonal pyramidal

(b)

electron pair geometry, tetrahedral

molecular geometry, bent

(c)

electron pair geometry, linear

molecular geometry, linear

(d)

electron pair geometry, tetrahedral

molecular geometry, bent

133

9.73 (a) $\left[:\overset{..}{\underset{..}{F}}—\overset{..}{\underset{..}{Cl}}—\overset{..}{\underset{..}{F}}: \right]^+$

electron-pair geometry, tetrahedral

molecular geometry, bent

(c) $\left[:\overset{..}{\underset{..}{O}}—\overset{\overset{..}{O}}{\underset{\underset{..}{O}}{P}}—\overset{..}{\underset{..}{O}}: \right]^{3-}$

electron-pair geometry, tetrahedral

molecular geometry, tetrahedral

(b) $\left[:\overset{..}{\underset{..}{Cl}}—\overset{\overset{..}{Cl}:}{Sn}—\overset{..}{\underset{..}{Cl}}: \right]^-$

electron-pair geometry, tetrahedral

molecular geometry, trigonal pyramidal

(d) $\overset{..}{\underset{..}{S}}=C=\overset{..}{\underset{..}{S}}$

electron-pair geometry, linear

molecular geometry, linear

9.74 (a) $\overset{..}{\underset{..}{O}}=C=\overset{..}{\underset{..}{O}}$

electron-pair geometry, linear

molecular geometry, linear

(c) $\overset{..}{\underset{..}{O}}=\overset{..}{O}—\overset{..}{\underset{..}{O}}:$

electron-pair geometry, trigonal planar

molecular geometry, bent

(b) $\left[\overset{..}{\underset{..}{O}}=\overset{..}{N}—\overset{..}{\underset{..}{O}}: \right]^-$

electron-pair geometry, trigonal planar

molecular geometry, bent

(d) $\left[:\overset{..}{\underset{..}{O}}—\overset{..}{Cl}—\overset{..}{\underset{..}{O}}: \right]^-$

electron-pair geometry, tetrahedral

molecular geometry, bent

Ozone (c) and nitrite ion (b) are isoelectronic (18 electrons) and have identical electron-pair and molecular geometries.

9.75 (a) $\left[:\overset{..}{\underset{..}{O}}—\overset{\overset{..}{O}:}{C}—\overset{..}{\underset{..}{O}}: \right]^{2-}$

electron-pair geometry, trigonal planar

molecular geometry, trigonal planar

(c) $\left[:\overset{..}{\underset{..}{O}}—\overset{\overset{..}{O}:}{S}—\overset{..}{\underset{..}{O}}: \right]^{2-}$

electron-pair geometry, tetrahedral

molecular geometry, trigonal pyramidal

(b) $\left[:\overset{..}{\underset{..}{O}}—\overset{\overset{..}{O}:}{N}—\overset{..}{\underset{..}{O}}: \right]^-$

electron-pair geometry, trigonal planar

molecular geometry, trigonal planar

(d) $\left[:\overset{..}{\underset{..}{O}}—\overset{\overset{..}{O}:}{Cl}—\overset{..}{\underset{..}{O}}: \right]^-$

electron-pair geometry, tetrahedral

molecular geometry, trigonal pyramidal

Ions (a) and (b) are isoelectronic (24 valence electrons) and have identical electron-pair and molecular geometries. Molecules (c) and (d) are also isoelectronic (26 valence electrons) and have identical electron-pair and molecular geometries.

9.76   (a)

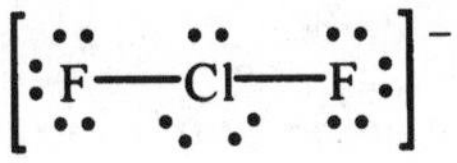

electron-pair geometry, trigonal bipyramid

molecular geometry, linear

(b)

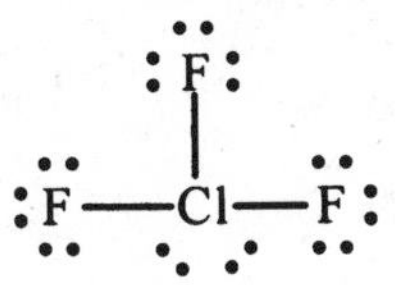

electron-pair geometry = trigonal bipyramid

molecular geometry, T-shaped

(c)

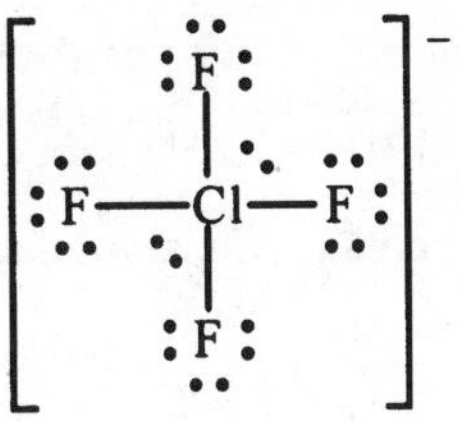

electron-pair geometry, octahedral

molecular geometry, square planar

(d)

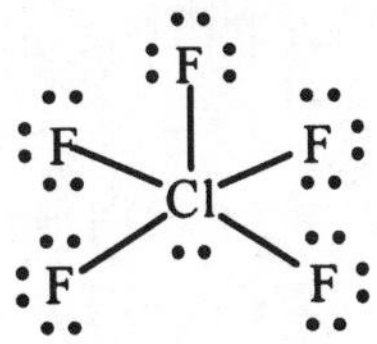

electron-pair geometry, octahedral

molecular geometry, square pyramidal

9.77   (a)

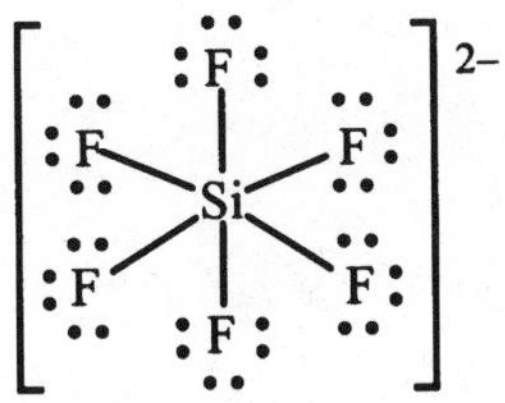

electron-pair geometry, octahedral

molecular geometry, octahedral

(b)

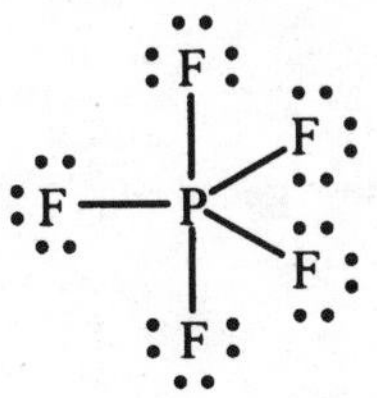

electron-pair geometry, trigonal bipyramid

molecular geometry, trigonal bipyramid

(c)

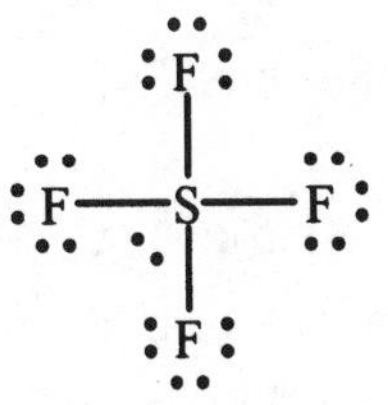

electron-pair geometry, trigonal bipyramid

molecular geometry, seesaw

(d)

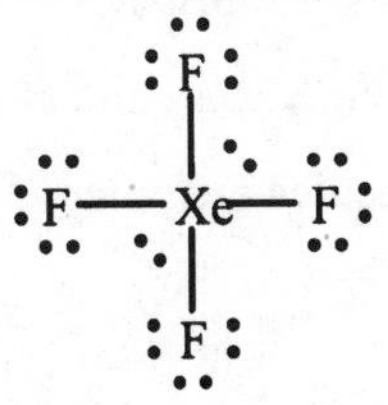

electron-pair geometry, octahedral

molecular geometry, square planar

9.78   (a) O—S—O in SO_2 = 120°

(b) F—B—F in BF_3 = 120°

(c) Cl—C—Cl in Cl_2CO = 120°

(d) H—C—H = 109°   C—C≡N = 180°

9.79   (a) Cl—S—Cl in SCl_2 = 109°

(b) N—N—O in N_2O = 180°

(c) angle 1 = 109°; angle 2 = 120°; angle 3 = 109°

9.80   angle 1 = 120°; angle 2 = 109°; angle 3 = 120°; angle 4 = 109°; angle 5 = 109°

The —CH_2—$CH(NH_2)$—CO_2H chain cannot be linear because the first two carbon atoms have bond angles of 109° (with their connecting atoms) and the third carbon has a 120° bond angle with the C and O on either side.

9.81   angle 1 = 109°; angle 2 = 120°; angle 3 = 120°

9.82   Molecule $\Delta\chi$ for bond

H_2O O—H = 3.5 − 2.1 = 1.4

NH_3 N—H = 3.0 − 2.1 = 0.9

CO_2 O—C = 3.5 − 2.5 = 1.0

ClF   F—Cl = 4.0 − 3.0 = 1.0

CCl_4 Cl—C = 3.0 − 2.5 = 0.5

(i)   The bonds are most polar in H_2O.

(ii) CO_2 and CCl_4 are nonpolar molecules.

(iii) The F atom in ClF is more negatively charged.

9.83   Molecule $\Delta\chi$ for bond

CH_4 C—H = 2.5 − 2.1 = 0.4

NCl_3 N—Cl = 3.0 − 3.0 = 0

BF_3 F—B = 4.0 − 2.0 = 2.0

CS_2 C—S = 2.5 − 2.5 = 0

(i)   The B—F bonds in BF_3 are the most polar.

(ii) None of the molecules are polar. NCl_3 has a trigonal pyramidal molecular geometry, but its bonds are nonpolar.

9.84

Molecule	$\Delta\chi$ for bond	molecular geometry	molecular polarity
$BeCl_2$	Cl—Be = 3.0 − 1.5 = 1.5	linear	nonpolar
HBF_2	H—B = 2.1 − 2.0 = 0.1		
	F—B = 4.0 − 2.0 = 2.0	trigonal planar	polar

F atoms negative end of dipole; H positive end of dipole

CH_3Cl $Cl—C = 3.0 - 2.5 = 0.5$

$C—H = 2.5 - 2.1 = 0.4$ tetrahedral   polar

Cl negative end of dipole; H atoms positive end of dipole

SO_3 $S—O = 2.5 - 3.5 = 1.0$ trigonal planar   nonpolar

9.85

Molecule	$\Delta\chi$ for bond	molecular geometry	molecular polarity
CO	$C—O = 2.5 - 3.5 = 1.0$	linear	polar
BCl_3	$B—Cl = 2.0 - 3.0 = 1.0$	trigonal planar	nonpolar
CF_4	$C—F = 2.5 - 4.0 = 1.5$	tetrahedral	nonpolar
PCl_3	$P—Cl = 2.1 - 3.0 = 0.9$	trigonal pyramidal	polar
GeH_4	$Ge—H = 1.9 - 2.1 = 0.2$	tetrahedral	nonpolar

BCl_3, CF_4, and GeH_4 are nonpolar molecules; CF_4 has the most polar bonds.

9.86   (a)   :O≡C—O: ⟷   O=C=O   ⟷   :O—C≡O:

       (b)   [:N≡N—N:]⁻   ⟷   [N=N=N]⁻   ⟷   [:N—N≡N:]⁻

       (c)   [:C≡N—O:]⁻   ⟷   [C=N=O]⁻   ⟷   [:C—N≡O:]⁻

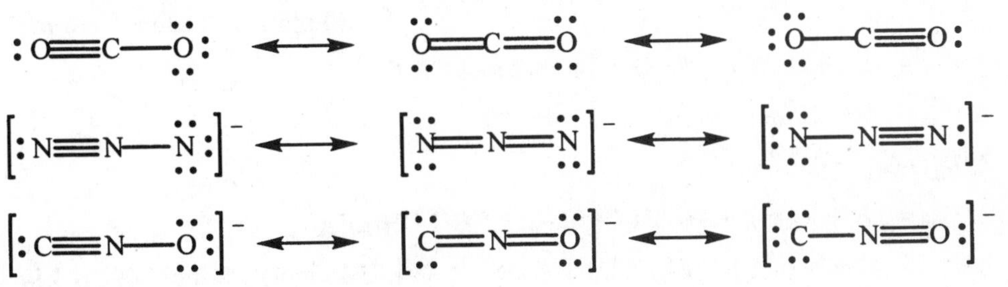

All three have 16 valence electrons and are linear

9.87   The N—O bonds in NO_2^- have a bond order of 1.5 while in NO_2^+ the bond order is 2. The shorter bonds (110 pm) are the N—O bonds with the higher bond order (2) while the N—O bonds with a bond order of 1.5 are longer (124 pm).

9.88 NO_2^- has a smaller bond angle (about 120°) than NO_2^+ (180°). The former has a trigonal-planar electron pair geometry, whereas the latter is linear.

9.89 ClF_2^+ [:F—Cl—F:]⁺ ClF_2^- [:F—Cl—F:]⁻

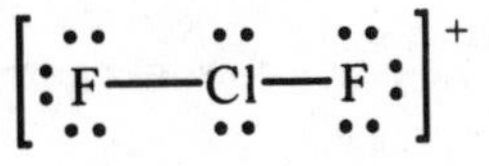

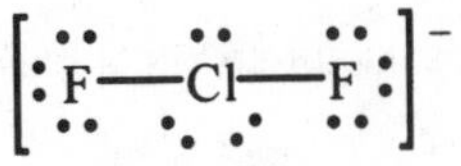

       F—Cl—F = 109°   F—Cl—F = 180°

ClF_2^- has a greater bond angle because there is an additional lone pair of electrons around the central atom.

9.90   [:C≡N:]⁻

The negative (formal) charge resides on C, so the H^+ should attach to that atom and form HCN.

9.91

$$\left[\begin{array}{c} \ddot{:}\ddot{O}\ddot{:} \\ \ddot{:}\ddot{O}{-}S{-}\ddot{O}\ddot{:} \end{array} \right]^{2-}$$ The H^+ will attach to the oxygen atom of SO_3^{2-}

9.92   Two N—O single bonds are broken and one O=O double bond is formed in the reaction

$\Delta H°_{rxn} = 2 \text{ mol} \cdot D_{N-O} - 1 \text{ mol} \cdot D_{O=O}$

$\Delta H°_{rxn} = 2 \text{ mol} \cdot 201 \text{ kJ/mol} - 1 \text{ mol} \cdot 498 \text{ kJ/mol}$

$\Delta H°_{rxn} = -96 \text{ kJ}$

9.93   (a)   Two O—H bonds do not change during the reaction.

$\Delta H°_{rxn} = (6 \text{ mol} \cdot D_{C-H} + 2 \text{ mol} \cdot D_{C-O} + 3 \text{ mol} \cdot D_{O=O}) - (4 \text{ mol} \cdot D_{C=O} + 6 \text{ mol} \cdot D_{O-H})$

$\Delta H°_{rxn} = (6 \text{ mol} \cdot 413 \text{ kJ/mol} + 2 \text{ mol} \cdot 358 \text{ kJ/mol} + 3 \text{ mol} \cdot 498 \text{ kJ/mol})$

$- (4 \text{ mol} \cdot 732 \text{ kJ/mol} + 6 \text{ mol} \cdot 463 \text{ kJ/mol})$

$\Delta H°_{rxn} = -1018 \text{ kJ}$ for the combustion of 2 mol CH_3OH

$\Delta H°_{rxn} = -509 \text{ kJ/mol } CH_3OH$

(b) $\Delta H_f°[O_2(g)] = 0 \text{ kJ/mol}$

$\Delta H°_{rxn} = \Delta H_f°[CO_2(g)] + \Delta H_f°[H_2O(g)] - \Delta H_f°[CH_3OH(g)]$

$\Delta H°_{rxn} = 2 \text{ mol} \cdot (-393.509 \text{ kJ/mol}) + 4 \text{ mol} \cdot (-241.83 \text{ kJ/mol}) - 2 \text{ mol} \cdot (-201 \text{ kJ/mol})$

$\Delta H°_{rxn} = -1352 \text{ kJ}$ for the combustion of 2 mol CH_3OH

$\Delta H°_{rxn} = -676 \text{ kJ/mol } CH_3OH$

9.94   The F^- ion has a very small radius when compared to the trend in ionic radii within the halide ions (see Figure 8.13). This results in a larger attractive force between the ions in NaF.

9.95   (a) $$\left[:C{\equiv}N{-}\ddot{O}: \right]^{-} \longleftrightarrow \left[\ddot{C}{=}N{=}\ddot{O} \right]^{-} \longleftrightarrow \left[:\ddot{C}{-}N{\equiv}O: \right]^{-}$$

(b)   −1   1   −1   −2   1   0   −3   1   1

The first resonance structure is most reasonable because the negative formal charge is on the most electronegative atom.

(c)   Carbon, the least electronegative element in the ion, has a negative formal charge. In addition, all three resonance structures have an unfavorable charge distribution.

9.96   (a)   angle 1 = 120°; angle 2 = 180°; angle 3 = 120°

(b)   The C=C bond is shorter than the C—C bond

(c)   The C=C bond is stronger than the C—C bond

(d)   The C≡N bond is the most polar; $\Delta\chi = 3.0 - 2.5 = 0.5$

9.97   (a) angle 1 = 120°; angle 2 = 109°, angle 3 = 120°

        (b) The C=O bond is the shortest carbon-oxygen bond in the molecule.

        (c) The O—H bond is the most polar; $\Delta\chi = 3.5 - 2.1 = 1.4$

9.98   (a) The three lone pairs of XeF_2 occupy the equatorial positions. There the angles between lone pairs are
             120°, so there is less lone pair/lone pair repulsion with this arrangement.

        (b) The two lone pairs on the Cl atom occupy the equatorial positions. The reasoning is the same as for
             XeF_2.

9.99

        The electron-pair geometry is trigonal planar, the molecular geometry is trigonal planar, and all bond
        angles are approximately 120°.

9.100   (a) angle 1 = 109°; angle 2 = 120°; angle 3 = 109°; angle 4 = 109°; angle 5 = 109°

        (b) The C=O bond is the most polar bond.

9.101   As the bond order successively increases the bond distance decreases, causing an increase in repulsive forces
        between both the nuclei and the bonding and nonbonding electrons of the atoms in the bond.

9.102   Four N—H bonds do not change during the reaction

        $\Delta H°_{rxn} = 2 \text{ mol} \cdot D_{C-N} + 1 \text{ mol} \cdot D_{C=O} - (1 \text{ mol} \cdot D_{N-N} + 1 \text{ mol} \cdot D_{C\equiv O})$

        $\Delta H°_{rxn} = 2 \text{ mol} \cdot 305 \text{ kJ/mol} + 1 \text{ mol} \cdot 745 \text{ kJ/mol} - (1 \text{ mol} \cdot 163 \text{ kJ/mol} + 1 \text{ mol} \cdot 1046 \text{ kJ/mol})$

        $\Delta H°_{rxn} = 146 \text{ kJ}$

9.103   (a)

             In this resonance structure there is a +1 formal charge on N whereas the other resonance structure has 0
             formal charge on both O and N.

        (b) The 120° bond angle suggest that his resonance structure may contribute to the resonance hybrid.

9.104   (a) S: $6 - 4 - \frac{1}{2}(4) = 0$ O: $6 - 4 - \frac{1}{2}(4) = 0$

        (b) angle 1 = 109°; angle 2 = 109°; angle 3 = 120°

        (c) The C=C bonds are shorter than the C—C bonds

        (d) The C–O bond is most polar

(e) The molecule is polar

(f) The four C atoms are planar and trigonal, so the ring as a whole is planar.

9.105   (a) Two C—H bonds and one O=O bond are broken and two O—C bonds and two H—O   bonds are
        formed in the reaction

$\Delta H°_{rxn} = (2 \text{ mol} \cdot D_{C—H} + 1 \text{ mol} \cdot D_{O=O}) - (2 \text{ mol} \cdot D_{O—C} + 2 \text{ mol} \cdot D_{H—O})$

$\Delta H°_{rxn} = (2 \text{ mol} \cdot 413 \text{ kJ/mol} + 1 \text{ mol} \cdot 498 \text{ kJ/mol}) - (2 \text{ mol} \cdot 358 \text{ kJ/mol} + 2 \text{ mol} \cdot 463 \text{ kJ/mol})$

$\Delta H°_{rxn} = -318 \text{ kJ}$ exothermic

(b) Acetone is polar

(c) The O—H hydrogen atoms are the most positive in dihydroxyacetone

9.106

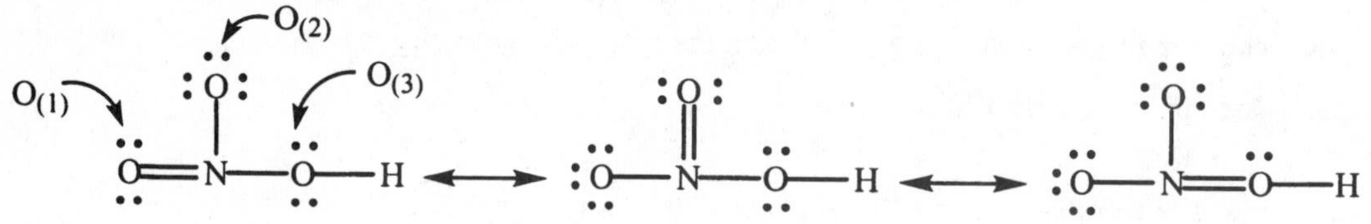

$O_{(1)} = 0$ $O_{(1)} = -1$ $O_{(1)} = -1$

$O_{(2)} = -1$ $O_{(2)} = 0$ $O_{(2)} = -1$

$O_{(3)} = 0$ $O_{(3)} = 0$ $O_{(3)} = 1$

$H = 0$ $H = 0$ $H = 0$

$N = 1$ $N = 1$ $N = 1$

The third resonance structure is the least important since it has a positive formal charge on one of the

oxygen atoms.

9.107   (a)

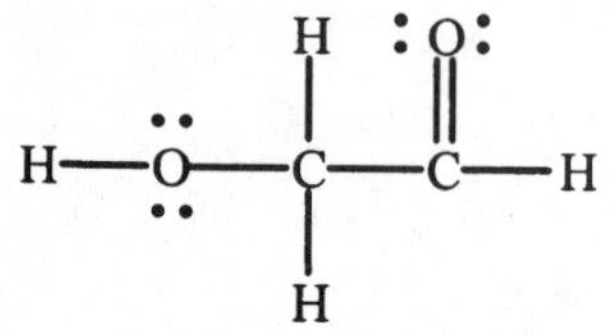

H—O—C = 109°; O—C—H = 109°; O—C—C = 109°; H—C—C = 109°

C—C=O = 120°; C—C—H = 120°; O=C—H = 120°

(b) H—C≡C—C≡N:

9.108   (a) The C=C bond is stronger than the C—C bond

(b) The C—C bond is longer

(c) Ethylene is nonpolar; acrolein is polar

(d) Four C—H bonds and one C=C bond do not change during the reaction

$\Delta H°_{rxn} = 1 \text{ mol} \cdot D_{C=O} - (1 \text{ mol} \cdot D_{C—C} + 1 \text{ mol} \cdot D_{C=O})$

$\Delta H°_{rxn} = 1 \text{ mol} \cdot 1046 \text{ kJ/mol} - (1 \text{ mol} \cdot 346 \text{ kJ/mol} + 1 \text{ mol} \cdot 745 \text{ kJ/mol})$

$\Delta H°_{rxn} = -45 \text{ kJ}$ exothermic

9.109   Two C—H bonds do not change during the reaction

$\Delta H^{\circ}_{rxn} = 1\ mol \cdot D_{C \equiv C} + 1\ mol \cdot D_{Cl-Cl} - (1\ mol \cdot D_{C=C} + 2\ mol \cdot D_{C-Cl})$

$\Delta H^{\circ}_{rxn} = 1\ mol \cdot 835\ kJ/mol + 1\ mol \cdot 242\ kJ/mol - (1\ mol \cdot 610\ kJ/mol + 2\ mol \cdot 339\ kJ/mol)$

$\Delta H^{\circ}_{rxn} = -211\ kJ$

9.110   (a) angle 1 = 109°; angle 2 = 120°; angle 3 = 120°; angle 4 = 109°; angle 5 = 109°

          (b) The O—H bonds are most polar

9.111   The data collected from the models on the CD-ROM, show that carbon-carbon bonds are generally shorter
          as the bond order increases.

Name	Bond Distance (Å)	Bond Order
Ethane	1.540	1
Butane	1.540	1
Ethylene	1.352	2
Acetylene	1.226	3
Benzene	1.397	2.5

9.112   (a)

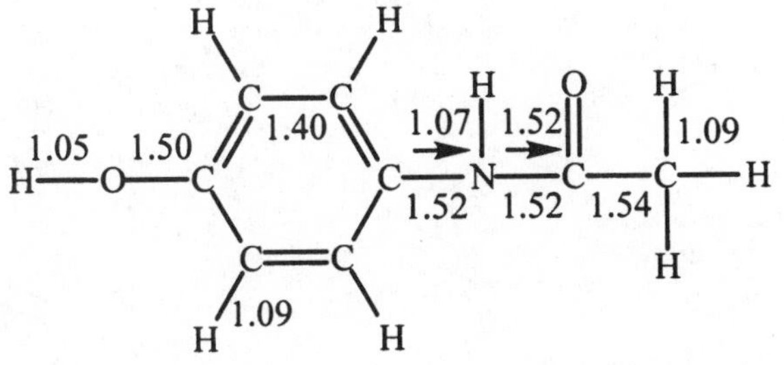

Bond angles in the ring and around the OH, NH and C=O groups are 120°. Bond angles around the
CH₃ group are 109°.

          (b)

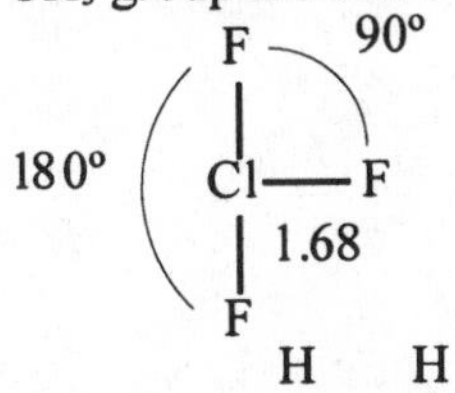

          (c)

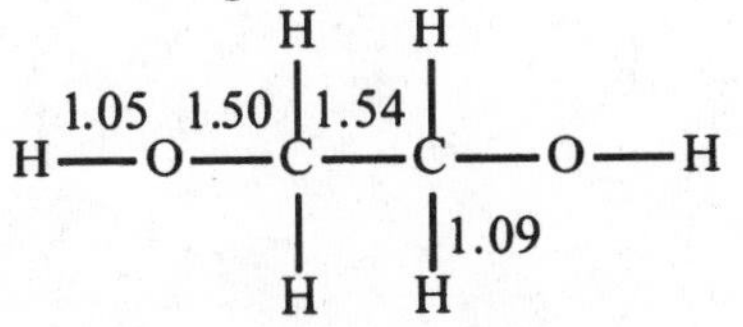

All bond angles are 109°.

9.113   (a) BF₃ is not a polar molecule. HBF₂ and H₂BF are polar molecules

          (b) BeCl₂ is not a polar molecule. BeClBr is a polar molecule.

Chapter 10
Bonding and Molecular Structure:
Orbital Hybridization and Molecular Orbitals

INSTRUCTOR'S NOTES

About three or four, 50-minute lectures are scheduled for this chapter. The emphasis is on valence bond theory, with only about one and a half lectures on molecular orbital theory. The following computer programs may be used for this material.

(a) ChemDraw, a drawing program for the Macintosh, is produced by CambridgeSoft Corporation

(b) There are many molecular modeling programs on the market that can be used to build molecular models and hybrid and molecular orbitals. There are some molecular orbitals on the *General Chemistry Interactive CD-ROM* that can be viewed using the *CAChe Visualizer for Education* (also available on the CD-ROM).

SUGGESTED DEMONSTRATIONS

1.   Orbital Overlap

- For an overhead demonstration of orbital overlap, see Rothchild, R. "Efficiency of Orbital Overlap: Visual Demonstration," *Journal of Chemical Education*, **1981**, *58*, 757.

2.   Hybrid Orbitals

- In these lectures it is most useful to show models of molecules with the hybrid orbitals in place. Suitable models can be obtained from Aldrich Chemical Company.

- For a demonstration of orbital hybridization see Emerson, D. W. "A Colorful Demonstration to Simulate Orbital Hybridization," *Journal of Chemical Education*, **1988**, *65*, 454.

3.   Molecular Orbital Theory

- Shakhashiri, B. Z.; Dirreen, G. E.; Williams, L. G.; Smith, S. R. "Paramagnetism and Color of Liquid Oxygen: A Lecture Demonstration," *Journal of Chemical Education* **1980**, *57*, 373.

- Saban, G. H.; Moran, T. F. "A Simple Demonstration of O_2 Paramagnetism. A Macroscopically Observable Difference Between VB and MO Approaches to Bonding Theory," *Journal of Chemical Education* **1973**, *50*, 217.

- See the *General Chemistry Interactive CD-ROM* for a demonstration of the paramagnetism of liquid oxygen.

Solutions to Study Questions

10.1 The electron density of a sigma bond is greatest along the axis of the bond while in a pi bond the overlap region is above and below the axis of the bond.

10.2 The maximum number of hybrid orbitals that a carbon atom can form is four and the minimum number that can be formed is two. Carbon has only four valence orbitals, one s and three p, so it cannot form more than four hybrid orbitals.

10.3 sp: 180° sp^2: 120° sp^3: 109°

10.4 For atoms with sp-hybridization, two unhybridized p orbitals remain. Two π bonds can form.

10.5   tetrahedral: sp^3 octahedral: sp^3d^2

   linear: sp trigonal-bipyramidal: sp^3d

   trigonal-planar: sp^2

10.6   (a) CF_4 is isoelectronic with BF_4^- (32 valence electrons)

   (b) SiF_4 (32 valence electrons) and SF_4 (34 valence electrons) are not isoelectronic

   (c) BF_4^-: sp^3 SiF_4: sp^3 SF_4: sp^3d

10.7 XeF_4: sp^3d^2

10.8 A third period element may form up to six hybrid orbitals (S can be sp^3d^2 hybridized).

10.9 In contrast to the localized bond and lone pair electrons of valence bond theory, molecular orbital theory assumes that pure atomic orbitals of the atoms in the molecule combine to produce orbitals that are spread out over several atoms or the entire molecule.

10.10   (a) The total number of molecular orbitals is always equal to the total number of atomic orbitals contributed by the atoms that have combined.

   (b) The bonding molecular orbital is lower in energy than the parent orbitals, and the antibonding orbital is higher in energy.

   (c) The electrons of the molecule are assigned to orbitals of successively higher energy according to the Pauli exclusion principle and Hund's rule.

   (d) Atomic orbitals combine to form molecular orbitals most effectively when the atomic orbitals are of similar energy.

10.11   Bonding MO   Antibonding MO

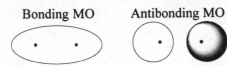

The bonding MO has a region of electron density directly along the bond axis. The antibonding MO has a nodal plane between the nuclei, an area of zero probability of finding an electron.

10.12   The higher the bond order, the shorter the bond length and the larger the bond energy. Acetylene has a carbon-carbon triple bond (bond order = 3), so it has the shortest and strongest carbon-carbon bond. Ethane has a carbon-carbon single bond (bond order = 1), so it has the longest and weakest carbon-carbon bond.

10.13   Molecular orbital theory correctly predicts the electronic structures for odd-electron molecules and other molecules such as O_2 that do not follow the electron-pairing assumptions of the Lewis dot structure approach.

10.14   The term localized as it pertains to bonding theories refers to the idea that electron pairs are contained (or localized) in orbitals between two atoms, while delocalized refers to the orbitals (in MO theory) that are thought of as being spread out (or delocalized) over the entire molecule.

10.15   Valence bond theory uses resonance to explain the bond order of 1.5 in O_3. Molecular orbital theory uses three π molecular orbitals (bonding, nonbonding, and antibonding) combined with sigma bonding and antibonding molecular orbitals to explain the bond order.

10.16   An insulator has a large band gap between valence and conduction bands, whereas the bands in a metal have no separation.

10.17   The conductivity of extrinsic semiconductors is controlled by adding small amounts of impurities. Intrinsic semiconductors are pure elements.

10.18

$$\begin{array}{c} \ddot{:}\ddot{F}\ddot{:} \\ | \\ :\ddot{F}-\ddot{N}-\ddot{F}: \end{array}$$

The electron pair geometry is tetrahedral and the molecular geometry is trigonal pyramidal. The N atom is sp^3 hybridized. Three of these hybrid orbitals each overlap a fluorine $2p$ orbital to form three N—F sigma bonds.

10.19 $\left[:\ddot{F}-\overset{..}{\underset{..}{Cl}}-\ddot{F}: \right]^+$

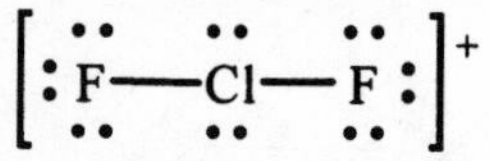

The electron-pair geometry is tetrahedral, and the molecular geometry is bent. The Cl atom is sp^3 hybridized. Two of these hybrid orbitals each overlap a fluorine $2p$ orbital to form two Cl—F sigma bonds.

10.20
$$:\overset{\overset{\displaystyle :\ddot{Cl}:}{|}}{\underset{\underset{\displaystyle H}{|}}{C}}:$$
: Cl— C —Cl :

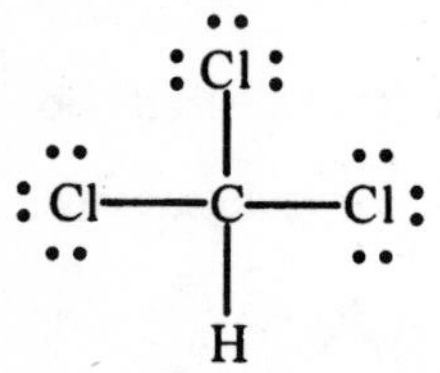

The electron-pair and molecular geometries are tetrahedral. The C atom is sp^3 hybridized. Three of these hybrid orbitals each overlap with a chlorine $3p$ orbital to form three C—Cl sigma bonds. One hybrid orbital overlaps with a hydrogen $1s$ orbital to from a C—H sigma bond.

10.21
$$\left[\begin{array}{c} :\ddot{F}: \\ | \\ :\ddot{F}-Al-\ddot{F}: \\ | \\ :\ddot{F}: \end{array} \right]^-$$

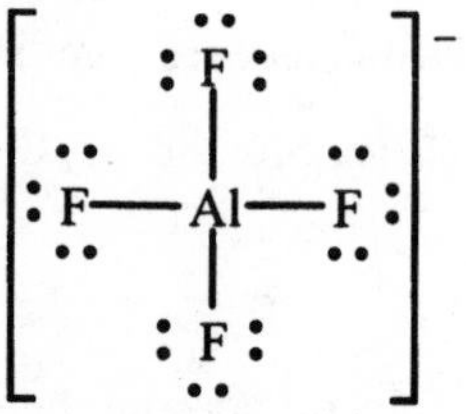

The electron-pair and molecular geometries are tetrahedral. The Al atom is sp^3 hybridized. Each of these orbitals overlaps a fluorine $2p$ orbital to form four Al—F sigma bonds.

10.22   (a) $\underline{B}Br_3$ sp^2 (c) $\underline{C}H_2Cl_2$ sp^3

         (b) $\underline{C}O_2$ sp (d) $\underline{C}O_3^{2-}$ sp^2

10.23   (a) $\underline{C}Se_2$ sp (c) $\underline{C}H_2O$ sp^2

         (b) $\underline{S}O_2$ sp^2 (d) $\underline{N}H_4^+$ sp^3

10.24   (a) C: sp^3 O: sp^3

         (b) From left to right: sp^3, sp^2, sp^2

         (c) N: sp^3 $\underline{C}H_2$: sp^3 $\underline{C}O_2H$: sp^2

10.25   underlined atom   hybrid orbital set

         (a)   N   both N atoms are sp^3 hybridized

                  C sp^2

         (b)   C of CH_3 sp^3

                  C of C=C and C=O   both C atoms are sp^2 hybridized

(c)   C of C=C sp^2

         C of C≡N sp

10.26

	electron-pair geometry	molecular geometry	hybridization
(a)	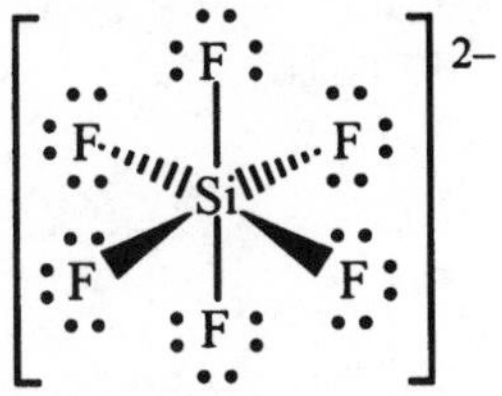 octahedral	octahedral	sp^3d^2
(b)	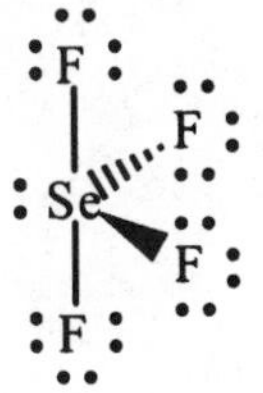 trigonal bipyramidal	see-saw	sp^3d
(c)	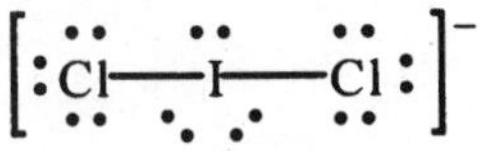 trigonal bipyramidal	linear	sp^3d
(d)	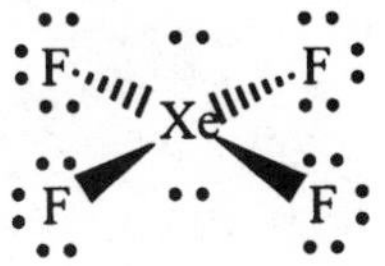 octahedral	square planar	sp^3d^2

10.27

	electron-pair geometry	molecular geometry	hybridization
(a)	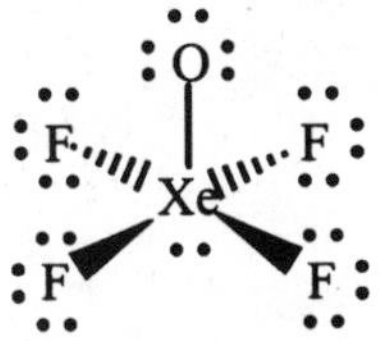 octahedral	square pyramid	sp^3d^2
(b)	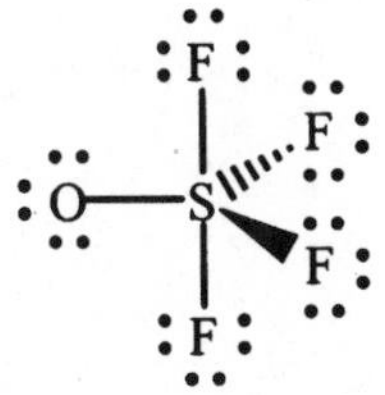 trigonal bipyramidal	see-saw	sp^3d
(c)	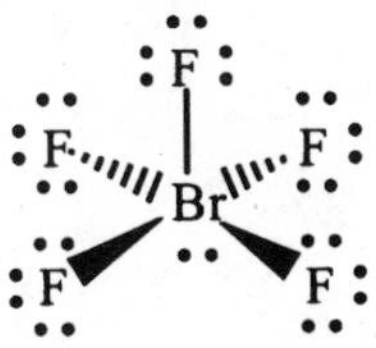 octahedral	square pyramid	sp^3d^2
(d)	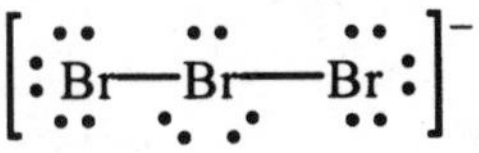 trigonal bipyramidal	linear	sp^3d

10.28

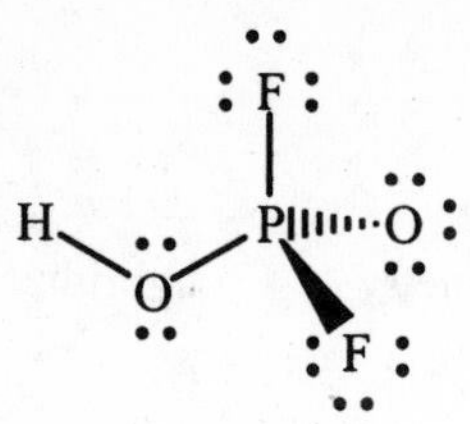

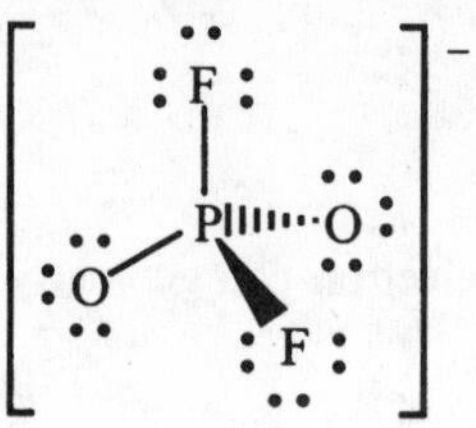

32 valence electrons

tetrahedral

sp^3

32 valence electrons

tetrahedral

sp^3

10.29

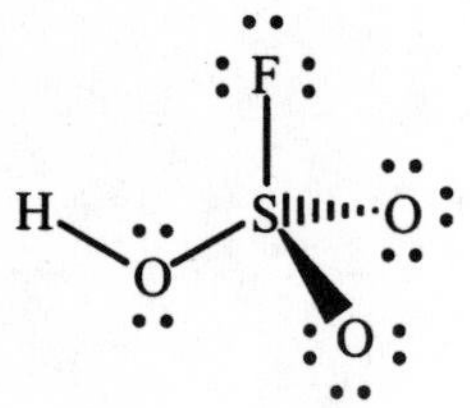

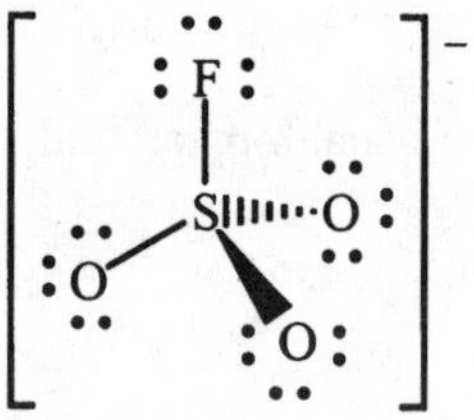

32 valence electrons

tetrahedral

sp^3

32 valence electrons

tetrahedral

sp^3

10.30   The C atom is sp^2 hybridized. Two of the sp^2 hybrid orbitals are used to form C—Cl σ bonds. The third is used to form the C—O σ bond. The p orbital not used in the C atom hybrid orbitals is used to form the CO π bond.

10.31 sp^3

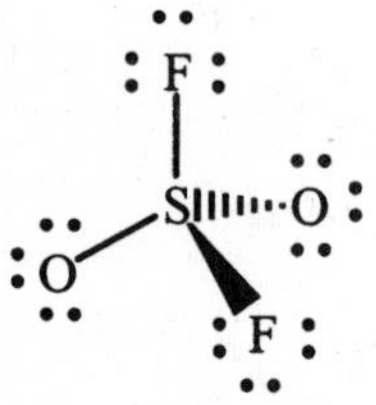

10.32 (a)

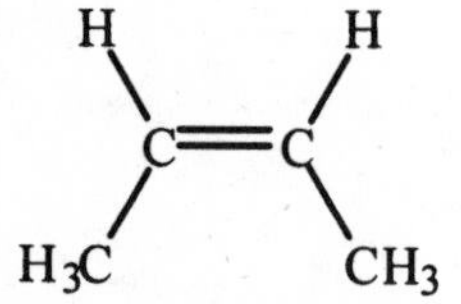

cis isomer

(b)

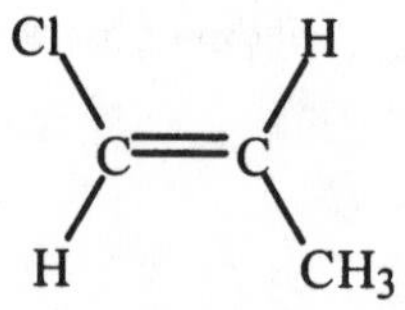

trans isomer

10.33 (a)

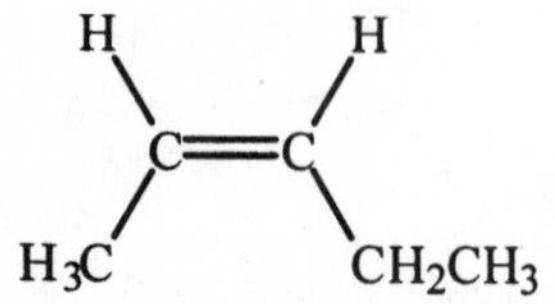

cis isomer

(c)

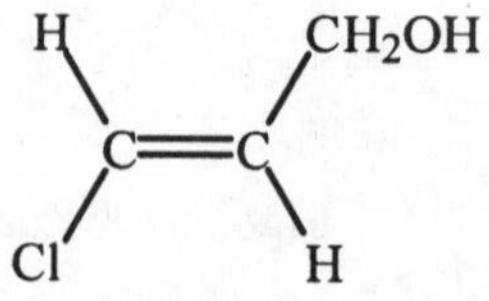

trans isomer

(b) *cis* and *trans* isomers not possible

10.34 H_2^+: $(\sigma_{1s})^1$ Bond order $= \frac{1}{2}(1-0) = \frac{1}{2}$ weaker H—H bond

       H_2: $(\sigma_{1s})^2$ Bond order $= \frac{1}{2}(2-0) = 1$ stronger H—H bond

10.35 Li_2^+: $(\sigma_{1s})^2(\sigma*_{1s})^2(\sigma_{2s})^1(\sigma*_{2s})^0$ Bond order $= \frac{1}{2}(3-2) = \frac{1}{2}$

       Li_2^- $(\sigma_{1s})^2(\sigma*_{1s})^2(\sigma_{2s})^2(\sigma*_{2s})^1$ Bond order $= \frac{1}{2}(4-3) = \frac{1}{2}$

       Li_2 $(\sigma_{1s})^2(\sigma*_{1s})^2(\sigma_{2s})^2(\sigma*_{2s})^0$ Bond order $= \frac{1}{2}(4-2) = 1$

The bond order of Li_2 is greater than that of either of its ions.

10.36

$\sigma*_{2p}$

$\pi*_{2p}$

σ_{2p}

π_{2p}

$\sigma*_{2s}$

σ_{2s}

The C_2^{2-} ion has a bond order of $\frac{1}{2}(8-2) = 3$ (one σ bond and two π bonds). The C_2 molecule has two fewer electrons and a bond order of $\frac{1}{2}(6-2) = 2$. The C_2^{2-} ion is diamagnetic.

10.37 O_2:   [core electrons]$(\sigma_{2s})^2(\sigma*_{2s})^2(\pi_{2p})^4(\sigma_{2p})^2(\pi*_{2p})^2$

       O_2^-:   [core electrons]$(\sigma_{2s})^2(\sigma*_{2s})^2(\pi_{2p})^4(\sigma_{2p})^2(\pi*_{2p})^3$

       O_2^{2-}:   [core electrons]$(\sigma_{2s})^2(\sigma*_{2s})^2(\pi_{2p})^4(\sigma_{2p})^2(\pi*_{2p})^4$

Property	O_2	O_2^-	O_2^{2-}
(a) magnetic character	paramagnetic	paramagnetic	diamagnetic
(b) net number of σ bonds	1	1	1
net number of π bonds	1	$\frac{1}{2}$	0
(c) bond order	2	1.5	1
(d) bond length	short	medium	long

10.38   (a)   [core electrons]$(\sigma_{2s})^2(\sigma*_{2s})^2(\pi_{2p})^4(\sigma_{2p})^2$

       (b)   The HOMO is σ_{2p}

       (c)   diamagnetic

       (d)   Bond order $= \frac{1}{2}(8-2) = 3$ One σ bond and two π bonds

10.39   (a)   The NO^+ ion has an even number of valence electrons (10 electrons) and so is predicted to be diamagnetic.

       (b) NO^+: [core electrons]$(\sigma_{2s})^2(\sigma*_{2s})^2(\pi_{2p})^4(\sigma_{2p})^2$ The HOMO is σ_{2p}

       (c)   Bond order $= \frac{1}{2}(8-2) = 3$

       (d)   The bond order of NO is 2.5, whereas that of NO^+ is 3. Therefore, NO^+ has a stronger bond than NO.

10.40 A single magnesium atom has one $2s$ and three $2p$ valence orbitals that it can contribute to metallic bonding, and four molecular orbitals are possible. From 100 atoms, 400 molecular orbitals are formed. Each magnesium atom contributes two valence electrons, for a total of 200 electrons. Each molecular orbital is capable of holding 2 electrons, so 100 of the orbitals are populated.

10.41 Each lithium atom contributes one valence electron, for a total of $1 \times (6.022 \times 10^{23})$ electrons. The band of orbitals can hold a total of $8 \times (6.022 \times 10^{23})$ electrons, so one-eighth of the orbitals will be filled up to the Fermi level.

10.42 (a) SO_2 120° sp^2

(b) SO_3 120° sp^2

(c) SO_3^{2-} 109° sp^3

(d) SO_4^{2-} 109° sp^3

SO_2 and SO_3 have the same bond angle and the S atom in each uses the same hybrid orbitals. SO_3^{2-} and SO_4^{2-} have the same bond angle and the S atom in each uses the same hybrid orbitals.

10.43

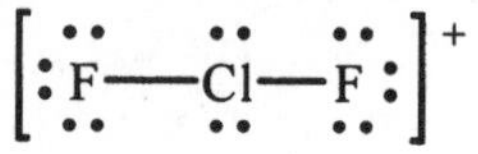

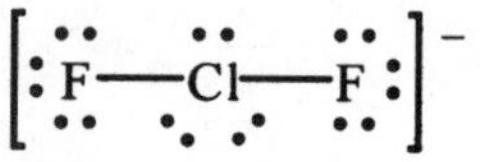

electron-pair geometry	tetrahedral	trigonal bipyramidal
molecular geometry	bent	linear
Cl atom hybridization	sp^3	sp^3d

10.44

electron-pair geometry: trigonal pyramidal

molecular geometry: bent

O—N—O bond angle = 120°

Average bond order = $^3/_2$

N atom hybridization: sp^2

10.45

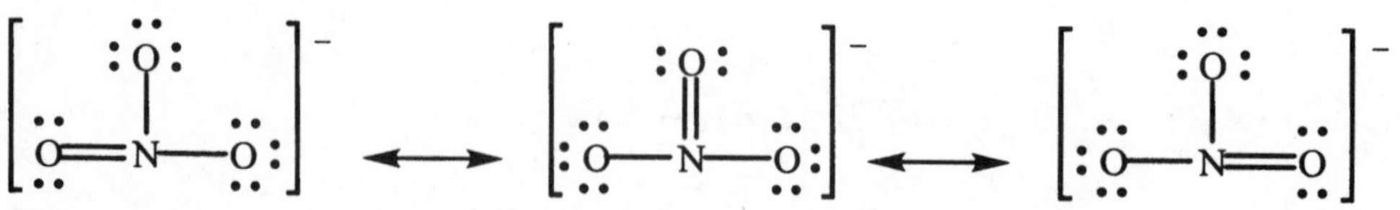

The N atom hybridization is the same in each structure (sp^2). The three sp^2 hybrid orbitals are used to form N—O σ bonds. The p orbital not used in the N atom hybrid orbitals is used to form the NO π bond.

10.46   :N≡N—Ö: ⟷   N̈=N=Ö̈ ⟷   :N̈—N≡O:

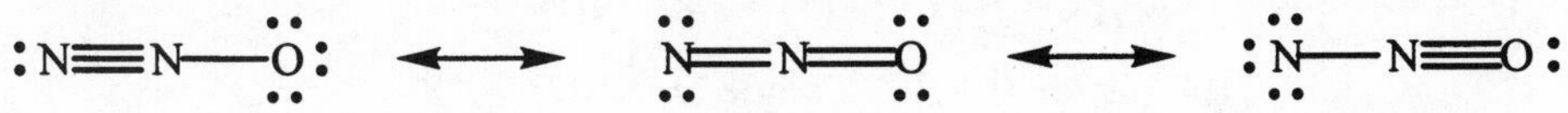

In each structure the central N atom is *sp* hybridized. The other N atom hybridization changes from *sp* to *sp²* to *sp³*. The two *sp* hybrid orbitals on the central N atom are used to form N—N and N—O σ bonds. The two *p* orbitals not used in the N atom hybridization are used to form NN and NO π bonds.

10.47

	O—C—O bond angle	CO bond order	C atom hybridization
CO_2	180°	2	*sp*
CO_3^{2-}	120°	$^4/_3$	*sp²*

10.48   (a) carbon 1: *sp²*   carbon 2: *sp²*

(b) angle A = 120°; angle B = 120°; angle C = 120°

(c) No, *cis-trans* isomerism is not possible

10.49   (a) CH_3 carbon atom: *sp³*

C=N carbon atom: *sp²*

N atom: *sp²*

(b) C—N—O angle = 120°

10.50   (a) All three molecules have the same molecular formula, C_2H_4O. They are isomers.

(b) Both carbon atoms in ethylene oxide are *sp³* hybridized. The CH_3 carbon in acetaldehyde is *sp³* hybridized and the C=O carbon is *sp²* hybridized. Both carbon atoms in vinyl alcohol are *sp²* hybridized.

(c)

	H—C—H angle
ethylene oxide	109°
acetaldehyde	109°
vinyl alcohol	120°

(d) All three molecules are polar.

(e) Vinyl alcohol has the strongest carbon-carbon bond, and acetaldehyde has the strongest carbon-oxygen bond.

10.51   (a) angle A = 120°; angle B = 109°; angle C = 109°; angle D = 120°

(b) carbon 1: *sp²*; carbon 2: *sp²*; carbon 3: *sp³*

10.52   (a) 1 π bond and 11 σ bonds.

(b) C(1) = *sp³*, C(2) = *sp²*, O(3) = *sp³*

(c) The C=O bond is the shortest and strongest CO bond.

(d) angle A = 109°, angle B = 109°, angle C = 120°

10.53   (a) $C(1) = sp^2$; $O(2) = sp^3$; $N(3) = sp^3$; $C(4) = sp^3$; $P(5) = sp^3$

(b)   angle A = 120°; angle B = 109°; angle C = 109°; angle D = 109°

(c)   The P—O and O—H bonds are most polar ($\Delta\chi = 1.4$)

10.54   (a)   The geometry about the boron atom is trigonal planar in BF_3, tetrahedral in H_3N—BF_3.

(b)   Boron is sp^2 hybridized in BF_3, sp^3 hybridized in H_3N—BF_3.

(c)   Yes

10.55   (a)   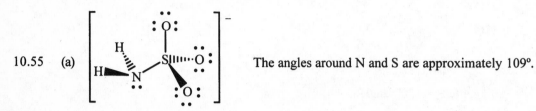   The angles around N and S are approximately 109°.

(b)   The hybridization of the N atom does not change (sp^3 in NH_2^- and $H_2N{\rightarrow}SO_3^-$). The S atom hybridization changes from sp^2 in SO_3 to sp^3 in $H_2N{\rightarrow}SO_3^-$.

10.56   (a) sp^3d in SbF_5, sp^3d^2 in SbF_6^-

(b) $\left[H\text{——}\overset{\bullet\bullet}{\underset{\bullet\bullet}{F}}\text{——}H \right]^+$ The geometry of H_2F^+ is bent, and the F atom is sp^3 hybridized.

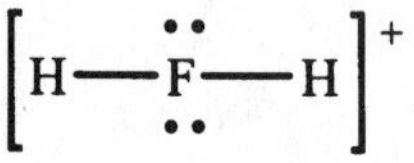

10.57

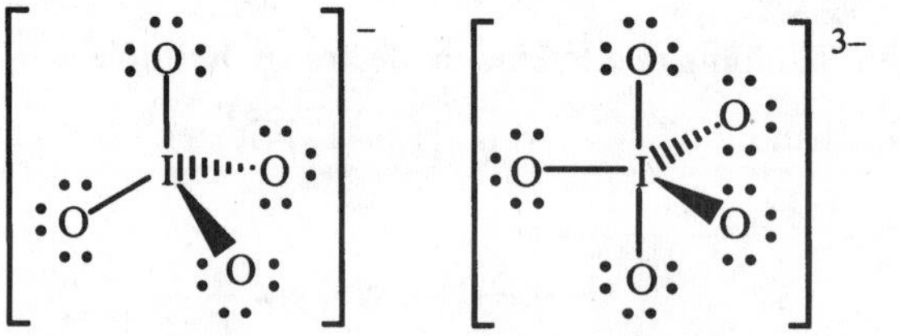

electron-pair geometry	tetrahedral	trigonal bipyramidal
molecular geometry	tetrahedral	trigonal bipyramidal
hybridization of I atom	sp^3	sp^3d

10.58   (a)   The C=O bond is the most polar bond in the molecule.

(b)   There are 18 σ bonds and 5 π bonds in the molecule.

(c)   The *trans* isomer is shown. The *cis* isomer is

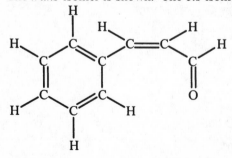

(d) All carbon atoms in the molecule are sp^2 hybridized.

(e) All three angles are 120°.

10.59

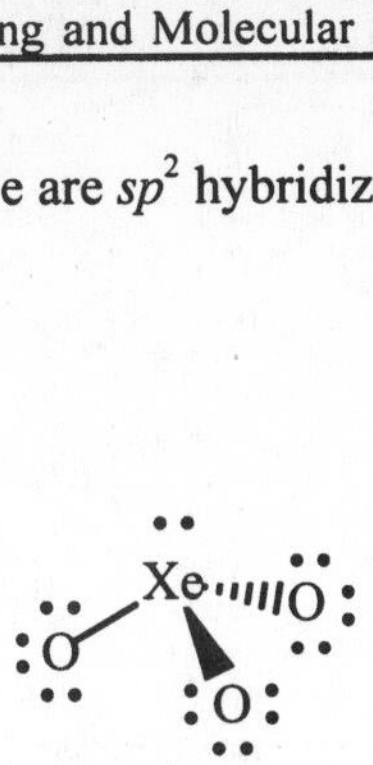

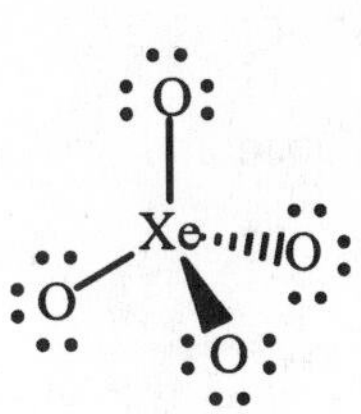

Electron-pair geometry	tetrahedral	tetrahedral
Molecular geometry	trigonal pyramidal	tetrahedral
Xe	sp^3 hybridized	sp^3 hybridized

10.60 (a) 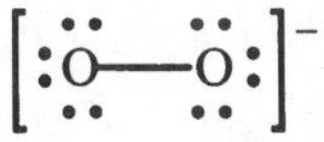 $\left[:\overset{..}{\underset{..}{O}}\text{—}\overset{..}{\underset{..}{O}}: \right]^-$ bond order = 1

(b) [core electrons]$(\sigma_{2s})^2(\sigma*_{2s})^2(\pi_{2p})^4(\sigma_{2p})^2(\pi*_{2p})^4$ bond order = $^1/_2(8-6)=1$

(c) Yes, the two bonding theories lead to the same magnetic character (diamagnetic) and bond order.

10.61 N_2 [core electrons]$(\sigma_{2s})^2(\sigma*_{2s})^2(\pi_{2p})^4(\sigma_{2p})^2$

N_2^+ [core electrons]$(\sigma_{2s})^2(\sigma*_{2s})^2(\pi_{2p})^4(\sigma_{2p})^1$

N_2^- [core electrons]$(\sigma_{2s})^2(\sigma*_{2s})^2(\pi_{2p})^4(\sigma_{2p})^2(\pi*_{2p})^1$

		N_2	N_2^+	N_2^-
(a)		diamagnetic	paramagnetic	paramagnetic
(b)		2 π bonds	2 π bonds	1 ½ π bonds
(c)	bond order	3	2 ½	2 ½

(d) $N_2 < N_2^+ \approx N_2^-$

—increasing bond length→

(e) $N_2^+ \approx N_2^- < N_2$

—increasing bond strength→

10.62 B_2 and O_2 are diamagnetic, Li_2, B_2, and F_2 have a bond order of 1, C_2 and O_2 have a bond order of 2, and N_2 has the highest bond order, 3.

10.63

Molecule or ion	Magnetic behavior	HOMO
NO	paramagnetic	$\pi*$
Ne_2^+	paramagnetic	$\sigma*_{2p}$
OF^-	diamagnetic	$\pi*$
CN	paramagnetic	σ_{2p}
O_2^{2-}	diamagnetic	$\pi*$

10.64   CN   [core electrons]$(\sigma_{2s})^2(\sigma^*_{2s})^2(\pi_{2p})^4(\sigma_{2p})^1$

(a)   The HOMO is σ_{2p}

(b)   Bond order = $\frac{1}{2}(7 - 2) = 2\frac{1}{2}$

(c)   One-half net σ bond and two net π bonds

(d)   paramagnetic

10.65   (a) C_6 ring carbon atoms: sp^2; side chain carbon atoms: sp^3; N atom: sp^3

(b)   angle A = 120°; angle B = 109°; angle C = 109°

(c)   23 σ bonds and 3 π bonds

(d)   The molecule is polar

(e)   The H^+ ion attaches to the most electronegative atom in the molecule, N

10.66   (a)   All of the C atoms are sp^3 hybridized

(b)   C—O—H angle = 109°

(c)   The molecule is polar

(d)   The six-member ring is non-planar. The ring could only be planar if the carbon atoms were sp^2 hybridized as in benzene.

10.67

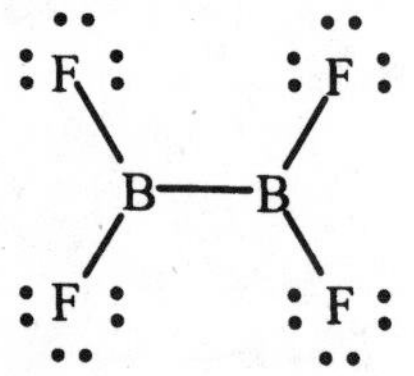

B is sp^2 hybridized, F—B—B = 120°

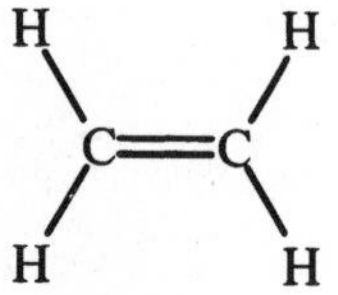

C is sp^2 hybridized, H—C—C = 120°

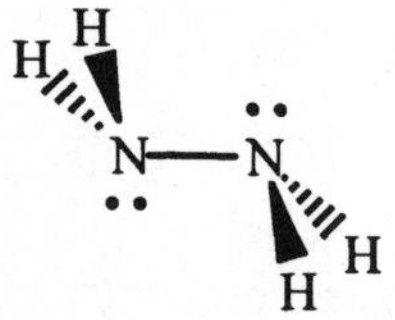

N is sp^3 hybridized, H—N—N = 109°

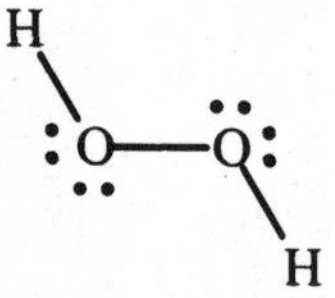

O is sp^3 hybridized, H—O—O = 109°

10.68   In a conductor, the valence band is only partially filled, allowing for relatively easy promotion to slightly higher energy levels. In an insulator, however, the valence band is completely filled, and the band gap between the valence band and conduction band is relatively large.

10.69   The band gap in silicon is smaller than that in diamond, so it is a better conductor.

10.70   Germanium should be a better conductor than diamond due to its smaller band gap, but it should be a much poorer conductor than a metal such as lithium.

10.71   Nitrogen exits as discrete N_2 molecules with localized orbitals, not "supermolecules" held together by delocalized bonds.

10.72   (a) C atom: sp^2; N atom: sp^3

       (b) Another resonance structure (showing only the peptide linkage and the formal charges on O and N) is

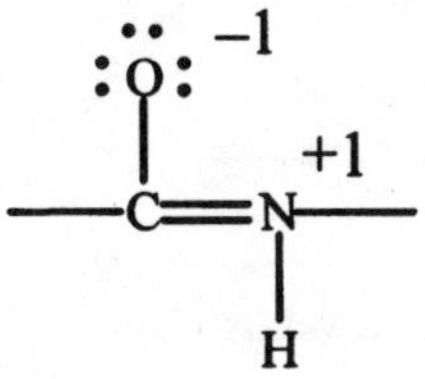

This resonance structure is less important owing to the separation of charges.

       (c) The fact that the amide link is planar indicates that the resonance structure shown above has some importance.

10.73   (a) The keto and enol forms are not resonance structures because both electron pairs and atoms have been rearranged.

       (b) The terminal —CH₃ carbon atoms are sp^3 hybridized and the three central carbon atoms are sp^2 hybridized in the enol form. In the keto form, the terminal —CH₃ carbon atoms and the central C atom are sp^3 hybridized and the two C=O carbon atoms are sp^2 hybridized.

       (c)

Enol form:	—CH₃ carbon atoms	tetrahedral
	central three carbon atoms	trigonal planar
Keto form:	—CH₃ carbon atoms	tetrahedral
	central —CH₂— carbon atom	tetrahedral
	C=O carbon atoms	trigonal planar

Only the center carbon atom changes geometry, from trigonal planar to tetrahedral

       (d)

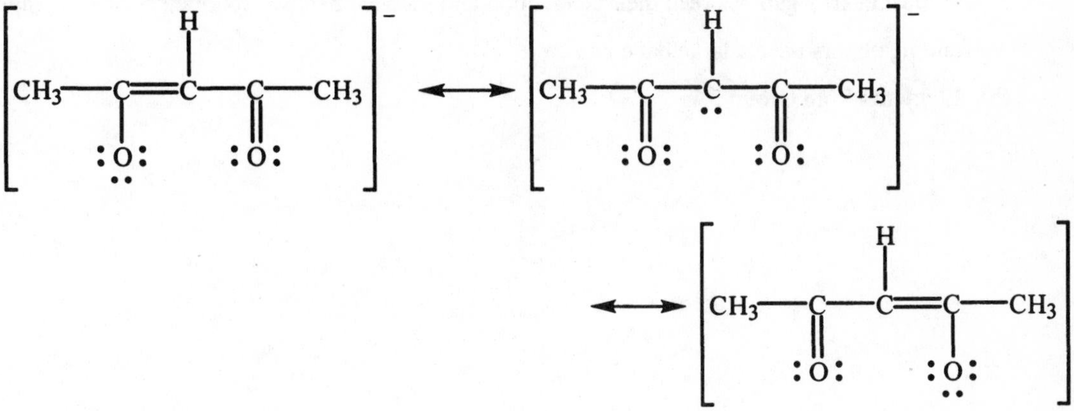

       (e) Not possible for either form

10.74   (a) Even though the atoms are sp^3 hybridized, the bond angles in the three-member ring must be 60°.

        (b) sp^3

        (c) Because the angles are significantly less than the expected value of 109°, the ring structure is strained and relatively easy to break. (The molecule is reactive.)

10.75   (a) The attractive forces must be greater than the repulsive forces if a covalent bond is to form.

        (b) When the atoms are widely separated, attractive and repulsive forces are minimized. As they approach each other, attractive forces increase until the energy reaches a minimum. As they approach still more closely, repulsive forces are maximized.

        (c) Unlike fluorine, neon does not have any orbitals with a single, unpaired electron.

10.76   (a) The number of hybrid orbitals is always equal to the number of atomic orbitals used.

        (b) No. All hybrid orbital sets involve an s orbital.

        (c) The energy of the hybrid orbital set is the weighted average of the energy of the combining atomic orbitals.

        (d) The shapes are identical. They are oriented in different directions in space.

        (e) As in (d), these hybrid orbitals have the same shape, but they are oriented in different planes.

10.77   (a) and (b) See the explanations on the Screen 10.7 "A Closer Look" sidebar.

        (c) C(1) sp^3; C(2) sp^2; C(3) sp^2

10.78   The molecule with the double bond requires a great deal more energy because the π bond must be broken in order for the ends of the molecule to rotate relative to each other.

10.79   The band is only half-filled because lithium has only one electron in the $2s$ orbital.

10.80   (a) Semiconductors have a filled valence band and conduct with a small input of energy because of the modest energy gap between their conduction and valence bands. Conductors have a small band gap and insulators have a large band gap.

        (b) Elements from Group 3A

Chapter 11
Carbon: More Than Just Another Element

INSTRUCTOR'S NOTES

The major theme of this chapter is the structure and reactivity of organic compounds. In presenting chemical reactivity, we introduce only a very few reaction types and then encourage the student to see how these could be put together to synthesize more complex organic compounds. As one can see from this chapter, we also believe it is important to use models when teaching the subject. The students needs to be trained to see molecular structures in three dimensions.

Many of the figures in the textbook and in this Manual were prepared using "ChemDraw" from CambridgeSoft Corporation. The molecular models pictured in this chapter were created using the CAChe modeling program, and all the models are included in the models folder on the *General Chemistry Interactive CD-ROM*.

SUGGESTED DEMONSTRATIONS

1. Organic Demonstrations

    - Silversmith, E. F. "Organic Lecture Demonstrations," *Journal of Chemical Education* **1988**, *65*, 70.

    - Bronice, R. "Saturated and Unsaturated Fats: An Organic Chemistry Demonstration," *Journal of Chemical Education* **1985**, *62*, 320.

2. Polymers

    - Shakhashiri, B. Z. *Chemical Demonstrations: A Handbook for Teachers of Chemistry*; University of Wisconsin Press, 1983; Vol. 1.

    - Kolb, K. E.; Kolb, D. K. "Method for Separating or Identifying Plastics," *Journal of Chemical Education* **1991**, *68*, 348.

    - Cross-linked polyvinyl alcohol (Figure 11.15) is a student favorite. About 40 grams of PVA are dissolved by heating in a liter of water. (Leave several hours for this process.) Solid sodium borate is stirred into a small quantity of this solution until cross-linking occurs to give the slimy material. To make the demonstration even more graphic, the slime can be colored with food coloring.

    - Nylon-66 is quite simple to synthesize (Figure 11.18). With care our students once were able to pull a continuous filament that stretched from the front of a large lecture room to the back.

    - Sperling, L. H. "On the Cross-Linked Structure of Rubber," *Journal of Chemical Education* **1982**, *59*, 651.

Solutions to Study Questions

11.1

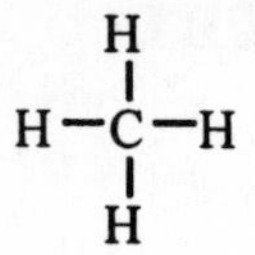

methane — four single bonds

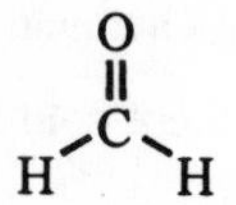

formaldehyde — one double bond and two single bonds

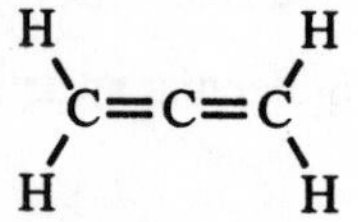

allene — two double bonds

H—C≡C—H — acetylene — one single bond and one triple bond

11.2   The restricted rotation around C=C double bonds is due to the π bond formed from overlap of unhybridized *p* orbitals on adjacent carbon atoms. Rotation around a C=C bond breaks this π bond, which requires more energy than rotation around a carbon-carbon sigma bond.

11.3   (a)

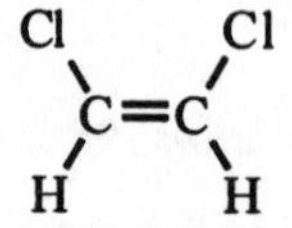

cis isomer 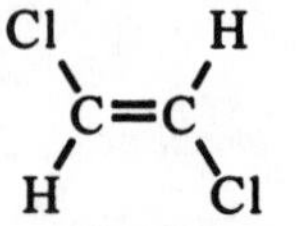   *trans* isomer

(b)

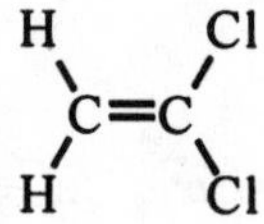

11.4

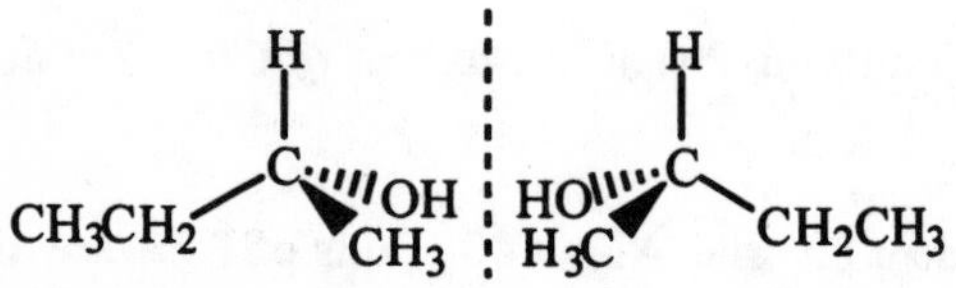

The chiral C atom is the atom to which the OH group is attached. Mirror images of the molecule are not superimposable.

11.5   There are five isomers with the formula C_6H_{14}, and they are shown in Example 11.1 (page 428). None of the five isomers are chiral.

11.6

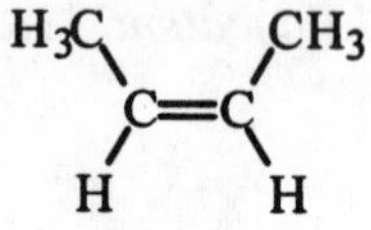

cis-2-butene 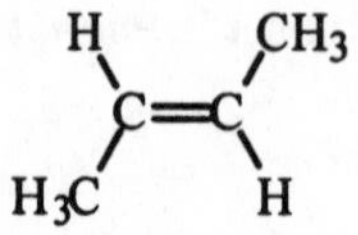   *trans*-2-butene 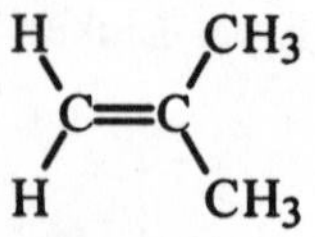   2-methylpropene 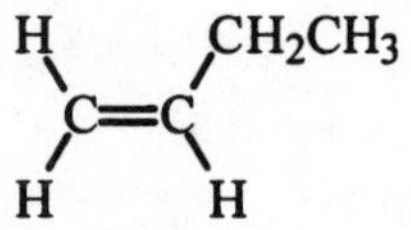   1-butene

11.7   (a) $\underset{H_3C}{\overset{H}{C}}=\underset{CH_3}{\overset{H}{C}}$ + H_2O → $H-\underset{CH_3}{\overset{H}{C}}-\underset{CH_3}{\overset{OH}{C}}-H$

(b) $\underset{H_3C}{\overset{H}{C}}=\underset{CH_3}{\overset{H}{C}}$ + H_2 → $H-\underset{CH_3}{\overset{H}{C}}-\underset{CH_3}{\overset{H}{C}}-H$

(c) $\underset{H_3C}{\overset{H}{C}}=\underset{CH_3}{\overset{H}{C}}$ + Br_2 → $H-\underset{CH_3}{\overset{H}{C}}-\underset{CH_3}{\overset{Br}{C}}-H$

(d) $\underset{H_3C}{\overset{H}{C}}=\underset{CH_3}{\overset{H}{C}}$ + Cl_2 → $H-\underset{CH_3}{\overset{Cl}{C}}-\underset{CH_3}{\overset{Cl}{C}}-H$

11.8   (a) $CH_3CH_2CH_2\overset{O}{\overset{\|}{C}}-OH$ butanoic acid

(b) $CH_3\overset{O}{\overset{\|}{C}}CH_2CH_3$ 2-butanone

(c)   NR

(d) $CH_3\underset{CH_3}{\overset{O}{\overset{\|}{C}HC}}-OH$ 2-methylpropanoic acid

11.9   (a) $H_3C-\overset{O}{\overset{\|}{C}}-OH + NaOH$ → $\left[H_3C-\overset{O}{\overset{\|}{C}}-O\right]^{-} Na^{+} + H_2O$

(b) $H_3C-\overset{H}{\overset{|}{N}}-H + HCl$ → $\left[H_3C-\underset{H}{\overset{H}{\overset{|}{\underset{|}{N}}}}-H\right]^{+} Cl^{-}$

11.10   (a) $H_3C-\overset{O}{\overset{\|}{C}}-OH$ + CH_3CH_2OH → $H_3C-\overset{O}{\overset{\|}{C}}-OCH_2CH_3$

(b) $\underset{\underset{\displaystyle H_2C-OC(CH_2)_{16}CH_3}{|}}{\overset{\displaystyle H_2C-OC(CH_2)_{16}CH_3}{\underset{|}{HC-OC(CH_2)_{16}CH_3}}}$ + 3 H_2O → $\underset{H_2COH}{\overset{H_2COH}{HCOH}}$ + 3 $R\overset{O}{\overset{\|}{C}}OH$

11.11 (a)

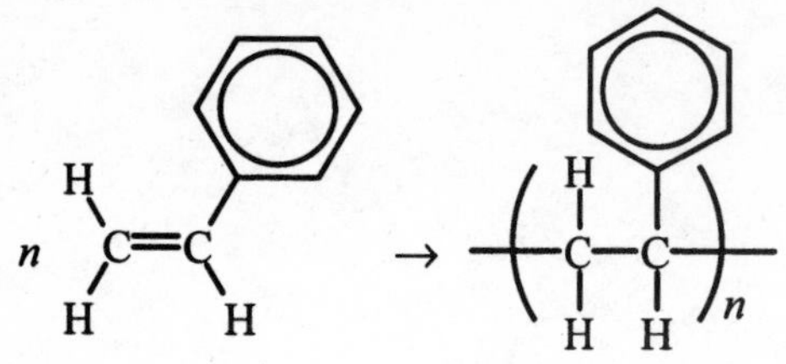

(b) 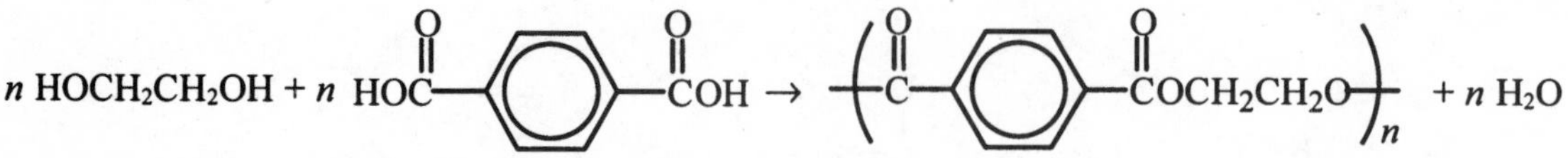 $n\ HOCH_2CH_2OH + n\ HOC$ $COH \rightarrow$ $+ n\ H_2O$

11.12 (a) 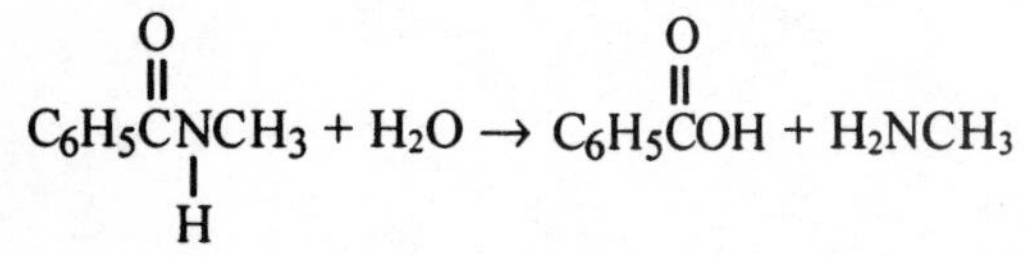 $C_6H_5\overset{O}{\overset{\|}{C}}\underset{\underset{H}{|}}{N}CH_3 + H_2O \rightarrow C_6H_5\overset{O}{\overset{\|}{C}}OH + H_2NCH_3$

(b) 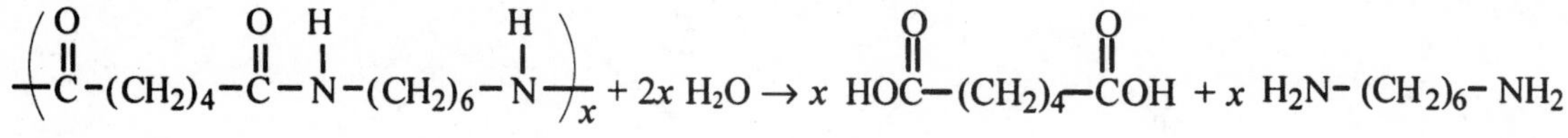 $+ 2x\ H_2O \rightarrow x\ HOC-(CH_2)_4-COH + x\ H_2N-(CH_2)_6-NH_2$

11.13 (a) carboxylic acid, ester

(b) carboxylic acid, amine

(c) alcohol, amide

11.14 (a) Crosslinking makes the material is very rigid and inflexible.

(b) The OH groups gives the polymer a high affinity for water.

(c) Hydrogen bonding allows the chains to form coils and sheets with high tensile strength.

11.15   The carbon marked * is the chiral carbon atom

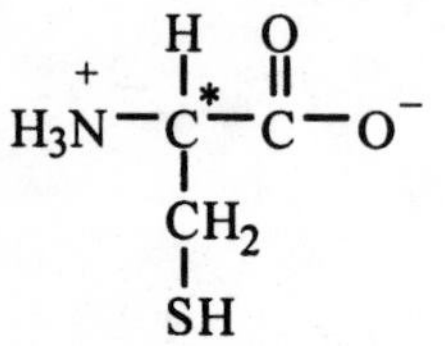

11.16 Heptane

11.17 $C_{12}H_{26}$

11.18 (c) $C_{14}H_{30}$ is an alkane

(b) C_5H_{10} could be a cycloalkane

11.19   2,2,4-trimethylpentane

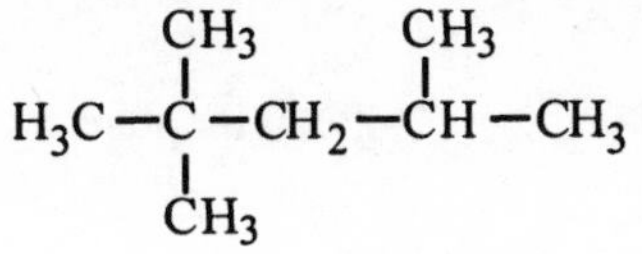

$$\underset{\overset{|}{CH_3}}{H_3C-\overset{\overset{CH_3}{|}}{\underset{|}{C}}-CH_2-\overset{\overset{CH_3}{|}}{CH}-CH_3}$$

Two other possible isomers: $H_3C-\overset{\overset{CH_3}{|}}{CH}-\overset{\overset{CH_3}{|}}{CH}-\overset{\overset{CH_3}{|}}{CH}-CH_3$ 2,3,4-trimethylpentane

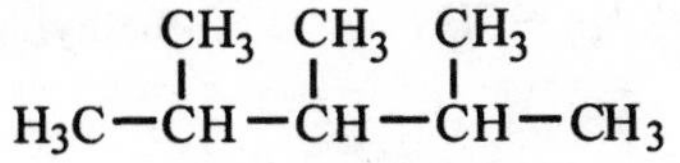

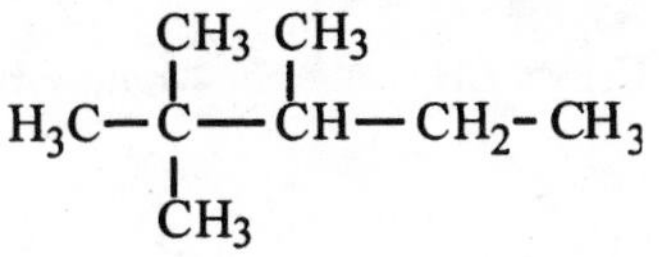

$H_3C-\overset{\overset{CH_3}{|}}{\underset{\underset{CH_3}{|}}{C}}-\overset{\overset{CH_3}{|}}{CH}-CH_2-CH_3$ 2,2,3-trimethylpentane

11.20   2,3-dimethylbutane

11.21   2,5-dimethylheptane

One possible isomer: $H_3C-\overset{\overset{CH_3}{|}}{\underset{\underset{CH_3}{|}}{C}}-CH_2-\overset{\overset{CH_3}{|}}{\underset{\underset{CH_3}{|}}{C}}-CH_3$ 2,2,4,4-tetramethylpentane

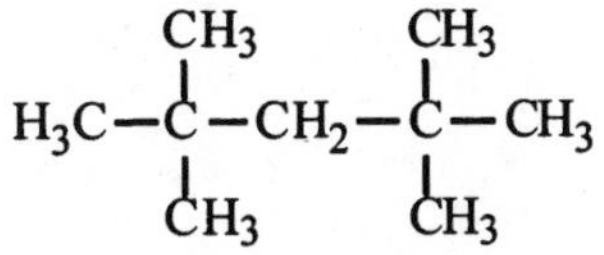

11.22   (a) $H_3C-\overset{\overset{CH_3}{|}}{\underset{\underset{CH_3}{|}}{CH}}-CH-CH_2-CH_2-CH_3$

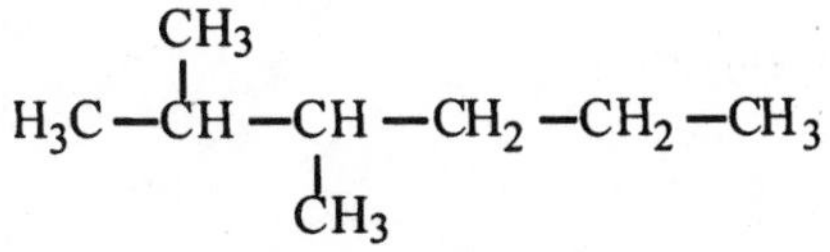

(b) $H_3C-\overset{\overset{CH_3}{|}}{\underset{\underset{CH_3}{|}}{CH}}-CH-CH_2-CH_2-CH_2-CH_2-CH_3$

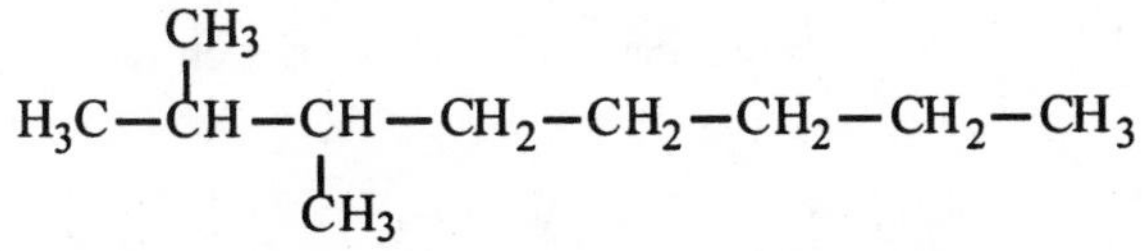

(c) $H_3C-CH_2-\overset{\overset{|}{CH_2}}{\underset{\underset{CH_3}{|}}{CH}}-CH_2-CH_2-CH_2-CH_3$

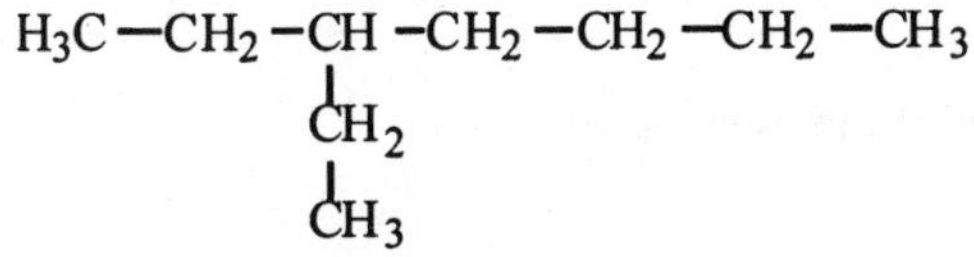

(d) $H_3C-\overset{\overset{CH_3}{|}}{CH}-\overset{\overset{|}{CH_2}}{\underset{\underset{CH_3}{|}}{CH}}-CH_2-CH_2-CH_3$

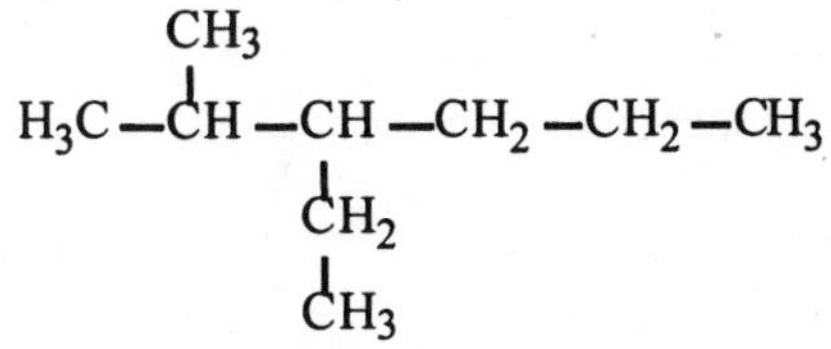

11.23 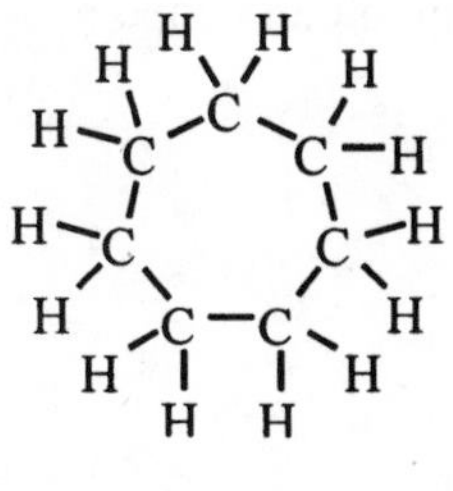   The ring is not planar. The geometry around each carbon atom is tetrahedral.

$$CH_3$$

11.24 $H_3C-CH-CH_2-CH_2-CH_2-CH_2-CH_3$ 2-methylheptane   not chiral

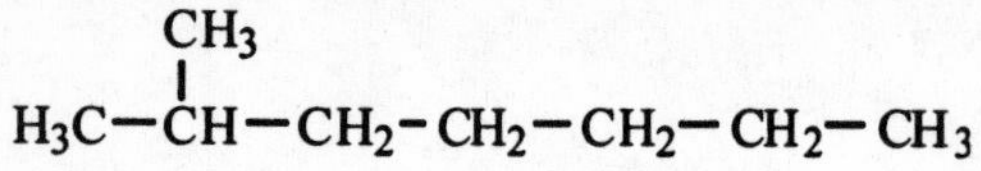

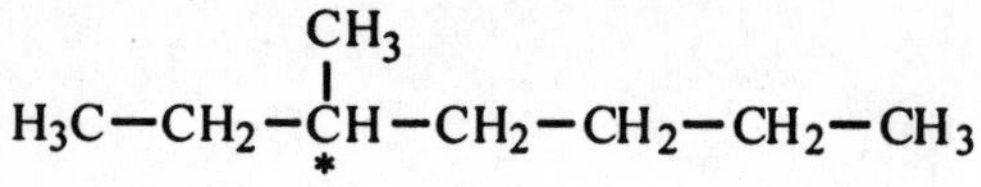

$$CH_3$$

$H_3C-CH_2-CH-CH_2-CH_2-CH_2-CH_3$ 3-methylheptane   chiral carbon (*)

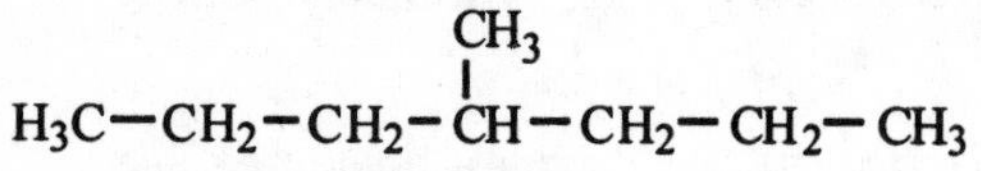

*

$$CH_3$$

$H_3C-CH_2-CH_2-CH-CH_2-CH_2-CH_3$ 4-methylheptane   not chiral

11.25

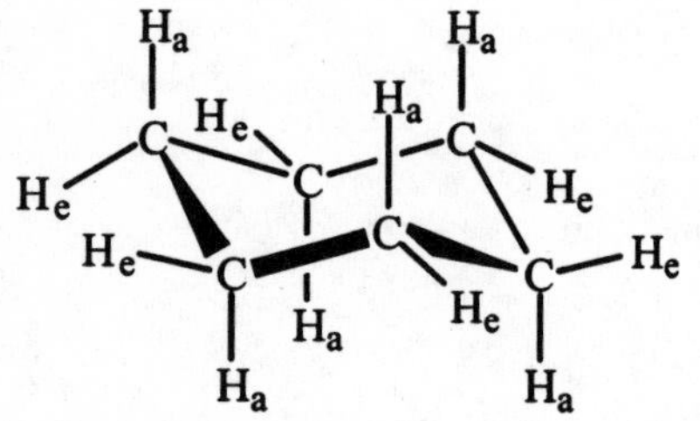

$$CH_3$$
$$CH_2$$

11.26 $H_3C-CH_2-CH-CH_2-CH_2-CH_2-CH_3$ 2-ethylheptane   not chiral

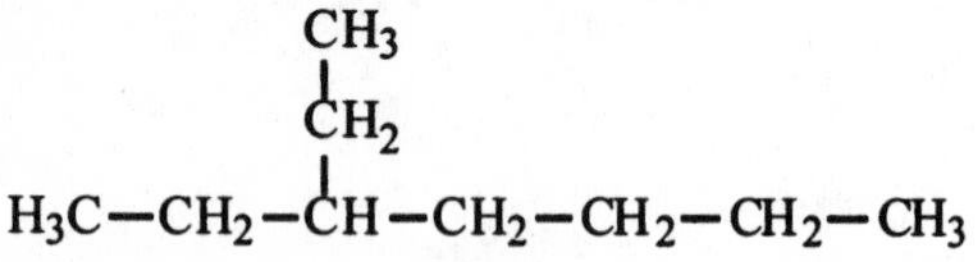

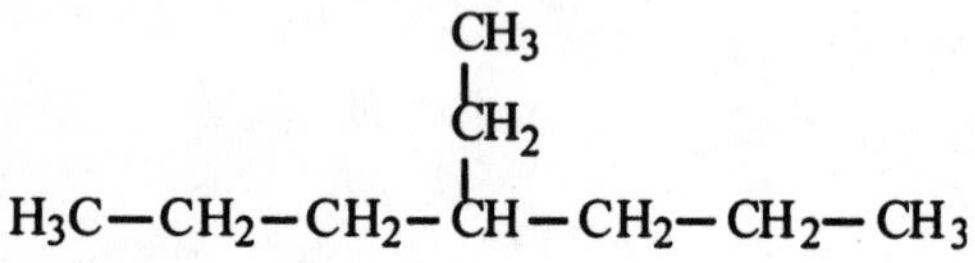

$$CH_3$$
$$CH_2$$

$H_3C-CH_2-CH_2-CH-CH_2-CH_2-CH_3$ 3-ethylheptane   not chiral

$$CH_3$$
$$CH_3 \quad CH_2$$

11.27 $H_3C-CH-CH-CH_2-CH_3$ 3-ethyl-2-methylpentane

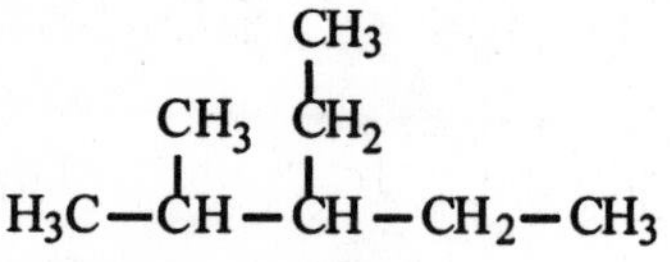

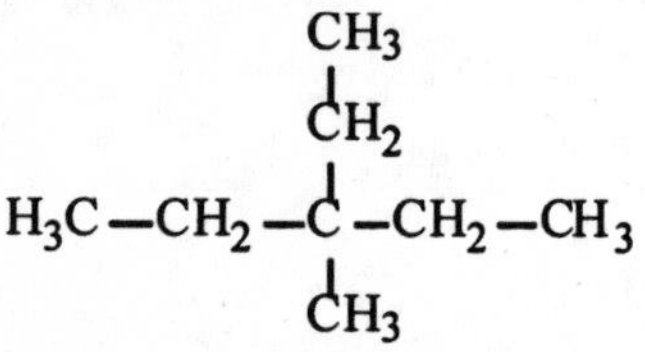

$$CH_3$$
$$CH_2$$

$H_3C-CH_2-C-CH_2-CH_3$ 3-ethyl-3-methylpentane

$$CH_3$$

11.28 C_4H_{10}, butane   Colorless gas at room temperature, insoluble in water

$C_{12}H_{26}$, dodecane   Colorless liquid at room temperature, insoluble in water, soluble in nonpolar solvent

11.29 (a) $CH_4 + 4\ Cl_2 \rightarrow CCl_4 + 4\ HCl$

(b) $C_6H_{12} + 9\ O_2 \rightarrow 6\ CO_2 + 6\ H_2O$

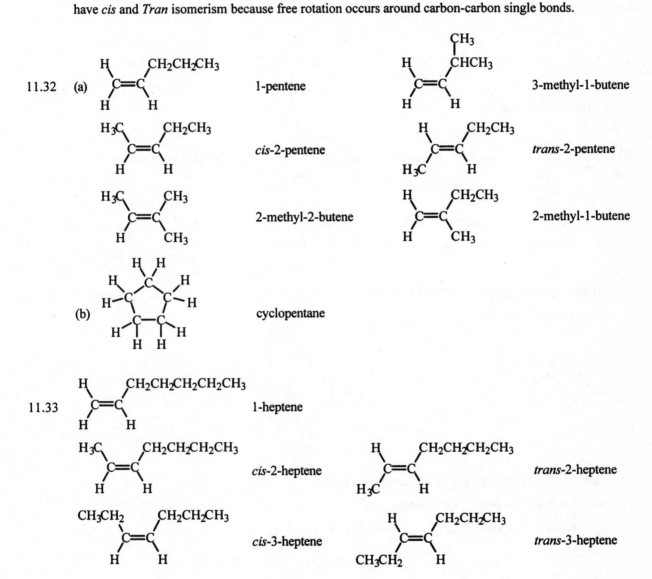

11.30

trans-4-methyl-2-hexene   cis-4-methyl-2-hexene

11.31   In order to have *cis* and *trans* isomers, the alkene must have different atoms or groups on the carbons

which are double bonded: That is, A ≠ B and X ≠ Y. Alkynes do not have *cis* and *trans*

isomerism because the *sp* hybridization of the carbon atoms produces a linear molecule. Alkenes do not

have *cis* and *Tran* isomerism because free rotation occurs around carbon-carbon single bonds.

11.32   (a)   1-pentene   3-methyl-1-butene

cis-2-pentene   trans-2-pentene

2-methyl-2-butene   2-methyl-1-butene

(b)   cyclopentane

11.33   1-heptene

cis-2-heptene   trans-2-heptene

cis-3-heptene   trans-3-heptene

11.34   (a) 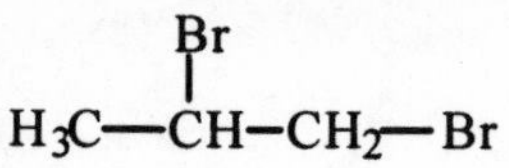 $H_3C-\underset{\underset{Br}{|}}{CH}-CH_2-Br$ 1,2-dibromopentane

(b) $CH_3CH_2CH_2CH_2CH_3$ pentane

11.35   (a) 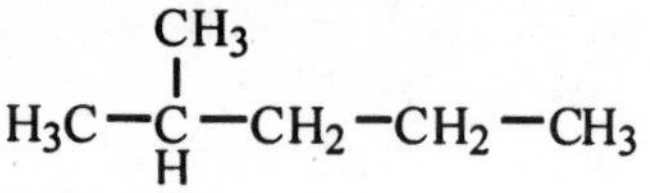 $H_3C-\underset{\underset{H}{|}}{\overset{\overset{CH_3}{|}}{C}}-CH_2-CH_2-CH_3$ 2-methylpentane

(b) 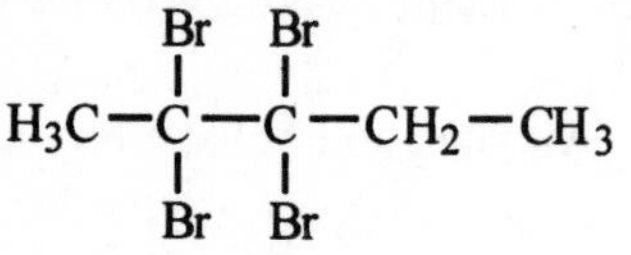 $H_3C-\underset{\underset{Br}{|}}{\overset{\overset{Br}{|}}{C}}-\underset{\underset{Br}{|}}{\overset{\overset{Br}{|}}{C}}-CH_2-CH_3$ 2,2,3,3-tetrabromopentane

11.36 $CH_3CH_2CH=CH_2$ 1-butene

11.37 $H_3C-\overset{\overset{CH_3}{|}}{C}=CHCH_2CH_2CH_3 + Br_2 \rightarrow H_3C-\underset{\underset{Br}{|}}{\overset{\overset{CH_3}{|}}{C}}-\underset{\underset{Br}{|}}{C}HCH_2CH_2CH_3$

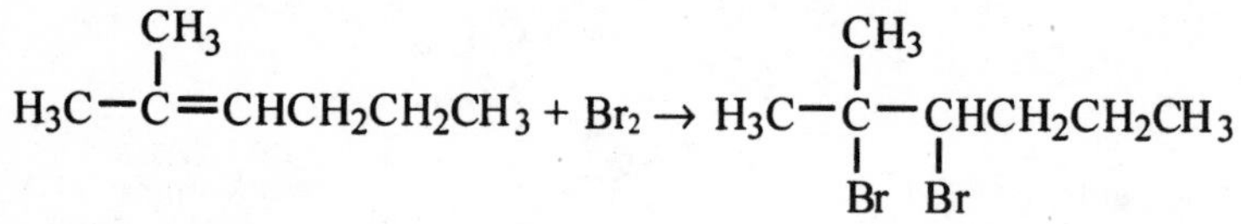

2-methyl-2-hexene

11.38 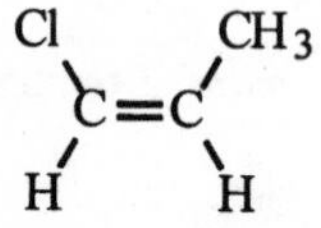   *cis*-1-chloropropene 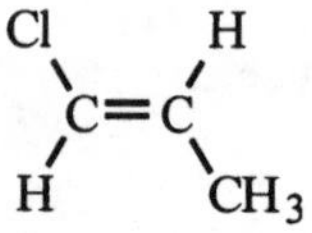   *trans*-1-chloropropene

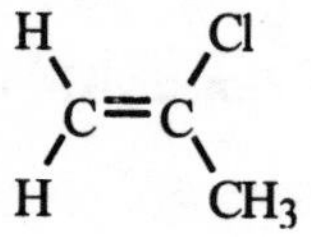

2-chloropropene 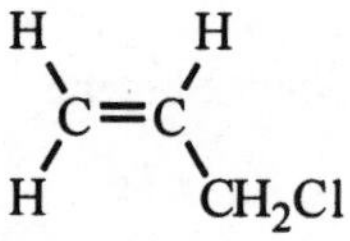   3-chloropropene

11.39   If the compound is an alkene it will react with bromine to form a substituted alkane. The alkane would not react with bromine.

11.40   (a) 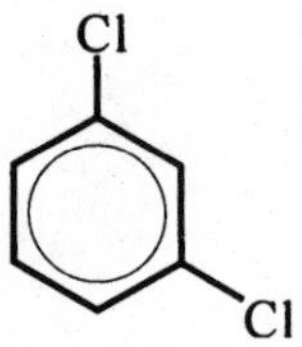   (b)

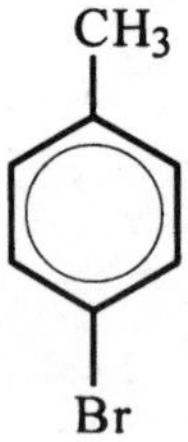

11.41   (a)   1-chloro-2-nitrobenzene (or *o*-chloronitrobenzene)

(b)   1,4-dinitrobenzene (or *p*-dinitrobenzene)

(c)   1-chloro-2-ethylbenzene (or *o*-chloroethylbenzene)

11.42   + CH_3CH_2Cl $\xrightarrow{AlCl_3}$ + HCl

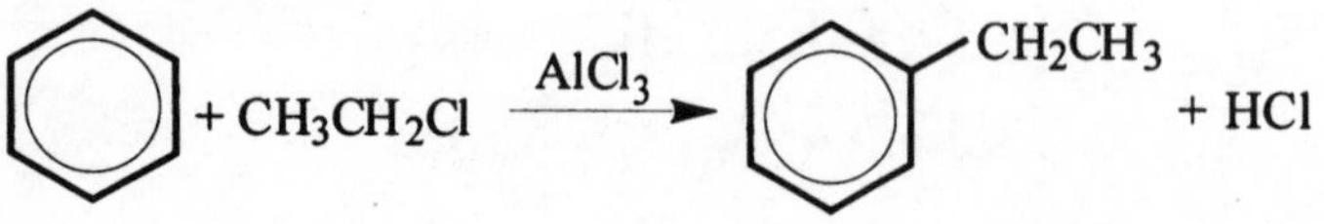

11.43 + $CH_3CH_2CH_2CH_2CH_2CH_2Cl$ $\xrightarrow{AlCl_3}$ $CH_2CH_2CH_2CH_2CH_2CH_3$ + HCl

11.44 + CH_3Cl $\xrightarrow{AlCl_3}$ 1,2,4-trimethylbenzene

11.45

11.46 (a) 1-propanol   primary

(b) 1-butanol   primary

(c) 2-methyl-2-propanol   tertiary

(d) 2-methyl-2-butanol   tertiary

11.47 (a) $HO-CH_2CH_2CH_2CH_3$ primary

(b) $CH_3\overset{\overset{\displaystyle OH}{|}}{C}HCH_2CH_3$ secondary

(c) $CH_3\overset{\overset{\displaystyle HO}{|}}{C}H\overset{\overset{\displaystyle CH_3}{|}}{\underset{\underset{\displaystyle CH_3}{|}}{C}}CH_3$ secondary

(c) $HO-CH_2CH_2\overset{\overset{\displaystyle CH_3}{|}}{\underset{\underset{\displaystyle CH_3}{|}}{C}}CH_3$ primary

11.48 (a) $C_2H_5NH_2$ $CH_3CH_2-\overset{\overset{\displaystyle H}{|}}{N}-H$

(b) $(C_3H_7)_2NH$ $CH_3CH_2CH_2-\overset{\overset{\displaystyle CH_2CH_2CH_3}{|}}{N}-H$

(c) $C_4H_9N(CH_3)_2$ $CH_3CH_2CH_2CH_2-\overset{\overset{\displaystyle CH_3}{|}}{N}-CH_3$

(d) $(C_2H_5)_3N$ $CH_3CH_2-\overset{\overset{\displaystyle CH_2CH_3}{|}}{N}-CH_2CH_3$

11.49 (a) propylamine

(b) trimethylamine

(c) ethylmethylamine

(d) hexylamine

11.50 $HO-CH_2CH_2CH_2CH_3$ 1-butanol $CH_3\overset{\overset{\displaystyle OH}{|}}{C}HCH_2CH_3$ 2-butanol

$HO-CH_2\overset{\overset{\displaystyle CH_3}{|}}{C}HCH_3$ 2-methyl-1-propanol $CH_3\overset{\overset{\displaystyle OH}{|}}{\underset{\underset{\displaystyle CH_3}{|}}{C}}CH_3$ 2-methyl-2-propanol

11.51 $H_2N-CH_2CH_2CH_2CH_3$ $CH_3\overset{\overset{\displaystyle NH_2}{|}}{C}HCH_2CH_3$ $H_2N-CH_2\overset{\overset{\displaystyle CH_3}{|}}{C}HCH_3$ $CH_3\overset{\overset{\displaystyle NH_2}{|}}{\underset{\underset{\displaystyle CH_3}{|}}{C}}CH_3$

11.52 (a) $C_6H_5NH_3^+(aq) + Cl^-(aq)$

(b) $(CH_3)_3NH^+(aq) + HSO_4^-(aq)$

11.53 (a) $CH_3CH_2CH_2CH_2-OH$ 1-butanol

(b) $CH_3\overset{\overset{\displaystyle OH}{|}}{C}HCH_2CH_2CH_2CH_3$ 2-hexanol

11.54 (a) $CH_3\overset{\overset{\displaystyle O}{\|}}{C}CH_2CH_2CH_3$ (b) $CH_3CH_2CH_2CH_2CH_2\overset{\overset{\displaystyle O}{\|}}{C}-H$ (c) $CH_3CH_2CH_2CH_2\overset{\overset{\displaystyle O}{\|}}{C}-OH$

11.55 (a) propanone; ketone   (b) butanal; aldehyde   (c) 2-pentanone; ketone

11.56 (a) 3-methylpentanoic acid; carboxylic acid

(b) methyl propanoate; ester

(c) butyl acetate, ester

(d) *p*-bromobenzoic acid; carboxylic acid

11.57 (a) $CH_3CH_2CH_2CH_2\overset{\overset{\displaystyle H_3C}{|}}{C}H-\overset{\overset{\displaystyle O}{\|}}{C}-OH$

(b) $CH_3CH_2CH_2\overset{\overset{\displaystyle O}{\|}}{C}OCH_2CH_2CH_2CH_3$

(c) $CH_3\overset{\overset{\displaystyle O}{\|}}{C}OCH_2CH_2CH_2CH_2CH_2CH_2CH_2CH_3$

11.58   (a) $CH_3CH_2CH_2CH_2\overset{\overset{\displaystyle O}{\|}}{C}-OH$ pentanoic acid

(b) $CH_3CH_2CH_2CH_2CH_2-OH$ 1-pentanol

(c) $CH_3\overset{\overset{\displaystyle OH}{|}}{C}HCH_2CH_2CH_2CH_2CH_2CH_3$ 2-octanol

(d)   no reaction

11.59   Reduction of 2-pentanone with $LiAlH_4$ or $NaBH_4$

11.60   First oxidize 1-propanol to propanoic acid using $KMnO_4$. Next react propanoic acid with 1-propanol in the presence of a strong acid to form the ester propyl propanoate and water.

11.61 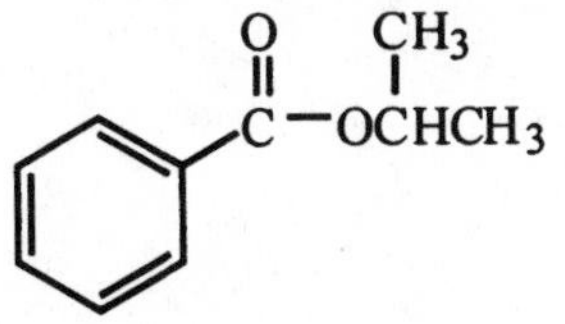   2-propyl benzoate

11.62 $CH_3\overset{\overset{\displaystyle O}{\|}}{C}O^-Na^+$ sodium acetate $HO-CH_2CH_2CH_2CH_3$ 1-butanol

11.63 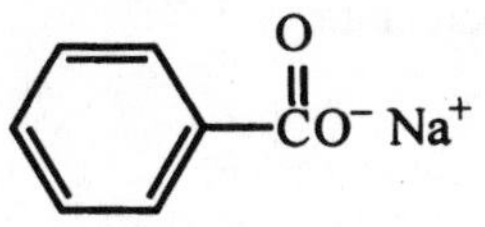   sodium benzoate $CH_3\overset{\overset{\displaystyle OH}{|}}{C}HCH_3$ 2-propanol

11.64   (a)   trigonal planar

(b)   120°

(c)   The molecule is chiral, carbon 2 is the chiral carbon atom

(d)   The —O—H hydrogen atom is acidic

11.65   (a)   120°

(b)   All of the C—O—H bond angles should be approximately 109°

(c)   The molecule is chiral, there are two chiral carbon atoms in the molecule

(d)   C=C

(e)   alcohol, alkene, ester

11.66   (a)   alcohol

(b)   amide

(c)   carboxylic acid

(d)   ester

11.67   (a) The alcohol is reduced to an alkane, $CH_3CH_2CH_2CH_3$, butane

(b) $CH_3CH_2\overset{\overset{\displaystyle O}{\|}}{C}-O\overset{\overset{\displaystyle CH_3}{|}}{C}HCH_2CH_3$ ester

(c) $CH_3CH_2CH_2OH$ 1-propanol

(d) $CH_3CH_2\overset{\overset{\displaystyle O}{\|}}{C}O^-\ Na^+$ sodium propanoate

11.68   (a)

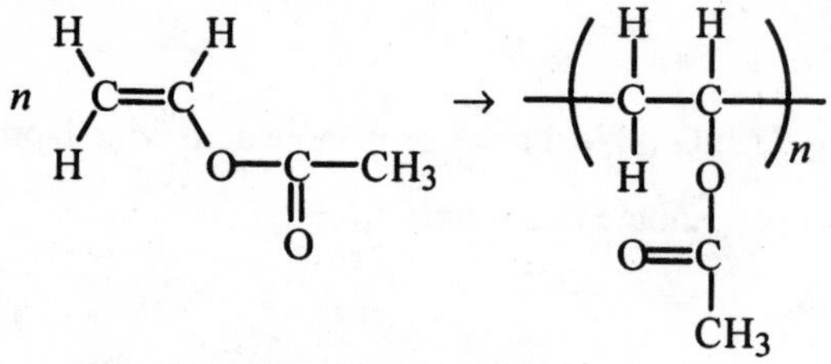

(b)

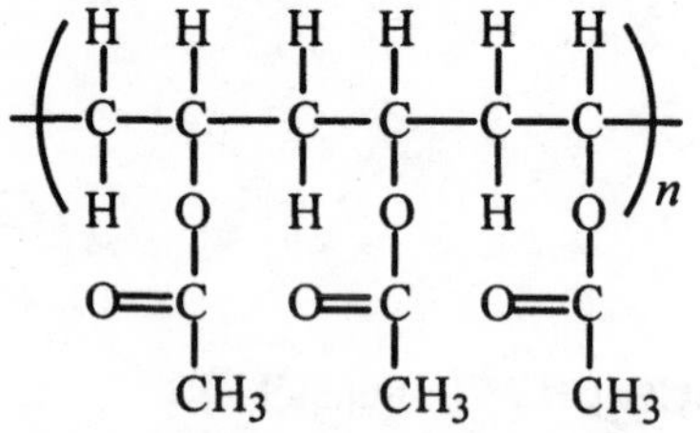

(c) Polyvinyl alcohol is made by hydrolyzing the ester groups in polyvinyl acetate.

11.69   (a)

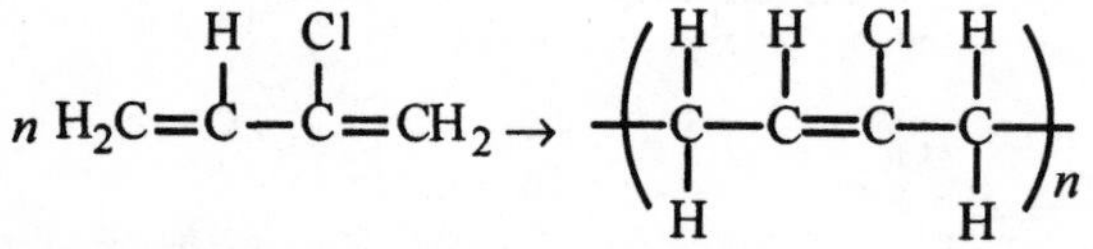

(b)

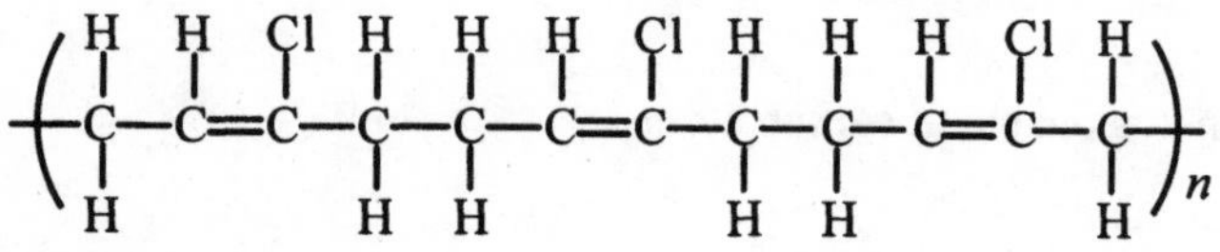

11.70

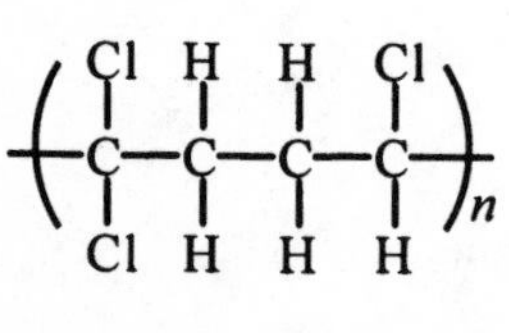

11.71

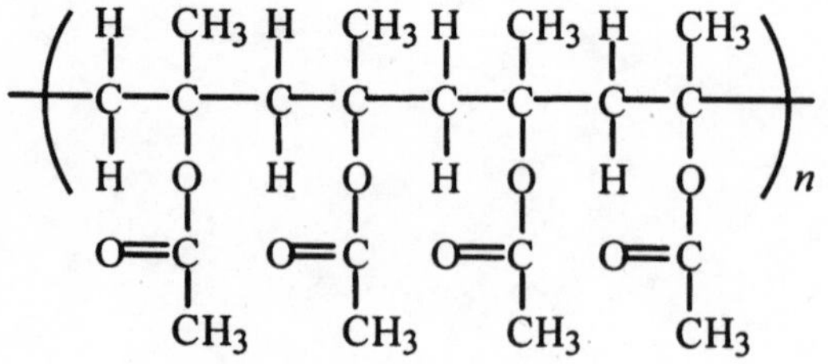

11.72 $^+H_3N-\underset{\underset{H}{|}}{\overset{\overset{H}{|}}{C}}-\underset{}{\overset{\overset{O}{||}}{C}}-\underset{}{\overset{\overset{H}{|}}{N}}-\underset{\underset{CH_2}{|}}{\overset{\overset{H}{|}}{C}}-\overset{\overset{O}{||}}{C}-\underset{}{\overset{\overset{H}{|}}{N}}-\underset{\underset{CH_3}{|}}{\overset{\overset{H}{|}}{C}}-\overset{\overset{O}{||}}{C}-O^-$

(imidazole ring with N and NH below CH_2)

11.73 $^+H_3N-\underset{\underset{CH_2}{|}}{\overset{\overset{H}{|}}{C}}-\overset{\overset{O}{||}}{C}-\underset{}{\overset{\overset{H}{|}}{N}}-\underset{\underset{CH_2}{|}}{\overset{\overset{H}{|}}{C}}-\overset{\overset{O}{||}}{C}-O^-$ with OH below each CH_2

serine + serine

$^+H_3N-\underset{\underset{CH_3}{|}}{\overset{\overset{H}{|}}{C}}-\overset{\overset{O}{||}}{C}-\underset{}{\overset{\overset{H}{|}}{N}}-\underset{\underset{CH_3}{|}}{\overset{\overset{H}{|}}{C}}-\overset{\overset{O}{||}}{C}-O^-$

alanine + alanine

$^+H_3N-\underset{\underset{CH_2}{|}}{\overset{\overset{H}{|}}{C}}-\overset{\overset{O}{||}}{C}-\underset{}{\overset{\overset{H}{|}}{N}}-\underset{\underset{CH_3}{|}}{\overset{\overset{H}{|}}{C}}-\overset{\overset{O}{||}}{C}-O^-$ with OH below CH_2

serine + alanine

$^+H_3N-\underset{\underset{CH_3}{|}}{\overset{\overset{H}{|}}{C}}-\overset{\overset{O}{||}}{C}-\underset{}{\overset{\overset{H}{|}}{N}}-\underset{\underset{CH_2}{|}}{\overset{\overset{H}{|}}{C}}-\overset{\overset{O}{||}}{C}-O^-$ with OH below CH_2

alanine + serine

11.74   (a) $H_3C-\underset{\underset{CH_3}{|}}{\overset{\overset{CH_3}{|}}{C}}-CH_2-CH_2-CH_3$

(b) $H_3C-CH_2-\underset{\underset{CH_2}{\underset{\underset{CH_3}{|}}{|}}}{\overset{\overset{CH_3}{\overset{\overset{CH_2}{|}}{|}}}{C}}-CH_2-CH_3$

(c) $H_3C-\underset{\underset{CH_3}{|}}{\overset{}{CH}}-\underset{\underset{CH_2}{\underset{\underset{CH_3}{|}}{|}}}{CH}-CH_2-CH_3$

(d) $H_3C-CH_2-\underset{\underset{CH_2}{\underset{\underset{CH_3}{|}}{|}}}{CH}-CH_2-CH_2-CH_3$

11.75   (a) $CH_3CH_2CH_2-OH$ 1-propanol   primary alcohol

$\underset{}{\overset{\overset{OH}{|}}{CH_3CHCH_3}}$ 2-propanol   secondary alcohol

$H_3C-O-CH_2CH_3$ ethylmethylether   ether

(b) $CH_3\overset{\overset{O}{||}}{C}CH_2CH_3$ $CH_3CH_2CH_2\overset{\overset{O}{||}}{CH}$

butanone   butanal

169

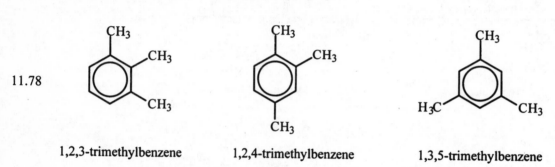

11.76 $HC-CH_2-CH_3$ (with Cl above and Cl below first C) $H_2C-CH-CH_3$ (Cl above each of first two C) $H_2C-CH_2-CH_2$ (Cl above first and third C) $H_3C-C-CH_3$ (Cl above and Cl below central C)

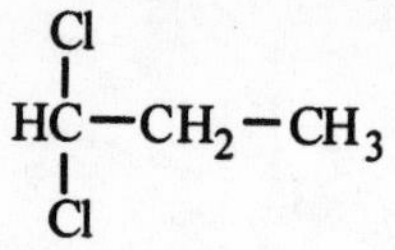

1,1-dichloropropane 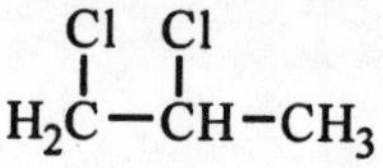   1,2-dichloropropane 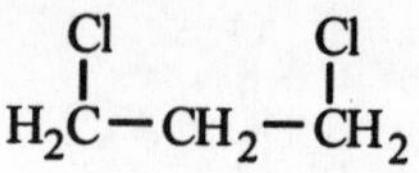   1,3-dichloropropane 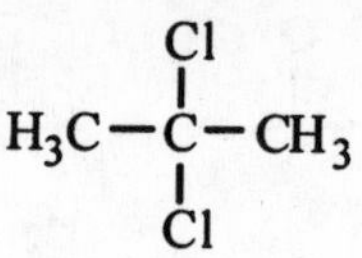   2,2-dichloropropane

11.77 $HC-CH_2-CH_3$ (Br above, Cl below first C) $H_2C-CH-CH_3$ (Br above first C, Cl above second C) $H_2C-CH-CH_3$ (Cl above first C, Br above second C)

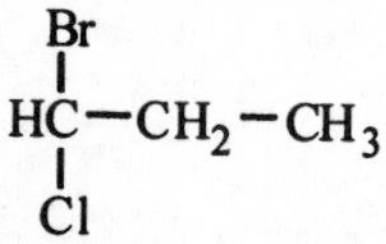

1-bromo-1-chloropropane 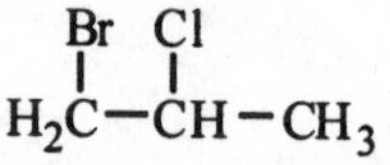   1-bromo-2-chloropropane 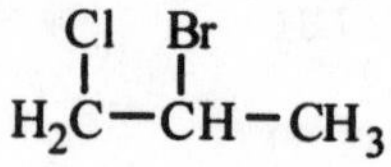   1-chloro-2-bromopropane

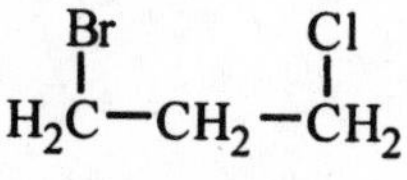

$H_2C-CH_2-CH_2$ (Br above first C, Cl above third C) $H_3C-C-CH_3$ (Br above, Cl below central C)

1-bromo-3-chlolorpropane 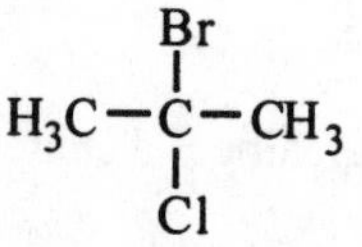   2-bromo-2-chloropropane

11.78

1,2,3-trimethylbenzene   1,2,4-trimethylbenzene   1,3,5-trimethylbenzene

11.79

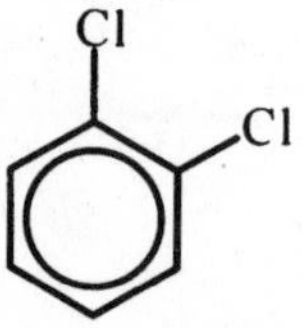

1,2-dichlorobenzene 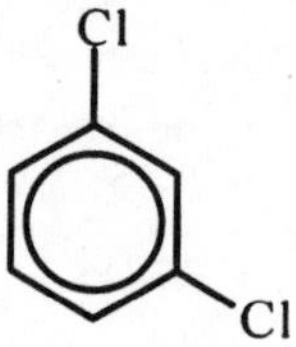   1,3-dichlorobenzene    1,4-dichlorobenzene

11.80   The —COOH group must be replaced with —H to convert lysine to cadaverine.

11.81

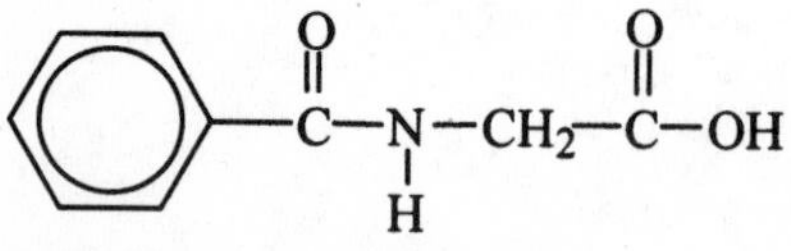

Hippuric acid is an acid because it contains a carboxylic acid group.

11.82

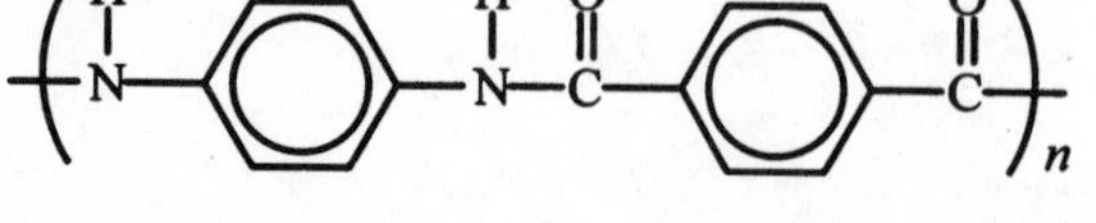

11.83

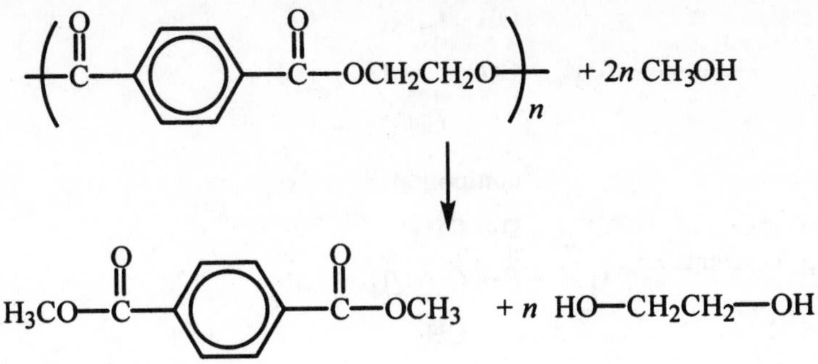

$$n \ H_3CO-\overset{\overset{\displaystyle O}{\|}}{C}-\text{(benzene ring)}-\overset{\overset{\displaystyle O}{\|}}{C}-OCH_3 \ + \ n \ HO-CH_2CH_2-OH$$

11.84

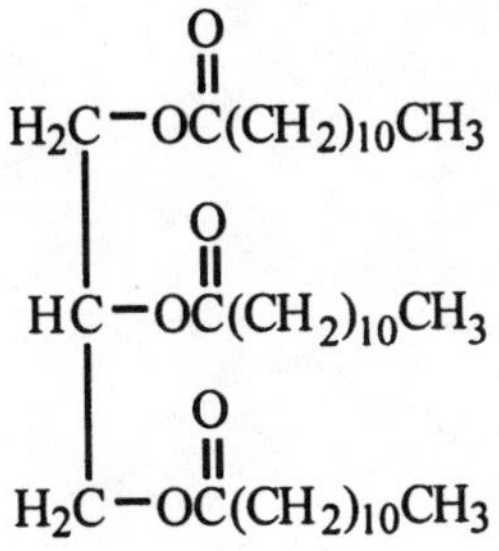

The saponification products are glycerol and sodium laurate

11.85

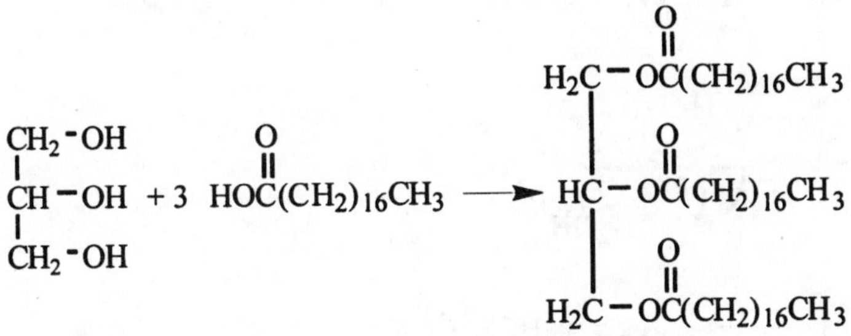

11.86   The liquid is cyclohexene.

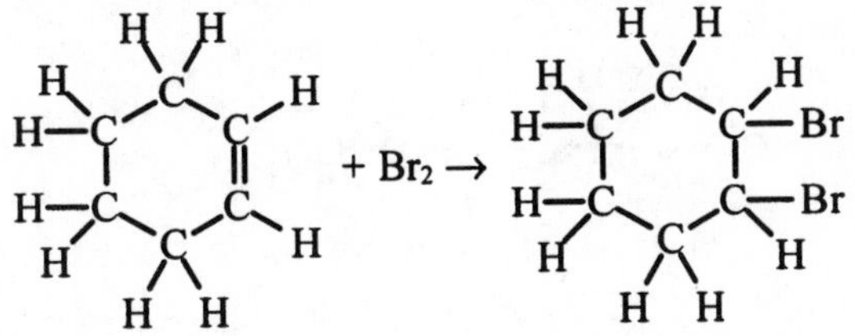

11.87

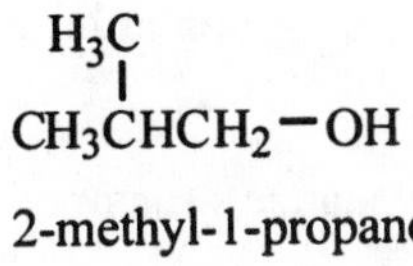

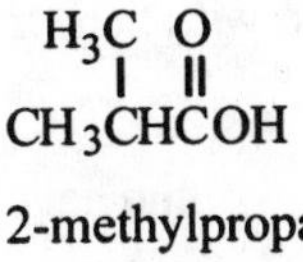

H_3C
$CH_3\overset{|}{C}HCH_2-OH$
2-methyl-1-propanol

$H_3C \ \ O$
$CH_3\overset{|}{C}H\overset{\|}{C}OH$
2-methylpropanoic acid

11.88   (a) 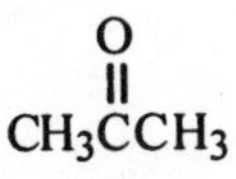 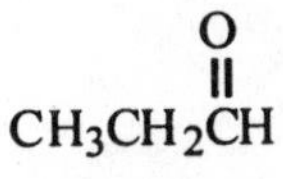 $CH_3\overset{\overset{\displaystyle O}{\|}}{C}CH_3$ 　 $CH_3CH_2\overset{\overset{\displaystyle O}{\|}}{C}H$

propanone 　 propanal

(b)   Only the aldehyde can be oxidized to a carboxylic acid. The correct structure is that of the aldehyde.

(c)   propanoic acid

11.89 $CH_3CH_2CH_2-OH$ 　 $CH_3\overset{\overset{\displaystyle OH}{|}}{C}HCH_3$ 　 $H_3C-O-CH_2CH_3$

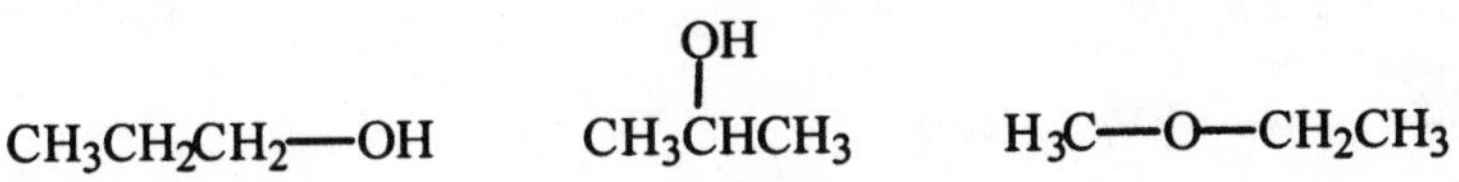

11.90 $H_2C=CH-\underset{\underset{CH_3}{|}}{\overset{\overset{CH_3}{|}}{C}}-CH_2-CH_3$ $\xrightarrow{+\;H_2O}$ $H_3C-\underset{}{\overset{\overset{OH}{|}}{CH}}-\underset{\underset{CH_3}{|}}{\overset{\overset{CH_3}{|}}{C}}-CH_2-CH_3$

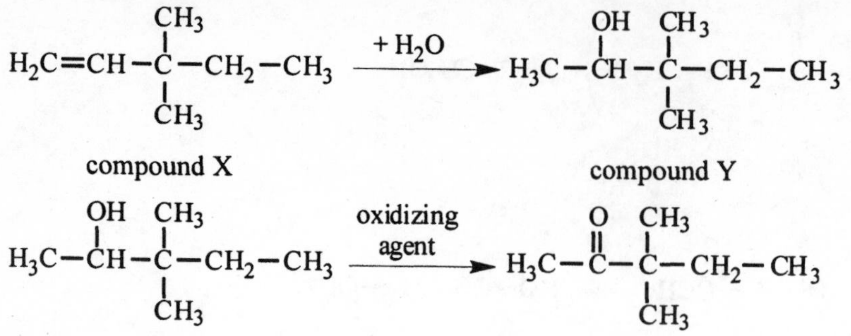

        compound X   compound Y

$H_3C-\overset{\overset{OH}{|}}{CH}-\underset{\underset{CH_3}{|}}{\overset{\overset{CH_3}{|}}{C}}-CH_2-CH_3$ $\xrightarrow[\text{agent}]{\text{oxidizing}}$ $H_3C-\overset{\overset{O}{\|}}{C}-\underset{\underset{CH_3}{|}}{\overset{\overset{CH_3}{|}}{C}}-CH_2-CH_3$

11.91 $CH_3CH_2\overset{\overset{O}{\|}}{C}-O-CH_3\; + H_2O\;\rightarrow CH_3CH_2\overset{\overset{O}{\|}}{C}-OH\; +\; HO-CH_3$

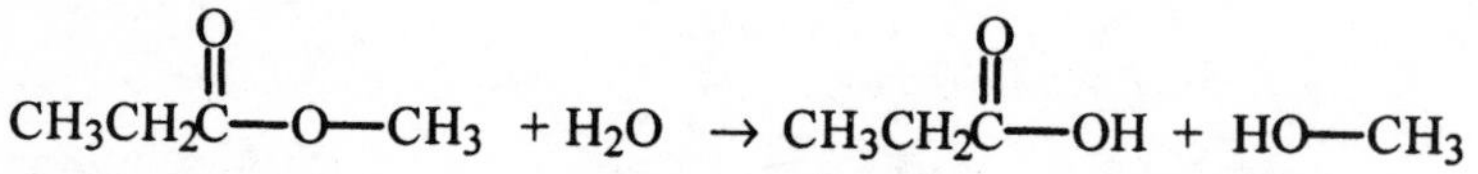

11.92   (a) $H_2C=CHCH_2OH$ $\xrightarrow[\text{catalyst}]{+\;H_2}$ $H_3C-CH_2CH_2OH$

        (b) 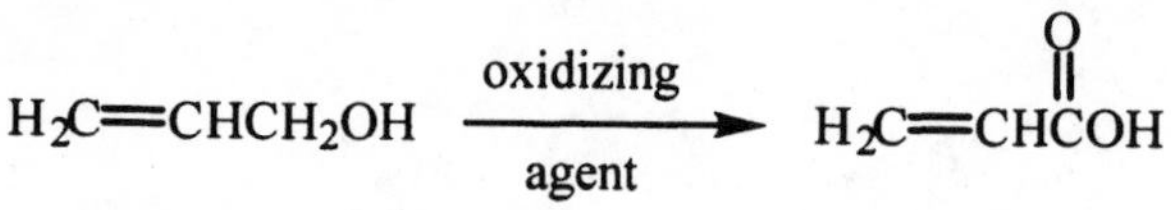 $H_2C=CHCH_2OH$ $\xrightarrow[\text{agent}]{\text{oxidizing}}$ $H_2C=CH\overset{\overset{O}{\|}}{C}OH$

        (c) $n\;\; H_2C=CHCH_2OH$ $\longrightarrow$ $\left(\!\!\begin{array}{c}\overset{\overset{H}{|}}{\underset{\underset{H}{|}}{C}}-\overset{\overset{H}{|}}{\underset{\underset{CH_2OH}{|}}{C}}\end{array}\!\!\right)_{\!n}$

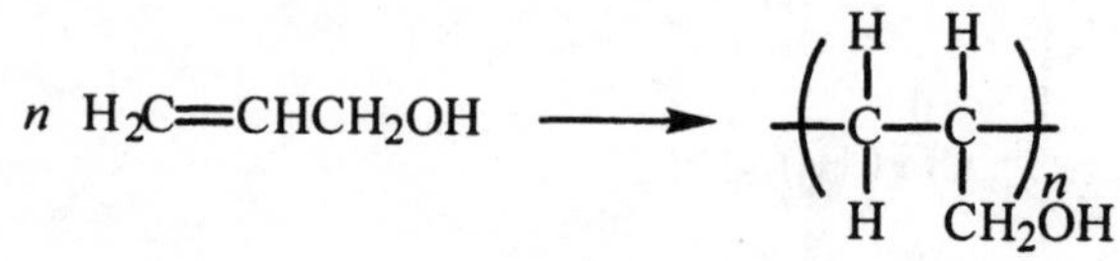

        (d)  $H_2C=CHCH_2OH + CH_3\overset{\overset{O}{\|}}{C}OH$ $\longrightarrow$ $H_2C=CHCH_2O\overset{\overset{O}{\|}}{C}CH_3 + H_2O$

11.93 $n\;\; HO-\underset{\underset{H}{|}}{\overset{\overset{H_3C}{|}}{C}}-\overset{\overset{O}{\|}}{C}-OH \rightarrow \left(\!\!\begin{array}{c}\underset{\underset{H}{|}}{\overset{\overset{H_3C}{|}}{C}}-\overset{\overset{O}{\|}}{C}-O\end{array}\!\!\right)_{\!n}$

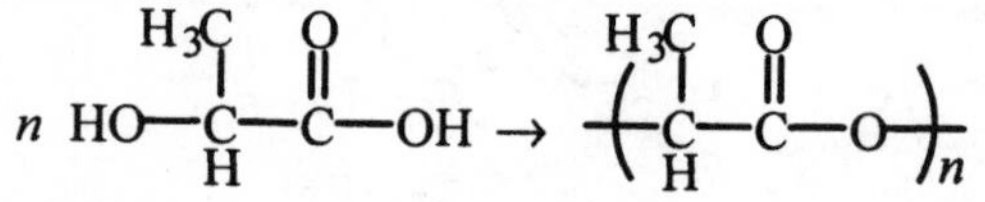

11.94 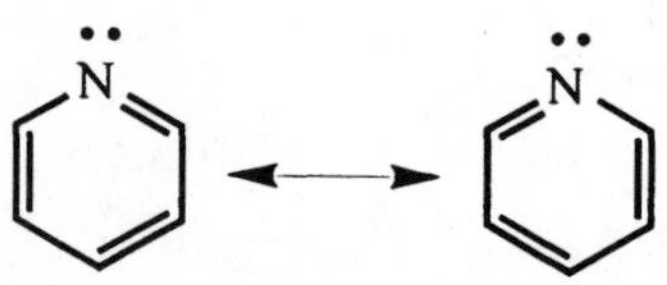   Pyridine is isoelectronic with benzene. A C—H group in benzene has

been replaced by an N atom in pyridine. Both benzene and pyridine have two resonance structures.

11.95 $C_2H_6(g) + {}^7/_2\,O_2(g) \rightarrow 2\;CO_2(g) + 3\;H_2O(g)$

        $C_2H_5OH(\ell) + 3\;O_2(g) \rightarrow 2\;CO_2(g) + 3\;H_2O(g)$

        (a)   Ethane:

                $\Delta H^\circ_{\text{combustion}} = \Delta H_f^\circ[CO_2(g)] + \Delta H_f^\circ[H_2O(g)] - \Delta H_f^\circ[C_2H_6(g)]$

                $\Delta H^\circ_{\text{combustion}} = 2\;\text{mol} \cdot (-393.509\;\text{kJ/mol}) + 3\;\text{mol} \cdot (-241.83\;\text{kJ/mol}) - 1\;\text{mol} \cdot (-83.85\;\text{kJ/mol})$

                $\Delta H^\circ_{\text{combustion}} = -1428.66\;\text{kJ}$

                $\dfrac{-1428.66\;\text{kJ}}{1\;\text{mol C}_2\text{H}_6} \cdot \dfrac{1\;\text{mol C}_2\text{H}_6}{30.0694\;\text{g}} = -47.51\;\text{kJ/g C}_2\text{H}_6$

Ethanol:

$\Delta H°_{combustion} = \Delta H_f°[CO_2(g)] + \Delta H_f°[H_2O(g)] - \Delta H_f°[C_2H_5OH(\ell)]$

$\Delta H°_{combustion} = 2 \text{ mol} \cdot (-393.509 \text{ kJ/mol}) + 3 \text{ mol} \cdot (-241.83 \text{ kJ/mol}) - 1 \text{ mol} \cdot (-277.0 \text{ kJ/mol})$

$\Delta H°_{combustion} = -1235.5 \text{ kJ}$

$$\frac{-1235.5 \text{ kJ}}{1 \text{ mol C}_2\text{H}_5\text{OH}} \cdot \frac{1 \text{ mol C}_2\text{H}_5\text{OH}}{46.0688 \text{ g}} = -26.82 \text{ kJ/g C}_2\text{H}_5\text{OH}$$

Ethane has a more negative enthalpy of combustion per gram.

(b) The heat realized by combustion of ethanol is less negative, so partially oxidizing ethane to form ethanol decreases the amount of energy per mole available from combustion of the substance.

11.96   Cyclopentane will not react with bromine, while 1-pentene will react with bromine.

11.97   2-propanol will react with an oxidizing agent such as $KMnO_4$, while methyl ethyl ether will not. In addition, 2-propanol is soluble in water, while methyl ethyl ether is not.

11.98   Symbol   (a) polymer   (b) common use

1   polyethylene terephthalate   2-L soda bottles

2   high-density polyethylene   milk and yogurt containers

3   polyvinyl chloride   shampoo bottles

4   low-density polyethylene   toiletries and cosmetics containers

5   polypropylene   syrup containers

(c) Assuming the plastic containers are crushed so they will not retain air, the PET plastics should sink in a water bath. HDPE and PP will float and can be skimmed off. By heating this mixture to approximately 140 °C, the HDPE will melt, allowing separation.

11.99   (a) $0.190 \text{ g CO}_2 \cdot \dfrac{1 \text{ mol CO}_2}{44.01 \text{ g}} \cdot \dfrac{1 \text{ mol C}}{1 \text{ mol CO}_2} = 0.00432 \text{ mol C}$

$0.00432 \text{ mol C} \cdot \dfrac{12.01 \text{ g}}{1 \text{ mol C}} = 0.0518 \text{ g C}$

$0.0388 \text{ g H}_2\text{O} \cdot \dfrac{1 \text{ mol H}_2\text{O}}{18.02 \text{ g}} \cdot \dfrac{2 \text{ mol H}}{1 \text{ mol H}_2\text{O}} = 0.00431 \text{ mol H}$

$0.00431 \text{ mol H} \cdot \dfrac{1.008 \text{ g}}{1 \text{ mol H}} = 0.00434 \text{ g H}$

0.125 g acid − 0.0518 g C − 0.00434 g H = 0.069 g O $0.069 \text{ g O} \cdot \dfrac{1 \text{ mol O}}{16.0 \text{ g}} = 0.0043 \text{ mol O}$

$\dfrac{0.00432 \text{ mol C}}{0.0043 \text{ mol O}} = \dfrac{1 \text{ mol C}}{1 \text{ mol O}}$ $\dfrac{0.00431 \text{ mol H}}{0.0043 \text{ mol O}} = \dfrac{1 \text{ mol H}}{1 \text{ mol O}}$ The empirical formula is CHO

(b) $0.03460 \text{ L} \cdot \dfrac{0.130 \text{ mol NaOH}}{1 \text{ L}} \cdot \dfrac{1 \text{ mol acid}}{2 \text{ mol NaOH}} = 0.00225 \text{ mol acid}$ $\dfrac{0.261 \text{ g}}{0.00225 \text{ mol}} = 116 \text{ g/mol}$

$\dfrac{116 \text{ g/mol}}{29.0 \text{ g/mol}} = 4$ The molecular formula is $(CHO)_2$ or $C_4H_4O_4$

(c) $HO-\overset{\overset{\textstyle O}{\|}}{C}-\underset{\underset{\textstyle H}{|}}{C}=\underset{\underset{\textstyle H}{|}}{C}-\overset{\overset{\textstyle O}{\|}}{C}-OH$

(d) All four carbon atoms are sp^2 hybridized

(e) 120°

11.100 (a) The C atoms of benzene are sp^2 hybridized (see page 396.) The C atoms of cyclohexane, C_6H_{12}, are sp^3 hybridized (page 431).

(b) π electron delocalization can occur in benzene because each C atom has an unhybridized p orbital perpendicular to the ring. Overlap of these orbitals leads to alternating π bonds.

(c) Cyclohexane cannot be planar because the geometry around each C atom is tetrahedral with bond angles of 109°.

11.101 (a) Two or more hydrocarbons with CC double bonds are added together.

(b) Hydrogenation of alkynes produces alkenes or alkanes.

(c) Alkanes do not contain a reactive double or triple carbon-carbon bond. Also, in alkanes the carbon atoms already have a maximum number of bonds, four.

11.102 (a) sp^3

(b) sp^2

(c) sp^2

(d) sp^3

(e) sp^3

11.103 (a) In a substitution reaction, one atom or group of atoms is substituted for another. In an elimination reaction, a small molecule is removed (eliminated) from a larger molecule.

(b) The elimination reaction produces an alkene while the hydrogenation reaction has an alkene as a reactant. Both involve a small molecule, either H_2 or H_2O, being added to or eliminated from an organic molecule.

11.104 (a) addition

(b) Oils generally have C=C double bonds in the long carbon chains of the fatty acids. Fats tend to have only C–C single bonds in these carbon chains (and the acid residues in fats are called saturated fatty acids). See page 454.

(c)   As noted in (b), oils have unsaturated fatty acids, which makes the fatty acid chains less flexible.

11.105   (a)   an amine and a carboxylic acid

(b)   See the answer to Study Question 72 in Chapter 10.

(c)   elimination

(d)   Yes. The tripeptide contains reactive amine and carboxylic acid groups at the ends of the molecule that can react with other amino acids to form a longer peptide chain.

(e) 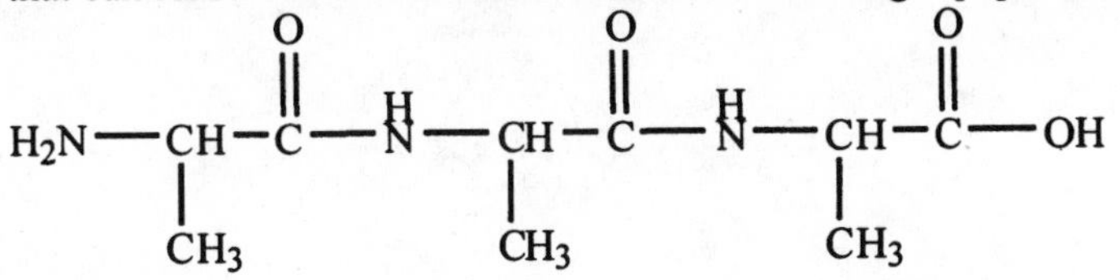
$$H_2N - CH - \overset{\overset{\displaystyle O}{\|}}{C} - \overset{H}{N} - CH - \overset{\overset{\displaystyle O}{\|}}{C} - \overset{H}{N} - CH - \overset{\overset{\displaystyle O}{\|}}{C} - OH$$
$$\quad\quad\quad | \quad\quad\quad\quad\quad\quad | \quad\quad\quad\quad\quad\quad\quad | $$
$$\quad\quad\quad CH_3 \quad\quad\quad\quad\quad\quad CH_3 \quad\quad\quad\quad\quad\quad CH_3$$

11.106   (a)   Double bonds. See also page 455.

(b)   Termination occurred when the chain reached 14 atoms. It could have been terminated earlier than this, or the chain could have continued to grow.

(c)   The termination step

(d)   Addition

11.107   (a)   The molecule must contain two reactive groups, such as OH, NH, or OCl groups.

(b)   The material is white and consists of a single long strand of polymer

(c)   The two molecules combined to make nylon-6,6 each contain 6 carbon atoms.

Chapter 12
Gases and Their Properties

INSTRUCTOR'S NOTES

In the first edition this chapter was placed in the first quarter of the book. However, it works well to place it somewhat later in the year, since we can then make a very nice connection between the phases of matter by covering the chapters on gases, liquids and solids, and solutions in that order. When discussing nonideal gases, we make the point that intermolecular forces play an important role, so it is a natural transition to move from there to the discussion of liquids and solids. It is important to emphasize that *this chapter can be used almost anywhere in the sequence of topics, as long as the basic ideas of stoichiometry have been covered.*

Three to four 50-minute lectures are normally given on this material. At the beginning of this series we take the opportunity to emphasize two reasons for studying gases and their behavior: (1) There are gases in the atmosphere and many of these and others are commercially important. We must understand how to deal with them. (2) The behavior of gases is well understood and can be modeled mathematically. This has two benefits: (a) This has led to a better understanding of other aspects of the physical world (such as the energy distribution in liquids). (b) It is important to recognize that nature and some aspects of social behavior can be subjected to mathematical models, an approach that is important in business and industry today.

Another very useful point to make is that one can clearly see the difference between a law (the ideal gas law and the laws on which it is based) and a theory (the kinetic molecular theory).

SUGGESTED DEMONSTRATIONS

1.   For a list of 26 demonstrations on "The Physical Behavior of Gases," see Shakhashiri, B. Z. *Chemical Demonstrations: A Handbook for Teachers of Chemistry*; University of Wisconsin Press, 1985; Vol. 2.

2.   Boyle's Law

   • To demonstrate Boyle's law, bring a bicycle pump to lecture.

   • Shakhashiri, B. Z. "Collapsing Can," *Chemical Demonstrations: A Handbook for Teachers of Chemistry*; University of Wisconsin Press, 1985; Vol. 2, pp. 6-8.

   • Boyle's law has been demonstrated in Figure 12.3 using a large syringe. Instead of lead shot in a beaker, one can also use a pile of textbooks to provide the pressure as described in Shakhashiri, B. Z. "Boyle's Law and the Mass of a Textbook," *Chemical Demonstrations: A Handbook for Teachers of Chemistry*; University of Wisconsin Press, 1985; Vol. 2, pp. 20-23. (For more on gas law demonstrations using syringes, see Davenport, D. *Journal of Chemical Education* **1962**, *39*, 252.)

3.   Charles's Law

- A favorite demonstration with the students in shown in Figure 12.5. Perhaps 15–20 balloons are passed out to students at the beginning of the lecture, and they are asked to blow them up and tie them off. When the demonstration begins, each of these students comes to the front of the room and places the balloon he or she has blown up in a large beaker of liquid nitrogen. After all the balloons have been placed in the beaker, they are poured out again and reinflate to their original volume when warmed back to room temperature. (However, a few may break, as they become twisted when frozen.)

- Shakhashiri, B. Z. "Charles Law," *Chemical Demonstrations: A Handbook for Teachers of Chemistry*; University of Wisconsin Press, 1985; Vol. 2, pp. 28-32.

4.   Avogadro's Law

- Shakhashiri, B. Z. "Avogadro's Hypothesis," *Chemical Demonstrations: A Handbook for Teachers of Chemistry*; University of Wisconsin Press, 1985; Vol. 2, pp. 44-47.

5.   Density

- Figure 12.7a illustrates the relative densities of two gases and is an easy demonstration. This can also be used to illustrate diffusion, since He atoms diffuse from a balloon much faster than Ar or air (O_2 and N_2).

6.   Molar Mass Determination

- Shakhashiri, B. Z. "Determination of the Molecular Mass of the Gas from a Butane Lighter," *Chemical Demonstrations: A Handbook for Teachers of Chemistry*; University of Wisconsin Press, 1985; Vol. 2, pp. 48-50.

7.   Diffusion and Effusion

- Release a small quantity of a concentrated scent (rose, lavender, or lemon oil) at the beginning of the lecture. The scent will fill the room.

- Keller, P. C. "A Simple Apparatus to Demonstrate Differing Gas Diffusion Rates (Graham's Law)," *Journal of Chemical Education* **1990**, *67*, 160.

- Shakhashiri, B. Z. "Graham's Law of Diffusion," *Chemical Demonstrations: A Handbook for Teachers of Chemistry*; University of Wisconsin Press, 1985; Vol. 2, pp. 69-71.

- Shakhashiri, B. Z. "Graham's Law of Effusion," *Chemical Demonstrations: A Handbook for Teachers of Chemistry*; University of Wisconsin Press, 1985; Vol. 2, pp. 72-74.

Solutions to Study Questions

12.1   Boyle's law states that the volume of a fixed amount of gas at a given temperature is inversely proportional to the pressure exerted by the gas. PV = constant

Charles's law states that if a given quantity of gas is held at a constant pressure, its volume is directly proportional to the Kelvin temperature. $\dfrac{V}{T}$ = constant

Avogadro's hypothesis states that the volume of a gas, at a given temperature and pressure, is directly proportional to the amount (mol) of gas. $\dfrac{V}{n}$ = constant

12.2   Under STP conditions, 0 °C (273.15 K) and 1 atm pressure, one mole of gas occupies 22.414 L.

12.3 $M = \dfrac{dRT}{P}$ Use density (g/L), temperature (K), and pressure (atm) to calculate molar mass.

12.4   The volume of a gas, at a given temperature and pressure, is directly proportional to the amount (mol) of gas. For the reaction $2\ H_2(g) + O_2(g) \rightarrow 2\ H_2O(g)$, 3 mol of H_2 at STP (67.2 L) would require 1.5 mol of O_2 (33.6 L) and produce 3 mol of H_2O (67.2 L).

12.5   The pressure of a mixture of gases is the sum of the partial pressures of the different gases in the mixture.
X_{O_2} = 0.21 P_{O_2} = 748 mm Hg · 0.21 = 160 mm Hg

12.6   (1) Gases consist of particles whose separation is much greater than the size of the particles themselves.
(2) The particles of a gas are in continual, random, and rapid motion. As they move, they collide with one another and with the walls of their container. (3) The average kinetic energy of gas particles is proportional to the gas temperature. All gases, regardless of their molecular mass, have the same average kinetic energy at the same temperature. Boyle's law states that pressure is proportional to $1/V$ when n and T are constant. If the temperature is constant, the average impact force of molecules of a given mass with the container walls must be constant. If n is kept constant while the volume of the container is made smaller, the number of collisions with the container walls per second must increase. This means that pressure increases as volume decreases at constant n and T.

12.7   In an ideal gas, it is assumed that gas molecules have very little volume when compared to the volume of the container they occupy, and that collisions between gas molecules are elastic. The ideal gas law is least accurate under conditions of high pressure or low temperature.

12.8 a: correction for intermolecular forces b: correction for molecular volume

12.9   The rate of effusion of a gas is inversely proportional to the square root of its molar mass

$$\frac{\text{Rate of effusion of gas 1}}{\text{Rate of effusion of gas 2}} = \sqrt{\frac{\text{molar mass of gas 2}}{\text{molar mass of gas 1}}}$$

$$\frac{1}{4} = \sqrt{\frac{2.02 \text{ g/mol}}{\text{molar mass of gas 1}}} \qquad \text{molar mass} = 32.3 \text{ g/mol} \qquad \text{The gas could be } O_2$$

12.10   (a) $440 \text{ mm Hg} \cdot \dfrac{1 \text{ atm}}{760 \text{ mm Hg}} = 0.58 \text{ atm}$

  (b) $0.58 \text{ atm} \cdot \dfrac{1.013 \text{ bar}}{1 \text{ atm}} = 0.59 \text{ bar}$

  (c) $440 \text{ mm Hg} \cdot \dfrac{101.325 \text{ kPa}}{760 \text{ mm Hg}} = 59 \text{ kPa}$

12.11 $210 \text{ mm Hg} \cdot \dfrac{1 \text{ atm}}{760 \text{ mm Hg}} = 0.28 \text{ atm}$

$0.28 \text{ atm} \cdot \dfrac{1.013 \text{ bar}}{1 \text{ atm}} = 0.28 \text{ bar}$

$210 \text{ mm Hg} \cdot \dfrac{101.325 \text{ kPa}}{760 \text{ mm Hg}} = 28 \text{ kPa}$

12.12   (a) $534 \text{ mm Hg} \cdot \dfrac{1.013 \text{ bar}}{760 \text{ atm}} = 0.71 \text{ bar}$ 0.754 is the higher pressure

  (b) $534 \text{ mm Hg} \cdot \dfrac{101.325 \text{ kPa}}{760 \text{ mm Hg}} = 71.2 \text{ kPa}$ 650 kPa is the higher pressure

  (c) $1.34 \text{ bar} \cdot \dfrac{1 \times 10^2 \text{ kPa}}{1 \text{ bar}} = 134 \text{ kPa}$ 934 kPa is the higher pressure

12.13 $363 \text{ mm Hg} \cdot \dfrac{1 \text{ atm}}{760 \text{ mm Hg}} = 0.478 \text{ atm}$ $363 \text{ kPa} \cdot \dfrac{1 \text{ atm}}{101.325 \text{ kPa}} = 3.58 \text{ atm}$

$0.523 \text{ bar} \cdot \dfrac{1 \text{ atm}}{1.013 \text{ bar}} = 0.516 \text{ atm}$ 0.256 atm < 363 mm Hg < 0.523 bar < 363 kPa

12.14 $P_2 = \dfrac{P_1 V_1}{V_2} = \dfrac{(67.5 \text{ mm Hg})(500. \text{ mL})}{125 \text{ mL}} = 270. \text{ mm Hg}$

12.15 $V_2 = \dfrac{P_1 V_1}{P_2} = \dfrac{(56.5 \text{ mm Hg})(125 \text{ mL})}{62.3 \text{ mm Hg}} = 113 \text{ mL}$

12.16 $V_2 = T_2 \left(\dfrac{V_1}{T_1} \right) = (310. \text{ K}) \left(\dfrac{3.5 \text{ L}}{295.2 \text{ K}} \right) = 3.7 \text{ L}$

12.17 $V_2 = T_2 \left(\dfrac{V_1}{T_1} \right) = (273 \text{ K}) \left(\dfrac{5.0 \text{ mL}}{295 \text{ K}} \right) = 4.6 \text{ mL}$

12.18 $P_2 = P_1 \left(\dfrac{T_2}{T_1} \right) = (380 \text{ mm Hg}) \left(\dfrac{273 \text{ K}}{298 \text{ K}} \right) = 350 \text{ mm Hg}$

12.19 $V_2 = V_1 \left(\dfrac{P_1}{P_2}\right)\left(\dfrac{T_2}{T_1}\right) = (25.0 \text{ mL})\left(\dfrac{436.5 \text{ mm Hg}}{94.3 \text{ mm Hg}}\right)\left(\dfrac{297.7 \text{ K}}{293.7 \text{ K}}\right) = 117 \text{ mL}$

12.20 $P_2 = P_1\left(\dfrac{T_2}{T_1}\right) = (360 \text{ mm Hg})\left(\dfrac{268.2 \text{ K}}{298.7 \text{ K}}\right) = 320 \text{ mm Hg}$

12.21 $P_2 = P_1\left(\dfrac{V_1}{V_2}\right)\left(\dfrac{T_2}{T_1}\right) = (165 \text{ mm Hg})\left(\dfrac{135 \text{ mL}}{252 \text{ mL}}\right)\left(\dfrac{273.2 \text{ K}}{295.7 \text{ K}}\right) = 81.7 \text{ mm Hg}$

12.22 $P_2 = P_1\left(\dfrac{V_1}{V_2}\right)\left(\dfrac{T_2}{T_1}\right) = (1.00 \text{ atm})\left(\dfrac{400. \text{ cm}^3}{50.0 \text{ cm}^3}\right)\left(\dfrac{350. \text{ K}}{288 \text{ K}}\right) = 9.72 \text{ atm}$

12.23 $V_2 = V_1\left(\dfrac{P_1}{P_2}\right)\left(\dfrac{T_2}{T_1}\right) = (1.2 \times 10^7 \text{ L})\left(\dfrac{737 \text{ mm Hg}}{600. \text{ mm Hg}}\right)\left(\dfrac{240. \text{ K}}{289.2 \text{ K}}\right) = 1.2 \times 10^7 \text{ L}$

The volume of gas is nearly the same (to 2 significant figures) at the higher altitude.

12.24 (a) $150 \text{ mL NO} \cdot \dfrac{1 \text{ L O}_2}{2 \text{ L NO}} = 75 \text{ mL O}_2$

 (b) $150 \text{ mL NO} \cdot \dfrac{2 \text{ L NO}_2}{2 \text{ L NO}} = 150 \text{ mL NO}_2$

12.25 $5.2 \text{ L C}_2\text{H}_6 \cdot \dfrac{7 \text{ L O}_2}{2 \text{ L C}_2\text{H}_6} = 18 \text{ L O}_2$

 $5.2 \text{ L C}_2\text{H}_6 \cdot \dfrac{6 \text{ L H}_2\text{O}}{2 \text{ L C}_2\text{H}_6} = 16 \text{ L H}_2\text{O}$

12.26 $1.25 \text{ g CO}_2 \cdot \dfrac{1 \text{ mol CO}_2}{44.01 \text{ g}} = 0.0284 \text{ mol CO}_2 \qquad 750. \text{ mL} \cdot \dfrac{1 \text{ L}}{10^3 \text{ mL}} = 0.750 \text{ L}$

 $P = \dfrac{nRT}{V} = \dfrac{(0.0284 \text{ mol})(0.082057 \text{ L}\cdot\text{atm/K}\cdot\text{mol})(295.7 \text{ K})}{0.750 \text{ L}} = 0.919 \text{ atm}$

12.27 $30.0 \text{ kg He} \cdot \dfrac{1000 \text{ g}}{1 \text{ kg}} \cdot \dfrac{1 \text{ mol He}}{4.003 \text{ g}} = 7490 \text{ mol He}$

 $V = \dfrac{nRT}{P} = \dfrac{(7490 \text{ mol})(0.082057 \text{ L}\cdot\text{atm/K}\cdot\text{mol})(295 \text{ K})}{1.20 \text{ atm}} = 1.51 \times 10^5 \text{ L}$

12.28 $2.2 \text{ g CO}_2 \cdot \dfrac{1 \text{ mol CO}_2}{44.0 \text{ g}} = 0.050 \text{ mol CO}_2 \qquad 313 \text{ mm Hg} \cdot \dfrac{1 \text{ atm}}{760 \text{ mm Hg}} = 0.418 \text{ atm}$

 $V = \dfrac{nRT}{P} = \dfrac{(0.050 \text{ mol})(0.082057 \text{ L}\cdot\text{atm/K}\cdot\text{mol})(295 \text{ K})}{0.418 \text{ atm}} = 2.9 \text{ L}$

12.29 $1.50 \text{ g C}_2\text{H}_5\text{OH} \cdot \dfrac{1 \text{ mol}}{46.07 \text{ g}} = 0.0326 \text{ mol C}_2\text{H}_5\text{OH} \qquad 251 \text{ cm}^3 \cdot \dfrac{1 \text{ mL}}{1 \text{ cm}^3} \cdot \dfrac{1 \text{ L}}{10^3 \text{ mL}} = 0.251 \text{ L}$

 $P = \dfrac{nRT}{V} = \dfrac{(0.0326 \text{ mol C}_2\text{H}_5\text{OH})(0.082057 \text{ L}\cdot\text{atm/K}\cdot\text{mol})(520 \text{ K})}{0.251 \text{ L}} = 5.6 \text{ atm}$

12.30 $737 \text{ mm Hg} \cdot \dfrac{1 \text{ atm}}{760 \text{ mm Hg}} = 0.970 \text{ atm}$

$n = \dfrac{PV}{RT} = \dfrac{(0.970 \text{ atm})(1.2 \times 10^7 \text{ L})}{(0.082057 \text{ L} \cdot \text{atm/K} \cdot \text{mol})(298 \text{ K})} = 4.8 \times 10^5 \text{ mol He}$

$4.8 \times 10^5 \text{ mol He} \cdot \dfrac{4.00 \text{ g}}{1 \text{ mol}} = 1.9 \times 10^6 \text{ g He}$

12.31 $n = \dfrac{PV}{RT} = \dfrac{(1.1 \text{ atm})(5.0 \text{ L})}{(0.082057 \text{ L} \cdot \text{atm/K} \cdot \text{mol})(298 \text{ K})} = 0.22 \text{ mol He}$

$0.22 \text{ mol He} \cdot \dfrac{4.00 \text{ g}}{1 \text{ mol}} = 0.88 \text{ g He}$

12.32 $0.20 \text{ mm Hg} \cdot \dfrac{1 \text{ atm}}{760 \text{ mm Hg}} = 2.6 \times 10^{-4} \text{ atm}$

$d = \dfrac{PM}{RT} = \dfrac{(2.6 \times 10^{-4} \text{ atm})(29 \text{ g/mol})}{(0.082057 \text{ L} \cdot \text{atm/K} \cdot \text{mol})(250 \text{ K})} = 3.7 \times 10^{-4} \text{ g/L}$

12.33 $233 \text{ mm Hg} \cdot \dfrac{1 \text{ atm}}{760 \text{ mm Hg}} = 0.307 \text{ atm}$

$d = \dfrac{PM}{RT} = \dfrac{(0.307 \text{ atm})(74.12 \text{ g/mol})}{(0.082057 \text{ L} \cdot \text{atm/K} \cdot \text{mol})(298 \text{ K})} = 0.929 \text{ g/L}$

12.34 $189 \text{ mm Hg} \cdot \dfrac{1 \text{ atm}}{760 \text{ mm Hg}} = 0.249 \text{ atm}$

$M = \dfrac{dRT}{P} = \dfrac{(0.355 \text{ g/L})(0.082057 \text{ L} \cdot \text{atm/K} \cdot \text{mol})(290. \text{ K})}{0.249 \text{ atm}} = 34.0 \text{ g/mol}$

12.35 $195 \text{ mm Hg} \cdot \dfrac{1 \text{ atm}}{760 \text{ mm Hg}} = 0.257 \text{ atm}$

$M = \dfrac{dRT}{P} = \dfrac{(1.25 \text{ g/L})(0.082057 \text{ L} \cdot \text{atm/K} \cdot \text{mol})(298.2 \text{ K})}{0.257 \text{ atm}} = 119 \text{ g/mol}$

12.36 $d = \dfrac{1.007 \text{ g}}{0.452 \text{ L}} = 2.23 \text{ g/L}$ $715 \text{ mm Hg} \cdot \dfrac{1 \text{ atm}}{760 \text{ mm Hg}} = 0.941 \text{ atm}$

$M = \dfrac{dRT}{P} = \dfrac{(2.23 \text{ g/L})(0.082057 \text{ L} \cdot \text{atm/K} \cdot \text{mol})(296 \text{ K})}{0.941 \text{ atm}} = 57.5 \text{ g/mol}$

12.37 $d = \dfrac{0.0125 \text{ g}}{0.165 \text{ L}} = 0.0758 \text{ g/L}$ $13.7 \text{ mm Hg} \cdot \dfrac{1 \text{ atm}}{760 \text{ mm Hg}} = 0.0180 \text{ atm}$

$M = \dfrac{dRT}{P} = \dfrac{(0.0758 \text{ g/L})(0.082057 \text{ L} \cdot \text{atm/K} \cdot \text{mol})(295.7 \text{ K})}{0.0180 \text{ atm}} = 102 \text{ g/mol}$

$\dfrac{102 \text{ g/mol}}{51 \text{ g/mol}} = 2$ The molecular formula is $(CHF_2)_2$ or $C_2H_2F_4$

12.38 $\quad d = \dfrac{12.5 \times 10^{-3}\ \text{g}}{0.125\ \text{L}} = 0.100\ \text{g/L} \qquad 24.8\ \text{mm Hg} \cdot \dfrac{1\ \text{atm}}{760\ \text{mm Hg}} = 0.0326\ \text{atm}$

$\qquad M = \dfrac{dRT}{P} = \dfrac{(0.100\ \text{g/L})(0.082057\ \text{L} \cdot \text{atm/K} \cdot \text{mol})(298\ \text{K})}{0.0326\ \text{atm}} = 74.9\ \text{g/mol}$

(d) B_6H_{10}

12.39 $\quad d = \dfrac{0.107\ \text{g}}{0.125\ \text{L}} = 0.856\ \text{g/L} \qquad 331\ \text{mm Hg} \cdot \dfrac{1\ \text{atm}}{760\ \text{mm Hg}} = 0.436\ \text{atm}$

$\qquad M = \dfrac{dRT}{P} = \dfrac{(0.856\ \text{g/L})(0.082057\ \text{L} \cdot \text{atm/K} \cdot \text{mol})(273.2\ \text{K})}{0.436\ \text{atm}} = 44.1\ \text{g/mol}$

12.40 $\quad 2.2\ \text{g Fe} \cdot \dfrac{1\ \text{mol Fe}}{55.9\ \text{g}} \cdot \dfrac{1\ \text{mol } H_2}{1\ \text{mol Fe}} = 0.039\ \text{mol } H_2$

$\qquad P = \dfrac{nRT}{V} = \dfrac{(0.039\ \text{mol})(0.082057\ \text{L} \cdot \text{atm/K} \cdot \text{mol})(298\ \text{K})}{10.0\ \text{L}} = 0.096\ \text{atm}$

12.41 $\quad 356\ \text{mm Hg} \cdot \dfrac{1\ \text{atm}}{760\ \text{mm Hg}} = 0.468\ \text{atm} \qquad 425\ \text{mm Hg} \cdot \dfrac{1\ \text{atm}}{760\ \text{mm Hg}} = 0.559\ \text{atm}$

$\qquad n = \dfrac{PV}{RT} = \dfrac{(0.468)(5.20\ \text{L})}{(0.082057\ \text{L} \cdot \text{atm/K} \cdot \text{mol})(298\ \text{K})} = 0.0996\ \text{mol SiH}_4$

$\qquad 0.0996\ \text{mol SiH}_4 \cdot \dfrac{2\ \text{mol } O_2}{1\ \text{mol SiH}_4} = 0.199\ \text{mol } O_2$

$\qquad V = \dfrac{nRT}{P} = \dfrac{(0.199\ \text{mol } O_2)(0.082057\ \text{L} \cdot \text{atm/K} \cdot \text{mol})(298\ \text{K})}{0.559\ \text{atm}} = 8.71\ \text{L}$

12.42 $\quad n = \dfrac{PV}{RT} = \dfrac{(1.3\ \text{atm})(75.0\ \text{L})}{(0.082057\ \text{L} \cdot \text{atm/K} \cdot \text{mol})(298\ \text{K})} = 4.0\ \text{mol } N_2$

$\qquad 4.0\ \text{mol } N_2 \cdot \dfrac{2\ \text{mol NaN}_3}{3\ \text{mol } N_2} \cdot \dfrac{65.0\ \text{g}}{1\ \text{mol NaN}_3} = 170\ \text{g NaN}_3$

12.43 $\quad 0.095\ \text{g } C_8H_{18} \cdot \dfrac{1\ \text{mol}}{114\ \text{g}} = 8.3 \times 10^{-4}\ \text{mol } C_8H_{18}$

$\qquad 8.3 \times 10^{-4}\ \text{mol } C_8H_{18} \cdot \dfrac{18\ \text{mol } H_2O}{2\ \text{mol } C_8H_{18}} = 0.0075\ \text{mol } H_2O$

$\qquad P_{H_2O} = \dfrac{n_{H_2O}RT}{V} = \dfrac{(0.0075\ \text{mol } H_2O)(0.082057\ \text{L} \cdot \text{atm/K} \cdot \text{mol})(303.2\ \text{K})}{4.75\ \text{L}} = 0.039\ \text{atm}$

$\qquad 8.3 \times 10^{-4}\ \text{mol } C_8H_{18} \cdot \dfrac{25\ \text{mol } O_2}{2\ \text{mol } C_6H_6} = 0.010\ \text{mol } O_2$

$\qquad P_{O_2} = \dfrac{n_{O_2}RT}{V} = \dfrac{(0.010\ \text{mol } O_2)(0.082057\ \text{L} \cdot \text{atm/K} \cdot \text{mol})(295\ \text{K})}{4.75\ \text{L}} = 0.053\ \text{atm}$

12.44 $\quad 1.00 \times 10^3\ \text{g} \cdot \dfrac{1\ \text{mol } N_2H_4}{32.05\ \text{g}} \cdot \dfrac{1\ \text{mol } O_2}{1\ \text{mol } N_2H_4} = 31.2\ \text{mol } O_2$

$\qquad P = \dfrac{nRT}{V} = \dfrac{(31.2\ \text{mol})(0.082057\ \text{L} \cdot \text{atm/K} \cdot \text{mol})(296\ \text{K})}{450\ \text{L}} = 1.7\ \text{atm}$

12.45 $767 \text{ mm Hg} \cdot \dfrac{1 \text{ atm}}{760 \text{ mm Hg}} = 1.01 \text{ atm}$

$n = \dfrac{PV}{RT} = \dfrac{(1.01 \text{ atm})(8.90 \text{ L})}{(0.082057 \text{ L} \cdot \text{atm/K} \cdot \text{mol})(295.2 \text{ K})} = 0.371 \text{ mol } CO_2$

$0.371 \text{ mol } CO_2 \cdot \dfrac{4 \text{ mol } KO_2}{2 \text{ mol } CO_2} \cdot \dfrac{71.10 \text{ g}}{1 \text{ mol } KO_2} = 52.7 \text{ g } KO_2$

12.46 $1.0 \text{ g} \cdot \dfrac{1 \text{ mol } H_2}{2.02 \text{ g}} = 0.50 \text{ mol } H_2$ $8.0 \text{ g} \cdot \dfrac{1 \text{ mol Ar}}{39.9 \text{ g}} = 0.20 \text{ mol Ar}$

$P_{H_2} = \dfrac{n_{H_2}RT}{V} = \dfrac{(0.50 \text{ mol})(0.082057 \text{ L} \cdot \text{atm/K} \cdot \text{mol})(300. \text{ K})}{3.0 \text{ L}} = 4.1 \text{ atm}$

$P_{Ar} = \dfrac{n_{Ar}RT}{V} = \dfrac{(0.20 \text{ mol})(0.082057 \text{ L} \cdot \text{atm/K} \cdot \text{mol})(300. \text{ K})}{3.0 \text{ L}} = 1.6 \text{ atm}$

$P_{total} = 4.1 \text{ atm} + 1.6 \text{ atm} = 5.7 \text{ atm}$

12.47 $\%N = 100.0 - (4.5\% \ H_2S + 3.0\% \ CO_2) = 92.5\% \ N$

The partial pressure of each gas is proportional to its percentage:

$P_{N_2} = (46 \text{ atm})(0.925) = 43 \text{ atm}$

$P_{H_2S} = (46 \text{ atm})(0.045) = 2.1 \text{ atm}$

$P_{CO_2} = (46 \text{ atm})(0.030) = 1.4 \text{ atm}$

12.48   (a) $\dfrac{\text{mol halothane}}{\text{mol } O_2} = \dfrac{170 \text{ mm Hg}}{570 \text{ mm Hg}} = 0.30$

(b) $160 \text{ g} \cdot \dfrac{1 \text{ mol } O_2}{32.0 \text{ g}} \cdot \dfrac{0.30 \text{ mol halothane}}{1 \text{ mol } O_2} \cdot \dfrac{197 \text{ g}}{1 \text{ mol halothane}} = 3.0 \times 10^2 \text{ g halothane}$

12.49   (a) $n = \dfrac{PV}{RT} = \dfrac{(1.00 \text{ atm})(12.5 \text{ L})}{(0.082057 \text{ L} \cdot \text{atm/K} \cdot \text{mol})(294.7 \text{ K})} = 0.517 \text{ mol He}$

$0.517 \text{ mol He} \cdot \dfrac{4.003 \text{ g}}{1 \text{ mol He}} = 2.07 \text{ g He}$

(b) $P = \dfrac{nRT}{V} = \dfrac{(0.517 \text{ mol He})(0.082057 \text{ L} \cdot \text{atm/K} \cdot \text{mol})(294.7 \text{ K})}{26 \text{ L}} = 0.48 \text{ atm}$

(c) $P_{O_2} = P_{total} - P_{He} = 1.00 \text{ atm} - 0.48 \text{ atm} = 0.52 \text{ atm}$

(d) $X_{He} = \dfrac{0.48 \text{ atm}}{1.00 \text{ atm}} = 0.48$ $X_{O_2} = \dfrac{0.52 \text{ atm}}{1.00 \text{ atm}} = 0.52$

12.50   (a)   The two gases are at the same temperature so the average kinetic energy per molecule is the same.

(b)   The molar mass of H_2 (2.02 g/mol) is less than the molar mass of CO_2 (44.0 g/mol). Flask A has molecules with higher average velocity.

(c)   At constant T and V, $n \propto P$. Flask B contains more molecules.

(d) $\dfrac{n_{H_2}}{n_{CO_2}} = \dfrac{(1 \text{ atm})(V)/(R)(273 \text{ K})}{(2 \text{ atm})(V)/(R)(298 \text{ K})} = \dfrac{0.5 \text{ mol } H_2}{1 \text{ mol } CO_2}$

1 mol CO_2 (44 g) has a greater mass than 0.5 mol H_2 (1.0 g). Flask B has a greater mass.

12.51   The molar mass of Ar (40 g/mol) is greater than the molar mass of N_2 (28 g/mol). Therefore, for samples with equal mass there are more moles of N_2 present than moles of Ar.

   (a)   True. There are more moles of N_2 present, so there are more molecules of N_2 present.

   (b)   False. Pressure is directly related to the number of moles of gas present. The pressure in the nitrogen flask is greater because there are more moles of N_2 present.

   (c)   False. The gas with the smaller molar mass (N_2) will have a greater velocity than the gas with the greater molar mass (Ar).

   (d)   True. The nitrogen molecules have a greater velocity than the argon molecules and there are more molecules of nitrogen present, so they will collide more frequently with the walls of the flask.

12.52 $$\frac{\text{rms speed } O_2}{\text{rms speed } CO_2} = \frac{4.28 \times 10^4 \text{ cm/s}}{\sqrt{\overline{u^2}}} = \sqrt{\frac{44.01 \text{ g/mol}}{32.00 \text{ g/mol}}} \qquad \sqrt{\overline{u^2}} \, (CO_2) = 3.65 \times 10^4 \text{ cm/s}$$

12.53 $$\sqrt{\overline{u^2}} = \sqrt{\frac{3RT}{M}} = \sqrt{\frac{3(8.3145 \text{ J/K} \cdot \text{mol})(298 \text{ K})}{28.01 \times 10^{-3} \text{ kg/mol}}} = 515 \text{ m/s}$$

   $$\frac{\text{rms speed CO}}{\text{rms speed Ar}} = \sqrt{\frac{39.95 \text{ g/mol}}{28.01 \text{ g/mol}}} = 1.194$$

12.54   Increasing average molecular speed: $CH_2F_2 < Ar < N_2 < CH_4$

   molar mass (g/mol)   51   40   28   16

12.55   Increasing average molecular speed: $OSCl_2 < Cl_2O < Cl_2 < SO_2$

   molar mass (g/mol):   119   87   71   64

12.56   (a) F_2 (38 g/mol) effuses faster than CO_2 (44 g/mol).

   (b) N_2 (28 g/mol) effuses faster than O_2 (32 g/mol).

   (c) C_2H_4 (28.1 g/mol) effuses faster than C_2H_6 (30.1 g/mol).

   (d) $CFCl_3$ (137 g/mol) effuses faster than $C_2Cl_2F_4$ (171 g/mol).

12.57   He will effuse faster $$\frac{\text{Rate of He effusion}}{\text{Rate of Ar effusion}} = \sqrt{\frac{39.9 \text{ g/mol}}{4.00 \text{ g/mol}}} = 3.16 \text{ times faster}$$

12.58 $$\frac{\text{Rate of He effusion}}{\text{Rate of unknown gas effusion}} = \frac{\text{Rate of He effusion}}{1/3(\text{Rate of He effusion})} = \sqrt{\frac{\text{unknown gas molar mass}}{4.00 \text{ g/mol}}}$$

   unknown gas molar mass = 36 g/mol

12.59 $\dfrac{\text{Rate of } I_2}{\text{Rate of uranium fluoride}} = \sqrt{\dfrac{\text{molar mass of uranium fluoride}}{\text{molar mass of iodine}}}$

$\dfrac{\left(\dfrac{0.0150 \text{ g}}{1 \text{ hr}} \cdot \dfrac{1 \text{ mol } I_2}{253.8 \text{ g}}\right)}{\left(\dfrac{0.0177 \text{ mg}}{1 \text{ hr}} \cdot \dfrac{1}{\text{molar mass}}\right)} = \sqrt{\dfrac{\text{molar mass of uranium fluoride}}{253.8 \text{ g/mol}}}$

$(0.00334)^2(\text{molar mass of uranium fluoride})^2 = \dfrac{\text{molar mass of uranium fluoride}}{253.8 \text{ g/mol}}$

molar mass of uranium fluoride = 353 g/mol

12.60 $P_{\text{ideal}} = \dfrac{nRT}{V} = \dfrac{(8.00 \text{ mol})(0.082057 \text{ L} \cdot \text{atm/K} \cdot \text{mol})(300.2 \text{ K})}{4.00 \text{ L}} = 49.3 \text{ atm}$

$\left(P + a\left[\dfrac{n}{V}\right]^2\right)(V - bn) = nRT$

$\left(P + (6.49 \text{ atm} \cdot L^2/\text{mol}^2)\left[\dfrac{8.00 \text{ mol}}{4.00 \text{ L}}\right]^2\right)\left(4.00 \text{ L} - [0.0562 \text{ L/mol}][8.00 \text{ mol}]\right)$

$= (8.00 \text{ mol})(0.082057 \text{ L} \cdot \text{atm/K} \cdot \text{mol})(300.2 \text{ K})$

$P = 29.5 \text{ atm}$

12.61 $165 \text{ g CO}_2 \cdot \dfrac{1 \text{ mol}}{44.01 \text{ g}} = 3.75 \text{ mol CO}_2$

(a) $P = \dfrac{nRT}{V} = \dfrac{(3.75 \text{ mol})(0.082057 \text{ L} \cdot \text{atm/K} \cdot \text{mol})(298 \text{ K})}{12.5 \text{ L}} = 7.33 \text{ atm}$

$\left(P + a\left[\dfrac{n}{V}\right]^2\right)(V - bn) = nRT$

(b) $\left(P + (3.59 \text{ atm} \cdot L^2/\text{mol}^2)\left[\dfrac{3.75 \text{ mol}}{12.5 \text{ L}}\right]^2\right)\left(12.5 \text{ L} - [0.0427 \text{ L/mol}][3.75 \text{ mol}]\right)$

$= (3.75 \text{ mol})(0.08206 \text{ L} \cdot \text{atm/K} \cdot \text{mol})(298 \text{ K})$

$P = 7.11 \text{ atm}$

12.62

	atm	mm Hg	kPa	bar
Standard atmosphere	1	760	101.325	1.013
Partial pressure of N_2 in the atmosphere	0.780	593	79.1	0.791
Tank of compressed H_2	131	99800	13300	133
Atmospheric pressure at the top of Mt. Everest	0.333	253	33.7	0.337

12.63 $\quad V = \pi\, r^2\, l = \pi \cdot (10.0 \text{ cm})^2 \cdot 20.0 \text{ m} \cdot \dfrac{10^2 \text{ cm}}{1 \text{ m}} \cdot \dfrac{1 \text{ mL}}{1 \text{ cm}^3} \cdot \dfrac{1 \text{ L}}{10^3 \text{ ml}} = 628 \text{ L}$

$\qquad 865 \text{ mm Hg} \cdot \dfrac{1 \text{ atm}}{760 \text{ mm Hg}} = 1.14 \text{ atm}$

$\qquad n = \dfrac{(1.14 \text{ atm})(628 \text{ L})}{(0.082057 \text{ L} \cdot \text{atm/K} \cdot \text{mol})(298 \text{ K})} = 29.2 \text{ mol CO}_2$

$\qquad 29.2 \text{ mol CO}_2 \cdot \dfrac{44.01 \text{ g}}{1 \text{ mol CO}_2} = 1290 \text{ g CO}_2$

12.64 $\quad 2.82 \text{ g H}_2\text{O} \cdot \dfrac{1 \text{ mol H}_2\text{O}}{18.02 \text{ g}} \cdot \dfrac{2 \text{ mol H}}{1 \text{ mol H}_2\text{O}} = 0.31 \text{ mol H}$

$\qquad$ At STP, 1 mol of a gas occupies 22.414 L

$\qquad 2.0 \text{ L CO}_2 \cdot \dfrac{1 \text{ mol CO}_2}{22.414 \text{ L}} \cdot \dfrac{1 \text{ mol C}}{1 \text{ mol CO}_2} = 0.089 \text{ mol C}$

$\qquad 0.5 \text{ L N}_2 \cdot \dfrac{1 \text{ mol N}_2}{22.414 \text{ L}} \cdot \dfrac{2 \text{ mol N}}{1 \text{ mol N}_2} = 0.045 \text{ mol N}$

$\qquad \dfrac{0.31 \text{ mol H}}{0.045 \text{ mol N}} = \dfrac{7 \text{ mol H}}{1 \text{ mol N}} \qquad \dfrac{0.089 \text{ mol C}}{0.045 \text{ mol N}} = \dfrac{2 \text{ mol C}}{1 \text{ mol N}} \qquad$ The empirical formula is C_2H_7N

12.65 $\quad T_2 = V_2\left(\dfrac{T_1}{V_1}\right) = (21.5 \text{ mL})\left(\dfrac{360 \text{ K}}{25.5 \text{ mL}}\right) = 310 \text{ K} = 30 \text{ °C}$

12.66 $\quad \sqrt{\overline{u^2}} = \sqrt{\dfrac{3RT}{M}} = \sqrt{\dfrac{3(8.314 \text{ J/K} \cdot \text{mol})(240 \text{ K})}{0.00400 \text{ kg/mol}}} = 1220 \text{ m/s}$

$\qquad$ New speed $= (1220 \text{ m/s})(1.10) = 1350 \text{ m/s}$

$\qquad 1350 \text{ m/s} = \sqrt{\dfrac{3(8.314 \text{ J/K} \cdot \text{mol})T}{0.00400 \text{ kg/mol}}} \qquad\qquad T = 290. \text{ K} = 17 \text{ °C}$

12.67 $\quad n_2 = n_1\left(\dfrac{T_1}{T_2}\right)$ and $n = \dfrac{\text{mass (g)}}{32.00 \text{ g/mol}}$

$\qquad \text{mass}_2 = \text{mass}_1\left(\dfrac{T_1}{T_2}\right) = (12.0 \text{ g})\left(\dfrac{300. \text{ K}}{278.2 \text{ K}}\right) = 12.9 \text{ g}$

12.68

	Helium balloon	Hydrogen balloon
Volume	V	$2 \times V$
Pressure	2 atm	1 atm
Temperature	296 K	268 K

(a) $\dfrac{n_{\text{He}}}{n_{\text{H}_2}} = \dfrac{PV/RT}{PV/RT} = \dfrac{(2 \text{ atm})(V)/(R)(296 \text{ K})}{(1 \text{ atm})(2 \times V)/(R)(268 \text{ K})} = \dfrac{0.9 \text{ mol He}}{1 \text{ mol H}_2}$

There are more moles of H_2 than He, so there are more molecules of H_2 than He.

(b) Assume that the hydrogen balloon contains 1 mol (2.02 g) of H_2. This must mean that the helium balloon contains 0.9 mol (3.6 g) of He. Therefore, there is a greater mass of helium present.

12.69 $T = \dfrac{PV}{nR} = \dfrac{(7.25 \text{ atm})(1.52 \text{ L})}{(0.406 \text{ mol})(0.082057 \text{ L} \cdot \text{atm/K} \cdot \text{mol})} = 331 \text{ K} = 58 \,^{\circ}\text{C}$

12.70   Assume the Mars atmosphere behaves as an ideal gas.

$n = \dfrac{PV}{RT} = \dfrac{\left(8 \text{ mm Hg} \cdot \dfrac{1 \text{ atm}}{760 \text{ mm Hg}}\right)\left(10. \text{ m}^3 \cdot \dfrac{10^3 \text{ L}}{1 \text{ m}^3}\right)}{(0.082057 \text{ L} \cdot \text{atm/K} \cdot \text{mol})(300. \text{ K})} = 4 \text{ mol}$

12.71 $2.25 \text{ g Si} \cdot \dfrac{1 \text{ mol Si}}{28.09 \text{ g}} = 0.0801 \text{ mol Si}$

$n_{\text{CH}_3\text{Cl}} = \dfrac{\left(585 \text{ mm Hg} \cdot \dfrac{1 \text{ atm}}{760 \text{ mm Hg}}\right)(6.56 \text{ L})}{(0.082057 \text{ L} \cdot \text{atm/K} \cdot \text{mol})(298 \text{ K})} = 0.206 \text{ mol CH}_3\text{Cl}$

$\dfrac{0.206 \text{ mol CH}_3\text{Cl}}{0.0801 \text{ mol Si}} = \dfrac{2.58 \text{ mol CH}_3\text{Cl}}{1 \text{ mol Si}} > \dfrac{2 \text{ mol CH}_3\text{Cl}}{1 \text{ mol Si}}$ Si is the limiting reactant

$0.0801 \text{ mol Si} \cdot \dfrac{1 \text{ mol (CH}_3)_2\text{SiCl}_2}{1 \text{ mol Si}} \cdot \dfrac{129.1 \text{ g}}{1 \text{ mol (CH}_3)_2\text{SiCl}_2} = 10.3 \text{ g (CH}_3)_2\text{SiCl}_2$

$P_{(\text{CH}_3)_2\text{SiCl}_2} = \dfrac{(0.0801 \text{ mol})(0.082057 \text{ L} \cdot \text{atm/K} \cdot \text{mol})(368 \text{ K})}{6.56 \text{ L}} = 0.369 \text{ atm}$

12.72 $0.450 \text{ g Ni} \cdot \dfrac{1 \text{ mol Ni}}{58.69 \text{ g}} = 0.00767 \text{ mol Ni}$

$n_{\text{CO}} = \dfrac{\left(418 \text{ mm Hg} \cdot \dfrac{1 \text{ atm}}{760 \text{ mm Hg}}\right)(1.50 \text{ L})}{(0.082057 \text{ L} \cdot \text{atm/K} \cdot \text{mol})(298.2 \text{ K})} = 0.0337 \text{ mol CO}$

$\dfrac{0.0337 \text{ mol CO}}{0.00767 \text{ mol Ni}} = \dfrac{4.40 \text{ mol CO}}{1 \text{ mol Ni}} > \dfrac{4 \text{ mol CO}}{1 \text{ mol Ni}}$ Ni is the limiting reactant

$0.00767 \text{ mol Ni} \cdot \dfrac{1 \text{ mol Ni(CO)}_4}{1 \text{ mol Ni}} \cdot \dfrac{170.7 \text{ g}}{1 \text{ mol Ni(CO)}_4} = 1.31 \text{ g Ni(CO)}_4$

12.73   (a) $O_2 < B_2H_6 < H_2O$

       (b) $P_{O_2} = 256 \text{ mm Hg} \cdot \dfrac{3 \text{ mol O}_2}{1 \text{ mol B}_2\text{H}_6} = 768 \text{ mm Hg}$

12.74 $100.00\% - (11.79\% \text{ C} + 69.57\% \text{ Cl}) = 18.64\% \text{ F}$ Assume 100.00 g compound

$$11.79 \text{ g C} \cdot \frac{1 \text{ mol C}}{12.011 \text{ g}} = 0.9816 \text{ mol C} \qquad\qquad 69.57 \text{ g Cl} \cdot \frac{1 \text{ mol Cl}}{35.453 \text{ g}} = 1.962 \text{ mol Cl}$$

$$18.64 \text{ g F} \cdot \frac{1 \text{ mol F}}{18.998 \text{ g}} = 0.9812 \text{ mol F}$$

$$\frac{0.9816 \text{ mol C}}{0.9812 \text{ mol F}} = \frac{1 \text{ mol C}}{1 \text{ mol F}} \qquad \frac{1.962 \text{ mol Cl}}{0.9812 \text{ mol F}} = \frac{2 \text{ mol Cl}}{1 \text{ mol F}} \qquad \text{The empirical formula is CCl}_2\text{F}$$

$$M = \frac{dRT}{P} = \frac{\left(\dfrac{0.107 \text{ g}}{0.458 \text{ L}}\right)(0.082057 \text{ L} \cdot \text{atm/K} \cdot \text{mol})(298 \text{ K})}{21.3 \text{ mm Hg} \cdot \dfrac{1 \text{ atm}}{760 \text{ mm Hg}}} = 204 \text{ g/mol}$$

$$\frac{204 \text{ g/mol}}{102 \text{ g/mol}} = 2 \qquad\qquad \text{The molecular formula is (CCl}_2\text{F)}_2 \text{ or C}_2\text{Cl}_4\text{F}_2$$

12.75 $25.23 \text{ g S} \cdot \dfrac{1 \text{ mol}}{32.066 \text{ g}} = 0.7868 \text{ mol S}$

$$74.77 \text{ g F} \cdot \frac{1 \text{ mol}}{18.998 \text{ g}} = 3.935 \text{ mol F}$$

$$\frac{3.935 \text{ mol F}}{0.7868 \text{ mol S}} = \frac{5 \text{ mol F}}{1 \text{ mol S}} \qquad \text{The empirical formula is SF}_5$$

$$M = \frac{dRT}{P} = \frac{\left(\dfrac{0.0955 \text{ g}}{0.089 \text{ L}}\right)(0.082057 \text{ L} \cdot \text{atm/K} \cdot \text{mol})(318 \text{ K})}{83.8 \text{ mm Hg} \cdot \dfrac{1 \text{ atm}}{760 \text{ mm Hg}}} = 254 \text{ g/mol}$$

$$\frac{254 \text{ g/mol}}{127 \text{ g/mol}} = 2 \qquad\qquad \text{The molecular formula is (SF}_5)_2 \text{ or S}_2\text{F}_{10}$$

12.76 $0.95 \text{ g (NH}_4)_2\text{Cr}_2\text{O}_7 \cdot \dfrac{1 \text{ mol (NH}_4)_2\text{Cr}_2\text{O}_7}{252 \text{ g}} \cdot \dfrac{5 \text{ mol gas}}{1 \text{ mol (NH}_4)_2\text{Cr}_2\text{O}_7} = 0.019 \text{ mol gas produced}$

$$P_{\text{total}} = \frac{n_{\text{total}} RT}{V} = \frac{(0.018 \text{ mol})(0.082057 \text{ L} \cdot \text{atm/K} \cdot \text{mol})(296 \text{ K})}{15.0 \text{ L}} = 0.031 \text{ atm}$$

$$P_{\text{N}_2} = 0.031 \text{ atm} \cdot \frac{1 \text{ mol N}_2}{5 \text{ mol gas}} = 0.0061 \text{ atm} \qquad P_{\text{H}_2\text{O}} = 0.031 \text{ atm} \cdot \frac{4 \text{ mol H}_2\text{O}}{5 \text{ mol gas}} = 0.024 \text{ atm}$$

12.77   (a) $1.0 \text{ L H}_2 \cdot \dfrac{1 \text{ mol H}_2}{22.414 \text{ L}} = 0.045 \text{ mol H}_2$

(b) $1.0 \text{ L Ar} \cdot \dfrac{1 \text{ mol Ar}}{22.414 \text{ L}} = 0.045 \text{ mol Ar}$

(c) $n = \dfrac{PV}{RT} = \dfrac{(1.0 \text{ atm})(1.0 \text{ L})}{(0.082057 \text{ L} \cdot \text{atm/K} \cdot \text{mol})(300. \text{ K})} = 0.041 \text{ mol H}_2$

(d) $n = \dfrac{PV}{RT} = \dfrac{\left(900 \text{ mm Hg} \cdot \dfrac{1 \text{ atm}}{760 \text{ mm Hg}}\right)(1.0 \text{ L})}{(0.082057 \text{ L} \cdot \text{atm/K} \cdot \text{mol})(273 \text{ K})} = 0.05 \text{ mol He}$

The number of molecules is proportional to number of moles, so sample (d) contains the greatest number of molecules and sample (c) contains the smallest number of gas molecules. Argon has the greatest molar mass, so sample (b) contains the largest mass of gas (0.045 mol Ar · 39.9 g/mol = 1.8 g Ar).

12.78 $n_{N_2} = \dfrac{PV}{RT} = \dfrac{\left(713 \text{ mm Hg} \cdot \dfrac{1 \text{ atm}}{760 \text{ mm Hg}}\right)(0.295 \text{ L})}{(0.082057 \text{ L} \cdot \text{atm/K} \cdot \text{mol})(294.2 \text{ K})} = 0.0115 \text{ mol N}_2$

$0.0115 \text{ mol N}_2 \cdot \dfrac{1 \text{ mol NaNO}_2}{1 \text{ mol N}_2} \cdot \dfrac{69.00 \text{ g}}{1 \text{ mol NaNO}_2} = 0.791 \text{ g NaNO}_2$

$\dfrac{0.791 \text{ g NaNO}_2}{1.232 \text{ g sample}} \cdot 100\% = 64.2\%$

12.79   (a) $M = \dfrac{dRT}{P} = \dfrac{\left(\dfrac{92 \text{ g}}{1 \text{ m}^3} \cdot \dfrac{1 \text{ m}^3}{10^3 \text{ L}}\right)(0.082057 \text{ L} \cdot \text{atm/K} \cdot \text{mol})(210. \text{ K})}{42 \text{ mm Hg} \cdot \dfrac{1 \text{ atm}}{760 \text{ mm Hg}}} = 29 \text{ g/mol}$

(b) $X_{O_2} + X_{N_2} = 1$

$29 \text{ g/mol} = X_{O_2} \cdot \dfrac{32.0 \text{ g}}{1 \text{ mol O}_2} + (1 - X_{O_2}) \cdot \dfrac{28.0 \text{ g}}{1 \text{ mol N}_2}$

$X_{O_2} = 0.18$

$X_{N_2} = 0.82$

12.80   He: $P_2 = \dfrac{P_1 V_1}{V_2} = \dfrac{(145 \text{ mm Hg})(3.0 \text{ L})}{5.0 \text{ L}} = 87 \text{ mm Hg}$

Hg: $P_2 = \dfrac{P_1 V_1}{V_2} = \dfrac{(355 \text{ mm Hg})(2.0 \text{ L})}{5.0 \text{ L}} = 140 \text{ mm Hg}$

$P_{\text{total}} = 87 \text{ mm Hg} + 140 \text{ mm Hg} = 230 \text{ mm Hg}$

12.81 $7 \times 10^{-5} \text{ mg PH}_3 \cdot \dfrac{1 \text{ g}}{1000 \text{ mg}} \cdot \dfrac{1 \text{ mol PH}_3}{34 \text{ g}} = 2 \times 10^{-9} \text{ mol}$

$P = \dfrac{(2 \times 10^{-9} \text{ mol})(0.082057 \text{ L} \cdot \text{atm/K} \cdot \text{mol})(298 \text{ K})}{1 \text{ L}} = 5 \times 10^{-8} \text{ atm}$

12.82 $P_{F_2(\text{consumed})} = P_{\text{total}} - P_{Xe} - P_{F_2(\text{unreacted})} = 0.72 \text{ atm} - 0.12 \text{ atm} - 0.36 \text{ atm} = 0.24 \text{ atm}$

$n_F = \dfrac{(0.24 \text{ atm})(0.25 \text{ L})}{(0.082057 \text{ L} \cdot \text{atm/K} \cdot \text{mol})(273.2 \text{ K})} \cdot \dfrac{2 \text{ mol F}}{1 \text{ mol F}_2} = 0.0054 \text{ mol F}$

$n_{Xe} = \dfrac{(0.12 \text{ atm})(0.25 \text{ L})}{(0.082057 \text{ L} \cdot \text{atm/K} \cdot \text{mol})(273.2 \text{ K})} = 0.0013 \text{ mol Xe}$

$\dfrac{0.0054 \text{ mol F}}{0.0013 \text{ mol Xe}} = \dfrac{4 \text{ mol F}}{1 \text{ mol Xe}}$ The empirical formula is XeF_4

12.83 $n = \dfrac{PV}{RT} = \dfrac{\left(17.2 \text{ mm Hg} \cdot \dfrac{1 \text{ atm}}{760 \text{ mm Hg}}\right)(1.850 \text{ L})}{(0.082057 \text{ L} \cdot \text{atm/K} \cdot \text{mol})(294 \text{ K})} = 0.00174 \text{ mol gas}$

$M = \dfrac{0.150 \text{ g}}{0.00174 \text{ mol}} = 86.4 \text{ g/mol}$ The gas is probably ClO_2F (86.4 g/mol)

12.84   Helium pressure = gauge pressure + barometric pressure = 22 mm Hg + 755 mm Hg = 777 mm Hg

$$n = \frac{PV}{RT} = \frac{\left(777 \text{ mm Hg} \cdot \frac{1 \text{ atm}}{760 \text{ mm Hg}}\right)(0.305 \text{ L})}{(0.082057 \text{ L} \cdot \text{atm/K} \cdot \text{mol})(298 \text{ K})} = 0.0128 \text{ mol He}$$

12.85   Theoretical yield of acetylene:

$$2.65 \text{ g CaC}_2 \cdot \frac{1 \text{ mol CaC}_2}{64.10 \text{ g}} \cdot \frac{1 \text{ mol C}_2\text{H}_2}{1 \text{ mol CaC}_2} = 0.0413 \text{ mol C}_2\text{H}_2$$

Actual yield of acetylene:

$$n_{\text{C}_2\text{H}_2} = \frac{\left(735.2 \text{ mm Hg} \cdot \frac{1 \text{ atm}}{760 \text{ mm Hg}}\right)(0.795 \text{ L})}{(0.082057 \text{ L} \cdot \text{atm/K} \cdot \text{mol})(298.4 \text{ K})} = 0.0314 \text{ mol C}_2\text{H}_2$$

$$\frac{0.0314 \text{ mol C}_2\text{H}_2}{0.0413 \text{ mol C}_2\text{H}_2} \cdot 100\% = 76.0\%$$

12.86 $\dfrac{n}{V} = \dfrac{P}{RT} = \dfrac{23.8 \text{ mm Hg} \cdot \dfrac{1 \text{ atm}}{760 \text{ mm Hg}}}{(0.082057 \text{ L} \cdot \text{atm/K} \cdot \text{mol})(298 \text{ K})} = 0.00128 \text{ mol/L}$

$$\frac{0.00128 \text{ mol}}{1 \text{ L}} \cdot \frac{6.022 \times 10^{23} \text{ molecules}}{1 \text{ mol}} \cdot \frac{1 \text{ L}}{10^3 \text{ mL}} \cdot \frac{1 \text{ mL}}{1 \text{ cm}^3} = 7.7 \times 10^{17} \text{ molecules/cm}^3$$

12.87 $n_{\text{O}_2} = \dfrac{\left(735 \text{ mm Hg} \cdot \dfrac{1 \text{ atm}}{760 \text{ mm Hg}}\right)(0.327 \text{ L})}{(0.082057 \text{ L} \cdot \text{atm/K} \cdot \text{mol})(292 \text{ K})} = 0.0132 \text{ mol O}_2$

$$0.0132 \text{ mol O}_2 \cdot \frac{2 \text{ mol KClO}_3}{3 \text{ mol O}_2} \cdot \frac{122.5 \text{ g}}{1 \text{ mol KClO}_3} = 1.08 \text{ g KClO}_3$$

$$\frac{1.08 \text{ g KClO}_3}{1.56 \text{ g mixture}} \cdot 100\% = 69.1\%$$

12.88 $P_{\text{total}} = P_{\text{H}_2\text{O}} + P_{\text{O}_2} + P_{\text{CO}_2} + P_{\text{N}_2}$

$P_{\text{N}_2} = 253 \text{ mm Hg} - 47.1 \text{ mm Hg} - 35 \text{ mm Hg} - 7.5 \text{ mm Hg}$

$P_{\text{N}_2} = 163 \text{ mm Hg}$

12.89   (a) $NO_2 < O_2 < NO$

   (b) $150 \text{ mm Hg} \cdot \dfrac{1 \text{ mol O}_2}{2 \text{ mol NO}} = 75 \text{ mm Hg}$

   (c) $150 \text{ mm Hg} \cdot \dfrac{2 \text{ mol NO}_2}{2 \text{ mol NO}} = 150 \text{ mm Hg}$

12.90   (a)   There are more moles of O_2 in the flask (oxygen has a smaller molar mass), so the oxygen has a greater partial pressure.

   (b)   Oxygen has a smaller molar mass so its molecules have the greater average speed.

   (c)   The gases are at the same temperature so the average kinetic energy is the same for both gases.

12.91   (a) True

        (b) False   Nitrogen (N_2) has a smaller molar mass than O_2, so an equal mass of N_2 contains more moles and more molecules than the O_2 sample

12.92   (a) Acetylene has a smaller molar mass, so there are more moles of gas in the acetylene cylinder and thus the pressure is greater.

        (b) The acetylene cylinder has a greater number of molecules.

12.93   At a constant pressure, the number of moles of a gas is inversely proportional to the temperature of the gas. Therefore flask B (at a lower temperature) contains more moles (and more molecules) of oxygen.

12.94   (a) probably not a gas (a gas would expand more)

        (b) probably not a gas (density = 8.2 g/mL, too large for a gas)

        (c) insufficient information (could also be a liquid or a solid)

        (d) gas

12.95   (a) more significant

        (b) more significant

        (c) less significant

12.96   (a) All four tires have the same pressure, temperature, and volume. They have the same number of gas molecules.

        (b) 160. g/16.0 g = 10 times heavier

        (c) All the molecules have the same kinetic energy (they have the same temperature). Helium is the lightest gas of the four, so its molecules have the greatest average speed.

12.97 P_{CO_2} = 1.56 atm − 1.34 atm = 0.22 atm

$$n_{CO_2} = \frac{PV}{RT} = \frac{(0.22 \text{ atm})(0.55 \text{ L})}{(0.082057 \text{ L} \cdot \text{atm/K} \cdot \text{mol})(297 \text{ K})} = 0.0050 \text{ mol CO}_2$$

$$0.0050 \text{ mol CO}_2 \cdot \frac{44.0 \text{ g}}{1 \text{ mol CO}_2} = 0.22 \text{ g CO}_2$$

$$P_{O_2} = \frac{nRT}{V} = \frac{\left(0.0870 \text{ g} \cdot \frac{1 \text{ mol O}_2}{32.00 \text{ g}}\right)(0.082057 \text{ L} \cdot \text{atm/K} \cdot \text{mol})(297 \text{ K})}{0.55 \text{ L}} = 0.12 \text{ atm}$$

P_{CO} = 1.56 atm − 0.22 atm − 0.12 atm = 1.22 atm

$$n_{CO_2} = \frac{PV}{RT} = \frac{(1.22 \text{ atm})(0.55 \text{ L})}{(0.082057 \text{ L} \cdot \text{atm/K} \cdot \text{mol})(297 \text{ K})} = 0.028 \text{ mol CO}$$

$$0.028 \text{ mol CO} \cdot \frac{28.0 \text{ g}}{1 \text{ mol CO}} = 0.77 \text{ g CO}$$

12.98 $CH_4(g) + 2\ O_2(g) \rightarrow CO_2(g) + 2\ H_2O(g)$

Assume a one-minute time period:

$$n_{CH_4} = \frac{\left(773\ mm\ Hg \cdot \dfrac{1\ atm}{760\ mm\ Hg}\right)(5.0\ L)}{(0.082057\ L \cdot atm/K \cdot mol)(301\ K)} = 0.21\ mol\ CH_4$$

$$0.21\ mol\ CH_4 \cdot \frac{2\ mol\ O_2}{1\ mol\ CH_4} = 0.41\ mol\ O_2$$

$$V_{O_2} = \frac{(0.41\ mol\ O_2)(0.082057\ L \cdot atm/K \cdot mol)(299\ K)}{742\ mm\ Hg \cdot \dfrac{1\ atm}{760\ mm\ Hg}} = 10\ L\ O_2$$

The oxygen must be supplied to the burner at a rate of 10 L/min.

12.99 $$n_{CO_2} = \frac{PV}{RT} = \frac{\left(44.9\ mm\ Hg \cdot \dfrac{1\ atm}{760\ mm\ Hg}\right)(1.50\ L)}{(0.082057\ L \cdot atm/K \cdot mol)(298\ K)} = 0.00362\ mol\ CO_2$$

$$0.00362\ mol\ CO_2 \cdot \frac{1\ mol\ CO}{1\ mol\ CO_2} \cdot \frac{28.01\ g}{1\ mol\ CO} = 0.102\ g\ CO$$

mass of Fe in sample = 0.142 g sample − 0.102 g CO = 0.040 g Fe

$$0.040\ g\ Fe \cdot \frac{1\ mol\ Fe}{55.8\ g} = 7.3 \times 10^{-4}\ mol\ Fe$$

$$\frac{0.00362\ mol\ CO}{7.3 \times 10^{-4}\ mol\ Fe} = \frac{5\ mol\ CO}{1\ mol\ Fe} \qquad \text{The empirical formula is Fe(CO)}_5$$

12.100 $$n_{CO_2} = n_{MCO_3} = \frac{\left(69.8\ mm\ Hg \cdot \dfrac{1\ atm}{760\ mm\ Hg}\right)(0.285\ L)}{(0.082057\ L \cdot atm/K \cdot mol)(298\ K)} = 0.00107\ mol\ MCO_3$$

$$\frac{0.158\ g\ MCO_3}{0.00107\ mol\ MCO_3} = 148\ g/mol$$

148 g/mol = $M_{metal} + M_{CO_3}$ = M_{metal} + 60.0 g/mol

M_{metal} = 88 g/mol   The metal is probably Sr (87.6 g/mol)

12.101 $P_{SiH_4} = X_{SiH_4} P_{total} = \dfrac{1\ mol\ SiH_4}{3\ mol\ total} \cdot 120\ mm\ Hg = 40\ mm\ Hg$

P_{O_2} = 120 mm Hg − 40 mm Hg = 80 mm Hg

When reaction is complete, H_2O is the only gas present in the flask. $P_{H_2O} = P_{O_2}$ =80 mm Hg

12.102   (a) $$n_{ClF_3} = \frac{PV}{RT} = \frac{\left(250\ mm\ Hg \cdot \dfrac{1\ atm}{760\ mm\ Hg}\right)(2.5\ L)}{(0.082057\ L \cdot atm/K \cdot mol)(293\ K)} = 0.034\ mol\ ClF_3$$

$$0.034\ mol\ ClF_3 \cdot \frac{6\ mol\ NiO}{4\ mol\ ClF_3} \cdot \frac{74.7\ g}{1\ mol\ NiO} = 3.8\ g\ NiO$$

(b) Partial pressures:

$$0.034 \text{ mol ClF}_3 \cdot \frac{3 \text{ mol O}_2}{4 \text{ mol ClF}_3} = 0.026 \text{ mol O}_2$$

$$0.034 \text{ mol ClF}_3 \cdot \frac{2 \text{ mol Cl}_2}{4 \text{ mol ClF}_3} = 0.017 \text{ mol Cl}_2$$

$$P_{O_2} = \frac{nRT}{V} = \frac{(0.026 \text{ mol})(0.082057 \text{ L} \cdot \text{atm/K} \cdot \text{mol})(293 \text{ K})}{2.5 \text{ L}} = 0.25 \text{ atm} = 190 \text{ mm Hg}$$

$$P_{Cl_2} = \frac{nRT}{V} = \frac{(0.017 \text{ mol})(0.082057 \text{ L} \cdot \text{atm/K} \cdot \text{mol})(293 \text{ K})}{2.5 \text{ L}} = 0.16 \text{ atm} = 120 \text{ mm Hg}$$

$$P_{total} = 190 \text{ mm Hg} + 120 \text{ mm Hg} = 310 \text{ mm Hg}$$

12.103 (a) $0.136 \text{ g} \cdot \dfrac{1 \text{ mol NaBH}_4}{37.83 \text{ g}} \cdot \dfrac{1 \text{ mol B}_2\text{H}_6}{2 \text{ mol NaBH}_4} = 0.00180 \text{ mol B}_2\text{H}_6$

$$P = \frac{nRT}{V} = \frac{\left(0.00180 \text{ mol}\right)(0.082057 \text{ L} \cdot \text{atm/K} \cdot \text{mol})(298 \text{ K})}{2.75 \text{ L}} = 0.0160 \text{ atm}$$

(b) $P_{H_2} = 0.0160 \text{ atm} \cdot \dfrac{2 \text{ mol H}_2}{1 \text{ mol B}_2\text{H}_6} = 0.0320 \text{ atm}$

$P_{total} = 0.0160 \text{ atm} + 0.0320 \text{ atm} = 0.0480 \text{ atm}$

12.104 (a) Determine the limiting reactant and maximum yield of NaN_3:

$$65.0 \text{ g Na} \cdot \frac{1 \text{ mol}}{23.00 \text{ g}} = 2.83 \text{ mol Na}$$

$$n_{N_2O} = \frac{(2.12 \text{ atm})(35.0 \text{ L})}{(0.082057 \text{ L} \cdot \text{atm/K} \cdot \text{mol})(296 \text{ K})} = 3.05 \text{ mol N}_2\text{O}$$

$$\frac{3.05 \text{ mol N}_2\text{O}}{2.83 \text{ mol Na}} = \frac{1.08 \text{ mol N}_2\text{O}}{1 \text{ mol Na}} > \frac{0.75 \text{ mol N}_2\text{O}}{1 \text{ mol Na}} \qquad \text{Na is the limiting reactant}$$

$$2.83 \text{ mol Na} \cdot \frac{1 \text{ mol NaN}_3}{4 \text{ mol Na}} \cdot \frac{65.02 \text{ g}}{1 \text{ mol NaN}_3} = 45.9 \text{ g NaN}_3$$

(b) $\left[:N \equiv N - \ddot{\underset{\cdot\cdot}{N}}:\right]^- \longleftrightarrow \left[\ddot{\underset{\cdot\cdot}{N}} = N = \ddot{\underset{\cdot\cdot}{N}}\right]^- \longleftrightarrow \left[:\ddot{N} - N \equiv N:\right]^-$

     0   +1   −2   −1   +1   −1   −2   +1   0

The formal charges (shown below the resonance structures) indicate that the center resonance structure is most likely.

(c) The azide ion is linear.

12.105 (a) $7 + 2(6) = 19$ valence electrons

(b) $\left[:\ddot{\underset{\cdot\cdot}{O}} - \ddot{\underset{\cdot\cdot}{Cl}} - \ddot{\underset{\cdot\cdot}{O}}:\right]^-$

(c) sp^3 The ion is bent

(d) Ozone has a larger bond angle. The central atom is sp^2 hybridized. $\ddot{O} = \ddot{O} - \ddot{\underset{\cdot\cdot}{O}}:$

(e) $15.6 \text{ g NaClO}_2 \cdot \dfrac{1 \text{ mol NaClO}_2}{90.44 \text{ g}} = 0.172 \text{ mol NaClO}_2$

$$n_{Cl_2} = \frac{PV}{RT} = \frac{\left(1050 \text{ mm Hg} \cdot \dfrac{1 \text{ atm}}{760 \text{ mm Hg}}\right)(1.45 \text{ L})}{(0.082057 \text{ L} \cdot \text{atm/K} \cdot \text{mol})(295 \text{ K})} = 0.0828 \text{ mol Cl}_2$$

$\dfrac{0.172 \text{ mol NaClO}_2}{0.0828 \text{ mol Cl}_2} = \dfrac{2.08 \text{ mol NaClO}_2}{1 \text{ mol Cl}_2} > \dfrac{2 \text{ mol NaClO}_2}{1 \text{ mol Cl}_2}$ Cl_2 is the limiting reactant

$0.0828 \text{ mol Cl}_2 \cdot \dfrac{2 \text{ mol ClO}_2}{1 \text{ mol Cl}_2} \cdot \dfrac{67.45 \text{ g}}{1 \text{ mol ClO}_2} = 11.2 \text{ g ClO}_2$

12.106   (a)   A gas will likely become a solid long before reaching the vicinity of absolute zero.

(b)   The N_2 and H_2 are in the correct stoichiometric ratio and will produce 8 molecules of NH_3. The volume of NH_3 will be twice that of the volume of N_2 and $^2/_3$ that of the H_2 (at the same T and P).

12.107   (a)   The simulation allows you to vary three factors (pressure, temperature, and mass) while volume is held constant. Plot volume and either pressure, temperature, or mass (while the other two are held constant) to discover the gas laws.

(b)   Volume and temperature are directly related. This is an illustration of Charles's Law.

(c) $V = \dfrac{nRT}{P} = \dfrac{\left(0.180 \text{ g} \cdot \dfrac{1 \text{ mol N}_2}{28.01 \text{ g}}\right)(0.082057 \text{ L} \cdot \text{atm/K} \cdot \text{mol})(373 \text{ K})}{200 \text{ mm Hg} \cdot \dfrac{1 \text{ atm}}{760 \text{ mm Hg}}} = 0.75 \text{ L}$

12.108   (a)   All of these foods have distinctive odors, which reach our noses by diffusion.

(b)   Speed of gas molecules is related to the square root of the absolute temperature, so a doubling of the temperature will lead to an increase of about $(2)^{1/2}$ or 1.4.

(c)   No.

12.109   (a)   Pressure is a force that arises from collisions of molecules with a surface.

12.110   (a)   As molar mass increases, gas speed decreases.

(b)   As temperature increases, gas speed increases.

12.111   (a) NH_3 molecules have a smaller molar mass than HCl molecules

(b) $NH_4Cl(s)$

Chapter 13
Intermolecular Forces, Liquids, and Solids

INSTRUCTOR'S NOTES

We believe the material in this chapter has been neglected in introductory courses, particularly the matter of intermolecular forces. Therefore, we set aside 5-6 lecture periods for this chapter.

The ionic and molecular solids pictured in this chapter can be found on the *General Chemistry Interactive CD-ROM* in the solids folder. The ionic solids pictured have been manipulated (by changing the ionic radii) in order to make the ions appear with the correct radius.

SUGGESTED DEMONSTRATIONS

1.   Vapor Pressure

   • We have searched for good demonstrations of vapor pressure for some time. One of the demonstrations we use is a so-called "Love Meter", a toy that can be obtained in novelty and gift shops. The closed, thin-walled glass vessel contains methyl chloride (bp –23.7 °C). Warming the vessel in your hand raises the vapor pressure of the liquid and forces the liquid to another compartment of the vessel.

2.   Solids

   • Molecular models are invaluable to show intermolecular forces and solid state structures. Various kinds of kits are available from Aldrich Chemical Company.

   • The Klinger Educational Products Corp. (112-19 14th Road, College Point, New York, NY 11356-1453) sells a very large number of models of various solids.

   • The Institute for Chemical Education (Department of Chemistry, University of Wisconsin - Madison, 1101 University Ave., Madison, WI 53706) offers a Solid State Model Kit that can be used to illustrate the variety of unit cells.

   • The close packing of spheres (such as the photos on page 541) is easy to do on an overhead projector. We have also used oranges and grapefruits, as well as Styrofoam balls.

Solutions to Study Questions

13.1   dipole-dipole, hydrogen bonding, dipole/induced dipole, induced dipole/induced dipole (London dispersion forces), ion-dipole

13.2   Water is a polar molecule and carbon dioxide has polar bonds (but is a nonpolar molecule). The negative end of the water dipole can interact with the positive end of the carbon-oxygen bond dipole in a dipole/induced dipole interaction.

13.3   dipole/induced dipole forces

13.4   N, O, and F   The electronegativities of the elements N, O, and F are among the highest of all the elements, whereas the electronegativity of hydrogen is much lower. The large difference in electronegativity means that the N—H, O—H, and F—H bonds are very polar.

13.5   As water is cooled from 4 °C to 0 °C, the molecules begin to cluster in ice-like arrangements with open-cage structures. The density decreases until the ice is formed, which consists of an extensive cage-like structure due to hydrogen bonding between water molecules.

13.6   Water has extensive hydrogen bonding. Raising the temperature of a sample of water disrupts hydrogen bonds and requires heat, so water has a high heat capacity. Large bodies of water can moderate temperature changes by giving up heat to the atmosphere when air temperature is lower than water temperature.

13.7   Heat from your body is consumed when sweat evaporates from your skin, and your body is cooled.

13.8   Generally, the boiling points of the EH_3 compounds increases with molar mass because of increasing dispersion forces. The boiling point of NH_3 does not follow this trend because of strong hydrogen bonds that exist between ammonia molecules.

13.9   Oils consist of long-chain molecules that are floppy and become entangled with one another, resulting in a viscous liquid. Benzene has a much smaller molar mass and a ring structure. The forces between benzene molecules are much weaker, so it is not viscous.

13.10   Simple cubic: eight identical atoms, molecules, or ions at the corners of a cube
        Body-centered cubic: a simple cubic arrangement plus an additional particle at the center of the cube
        Face-centered cubic: a simple cubic arrangement plus an additional particle on each face of the cube

13.11 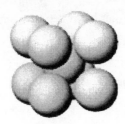   2 net atoms per unit cell

13.12   When a salt crystal is cleaved, the smaller cubes that form are smaller versions of the macroscopic crystal. This is evidence for the underlying lattice structure. Glass is an amorphous solid that has no long-range order, so when it breaks it leaves randomly shaped pieces.

13.13   Ionic solids have very high melting points.

13.14   See Figure 13.35

13.15   Because ice is less dense than liquid water, ice and water in equilibrium respond to increased pressure (at constant T) by melting ice to form more water because the same mass of water requires less volume.

13.16   (a) hydrogen bonding

      (b) induced dipole/induced dipole

      (c) hydrogen bonding

13.17   solid iodine: induced dipole/induced dipole

      CH_3OH: hydrogen bonding

      I_2 and CH_3OH: induced dipole/dipole

13.18   (a) induced dipole/induced dipole   (c) dipole-dipole

      (b) induced dipole/induced dipole   (d) hydrogen bonding

13.19   (a) induced dipole/induced dipole   (c) dipole-dipole

      (b) hydrogen bonding   (d) induced dipole/induced dipole

13.20   Based on increasing molar mass: $CH_4 < Ne < CO < CCl_4$

                                       —increasing intermolecular forces→

      However, boiling points are in the order   Ne (–246 °C) < CO (–192 °C) < CH_4 (–162 °C) < CCl_4 (77 °C)

      CH_4, Ne, and CO are gases at 25 °C and 1 atm

13.21   He < $CH_3CH_2CH_2CH_3$ < CH_3OH

      —increasing intermolecular forces→

      He and $CH_3CH_2CH_2CH_3$ are gases at 25 °C and 1 atm

13.22   (c) HF, (d) CH_3CO_2H, and (f) CH_3OH would be expected to form intermolecular hydrogen bonds in the liquid state

13.23 HCO_2H would be expected to form intermolecular hydrogen bonds in the liquid state.

13.24 $125 \text{ mL} \cdot \dfrac{0.7849 \text{ g}}{1 \text{ mL}} \cdot \dfrac{1 \text{ mol}}{46.069 \text{ g}} \cdot \dfrac{42.32 \text{ kJ}}{1 \text{ mol}} = 90.1 \text{ kJ}$

13.25 $0.500 \text{ mL} \cdot \dfrac{13.53 \text{ g}}{1 \text{ mL}} \cdot \dfrac{1 \text{ mol}}{200.59 \text{ g}} \cdot \dfrac{59.11 \text{ kJ}}{1 \text{ mol}} = 1.99 \text{ kJ}$

13.26   (a) Approximately 150 mm Hg. Appendix G shows a value of 149.4 mm Hg

(b) 93 °C

(c) Ethanol (520 mm Hg) has a higher vapor pressure at 70 °C than water (225 mm Hg)

13.27   (a) Approximately 400 mm Hg.

(b) diethyl ether < ethanol < water

(c) diethyl ether is a gas, and ethanol and water are in the liquid phase

13.28   The vapor pressure of diethyl ether at 30 °C is approximately 600 mm Hg.

$$n = \frac{PV}{RT} = \frac{\left(600 \text{ mm Hg} \cdot \dfrac{1 \text{ atm}}{760 \text{ mm Hg}}\right)(0.100 \text{ mL})}{(0.082057 \text{ L} \cdot \text{atm/K} \cdot \text{mol})(303 \text{ K})} = 0.0032 \text{ mol}$$

$0.0032 \text{ mol} \cdot \dfrac{74.1 \text{ g}}{1 \text{ mol}} = 0.24 \text{ g}$ diethyl ether needed to create pressure of 600 mm Hg in flask

There is enough diethyl ether available (1.0 g) to create a pressure of 600 mm Hg. When the flask is cooled, some ether will condense to a liquid.

13.29   (a) As the water cools, the vapor pressure of the water decreases, resulting in a decrease in the total pressure inside the bottle. The bottle will collapse because the pressure inside is less than the external pressure.

(b) The normal boiling point of diethyl ether is 34.6 °C so the liquid will evaporate completely at body temperature (37 °C).

13.30   (a) O_2 (higher molar mass)   (c) HF (hydrogen bonding)

(b) SO_2 (polar molecule)   (d) GeH_4 (higher molar mass)

13.31 $CH_4 < CO < NH_3 < SCl_2$ (predicted based on increasing molar mass)

$CO < CH_4 < NH_3 < SCl_2$ (actual order of increasing boiling point)

—increasing boiling point→

13.32   (a) CS₂: 620 mm Hg   CH₃NO₂: 80 mm Hg

         (b)   induced dipole/induced dipole   dipole-dipole

         (c)   46 °C   100 °C

         (d) 39 °C

         (e) 34 °C

13.33   (a) increase

         (b) increases

         (c) does not change

         (d) increases

13.34   A gas can be liquefied at or below its critical temperature. The critical temperature for CO (132.9 K) is
         below room temperature (298 K), so CO cannot be liquefied at or above room temperature.

13.35   The critical temperature for propane is well above room temperature, so propane can be liquefied.
         Liquefied propane is commonly used for heating and cooking.

13.36   Two possible unit cells: Each unit cell contains 1 A square and 8 B squares, so the
                                                       simplest formula is AB₈

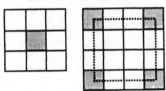

13.37   The area inside the box is a unit cell. Each unit cell contains 2 A squares and 2 B squares,
         so the simplest formula is AB.

13.38   8 corner Ti × ¹/₈ = 1 Ti   12 edge O × ¹/₄ = 3 O   1 internal Ca = 1 Ca
         The formula is CaTiO₃

13.39   8 corner Ti × ¹/₈ = 1 Ti   4 face O × ¹/₂ = 2 O
         1 internal Ti   = 1 Ti   2 internal O   = 2 O
         _____   _____
                            = 2 Ti total   = 4 O total
         There are two TiO₂ units per unit cell.

13.40   8 corner O × ¹/₈ = 1 O
         1 internal O   = 1 O   4 internal Cu = 4 Cu
         _____   _____
                           = 2 O total   = 4 Cu total

There is a ratio of two copper ions to one oxide ion for a formula of Cu_2O. The oxidation number of copper is +1.

13.41   (a)   face-centered cubic

(b)   tetrahedral holes

(c)   (8 corner $Ca^{2+} \times {}^1/_8$) + (6 face $Ca^{2+} \times {}^1/_2$) = 4 Ca^{2+} 8 internal $F^- = 8\ F^-$

The formula is CaF_2

13.42   (a)   (8 corner $C \times {}^1/_8$) + (6 face $C \times {}^1/_2$) + (4 internal C) = 8 C atoms/unit cell

(b)   face-centered cubic arrangement with carbon atoms in tetrahedral holes

13.43   (a)   induced dipole/induced dipole

(b)   Since there are only weak intermolecular forces between the layers in graphite, the layers slide over each other easily, giving graphite a slippery feel. Pushing a pencil lead against paper causes some of the carbon layers to rub off, leaving a black mark

13.44 $15.5\ g \cdot \dfrac{1\ mol\ C_6H_6}{78.11\ g} \cdot \dfrac{9.95\ kJ}{1\ mol} = 1.97\ kJ$ heat evolved (−1.97 kJ)

+1.97 kJ of heat must be absorbed to convert the solid to a liquid.

13.45   The total heat required is the sum of the heat required to (1) heat the solid from 25 °C to its melting point and (2) liquefy the solid at its melting point.

q_{solid} = 5.00 g Ag $\cdot$ 0.235 J/g·K $\cdot$ (1235 K − 298 K) = 1.10×10^3 J

$q_{melting}$ = 5.00 g Ag $\cdot \dfrac{1\ mol}{107.9\ g} \cdot \dfrac{11.3\ kJ}{1\ mol} \cdot \dfrac{10^3\ J}{1\ kJ}$ = 5.24×10^2 J

q_{total} = (1.10×10^3 J) + (5.24×10^2 J) = 1.62×10^3 J

13.46   (a)   The positive slope of the solid/liquid equilibrium line indicates that liquid CO_2 is less dense than solid CO_2.

(b)   gas phase

(c)   31 °C

13.47   (a)   Xenon is a gas at room temperature and 1.0 atm pressure.

(b)   Xenon is a liquid at 0.75 atm pressure and −114 °C.

(c)   When the pressure on a sample of liquid xenon is 380 mm Hg (0.5 atm), the temperature is between −117 and −119 °C.

(d)   At −122 °C, the vapor pressure of solid xenon is 0.25 atm.

(e)   The solid phase is more dense than the liquid phase because the solid–liquid equilibrium line has a positive slope.

13.48   The total heat required is the sum of the heat required to (1) heat the liquid from –50.0 °C to its boiling
point, (2) vaporize the gas, and (3) heat the vapor to 0.0 °C.

$$q_{liquid} = 12 \text{ kg} \cdot \frac{10^3 \text{ g}}{1 \text{ kg}} \cdot 4.7 \text{ J/g·K} \cdot (239.9 \text{ K} - 223.2 \text{ K}) \cdot \frac{1 \text{ kJ}}{10^3 \text{ J}} = 9.4 \times 10^2 \text{ kJ}$$

$$q_{evaporation} = 12 \text{ kg} \cdot \frac{10^3 \text{ g}}{1 \text{ kg}} \cdot \frac{1 \text{ mol}}{17.0 \text{ g}} \cdot \frac{23.33 \text{ kJ}}{1 \text{ mol}} = 1.6 \times 10^4 \text{ kJ}$$

$$q_{vapor} = 12 \text{ kg} \cdot \frac{10^3 \text{ g}}{1 \text{ kg}} \cdot 2.2 \text{ J/g·K} \cdot (273.2 \text{ K} - 239.9 \text{ K}) \cdot \frac{1 \text{ kJ}}{10^3 \text{ J}} = 8.8 \times 10^2 \text{ kJ}$$

$$q_{total} = 9.4 \times 10^2 \text{ kJ} + 1.6 \times 10^4 \text{ kJ} + 8.8 \times 10^2 \text{ kJ} = 1.8 \times 10^4 \text{ kJ}$$

13.49   The total heat required is the sum of the heat required to (1) cool the gas from 40.0 °C to its boiling point,
(2) condense the gas, and (3) cool the liquid to –40.0 °C.

$$q_{gas} = 20.0 \text{ g CCl}_2\text{F}_2 \cdot \frac{1 \text{ mol}}{120.9 \text{ g}} \cdot 117.2 \text{ J/mol·K} \cdot (243.4 \text{ K} - 313.2 \text{ K}) = -1350 \text{ J}$$

$$q_{condensation} = 20.0 \text{ g CCl}_2\text{F}_2 \cdot \frac{1 \text{ mol}}{120.9 \text{ g}} \cdot \frac{-20.11 \text{ kJ}}{1 \text{ mol}} \cdot \frac{10^3 \text{ J}}{1 \text{ kJ}} = -3330 \text{ J}$$

$$q_{liquid} = 20.0 \text{ g CCl}_2\text{F}_2 \cdot \frac{1 \text{ mol}}{120.9 \text{ g}} \cdot 72.3 \text{ J/mol·K} \cdot (233.2 \text{ K} - 243.4 \text{ K}) = -122 \text{ J}$$

$$q_{total} = (-1350 \text{ J}) + (-3330 \text{ J}) + (-122 \text{ J}) = -4.80 \times 10^3 \text{ J}$$

13.50 $Ar < CO_2 < CH_3OH$

—increasing intermolecular forces→

13.51   (a) induced dipole/induced dipole forces

(b) hydrogen bonding

13.52
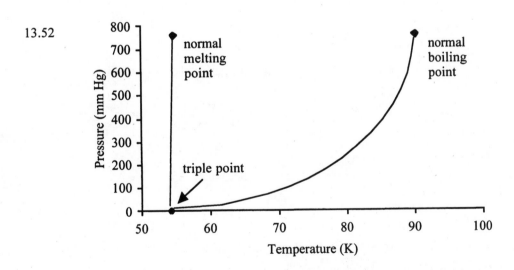

The estimated vapor pressure at 77 K is approximately 200 mmHg. The solid-liquid equilibrium line has
a positive slope, so the density of liquid O_2 is less than that of solid O_2.

13.53   Since cooking oil does not mix with water, the two substances have different types of intermolecular forces. Water is a polar molecule, and strong hydrogen bonding occurs between water molecules. The molecules in cooking oil are likely nonpolar.

13.54   Acetone readily absorbs water because hydrogen bonding occurs between the molecules.

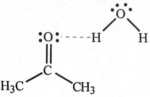

13.55 $1.0 \times 10^3 \text{ mL} \cdot \dfrac{1 \text{ cm}^3}{1 \text{ mL}} \cdot \dfrac{0.785 \text{ g}}{1 \text{ cm}^3} \cdot \dfrac{1 \text{ mol}}{46.07 \text{ g}} = 17 \text{ mol C}_2\text{H}_5\text{OH}$

$V_{\text{room}} = 3.0 \text{ m} \cdot 2.5 \text{ m} \cdot 2.5 \text{ m} \cdot \left(\dfrac{10^2 \text{ cm}}{1 \text{ m}}\right)^3 \cdot \dfrac{1 \text{ mL}}{1 \text{ cm}^3} \cdot \dfrac{1 \text{ L}}{10^3 \text{ mL}} = 1.9 \times 10^4 \text{ L}$

$n = \dfrac{PV}{RT} = \dfrac{\left(59 \text{ mm Hg} \cdot \dfrac{1 \text{ atm}}{760 \text{ mm Hg}}\right)(1.9 \times 10^4 \text{ L})}{(0.082057 \text{ L} \cdot \text{atm/K} \cdot \text{mol})(298 \text{ K})} = 60. \text{ mol ethanol}$

Less ethanol is available (17 mol) than would be required to completely fill the room with vapor (60. mol), so all of the ethanol will evaporate.

13.56   The viscosity of ethylene glycol is greater than that of ethanol since ethylene glycol contains two O—H groups per molecule while ethanol has only one.

13.57   (a) ICl (polar molecule)

(b) krypton (greater molar mass)

(c) CH₃CH₂OH (hydrogen bonding)

13.58   The meniscus is concave since there are adhesive forces between the methanol and the silicate of the glass.

13.59   (a) 350 mm Hg

(b) ethanol (lower vapor pressure at every temperature)

(c) 84 °C

(d) CS₂: 46 °C   C₂H₂OH: 78 °C   C₇H₁₆: 99 °C

(e) CS₂: gas   C₂H₂OH: gas   C₇H₁₆: liquid

13.60   (a) Water has two O—H bonds and two lone pairs on oxygen, and ethanol has only one O—H bond. This leads to less extensive hydrogen bonding in ethanol and a lower boiling point than water.

(b) The water molecules interact extensively with the ethanol molecules (through hydrogen bonding) and can therefore occupy less than the anticipated 100 mL.

13.61 $CO_2 < CH_3Cl < HCO_2H$

—increasing intermolecular forces→

13.62 $(\text{face diagonal})^2 = (\text{edge length})^2 + (\text{edge length})^2$

face diagonal $= \sqrt{2} \cdot$ edge length

face diagonal $= \sqrt{2} \cdot 409$ pm

face diagonal $= 578$ pm

radius $= \dfrac{578\,\text{pm}}{4} = 145$ pm

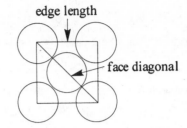

13.63   (a)   body-centered cubic

(b) $(8 \text{ corner W} \times {}^1/_8) + (1 \text{ internal W}) = 2$ W atoms/unit cell

(c) $(\text{cube diagonal})^2 = (\text{edge length})^2 + (\text{face diagonal})^2$

$(\text{cube diagonal})^2 = (\text{edge length})^2 + (\sqrt{2} \cdot \text{edge length})^2$

cube diagonal $= \sqrt{3} \cdot (\text{edge length})$

cube diagonal $= \sqrt{3} \cdot 316.5$ pm

cube diagonal $= 548$ pm

radius $= \dfrac{548\,\text{pm}}{4} = 137$ pm

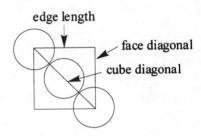

13.64

8 corner Ca $\times {}^1/_8$	= 1 Ca	8 edge C $\times {}^1/_4$	= 2 C
1 internal Ca	= 1 Ca	2 internal C	= 2 C
	= 2 Ca total		= 4 C total

There is a ratio of two calcium ions to four carbon ions for a formula of CaC_2.

13.65   In a face-centered cubic lattice of anions (X) there are a total of four anions per unit cell.

Type of holes occupied by cation (M)	Number of cations per unit cell	Formula of salt
all tetrahedral holes	8	M_2X
half of the tetrahedral holes	4	MX
all octahedral holes	4	MX

It is not possible to have a cation:anion ratio of 3:1.

13.66   No. The sodium chloride unit cell contains four anions and four cations. It cannot have a 1:2 cation:anion stoichiometry.

13.67   1-propanol has stronger intermolecular forces (hydrogen bonding) than methyl ethyl ether (dipole-dipole).

13.68   Two pieces of evidence for $H_2O(\ell)$ having considerable intermolecular attractive forces:

(1) Based on the trend for Group VIA hydrides, the boiling point of water should be approximately −80 °C. The actual boiling point (100 °C) reflects the significant hydrogen bonding present.

(2) Liquid water has a heat capacity of 4.184 J/g·K, higher than almost all other liquids. This reflects the fact that it takes a relatively large amount of energy to overcome intermolecular forces in order to raise the temperature of a sample of water.

13.69   The frost–free refrigerator's freezer is warmed periodically to near the freezing point of water. This allows the vapor pressure of the ice to increase so that sublimation readily occurs, keeping the frost from accumulating in the freezer. It would therefore make the hailstones disappear over time. No such mechanism exists in the older non–frost–free refrigerator.

13.70   When the water vapor in the can comes in contact with the cold water in the pan, the vapor condenses, decreasing the vapor pressure inside the can. The pressure inside the can is now lower than the atmospheric pressure outside the can, causing the can to collapse.

13.71 $C_2H_6 < HCl < CH_3OH$

—increasing molar enthalpy of vaporization→

13.72   (a)   −27 °C

(b)   6.5 atm

(c)   The flow is rapid at first because the liquid has vaporized to form the maximum amount of vapor possible at that temperature, with a pressure of approximately 6.5 atm. As the gas leaves the cylinder, additional liquid vaporizes in an attempt to reach liquid-vapor equilibrium. The flow becomes much slower because the pressure in the cylinder has dropped and cannot increase unless the cylinder is closed or enough heat is supplied to vaporize the remaining liquid. This vaporization requires energy, so the temperature of the cylinder drops and ice forms on the outside of the cylinder.

(d)   (ii) Cool the cylinder to −78 °C and open the valve. Cooling the cylinder will condense the vapor, allowing it to be easily removed as a liquid.

13.73   A gas can be liquefied at or below its critical temperature. The critical temperature for CF_4 (−45.7 °C) is below room temperature (25 °C), so it cannot be liquefied at room temperature.

13.74 (a) 80.1 °C

(b) When P = 250 mm Hg, T = 47 ° C   When P = 650 mm Hg, T = 77 °C

Vapor pressure vs Temperature

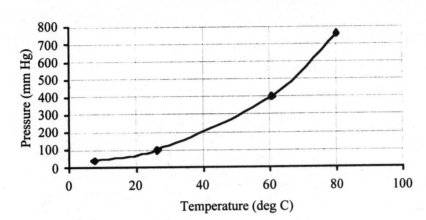

(c) $\ln\left(\dfrac{400.\ mm\ Hg}{100.\ mm\ Hg}\right) = \dfrac{\Delta H_{vap}}{0.0083145\ kJ/K{\cdot}mol}\left(\dfrac{1}{299.3\ K} - \dfrac{1}{333.8\ K}\right)$

ΔH_{vap} = 33.4 kJ/mol

13.75 **NOTE:** Temperature and Vapor Pressure data are reversed in the problem. The correct data table is:

Temperature (°C)	Vapor Pressure (mm Hg)
25.	13.6
50.	45.3
75.	127.2
100.	310.8

$\ln\left(\dfrac{45.3\ mm\ Hg}{13.6\ mm\ Hg}\right) = \dfrac{\Delta H_{vap}}{0.0083145\ kJ/K{\cdot}mol}\left(\dfrac{1}{298\ K} - \dfrac{1}{323\ K}\right)$

ΔH_{vap} = 38.5 kJ/mol

Use this value to calculate the temperature when vapor pressure = 760 mm Hg

$\ln\left(\dfrac{760\ mm\ Hg}{13.6\ mm\ Hg}\right) = \dfrac{38.5\ kJ/mol}{0.0083145\ kJ/K{\cdot}mol}\left(\dfrac{1}{298\ K} - \dfrac{1}{T_2}\right)$

T_2 = 402 K (129 °C)   The actual boiling point is 126 °C

13.76   Unit cell volume:

$$\frac{4 \text{ Ir atoms}}{\text{unit cell}} \cdot \frac{192.22 \text{ g}}{1 \text{ mol Ir}} \cdot \frac{1 \text{ cm}^3}{22.56 \text{ g}} \cdot \frac{1 \text{ mol Ir}}{6.0221 \times 10^{23} \text{ atoms}} = 5.659 \times 10^{-23} \text{ cm}^3$$

Unit cell edge length:

$V = 5.659 \times 10^{-23} \text{ cm}^3 = (\text{edge length})^3$

edge length $= \sqrt[3]{5.659 \times 10^{-23} \text{ cm}^3} = 3.839 \times 10^{-8} \text{ cm}$

face diagonal $= 4 \cdot \text{radius} = \sqrt{2} \cdot \text{edge length}$

radius $= \dfrac{\sqrt{2} \cdot (3.839 \times 10^{-8} \text{ cm})}{4} = 1.357 \times 10^{-8} \text{ cm} = 135.7 \text{ pm}$

13.77   Unit cell volume:

$$\frac{40.08 \text{ g}}{1 \text{ mol Ca}} \cdot \frac{1 \text{ cm}^3}{1.54 \text{ g}} \cdot \frac{1 \text{ mol Ca}}{6.022 \times 10^{23} \text{ atoms}} \cdot \frac{4 \text{ Ca atoms}}{\text{unit cell}} = 1.73 \times 10^{-22} \text{ cm}^3$$

Unit cell edge length:

$V = 1.73 \times 10^{-22} \text{ cm}^3 = (\text{edge length})^3$

edge length $= \sqrt[3]{1.73 \times 10^{-22} \text{ cm}^3} = 5.57 \times 10^{-8} \text{ cm}$

face diagonal $= 4 \cdot \text{radius} = \sqrt{2} \cdot \text{edge length}$

radius $= \dfrac{\sqrt{2} \cdot (5.57 \times 10^{-8} \text{ cm})}{4} = 1.97 \times 10^{-8} \text{ cm} = 197 \text{ pm}$

13.78   Assume that copper has a face-centered cubic unit cell. Calculate the density of the unit cell based on this assumption and compare it with the actual density of copper:

mass of one Cu atom $= \dfrac{63.546 \text{ g}}{1 \text{ mol Cu}} \cdot \dfrac{1 \text{ mol Cu}}{6.02214 \times 10^{23} \text{ atoms}} = 1.0552 \times 10^{-22} \text{ g}$

mass of unit cell $= \dfrac{1.0552 \times 10^{-22} \text{ g}}{1 \text{ Cu atom}} \cdot \dfrac{4 \text{ Cu atoms}}{1 \text{ unit cell}} = 4.2208 \times 10^{-22} \text{ g/unit cell}$

face diagonal $= 4 \cdot \text{atom radius} = \sqrt{2} \cdot \text{edge length}$

edge length $= \dfrac{4 \cdot \text{atom radius}}{\sqrt{2}} = \dfrac{4 \cdot 127.8 \text{ pm}}{\sqrt{2}} = 361.5 \text{ pm} = 3.615 \times 10^{-8} \text{ cm}$

unit cell volume $= (\text{edge length})^3 = (3.615 \times 10^{-8} \text{ cm})^3 = 4.723 \times 10^{-23} \text{ cm}^3$

unit cell density $= \dfrac{4.2208 \times 10^{-22} \text{ g}}{4.723 \times 10^{-23} \text{ cm}^3} = 8.937 \text{ g/cm}^3$

The calculated density closely matches the actual density (8.95 g/cm^3) so the copper unit cell is most likely face-centered cubic.

13.79   Assume that vanadium metal has a face–centered cubic unit cell. Calculate the density of the unit cell based on this assumption and compare it with the actual density of vanadium:

$$\text{mass of one V atom} = \frac{50.94 \text{ g}}{1 \text{ mol V}} \cdot \frac{1 \text{ mol V}}{6.022 \times 10^{23} \text{ atoms}} = 8.459 \times 10^{-23} \text{ g}$$

$$\text{mass of unit cell} = \frac{8.459 \times 10^{-23} \text{ g}}{1 \text{ V atom}} \cdot \frac{4 \text{ V atoms}}{1 \text{ unit cell}} = 3.384 \times 10^{-22} \text{ g/unit cell}$$

$$\text{face diagonal} = 4 \cdot \text{atom radius} = \sqrt{2} \cdot \text{edge length}$$

$$\text{edge length} = \frac{4 \cdot \text{atom radius}}{\sqrt{2}} = \frac{4 \cdot 132 \text{ pm}}{\sqrt{2}} = 373 \text{ pm} = 3.73 \times 10^{-8} \text{ cm}$$

$$\text{unit cell volume} = (\text{edge length})^3 = (3.73 \times 10^{-8} \text{ cm})^3 = 5.19 \times 10^{-23} \text{ cm}^3$$

$$\text{unit cell density} = \frac{3.384 \times 10^{-22} \text{ g}}{5.19 \times 10^{-23} \text{ cm}^3} = 6.52 \text{ g/cm}^3$$

The calculated density does not agree with the actual density (6.11 g/cm^3). If the unit cell is assumed to be body–centered cubic, the calculated density is 5.97 g/cm^3; simple cubic results in a calculated density of 4.60 g/cm^3. The vanadium unit cell is most likely body–centered cubic.

13.80   Calculate the mass of one iron atom and compare this to the mass of one mole of iron.

$$V = \left(286.65 \text{ pm} \cdot \frac{1 \text{ m}}{10^{12} \text{ pm}} \cdot \frac{10^2 \text{ cm}}{1 \text{ m}} \right)^3 = 2.3554 \times 10^{-23} \text{ cm}^3$$

$$2.3554 \times 10^{-23} \text{ cm}^3 \cdot \frac{7.874 \text{ g}}{1 \text{ cm}^3} \cdot \frac{1 \text{ unit cell}}{2 \text{ Fe atoms}} = 9.2730 \times 10^{-23} \text{ g/Fe atom}$$

$$\frac{55.845 \text{ g/1 mol Fe}}{9.2730 \times 10^{-23} \text{ g/Fe atom}} = 6.0223 \times 10^{23} \text{ Fe atoms/mol}$$

13.81   Calculate the mass of one CaF_2 ion pair and compare this to the mass of one mole of CaF_2:

$$(5.46295 \times 10^{-8} \text{ cm})^3 \cdot \frac{3.1805 \text{ g}}{1 \text{ cm}^3} \cdot \frac{1 \text{ unit cell}}{4 \text{ CaF}_2} = 1.2963 \times 10^{-22} \text{ g/CaF}_2$$

$$\frac{78.077 \text{ g/1 mol CaF}_2}{1.2963 \times 10^{-22} \text{ g/CaF}_2} = 6.0230 \times 10^{23} \text{ CaF}_2\text{/mol}$$

13.82 $$\frac{n}{V} = \frac{P}{RT} = \frac{0.00169 \text{ mm Hg} \cdot \dfrac{1 \text{ atm}}{760 \text{ mm Hg}}}{(0.082057 \text{ L} \cdot \text{atm/K} \cdot \text{mol})(297 \text{ K})} = 9.12 \times 10^{-8} \text{ mol/L}$$

$$\frac{9.12 \times 10^{-8} \text{ mol}}{1 \text{ L}} \cdot \frac{6.022 \times 10^{23} \text{ atoms}}{1 \text{ mol}} \cdot \frac{1 \text{ L}}{10^{-3} \text{ m}^3} = 5.49 \times 10^{19} \text{ atoms/m}^3$$

13.83   Diagram A:

$$\frac{\text{area covered by circles}}{\text{total area}} = \frac{\text{area of one circle}}{(2 \cdot r_{\text{circle}})^2} = \frac{\pi r^2}{4 r^2} = 0.785 = 78.5\%$$

Diagram B:

$$\text{area of triangle} = \frac{1}{2} \cdot \text{base} \cdot \text{height} = \frac{1}{2} \cdot (2\,r) \cdot (\sqrt{3}\,r)$$

$$\text{area covered by circles} = \frac{1}{2} \cdot \text{area of circle} = \frac{1}{2} \cdot \pi\,r^2$$

$$\frac{\text{area covered}}{\text{area of triangle}} = \frac{\frac{1}{2} \cdot \pi\,r^2}{\frac{1}{2} \cdot (2\,r) \cdot (\sqrt{3}\,r)} = 0.907 = 90.7\%$$

13.84 $\text{percentage of empty space} = \dfrac{\text{volume occupied by spheres}}{\text{total volume of unit cell}} \cdot 100\% = \dfrac{1 \text{ sphere} \cdot \frac{4}{3}(\pi r^3)}{(2 \cdot r)^3} \cdot 100\% = 52\%$

13.85   Assuming the spheres are packed in an identical way, the water levels will be identical. A face–centered cubic lattice, for example, uses 74% of the available volume, regardless of sphere size.

13.86   (a) In a related series of compounds, the boiling point generally increases with increasing intermolecular forces.

         (b) Polarity and mass.

13.87   (a) How easily the electron cloud in a molecule can be distorted to induce a temporary dipole

         (b) For nonpolar molecules, boiling point increases as molar mass increases. $F_2 < Cl_2 < Br_2$

13.88   (a) Crystalline solids have long-range order.

         (b) 12 unit cells

         (c) Salt and ice, crystalline; glass and wood, amorphous.

13.89   (a) The Na^+ ions are in an octahedral environment, surrounded by six chloride ions.

         (b) Calcium oxide has the same structure as sodium chloride. The Ca^{2+} ions are in a face-centered cubic arrangement and the O^{2-} ions fill octahedral holes. There are 4 Ca^{2+} ions and 4 O^{2-} ions per unit cell, a 1:1 ratio that matches the compound formula.

         (c) The Zn^{2+} ions are in a face-centered cubic arrangement and the S^{2-} ions fill half of the tetrahedral holes. There are 4 Zn^{2+} ions and 4 S^{2-} ions per unit cell, a 1:1 ratio that matches the compound formula.

         (d) Lead sulfide has the same structure as sodium chloride, not the same structure as ZnS. There are 4 Pb^{2+} ions and 4 S^{2-} ions per unit cell, a 1:1 ratio that matches the compound formula.

         (e) The Ca^{2+} ions are in a face-centered cubic arrangement and the F^- ions fill all of the tetrahedral holes. There are 4 Ca^{2+} ions and 8 F^- ions per unit cell, a 1:2 ratio that matches the compound formula. The CaF_2 and ZnS structures both have a face-centered cubic arrangement of cations. The ZnS structure fills half of the tetrahedral holes with anions and the CaF_2 structure fills all of the tetrahedral holes with anions.

Chapter 14
Solutions and Their Behavior

INSTRUCTOR'S NOTES

We generally cover all the topics in this chapter (except for Section 14.4) in 2-3 lectures. Students are able to deal with straightforward problems and discuss solution phenomena with little difficulty.

SUGGESTED DEMONSTRATIONS

1.   The Solution Process
   - Several demonstrations in Volume 1 of *Chemical Demonstrations* by Shakhashiri are suitable. Suggestions include "Chemical Cold Packs," "Crystallization from Supersaturated Solutions of Sodium Acetate," "Chemical Hot Packs," and "Endothermic Reactions of Hydrated Barium Chloride and Ammonium Salts."
   - A demonstration of Henry's Law, "Effect of Temperature and Pressure on the Solubility of Gases in Liquids," is contained in Volume 3 of the *Chemical Demonstrations* series. Also in Volume 3 are: "Getting Colder: Freezing-Point Depression," "Getting Hotter: Boiling Point Elevation by Nonvolatile Solutes," "Osmosis Through the Membrane of an Egg," and "Osmotic Pressure of a Sugar Solution."
   - Several of the photos in the chapter represent demonstrations we do in class. For example, Figure 14.1 shows the difference between molality and molarity, and Figure 14.5, showing the preferential solubility of iodine in CCl_4, is easy to do. One of our favorites is the frozen solution in Figure 14.13. We place an indicator in water and then allow the solution to freeze slowly in the freezer of a lab refrigerator. The result clearly shows that the solute concentrates in the solution and that the solid is pure solvent.

2.   Additional demonstrations
   - Mundell, D. W. "Heat of Solution and Colligative Properties: An Illustration of Enthalpy and Entropy," *Journal of Chemical Education* **1990**, *67*, 426.
   - Levy, J. B.; Hornack, F. M.; Levy, M. A. "Simple Determination of Henry's Law Constant for Carbon Dioxide," *Journal of Chemical Education* **1987**, *64*, 260.

Solutions to Study Questions

14.1   False. Colligative properties depend only on the number of solute particles per solvent molecule and not on the identity of the solute.

14.2   Raoult's law (change in vapor pressure) $P_{solv} = X_{solv}P^{\circ}_{solv}$

       Boiling point elevation $\Delta T_{bp} = K_{bp}m_{solute}$

       Freezing point depression $\Delta T_{fp} = K_{fp}m_{solute}$

       Osmotic pressure $\Pi = cRT$

14.3   molality: amount of solute per kilogram of solvent

       molarity: amount of solute per liter of solution

14.4   temperature, pressure, and the intermolecular forces between the gas and water molecules

14.5   When the solids dissolve in water, $CaCl_2$ produces three ions per mole of solute while NaCl produces only two moles of ions per mole of solute. The solution with a higher concentration of ions (particles) will have a lower freezing point.

14.6   The solution inside the cucumber has a higher solvent concentration than the concentrated salt solution. The solvent molecules flow out of the cucumber, and the cucumber shrivels.

14.7   Solubility is the concentration of solute in equilibrium with undissolved solute in a saturated solution. Add a known quantity of NaCl to 100 mL of water, making sure that enough NaCl is added so that some of the salt does not dissolve. Filter the solution and weight the undissolved salt. The difference between the original mass and the undissolved salt is the solubility of NaCl per 100 mL of water.

14.8   Using KF as an example:

       $KF(s) \rightarrow K^+(g) + F^-(g)$ ΔH = lattice energy

       $K^+(g) + F^-(g) \rightarrow K^+(aq) + F^-(aq)$ ΔH = enthalpy of solvation of the ions

---

       $KF(s) \rightarrow K^+(aq) + F^-(aq)$ ΔH = heat of solution

14.9   At the particulate level, Na^+ and Cl^- ions are still leaving the solid state and entering solution. Concurrently, solid NaCl is forming from Na^+ and Cl^- ions in solution.

14.10   Make a solution from a known quantity of solute (with unknown molar mass) and solvent. Measure the freezing point depression of the solution and use this to calculate the molality of the solution. From this determine the amount of solute (mol) in the solution. The ratio of the mass and amount of solute gives the molar mass.

14.11   Two or more nonpolar liquids (such as octane, C_8H_{18}, and carbon tetrachloride, CCl_4) frequently are miscible, just as are two or more polar liquids (such as water, H_2O, and ethanol, C_2H_5OH).

14.12   (a) ionic solid, soluble in water

(b) polar, soluble in water

(c) nonpolar, soluble in benzene

(d) ionic solid, soluble in water

(e) nonpolar, soluble in benzene

14.13   In a true solution, no settling of the solute is observed and the solute particles are ions or relatively small molecules. In a suspension, solute particles are visible and gradually settle to the bottom of the container. A colloidal dispersion is a state intermediate between a solution and a suspension.

14.14   A sol is a dispersion of a solid substance in a fluid medium (milk of magnesia) and a gel is a dispersion that has a structure that prevents it from being mobile (cheese).

14.15   The nonpolar oil molecules interact with the nonpolar hydrocarbon tails of the soap molecules, leaving the polar heads of the soap to interact with surrounding water molecules. The oil and water then mix. If the oily material on a piece of clothing or a dish also contains some dirt particles, the dirt can now be washed away.

14.16 $2.56 \text{ g} \cdot \dfrac{1 \text{ mol } C_4H_6O_4}{118.1 \text{ g}} = 0.0217 \text{ mol } C_4H_6O_4$

$500. \text{ mL} \cdot \dfrac{1 \text{ cm}^3}{1 \text{ mL}} \cdot \dfrac{1.00 \text{ g}}{1 \text{ cm}^3} \cdot \dfrac{1 \text{ mol } H_2O}{18.02 \text{ g}} = 27.7 \text{ mol } H_2O$

$M = \dfrac{\text{amount of solute}}{\text{volume of solution}} = \dfrac{0.0217 \text{ mol } C_4H_6O_4}{0.500 \text{ L}} = 0.0434 \text{ M}$

$m = \dfrac{\text{amount of solute}}{\text{kg of solvent}} = \dfrac{0.0217 \text{ mol } C_4H_6O_4}{500. \text{ g}} \cdot \dfrac{10^3 \text{ g}}{1 \text{ kg}} = 0.0434 \text{ } m$

$X_{acid} = \dfrac{0.0217 \text{ mol}}{0.0217 \text{ mol} + 27.7 \text{ mol}} = 0.000781$

$\text{Weight \%} = \dfrac{2.56 \text{ g}}{2.56 \text{ g} + 500. \text{ g}} \cdot 100\% = 0.509\%$

14.17 $45.0 \text{ g } C_{10}H_{16}O \cdot \dfrac{1 \text{ mol}}{152.2 \text{ g}} = 0.296 \text{ mol } C_{10}H_{16}O$

$425 \text{ mL } C_2H_5OH \cdot \dfrac{0.785 \text{ g}}{1 \text{ mL}} \cdot \dfrac{1 \text{ mol}}{46.07 \text{ g}} = 7.24 \text{ mol } C_2H_5OH$

$M = \dfrac{\text{amount of solute}}{\text{volume of solution}} = \dfrac{0.296 \text{ mol } C_{10}H_{16}O}{0.425 \text{ L } C_2H_5OH} = 0.696 \text{ M}$

$m = \dfrac{\text{amount of solute}}{\text{kg of solvent}} = \dfrac{0.296 \text{ mol } C_{10}H_{16}O}{425 \text{ mL } C_2H_5OH} \cdot \dfrac{1 \text{ mL}}{0.785 \text{ g}} \cdot \dfrac{10^3 \text{ g}}{1 \text{ kg}} = 0.886 \text{ } m$

$$X_{camphor} = \frac{0.296 \text{ mol}}{0.296 \text{ mol} + 7.24 \text{ mol}} = 0.0392$$

$$\text{Weight \%} = \frac{45.0 \text{ g}}{45.0 \text{ g} + \left(425 \text{ mL} \cdot \dfrac{0.785 \text{ g}}{1 \text{ mL}}\right)} \times 100\% = 11.9\%$$

14.18

Compound	Molality	Weight percent	Mole fraction
NaI	0.15	2.2	0.0027
C_2H_5OH	1.1	5.0	0.020
$C_{12}H_{22}O_{11}$	0.15	4.9	0.0027

NaI: 0.15 mol NaI dissolved in 1.0 kg H_2O

$$0.15 \text{ mol} \cdot \frac{150. \text{ g}}{1 \text{ mol}} = 23 \text{ g NaI} \qquad\qquad 1.0 \times 10^3 \text{ g} \cdot \frac{1 \text{ mol}}{18.0 \text{ g}} = 56 \text{ mol } H_2O$$

$$\text{Weight \%} = \frac{23 \text{ g}}{23 \text{ g} + 1.0 \times 10^3 \text{ g}} \cdot 100\% = 2.2\%$$

$$X_{NaI} = \frac{0.15 \text{ mol}}{0.15 \text{ mol} + 56 \text{ mol}} = 0.0027$$

C_2H_5OH: 5.0 g C_2H_5OH dissolved in 95.0 g H_2O

$$5.0 \text{ g} \cdot \frac{1 \text{ mol}}{46.1 \text{ g}} = 0.11 \text{ mol } C_2H_5OH \qquad\qquad 95.0 \text{ g} \cdot \frac{1 \text{ mol}}{18.02 \text{ g}} = 5.27 \text{ mol } H_2O$$

$$m = \frac{\text{amount of solute}}{\text{kg of solvent}} = \frac{0.11 \text{ mol } C_2H_5OH}{0.0950 \text{ kg } H_2O} = 1.1 \, m$$

$$X_{C_2H_5OH} = \frac{0.11 \text{ mol}}{0.11 \text{ mol} + 5.27 \text{ mol}} = 0.020$$

$C_{12}H_{22}O_{11}$: 0.15 mol $C_{12}H_{22}O_{11}$ dissolved in 1.0 kg H_2O

$$0.15 \text{ mol} \cdot \frac{342 \text{ g}}{1 \text{ mol}} = 51.3 \text{ g } C_{12}H_{22}O_{11} \qquad\qquad 1.0 \times 10^3 \text{ g} \cdot \frac{1 \text{ mol}}{18.0 \text{ g}} = 56 \text{ mol } H_2O$$

$$\text{Weight \%} = \frac{51.3 \text{ g}}{51.3 \text{ g} + 1.0 \times 10^3 \text{ g}} \cdot 100\% = 4.9\%$$

$$X_{C_{12}H_{22}O_{11}} = \frac{0.15 \text{ mol}}{0.15 \text{ mol} + 56 \text{ mol}} = 0.0027$$

14.19

Compound	Molality	Weight percent	Mole fraction
KNO_3	1.10	10.0	0.0194
CH_3CO_2H	0.0183	0.110	3.30×10^{-4}
HOC_2H_4OH	3.54	18.0	0.0599

KNO_3: 10.0 g KNO_3 dissolved in 90.0 g H_2O

$$10.0 \text{ g} \cdot \frac{1 \text{ mol}}{101.1 \text{ g}} = 0.0989 \text{ mol } KNO_3 \qquad\qquad 90.0 \text{ g} \cdot \frac{1 \text{ mol}}{18.02 \text{ g}} = 4.99 \text{ mol } H_2O$$

$$m = \frac{\text{amount of solute}}{\text{kg of solvent}} = \frac{0.0989 \text{ mol } KNO_3}{0.0900 \text{ kg } H_2O} = 1.10 \, m$$

$$X_{KNO_3} = \frac{0.0989 \text{ mol}}{0.0989 \text{ mol} + 4.99 \text{ mol}} = 0.0194$$

CH_3CO_2H: 0.0183 mol CH_3CO_2H dissolved in 1.00 kg H_2O

$$0.0183 \text{ mol} \cdot \frac{60.05 \text{ g}}{1 \text{ mol}} = 1.10 \text{ g } CH_3CO_2H \qquad\qquad 1.00 \times 10^3 \text{ g} \cdot \frac{1 \text{ mol}}{18.02 \text{ g}} = 55.5 \text{ mol } H_2O$$

$$\text{Weight \%} = \frac{1.10 \text{ g}}{1.10 \text{ g} + 1.00 \times 10^3 \text{ g}} \cdot 100\% = 0.110\%$$

$$X_{CH_3CO_2H} = \frac{0.0183 \text{ mol}}{0.0183 \text{ mol} + 55.5 \text{ mol}} = 3.30 \times 10^{-4}$$

$HOCH_2CH_2OH$: 18.0 g $HOCH_2CH_2OH$ dissolved in 82.0 g H_2O

$$18.0 \text{ g} \cdot \frac{1 \text{ mol}}{62.07 \text{ g}} = 0.290 \text{ mol } HOCH_2CH_2OH \qquad\qquad 82.0 \text{ g} \cdot \frac{1 \text{ mol}}{18.02 \text{ g}} = 4.55 \text{ mol } H_2O$$

$$m = \frac{\text{amount of solute}}{\text{kg of solvent}} = \frac{0.290 \text{ mol } HOCH_2CH_2OH}{0.0820 \text{ kg } H_2O} = 3.54 \text{ } m$$

$$X_{HOCH_2CH_2OH} = \frac{0.290 \text{ mol}}{0.290 \text{ mol} + 4.55 \text{ mol}} = 0.0599$$

14.20 $\quad \dfrac{0.200 \text{ mol } Na_2CO_3}{1 \text{ kg } H_2O} \cdot \dfrac{106.0 \text{ g}}{1 \text{ mol } Na_2CO_3} \cdot \dfrac{125 \text{ g } H_2O}{10^3 \text{ g/1 kg}} = 2.65 \text{ g } Na_2CO_3$

$$X_{Na_2CO_3} = \frac{0.200 \text{ mol } Na_2CO_3}{0.200 \text{ mol } Na_2CO_3 + \left(10^3 \text{ g} \cdot \dfrac{1 \text{ mol } H_2O}{18.02 \text{ g}}\right)} = 0.00359$$

14.21 $\quad \dfrac{0.0512 \text{ mol } NaNO_3}{1 \text{ kg } H_2O} \cdot \dfrac{85.00 \text{ g}}{1 \text{ mol } NaNO_3} \cdot \dfrac{500. \text{ g } H_2O}{10^3 \text{ g/1 kg}} = 2.18 \text{ g } NaNO_3$

$$X_{NaNO_3} = \frac{0.0512 \text{ mol } NaNO_3}{0.0512 \text{ mol } NaNO_3 + \left(10^3 \text{ g} \cdot \dfrac{1 \text{ mol } H_2O}{18.02 \text{ g}}\right)} = 9.22 \times 10^{-4}$$

14.22 $\quad 0.093 = \dfrac{x \text{ mol } C_3H_5(OH)_3}{x \text{ mol } C_3H_5(OH)_3 + \left(425 \text{ g} \cdot \dfrac{1 \text{ mol } H_2O}{18.02 \text{ g}}\right)} \qquad\qquad x = 2.4 \text{ mol } C_3H_5(OH)_3$

$$2.4 \text{ mol } C_3H_5(OH)_3 \cdot \frac{92.1 \text{ g}}{1 \text{ mol}} = 220 \text{ g } C_3H_5(OH)_3$$

$$m = \frac{2.4 \text{ mol } C_3H_5(OH)_3}{0.425 \text{ kg } H_2O} = 5.7 \text{ } m$$

14.23 $\quad 0.125 = \dfrac{x \text{ mol } HOCH_2CH_2OH}{x \text{ mol } HOCH_2CH_2OH + \left(955 \text{ g } H_2O \cdot \dfrac{1 \text{ mol}}{18.02 \text{ g}}\right)} \qquad\qquad x = 7.57 \text{ mol } HOCH_2CH_2OH$

$$7.57 \text{ mol } HOCH_2CH_2OH \cdot \frac{62.07 \text{ g}}{1 \text{ mol } HOCH_2CH_2OH} = 470. \text{ g } HOCH_2CH_2OH$$

$$m = \frac{7.57 \text{ mol } HOCH_2CH_2OH}{0.955 \text{ kg } H_2O} = 7.93 \text{ } m$$

14.24   (a)   Mass of solution = $1 \text{ L} \cdot \dfrac{1000 \text{ mL}}{1 \text{ L}} \cdot \dfrac{1.18 \text{ g}}{\text{mL}}$ = 1180 g solution

Mass of HCl = $1 \text{ L} \cdot \dfrac{12.0 \text{ mol HCl}}{1 \text{ L}} \cdot \dfrac{36.46 \text{ g}}{1 \text{ mol HCl}}$ = 438 g HCl

Mass of H_2O = 1180 g – 438 g = 742 g H_2O

$m = \dfrac{12.0 \text{ mol HCl}}{0.742 \text{ kg } H_2O}$ = 16.2 m

(b)   Weight % = $\dfrac{438 \text{ g HCl}}{1180 \text{ g solution}} \cdot 100\%$ = 37.1%

14.25   95.0 g $H_2SO_4 \cdot \dfrac{1 \text{ mol}}{98.08 \text{ g}}$ = 0.969 mol H_2SO_4

$m = \dfrac{0.969 \text{ mol } H_2SO_4}{0.0050 \text{ kg } H_2O}$ = 194 m

100.0 g solution $\cdot \dfrac{1 \text{ cm}^3}{1.84 \text{ g}} \cdot \dfrac{1 \text{ mL}}{1 \text{ cm}^3} \cdot \dfrac{1 \text{ L}}{10^3 \text{ mL}}$ = 0.0543 L solution

$M = \dfrac{0.969 \text{ mol } H_2SO_4}{0.0543 \text{ L solution}}$ = 17.8 M

14.26 $\dfrac{0.18 \text{ g Li}^+}{1 \times 10^6 \text{ g } H_2O} \cdot \dfrac{1 \text{ mol}}{6.941 \text{ g}} \cdot \dfrac{10^3 \text{ g}}{1 \text{ kg}}$ = 2.6×10^{-6} m

14.27   1 ppm = 1 g solute/10^6 g solvent, so 1 ppb = 1 g solute/10^9 g solvent

(a) $\dfrac{28 \text{ g Ag}}{1 \times 10^9 \text{ g } H_2O} \cdot \dfrac{1 \text{ mol Ag}}{108 \text{ g}} \cdot \dfrac{1000 \text{ g}}{1 \text{ kg}}$ = 2.6×10^{-7} m

(b) 1.0×10^2 g Ag $\cdot \dfrac{1 \times 10^9 \text{ g } H_2O}{28 \text{ g Ag}} \cdot \dfrac{1 \text{ L}}{1000 \text{ g}}$ = 3.6×10^6 L H_2O

14.28   (b) C_6H_6 and CCl_4 both are nonpolar molecules

(c) H_2O and CH_3CO_2H both are polar molecules

14.29   Acetone is a polar molecule, so the strong dipole–dipole interactions between acetone and water molecules lead to a high solubility of acetone in water.

14.30   LiCl(s) → LiCl(aq)

$\Delta H^{\circ}{}_{soln} = \Delta H_f^{\circ}[\text{LiCl(aq)}] - \Delta H_f^{\circ}[\text{LiCl(s)}]$ = –445.6 kJ/mol – (–408.6 kJ/mol) = –37.0 kJ/mol

The enthalpy of solution of LiCl is exothermic while that of NaCl is endothermic (+3.9 kJ/mol).

14.31 $NaClO_4$(s) → $NaClO_4$(aq)

$\Delta H^{\circ}{}_{soln} = \Delta H_f^{\circ}[\text{NaClO}_4\text{(aq)}] - \Delta H_f^{\circ}[\text{NaClO}_4\text{(s)}]$ = –369.5 kJ/mol – (–382.9 kJ/mol) = 13.4 kJ/mol

14.32   (c)   Raise the temperature of the solution and add some NaCl

14.33   As temperature increases the solubility of Li_2SO_4 decreases; additional solid should appear in the beaker. As temperature increases the solubility of LiCl increases; additional solid should dissolve.

14.34   (a) LiCl   Lithium ions are smaller than cesium ions

   (b) $Mg(NO_3)_2$ Magnesium has a larger positive charge (+2) than sodium (+1)

   (c) $NiCl_2$ Nickel has a larger positive charge (+2) than rubidium (+1) and it is a smaller ion

14.35 Mg^{2+} is most strongly hydrated because of its small size and large positive charge. Cs^+ is least strongly hydrated because of its large size and smaller positive charge.

14.36 $$S_{O_2} = k_H P_{O_2} = \frac{1.66 \times 10^{-6}\ M}{mm\ Hg} \cdot 40\ mm\ Hg = 7 \times 10^{-5}\ M$$

$$\frac{7 \times 10^{-5}\ mol\ O_2}{1\ L} \cdot \frac{32\ g}{1\ mol} = 0.002\ g\ O_2/L$$

14.37   Since the solubility of a gas generally decreases with increasing temperature, (a) 8.80×10^{-7} M/mm Hg is the only reasonable choice because it is less than the value of the constant at 25 °C.

14.38 $$P_{CO_2} = \frac{S_{CO_2}}{k_H} = \frac{0.0506\ M}{4.48 \times 10^{-5}\ M/mm\ Hg} = 1130\ mm\ Hg\ (1.49\ atm)$$

14.39 $P_{H_2} = P_{total} - P_{H_2O} = 760.0\ mm\ Hg - 23.8\ mm\ Hg = 736.2\ mm\ Hg$

$$S_{H_2} = \frac{1.07 \times 10^{-6}\ M}{mm\ Hg} \cdot 736.2\ mm\ Hg = 7.88 \times 10^{-4}\ M$$

$$\frac{7.88 \times 10^{-4}\ mol\ H_2}{1\ L} \cdot \frac{1\ L}{1000\ mL} \cdot \frac{2.016\ g}{1\ mol\ H_2} = 1.59 \times 10^{-6}\ g/mL$$

14.40 $35.0\ g \cdot \dfrac{1\ mol}{62.07\ g} = 0.564\ mol\ HOCH_2CH_2OH$ $500.0\ g \cdot \dfrac{1\ mol}{18.02\ g} = 27.75\ mol\ H_2O$

$$X_{H_2O} = \frac{27.75\ mol}{27.75\ mol + 0.564\ mol} = 0.980$$

$P_{H_2O} = X_{H_2O} P^o_{H_2O}$

$P_{H_2O} = (0.980)(35.7\ mm\ Hg) = 35.0\ mm\ Hg$

14.41 $9.00\ g \cdot \dfrac{1\ mol}{60.06\ g} = 0.150\ mol\ (NH_2)_2CO$ $10.0\ mL \cdot \dfrac{1.00\ g}{1\ mL} \cdot \dfrac{1\ mol}{18.02\ g} = 0.555\ mol\ H_2O$

$$X_{H_2O} = \frac{0.555\ mol}{0.555\ mol + 0.150\ mol} = 0.787$$

$P_{H_2O} = X_{H_2O} P^o_{H_2O}$

$P_{H_2O} = (0.787)(22.4\ mm\ Hg) = 17.6\ mm\ Hg$

14.42 $X_{H_2O} = \dfrac{P_{H_2O}}{P^o_{H_2O}} = \dfrac{457 \text{ mm Hg}}{525.8 \text{ mm Hg}} = 0.869$ $\qquad 2.00 \times 10^3 \text{ g} \cdot \dfrac{1 \text{ mol}}{18.02 \text{ g}} = 111 \text{ mol } H_2O$

$X_{H_2O} = 0.869 = \dfrac{111 \text{ mol } H_2O}{111 \text{ mol } H_2O + x \text{ mol } HOCH_2CH_2OH}$

$x = 16.7 \text{ mol } HOCH_2CH_2OH$

$16.7 \text{ mol } HOCH_2CH_2OH \cdot \dfrac{62.07 \text{ g}}{1 \text{ mol}} = 1040 \text{ g } HOCH_2CH_2OH$

14.43 $105 \text{ g} \cdot \dfrac{1 \text{ mol}}{253.8 \text{ g}} = 0.414 \text{ mol } I_2$ $\qquad 325 \text{ g} \cdot \dfrac{1 \text{ mol}}{153.8 \text{ g}} = 2.11 \text{ mol } CCl_4$

$X_{CCl_4} = \dfrac{2.11 \text{ mol}}{2.11 \text{ mol} + 0.414 \text{ mol}} = 0.836$

$P_{CCl_4} = X_{CCl_4} P^o_{CCl_4} = (0.836)(531 \text{ mm Hg}) = 444 \text{ mm Hg}$

14.44 $\Delta T_{bp} = (2.53 \text{ °C}/m) \left(\dfrac{0.200 \text{ mol solute}}{0.125 \text{ kg benzene}} \right) = 4.05 \text{ °C}$

$T_{bp} = 80.10 \text{ °C} + 4.05 \text{ °C} = 84.15 \text{ °C}$

14.45 $m_{urea} = \dfrac{15.0 \text{ g} \cdot \dfrac{1 \text{ mol urea}}{60.06 \text{ g}}}{0.500 \text{ kg } H_2O} = 0.500 \ m$

$\Delta T_{bp} = (0.5121 \text{ °C}/m)(0.500 \ m) = 0.256 \text{ °C}$

$T_{bp} = 100.00 \text{ °C} + 0.256 \text{ °C} = 100.26 \text{ °C}$

14.46 $m_{C_{12}H_{10}} = \dfrac{0.515 \text{ g} \cdot \dfrac{1 \text{ mol } C_{12}H_{10}}{154.2 \text{ g}}}{0.0150 \text{ kg } CHCl_3} = 0.223 \ m$

$\Delta T_{bp} = (3.63 \text{ °C}/m)(0.223 \ m) = 0.808 \text{ °C}$

$T_{bp} = 61.70 \text{ °C} + 0.808 \text{ °C} = 62.51 \text{ °C}$

14.47 $m_{caffeine} = \dfrac{0.755 \text{ g} \cdot \dfrac{1 \text{ mol caffeine}}{194.2 \text{ g}}}{0.0956 \text{ kg benzene}} = 0.0407 \ m$

$\Delta T_{bp} = (2.53 \text{ °C}/m)(0.0407 \ m) = 0.103 \text{ °C}$

$T_{bp} = 80.10 \text{ °C} + 0.103 \text{ °C} = 80.20 \text{ °C}$

14.48 $\Delta T_{bp} = 80.51 \text{ °C} - 80.10 \text{ °C} = 0.41 \text{ °C}$

$m_{C_{14}H_{10}} = \dfrac{\Delta T_{bp}}{K_{bp}} = \dfrac{0.41 \text{ °C}}{2.53 \text{ °C}/m} = 0.16 \ m$

$\dfrac{0.16 \text{ mol } C_{14}H_{10}}{1 \text{ kg benzene}} \cdot \dfrac{178 \text{ g}}{1 \text{ mol } C_{14}H_{10}} \cdot 0.0500 \text{ kg benzene} = 1.4 \text{ g } C_{14}H_{10}$

14.49 $\Delta T_{bp} = 104.4\ °C - 100.0\ °C = 4.4\ °C$

$$m_{solute} = \frac{\Delta T_{bp}}{K_{bp}} = \frac{4.4\ °C}{0.5121\ °C/m} = 8.6\ m$$

$$\frac{8.6\ mol\ C_3H_5(OH)_3}{1\ kg\ H_2O} \cdot 0.735\ kg\ H_2O = 6.3\ mol\ C_3H_5(OH)_3$$

$$6.3\ mol\ C_3H_5(OH)_3 \cdot \frac{92.1\ g}{1\ mol} = 580\ g\ C_3H_5(OH)_3$$

$$X_{glycerol} = \frac{6.3\ mol\ C_3H_5(OH)_3}{6.3\ mol\ C_3H_5(OH)_3 + \left(735\ g \cdot \dfrac{1\ mol\ H_2O}{18.02\ g}\right)} = 0.13$$

14.50   (a) $m_{ethanol} = \dfrac{\Delta T_{fp}}{K_{fp}} = \dfrac{-16.0\ °C}{-1.86\ °C/m} = 8.60\ m$

(b) $8.60\ mol\ C_2H_5OH \cdot \dfrac{46.07\ g}{1\ mol} = 396\ g\ C_2H_5OH$

$$\text{Weight \%} = \frac{396\ g\ C_2H_5OH}{396\ g\ C_2H_5OH + 1.00 \times 10^3\ g\ H_2O} \cdot 100\% = 28.4\%$$

14.51 $m_{solute} = \dfrac{\Delta T_{fp}}{K_{fp}} = \dfrac{-15.0\ °C}{-1.86\ °C/m} = 8.06\ m$

$$\frac{8.06\ mol\ HOCH_2CH_2OH}{1\ kg\ H_2O} \cdot \frac{62.07\ g}{1\ mol} \cdot 5.0\ kg\ H_2O = 2500\ g\ HOCH_2CH_2OH$$

14.52 $m_{sucrose} = \dfrac{15.0\ g \cdot \dfrac{1\ mol\ sucrose}{342.3\ g}}{0.225\ kg\ H_2O} = 0.195\ m$

$\Delta T_{fp} = (-1.86\ °C/m)(0.195\ m) = -0.362\ °C$

$T_{fp} = -0.362\ °C$

14.53 $11\ g\ C_2H_5OH \cdot \dfrac{1\ mol}{46.1\ g} = 0.24\ mol\ C_2H_5OH$ $m_{C_2H_5OH} = \dfrac{0.24\ mol\ C_2H_5OH}{0.089\ kg\ H_2O} = 2.7\ m$

$\Delta T_{fp} = (-1.86\ °C/m)(2.7\ m) = -5.0\ °C$

$T_{fp} = -5.0\ °C$ The solution will begin freeze if it is chilled to $-20\ °C$.

14.54 $\Delta T_{bp} = 80.26\ °C - 80.10\ °C = 0.16\ °C$

$$m_{solute} = \frac{\Delta T_{bp}}{K_{bp}} = \frac{0.16\ °C}{2.53\ °C/m} = 0.063\ m$$

$$\frac{0.063\ mol\ solute}{1\ kg\ benzene} \cdot 0.01112\ kg\ benzene = 7.0 \times 10^{-4}\ mol\ solute$$

$$\frac{0.255\ g}{7.0 \times 10^{-4}\ mol} = 360\ g/mol$$

$\dfrac{360\ g/mol}{184\ g/mol} = 2$ The molecular formula is $(C_{10}H_8Fe)_2$ or $C_{20}H_{16}Fe_2$

14.55 $\Delta T_{bp} = 62.22\ °C - 61.70\ °C = 0.52\ °C$

$$m_{BHA} = \frac{\Delta T_{bp}}{K_{bp}} = \frac{0.52\ °C}{3.63\ °C/m} = 0.14\ m$$

$$\frac{0.14\ mol\ BHA}{1\ kg\ CHCl_3} \cdot 0.0250\ kg\ CHCl_3 = 0.0035\ mol\ BHA$$

$$\frac{0.640\ g\ BHA}{0.0035\ mol\ BHA} = 180\ g/mol$$

14.56 $\Delta T_{bp} = 61.82\ °C - 61.70\ °C = 0.12\ °C$

$$m_{benzyl\ acetate} = \frac{\Delta T_{bp}}{K_{bp}} = \frac{0.12\ °C}{3.63\ °C/m} = 0.033\ m$$

$$\frac{0.033\ mol\ benzyl\ acetate}{1\ kg\ CHCl_3} \cdot 0.0250\ kg\ CHCl_3 = 8.3 \times 10^{-4}\ mol\ benzyl\ acetate$$

$$\frac{0.125\ g\ benzyl\ acetate}{8.3 \times 10^{-4}\ mol\ benzyl\ acetate} = 150\ g/mol$$

14.57 $\Delta T_{bp} = 80.34\ °C - 80.10\ °C = 0.24\ °C$

$$m_{anthracene} = \frac{\Delta T_{bp}}{K_{bp}} = \frac{0.24\ °C}{2.53\ °C/m} = 0.095\ m$$

$$\frac{0.095\ mol\ anthracene}{1\ kg\ benzene} \cdot 0.0300\ kg\ benzene = 0.0028\ mol\ anthracene$$

$$\frac{0.500\ g\ anthracene}{0.0028\ mol\ anthracene} = 180\ g/mol$$

$$\frac{180\ g/mol}{89\ g/mol} = 2 \qquad\qquad \text{The molecular formula is } (C_7H_5)_2 \text{ or } C_{14}H_{10}$$

14.58 $$m_{solute} = \frac{\Delta T_{fp}}{K_{fp}} = \frac{-0.040\ °C}{-1.86\ °C/m} = 0.022\ m$$

$$\frac{0.022\ mol\ solute}{1\ kg\ H_2O} \cdot 0.0500\ kg\ H_2O = 0.0011\ mol\ solute$$

$$\frac{0.180\ g\ solute}{0.0011\ mol\ solute} = 170\ g/mol$$

14.59 $$m_{solute} = \frac{\Delta T_{fp}}{K_{fp}} = \frac{-0.197\ °C}{-1.86\ °C/m} = 0.106\ m$$

$$\frac{0.106\ mol\ aluminon}{1\ kg\ H_2O} \cdot 0.0500\ kg\ H_2O = 0.00530\ mol\ aluminon$$

$$\frac{2.50\ g\ aluminon}{0.00530\ mol\ aluminon} = 472\ g/mol$$

14.60 $\Delta T_{fp} = 69.40\ °C - 70.03\ °C = -0.63\ °C$

$$m_{naphthalene} = \frac{\Delta T_{fp}}{K_{fp}} = \frac{-0.63\ °C}{-8.00\ °C/m} = 0.079\ m$$

$$\frac{0.079\ mol\ naphthalene}{1\ kg\ biphenyl} \cdot 0.0100\ kg\ biphenyl = 7.9 \times 10^{-4}\ mol\ naphthalene$$

$$\frac{0.100\ g\ naphthalene}{7.9 \times 10^{-4}\ mol\ naphthalene} = 130\ g/mol$$

14.61 $$m_{phenylcarbinol} = \frac{\Delta T_{fp}}{K_{fp}} = \frac{-0.36\ °C}{-1.86\ °C/m} = 0.19\ m$$

$$\frac{0.19\ mol\ phenylcarbinol}{1\ kg\ H_2O} \cdot 0.0250\ kg\ H_2O = 0.048\ mol\ phenylcarbinol$$

$$\frac{0.52\ g\ phenylcarbinol}{0.048\ mol\ phenylcarbinol} = 110\ g/mol$$

14.62 $$m_{LiF} = \frac{52.5\ g \cdot \dfrac{1\ mol\ LiF}{25.94\ g}}{0.306\ kg\ H_2O} = 6.61\ m$$

$\Delta T_{fp} = (-1.86\ °C/m)(6.61\ m)(2) = -24.6\ °C$

$T_{fp} = -24.6\ °C$

14.63 $$m_{NaCl} = \frac{\Delta t_{fp}}{K_{fp} \cdot i} = \frac{-10.\ °C}{(-1.86\ °C/m)(1.85)} = 2.9\ m$$

$$\frac{2.9\ mol\ NaCl}{1\ kg\ H_2O} \cdot \frac{58.5\ g}{1\ mol} \cdot 3.0\ kg\ H_2O = 510\ g\ NaCl$$

14.64

solute	solution concentration	particle concentration
(a) sugar	0.1 m	$(0.1 \times 1) = 0.1\ m$
(b) NaCl	0.1 m	$(0.1 \times 2) = 0.2\ m$
(c) $CaCl_2$	0.08 m	$(0.08 \times 3) = 0.24\ m$
(d) Na_2SO_4	0.04 m	$(0.04 \times 3) = 0.12\ m$

Freezing point decreases as the particle concentration increases:

0.1 m sugar > 0.04 m Na_2SO_4 > 0.1 m NaCl > 0.08 m $CaCl_2$

14.65	solute	solution concentration	particle concentration
	(a) ethylene glycol	0.20 m	$(0.20 \times 1) = 0.20\ m$
	(b) K_2SO_4	0.12 m	$(0.12 \times 3) = 0.36\ m$
	(c) $MgCl_2$	0.10 m	$(0.10 \times 3) = 0.30\ m$
	(d) KBr	0.12 m	$(0.12 \times 2) = 0.24\ m$

Freezing point decreases as the particle concentration increases:

0.20 m ethylene glycol > 0.12 m KBr > 0.10 m $MgCl_2$ > 0.12 m K_2SO_4

14.66 $3.00\ \text{g}\ C_9H_{11}NO_2 \cdot \dfrac{1\ \text{mol}}{165.2\ \text{g}} = 0.0182\ \text{mol}\ C_9H_{11}NO_2$ $\quad m_{C_9H_{11}NO_2} = \dfrac{0.0182\ \text{mol}\ C_9H_{11}NO_2}{0.09700\ \text{kg}\ H_2O} = 0.187\ m$

(a) $\Delta T_{fp} = K_{fp} m_{C_9H_{11}NO_2} = (-1.86\ °C/m)(0.187\ m) = -0.348\ °C$

$T_{fp} = -0.348\ °C$

(b) $\Delta T_{bp} = K_{bp} m_{C_9H_{11}NO_2} = (0.5121\ °C/m)(0.187\ m) = 0.0959\ °C$

$T_{fp} = 100.0959\ °C$

(c) $\Pi = cRT = \left(\dfrac{0.0182\ \text{mol}}{0.09700\ \text{L}}\right)(0.082057\ \text{L} \cdot \text{atm/K} \cdot \text{mol})(298\ \text{K}) = 4.58\ \text{atm}$

The osmotic pressure is large and can be measured with the least experimental error.

14.67 Concentration of ions in solution = (0.16 M)(1.9) = 0.30 M

$\Pi = cRT = (0.30\ \text{mol/L})(0.082057\ \text{L} \cdot \text{atm/K} \cdot \text{mol})(310.\ \text{K}) = 7.7\ \text{atm}$

14.68 $n = \dfrac{\Pi V}{RT} = \dfrac{\left(3.1\ \text{mm Hg} \cdot \dfrac{1\ \text{atm}}{760\ \text{mm Hg}}\right)(1.00\ \text{L})}{(0.082057\ \text{L} \cdot \text{atm/K} \cdot \text{mol})(298\ \text{K})} = 1.7 \times 10^{-4}\ \text{mol bovine insulin}$

$\dfrac{1.00\ \text{g}}{1.7 \times 10^{-4}\ \text{mol}} = 6.0 \times 10^{3}\ \text{g/mol}$

14.69 Concentration of ions in solution = (0.0120 M)(1.94) = 0.0233 M

$\Pi = cRT = (0.0233\ \text{mol/L})(0.08257\ \text{L} \cdot \text{atm/K} \cdot \text{mol})(273\ \text{K}) = 0.522\ \text{atm}$

14.70 (a) $BaCl_2(aq) + Na_2SO_4(aq) \rightarrow BaSO_4(s) + 2\ NaCl(aq)$

(b) Initially the $BaSO_4$ particles form a colloidal suspension.

(c) Over time the particles of $BaSO_4(s)$ grow and precipitate.

14.71 diameter = 1.0×10^{2} nm, radius = 50. nm

(a) $V = {}^4/_3\ \pi\ r^3 = {}^4/_3\ \pi\ (50.\ \text{nm})^3 = 5.2 \times 10^{5}\ \text{nm}^3$

$A = 4\ \pi\ r^2 = 4\ \pi\ (50.\ \text{nm})^2 = 3.1 \times 10^{4}\ \text{nm}^2$

(b) $1.0 \text{ cm}^3 \cdot \dfrac{1 \text{ sphere}}{5.2 \times 10^5 \text{ nm}^3} \cdot \left(\dfrac{10^7 \text{ nm}}{1 \text{ cm}}\right)^3 = 1.9 \times 10^{15} \text{ spheres}$

$1.9 \times 10^{15} \text{ spheres} \cdot \dfrac{3.1 \times 10^4 \text{ nm}^2}{1 \text{ sphere}} \cdot \left(\dfrac{1 \text{ m}}{10^9 \text{ nm}}\right)^2 = 60. \text{ m}^2$

14.72 Li_2SO_4 should have the more exothermic heat of hydration because the lithium ion is smaller than the cesium ion.

14.73   (a) The 0.10 m Na_2SO_4 solution has a higher particle concentration (0.30 m) so it should have the higher boiling point.

(b) The 0.30 m NH_4NO_3 solution has a lower particle concentration (0.60 m) so it should have the higher water vapor pressure.

14.74

solute	solution concentration	particle concentration
(a) $HOCH_2CH_2OH$	0.35 m	$(0.35 \times 1) = 0.35$ m
(b) sugar	0.50 m	$(0.50 \times 1) = 0.50$ m
(c) KBr	0.20 m	$(0.20 \times 2) = 0.40$ m
(d) Na_2SO_4	0.20 m	$(0.20 \times 3) = 0.60$ m

(i) Vapor pressure increases as the particle concentration decreases:

0.20 m Na_2SO_4 < 0.50 m sugar < 0.20 m KBr < 0.35 m $HOCH_2CH_2OH$

(ii) Boiling point increases as the particle concentration increases:

0.35 m $HOCH_2CH_2OH$ < 0.20 m KBr < 0.50 m sugar < 0.20 m Na_2SO_4

14.75   (a) Weight % $= \dfrac{1130 \text{ g NaCl}}{1130 \text{ g NaCl} + 7250 \text{ g H}_2\text{O}} \cdot 100\% = 13.5\%$

(b) $1130 \text{ g NaCl} \cdot \dfrac{1 \text{ mol}}{58.44 \text{ g}} = 19.3 \text{ mol NaCl}$ $7250 \text{ g H}_2\text{O} \cdot \dfrac{1 \text{ mol}}{18.02 \text{ g}} = 402 \text{ mol H}_2\text{O}$

$X_{NaCl} = \dfrac{19.3 \text{ mol NaCl}}{19.3 \text{ mol NaCl} + 402 \text{ mol H}_2\text{O}} = 0.0459$

(c) $m_{NaCl} = \dfrac{19.3 \text{ mol NaCl}}{7.25 \text{ kg H}_2\text{O}} = 2.67 \ m$

14.76 $53.0 \text{ g DMG} \cdot \dfrac{1 \text{ mol}}{116.1 \text{ g}} = 0.457 \text{ mol DMG}$ $525 \text{ g C}_2\text{H}_5\text{OH} \cdot \dfrac{1 \text{ mol}}{46.07 \text{ g}} = 11.4 \text{ mol C}_2\text{H}_5\text{OH}$

(a) $X_{DMG} = \dfrac{0.457 \text{ mol DMG}}{0.457 \text{ mol DMG} + 11.4 \text{ mol C}_2\text{H}_5\text{OH}} = 0.0385$

(b) $m_{DMG} = \dfrac{0.457 \text{ mol DMG}}{0.525 \text{ kg C}_2\text{H}_5\text{OH}} = 0.870 \ m$

(c) $P_{C_2H_5OH} = X_{C_2H_5OH} P^{\circ}_{C_2H_5OH} = (1 - 0.0386)(760 \text{ mm Hg}) = 731 \text{ mm Hg}$

(d) $\Delta T_{bp} = K_{bp} m_{C_2H_5OH} = (1.22 \, °C/m)(0.870 \, m) = 1.06 \, °C$

$T_{bp} = 78.4 \, °C + 1.06 \, °C = 79.5 \, °C$

14.77 $10.7 \, \text{mol NaOH} \cdot \dfrac{40.00 \, g}{1 \, \text{mol}} = 428 \, \text{g NaOH}$ $\qquad$ $1 \times 10^3 \, \text{g H}_2\text{O} \cdot \dfrac{1 \, \text{mol}}{18.02 \, g} = 55.5 \, \text{mol H}_2\text{O}$

$(428 \, g + 1000 \, g) \cdot \dfrac{1 \, cm^3}{1.33 \, g} \cdot \dfrac{1 \, mL}{1 \, cm^3} \cdot \dfrac{1 \, L}{10^3 \, mL} = 1.07 \, \text{L solution}$

(a) $X_{NaOH} = \dfrac{10.7 \, \text{mol NaOH}}{10.7 \, \text{mol NaOH} + 55.5 \, \text{mol H}_2\text{O}} = 0.162$

(b) Weight % $= \dfrac{428 \, \text{g NaOH}}{428 \, \text{g NaOH} + 1000 \, \text{g H}_2\text{O}} \cdot 100\% = 30.0\%$

(c) $M_{NaOH} = \dfrac{10.7 \, \text{mol NaOH}}{1.07 \, \text{L solution}} = 9.97 \, M$

14.78 $14.8 \, \text{mol NH}_3 \cdot \dfrac{17.03 \, g}{1 \, \text{mol}} = 252 \, \text{g NH}_3$ $\qquad$ $1000 \, \text{mL solution} \cdot \dfrac{0.90 \, g}{1 \, mL} = 9.0 \times 10^2 \, g = 0.90 \, \text{kg}$

$9.0 \times 10^2 \, \text{g solution} - 252 \, \text{g NH}_3 = 650 \, \text{g H}_2\text{O}$ $\qquad$ $650 \, \text{g H}_2\text{O} \cdot \dfrac{1 \, \text{mol}}{18.0 \, g} = 36 \, \text{mol H}_2\text{O}$

$m = \dfrac{14.8 \, \text{mol NH}_3}{0.65 \, \text{kg}} = 23 \, m$

$X_{NH_3} = \dfrac{14.8 \, \text{mol NH}_3}{14.8 \, \text{mol NH}_3 + 36 \, \text{mol H}_2\text{O}} = 0.29$

Weight % $= \dfrac{252 \, \text{g NH}_3}{9.0 \times 10^2 \, \text{g solution}} \cdot 100\% = 28\%$

14.79 $m_{Ca(NO_3)_2} = \dfrac{2.00 \, g \cdot \dfrac{1 \, \text{mol Ca(NO}_3)_2}{164.1 \, g}}{0.75 \, \text{kg H}_2\text{O}} = 0.016 \, m$

$m_{ions} = \dfrac{0.016 \, \text{mol Ca(NO}_3)_2}{1 \, \text{kg H}_2\text{O}} \cdot \dfrac{3 \, \text{mol ions}}{1 \, \text{mol Ca(NO}_3)_2} = 0.049 \, m$

14.80 $Na_2SO_4(s) \rightarrow 2 \, Na^+(aq) + SO_4^{2-}(aq)$

$\dfrac{0.100 \, \text{mol ions}}{1 \, \text{kg H}_2\text{O}} \cdot 0.125 \, \text{kg H}_2\text{O} = 0.0125 \, \text{mol ions}$

$0.0125 \, \text{mol ions} \cdot \dfrac{1 \, \text{mol Na}_2\text{SO}_4}{3 \, \text{mol ions}} \cdot \dfrac{142.0 \, g}{1 \, \text{mol Na}_2\text{SO}_4} = 0.592 \, \text{g Na}_2\text{SO}_4$

14.81

solute	solution concentration	particle concentration
(i) $HOCH_2CH_2OH$	0.20 m	$(0.20 \times 1) = 0.20 \, m$
(ii) $CaCl_2$	0.10 m	$(0.10 \times 3) = 0.30 \, m$
(iii) KBr	0.12 m	$(0.12 \times 2) = 0.24 \, m$
(iv) Na_2SO_4	0.12 m	$(0.12 \times 3) = 0.36 \, m$

(a) $0.12\ m\ Na_2SO_4$ Boiling point increases as the particle concentration increases

(b) $0.12\ m\ Na_2SO_4$ Freezing point decreases as the particle concentration increases

(c) $0.20\ m\ HOCH_2CH_2OH$ Vapor pressure increases as particle concentration decreases

14.82   (a) $0.20\ m$ KBr (higher particle concentration, $0.40\ m$)

(b) $0.10\ m\ Na_2CO_3$ (higher particle concentration, $0.30\ m$)

14.83 $m_{NaCl} = \dfrac{39.1\ g \cdot \dfrac{1\ mol\ NaCl}{58.44\ g}}{0.100\ kg\ H_2O} = 6.69\ m$

$\Delta T_{bp} = K_{bp} m_{NaCl} i = (0.5121\ °C/m)(6.69\ m)(1.85) = 6.34\ °C$

$T_{bp} = 100.00\ °C + 6.34\ °C = 106.34\ °C$

14.84 $m_{CaCl_2} = \dfrac{35.0\ g \cdot \dfrac{1\ mol\ CaCl_2}{111.0\ g}}{0.150\ kg\ H_2O} = 2.10\ m$

$\Delta T_{fp} = K_{fp} m_{CaCl_2} i = (-1.86\ °C/m)(2.10\ m)(2.7) = -10.6\ °C$

$T_{fp} = -10.6\ °C$

14.85 $\Delta T_{bp} = 61.82\ °C - 61.70\ °C = 0.12\ °C$

$m_{solute} = \dfrac{\Delta T_{bp}}{K_{bp}} = \dfrac{0.12\ °C}{3.63\ °C/m} = 0.033\ m$

$\dfrac{0.033\ mol\ solute}{1\ kg\ CHCl_3} \cdot 0.0250\ kg\ CHCl_3 = 8.3 \times 10^{-4}\ mol\ solute$

$\dfrac{0.135\ g\ solute}{8.3 \times 10^{-4}\ mol\ solute} = 160\ g/mol$

$\dfrac{160\ g/mol}{82\ g/mol} = 2$ The molecular formula is $(C_5H_6O)_2$ or $C_{10}H_{12}O_2$

14.86 $\Delta T_{fp} = 61.93\ °C - 61.70\ °C = 0.23\ °C$

$m_{solute} = \dfrac{\Delta T_{bp}}{K_{bp}} = \dfrac{0.23\ °C}{3.63\ °C/m} = 0.063\ m$

$\dfrac{0.063\ mol\ hexachlorophene}{1\ kg\ CHCl_3} \cdot 0.0250\ kg\ CHCl_3 = 0.0016\ mol\ hexachlorophene$

$\dfrac{0.640\ g\ hexachlorophene}{0.0016\ mol\ hexachlorophene} = 4.0 \times 10^2\ g/mol$

14.87   At 80 °C 1092 g NH_4CHO_2 will dissolve in 200 g of water (546 g/100 g). At 0 °C only 204 g NH_4CHO_2 will dissolve in 200 g of water (102 g/100 g).

1092 g – 204 g = 888 g NH_4CHO_2 precipitates at 0 °C

14.88 $S_{N_2} = (8.42 \times 10^{-7}\ M/mm\ Hg)(585\ mm\ Hg) = 4.93 \times 10^{-4}\ mol/L$

14.89 $15.5 \text{ mm Hg} \cdot 0.55 = 8.53 \text{ mm Hg}$

$$X_{H_2O} = \frac{P_{H_2O}}{P^o_{H_2O}} = \frac{8.53 \text{ mm Hg}}{15.5 \text{ mm Hg}} = 0.550 \qquad X_{C_3H_5(OH)_3} = 1 - 0.550 = 0.450$$

$$0.550 \text{ mol H}_2O \cdot \frac{18.02 \text{ g}}{1 \text{ mol}} = 9.91 \text{ g H}_2O \qquad 0.450 \text{ mol C}_3H_5(OH)_3 \cdot \frac{92.09 \text{ g}}{1 \text{ mol}} = 41.4 \text{ g C}_3H_5(OH)_3$$

$$\text{Weight \%} = \frac{41.4 \text{ g C}_3H_5(OH)_3}{41.4 \text{ g C}_3H_5(OH)_3 + 9.91 \text{ g H}_2O} \cdot 100\% = 80.7\%$$

14.90   (a) $c_{starch} = \dfrac{\Pi}{RT} = \dfrac{3.8 \text{ mm Hg} \cdot \dfrac{1 \text{ atm}}{760 \text{ mm Hg}}}{(0.082057 \text{ L} \cdot \text{atm/K} \cdot \text{mol})(298 \text{ K})} = 2.0 \times 10^{-4} \text{ mol/L}$

$$\frac{10.0 \text{ g/L}}{0.00020 \text{ mol/L}} = 4.9 \times 10^4 \text{ g/mol}$$

   (b) $\Delta T_{fp} = K_{fp} m_{solute} = (-1.86 \text{ °C/}m)(2.0 \times 10^{-4} \text{ } m) = -3.8 \times 10^{-4} \text{ °C}$

The very small change in the freezing point would make it very difficult to determine the molar mass of starch using freezing-point depression.

14.91 $5 \text{ g CH}_3CO_2H \cdot \dfrac{1 \text{ mol}}{60.0 \text{ g}} = 0.08 \text{ mol CH}_3CO_2H \qquad 95 \text{ g H}_2O \cdot \dfrac{1 \text{ mol}}{18.0 \text{ g}} = 5.3 \text{ mol H}_2O$

$$X_{CH_3CO_2H} = \frac{0.08 \text{ mol CH}_3CO_2H}{0.08 \text{ mol CH}_3CO_2H + 5.8 \text{ mol H}_2O} = 0.016$$

$$m_{CH_3CO_2H} = \frac{0.08 \text{ mol CH}_3CO_2H}{0.095 \text{ kg H}_2O} = 0.9 \text{ } m$$

$$\frac{5 \times 10^{-3} \text{ mg CH}_3CO_2H}{100 \text{ g solution} \cdot \dfrac{1 \text{ mL}}{1 \text{ g}} \cdot \dfrac{1 \text{ L}}{10^3 \text{ mL}}} = 0.05 \text{ mg/L} = 0.05 \text{ ppm}$$

Calculating molarity requires knowing the total volume of the solution. Without knowing the density of the acetic acid solution it is impossible to calculate the molarity of the solution.

14.92   Benzene solution:

$$\Delta T_{fp} = 3.37 \text{ °C} - 5.50 \text{ °C} = -2.13 \text{ °C}$$

$$m_{solute} = \frac{\Delta T_{bp}}{K_{bp}} = \frac{-2.13 \text{ °C}}{-5.12 \text{ °C/}m} = 0.416 \text{ } m$$

$$\frac{0.416 \text{ mol acetic acid}}{1 \text{ kg benzene}} \cdot 0.100 \text{ kg benzene} = 0.0416 \text{ mol acetic acid}$$

$$\frac{5.00 \text{ g acetic acid}}{0.0416 \text{ mol acetic acid}} = 120. \text{ g/mol}$$

Aqueous solution:

$\Delta T_{fp} = -1.49\ °C$

$$m_{solute} = \frac{\Delta T_{bp}}{K_{bp}} = \frac{-1.49\ °C}{-1.86\ °C/m} = 0.801\ m$$

$$\frac{0.801\ mol\ acetic\ acid}{1\ kg\ H_2O} \cdot 0.100\ kg\ H_2O = 0.0801\ mol\ acetic\ acid$$

$$\frac{5.00\ g\ acetic\ acid}{0.0801\ mol\ acetic\ acid} = 62.4\ g/mol$$

The actual molar mass of acetic acid is 60.05 g/mol. The aqueous solution calculated molar mass is slightly higher, suggesting that the i value for acetic acid is slightly greater than 1 (the acid is weakly ionized in solution). This is consistent with acetic acid being a weak acid in aqueous solution. The benzene solution calculated molar mass is twice the actual molar mass, suggesting that the acetic acid molecules form dimers in benzene.

14.93 $$m_{HOCH_2CH_2OH} = \frac{\Delta T_{fp}}{K_{fp}} = \frac{-15.0\ °C}{-1.86\ °C/m} = 8.06\ m$$

$\Delta T_{bp} = K_{bp}\,m_{HOCH_2CH_2OH} = (+0.5121\ °C/m)(8.06\ m) = 4.13\ °C$

$T_{bp} = 100.00\ °C + 4.13\ °C = 104.13\ °C$

14.94   The acetic acid only reacts with the calcium carbonate shell, not with the egg membrane. When the egg is placed in water, it swells because the concentration of solute is higher inside the egg than outside. There is therefore a net flow of water into the egg. The situation is opposite when the egg is placed in corn syrup. Water passes out of the egg from a solution of "low" solute concentration to one of relatively higher concentration.

14.95   All of the alcohols contain a polar —OH group that can interact with polar water molecules. The smaller alcohols are miscible with water because of this polar group. However, with an increase in the size of the hydrocarbon group, the organic group (the nonpolar part of the molecule) has become a larger fraction of the molecule, and properties associated with nonpolarity begin to dominate.

14.96   The C—C and C—H bonds in hydrocarbons being nonpolar would tend to make such dispersions hydrophobic. The C—O and O—H bonds in starch present opportunities for hydrogen bonding with water, and hence such dispersions are expected to be hydrophilic.

14.97   As lattice energy becomes more negative, solubility increases.

14.98 $Li_2SO_4(s) \rightarrow Li_2SO_4(aq)$

$\Delta H°_{soln} = \Delta H_f°[Li_2SO_4(aq)] - \Delta H_f°[Li_2SO_4(s)] = -1464.4$ kJ/mol $- (-1436.4$ kJ/mol$) = -28.0$ kJ/mol

$K_2SO_4(s) \rightarrow K_2SO_4(aq)$

$\Delta H°_{soln} = \Delta H_f°[K_2SO_4(aq)] - \Delta H_f°[K_2SO_4(s)] = -1414.0$ kJ/mol $- (-1437.7$ kJ/mol$) = 23.7$ kJ/mol

The enthalpy of solution for Li_2SO_4 is exothermic, and that for K_2SO_4 is endothermic

$LiCl(s) \rightarrow LiCl(aq)$

$\Delta H°_{soln} = \Delta H_f°[LiCl(aq)] - \Delta H_f°[LiCl(s)] = -445.6$ kJ/mol $- (-408.6$ kJ/mol$) = -37.0$ kJ/mol

$KCl(s) \rightarrow KCl(aq)$

$\Delta H°_{soln} = \Delta H_f°[KCl(aq)] - \Delta H_f°[KCl(s)] = -419.5$ kJ/mol $- (-436.7$ kJ/mol$) = 17.2$ kJ/mol

Again, the lithium salt has an exothermic enthalpy of solution and the potassium salt enthalpy of solution is endothermic.

14.99   The density of water is 0.997 g/cm^3, so 1000. mL of water will have a mass of 997 g.

$$\frac{997 \text{ g H}_2\text{O}}{1 \text{ L}} \cdot \frac{1 \text{ mol}}{18.02 \text{ g}} = 55.3 \text{ M}$$

$$\frac{55.3 \text{ mol H}_2\text{O}}{0.997 \text{ kg}} = 55.5 \text{ } m$$

14.100   liquid: $X_{toluene} = \dfrac{1.0 \text{ mol}}{1.0 \text{ mol} + 2.0 \text{ mol}} = 0.33$ $X_{benzene} = \dfrac{2.0 \text{ mol}}{2.0 \text{ mol} + 1.0 \text{ mol}} = 0.67$

$P_{total} = P_{toluene} + P_{benzene} = X_{toluene}P°_{toluene} + X_{benzene}P°_{benzene}$

$P_{total} = (0.33)(22 \text{ mm Hg}) + (0.67)(75 \text{ mm Hg}) = 7.3 \text{ mm Hg} + 50. \text{ mm Hg} = 57 \text{ mm Hg}$

vapor $X_{toluene} = \dfrac{P_{toluene}}{P°_{toluene}} = \dfrac{7.3 \text{ mm Hg}}{57 \text{ mm Hg}} = 0.13$ $X_{benzene} = \dfrac{P_{benzene}}{P°_{benzene}} = \dfrac{50. \text{ mm Hg}}{57 \text{ mm Hg}} = 0.87$

14.101 $50.0 \text{ mL C}_2\text{H}_5\text{OH} \cdot \dfrac{0.785 \text{ g}}{1 \text{ mL}} \cdot \dfrac{1 \text{ mol}}{46.07 \text{ g}} = 0.852 \text{ mol C}_2\text{H}_5\text{OH}$

$50.0 \text{ mL H}_2\text{O} \cdot \dfrac{1.00 \text{ g}}{1 \text{ mL}} \cdot \dfrac{1 \text{ mol}}{18.02 \text{ g}} = 2.77 \text{ mol H}_2\text{O}$

$X_{C_2H_5OH} = \dfrac{0.852 \text{ mol}}{0.852 + 2.77} = 0.235$

$P_{total} = P_{C_2H_5OH} + P_{H_2O} = X_{C_2H_5OH}P°_{C_2H_5OH} + (1 - X_{C_2H_5OH})P°_{H_2O}$

$P_{total} = (0.235)(43.6 \text{ mm Hg}) + (1 - 0.235)(17.5 \text{ mm Hg}) = 23.6 \text{ mm Hg}$

14.102 $m = \dfrac{2.0 \text{ g} \cdot \dfrac{1 \text{ mol C}_{13}\text{H}_{21}\text{ClN}_2\text{O}_2}{273 \text{ g}}}{0.0980 \text{ kg H}_2\text{O}} = 0.075 \text{ } m$

$i = \dfrac{\Delta T_{fp}}{K_{fp}m} = \dfrac{-0.237 \text{ °C}}{(-1.86 \text{ °C/}m)(0.075 \text{ } m)} = 1.7$

There are approximately 2 moles of ions in solution per mole of compound.

14.103 (a) $m_{maltose} = \dfrac{\Delta T_{fp}}{K_{fp}} = \dfrac{-0.229\ ^\circ C}{-1.86\ ^\circ C/m} = 0.123\ m$

$\dfrac{0.123\ mol\ maltose}{1\ kg\ H_2O} \cdot 0.09600\ kg\ H_2O = 0.0118\ mol\ maltose$

$\dfrac{4.00\ g\ maltose}{0.0118\ mol\ maltose} = 338\ g/mol$

(b) $100.00\ g\ solution \cdot \dfrac{1\ mL}{1.014\ g} = 98.62\ mL$ $c_{maltose} = \dfrac{4.00\ g \cdot \dfrac{1\ mol}{338\ g}}{0.09862\ L} = 0.120\ mol/L$

at 25 °C: $\Pi = cRT = (0.120\ mol/L)(0.082057\ L \cdot atm/K \cdot mol)(298\ K) = 2.93\ atm$

14.104 (a)   Assume a mass of 1×10^6 g seawater

Cl^- $1.95 \times 10^4\ g \cdot \dfrac{1\ mol}{35.45\ g} = 550.\ mol\ Cl^-$

Na^+ $1.08 \times 10^4\ g \cdot \dfrac{1\ mol}{22.99\ g} = 470.\ mol\ Na^+$

Mg^{2+} $1.29 \times 10^3\ g \cdot \dfrac{1\ mol}{24.31\ g} = 53.1.\ mol\ Mg^{2+}$

SO_4^{2-} $9.05 \times 10^2\ g \cdot \dfrac{1\ mol}{96.06\ g} = 9.42\ mol\ SO_4^{2-}$

Ca^{2+} $4.12 \times 10^2\ g \cdot \dfrac{1\ mol}{40.08\ g} = 10.3\ mol\ Ca^{2+}$

K^+ $3.80 \times 10^2\ g \cdot \dfrac{1\ mol}{39.10\ g} = 9.72\ mol\ K^+$

Br^- $67\ g \cdot \dfrac{1\ mol}{79.90\ g} = 0.84\ mol\ Br^-$

$m_{ions} = \dfrac{1103\ mol\ ions}{1 \times 10^3\ kg\ H_2O} = 1.103\ m$

$\Delta T_{fp} = K_{fp} m_{ions} = (-1.86\ ^\circ C/m)(1.103\ m) = -2.05\ ^\circ C$

$T_{fp} = -2.05\ ^\circ C$

(b) $\Pi = cRT = \left(\dfrac{1.103\ mol\ ions}{1\ L}\right)(0.082057\ L \cdot atm/K \cdot mol)(298\ K) = 27.0\ atm$

A pressure greater than 27.0 atm is required to purify seawater by reverse osmosis.

14.105 (a)   The 10 m tree is equal to a column of water 10^4 mm tall. The equivalent column of mercury would be

$10^4\ mm\ Hg \cdot \dfrac{1.0\ mm\ Hg}{13.6\ mm\ H_2O} = 735\ mm\ Hg$

$c = \dfrac{\Pi}{RT} = \dfrac{735\ mm\ Hg \cdot \dfrac{1\ atm}{760\ mm\ Hg}}{(0.082057\ L \cdot atm/K \cdot mol)(293\ K)} = 0.0402\ M$

(b)   Assuming the density of sap is 1.0 g/mL, the mass of 1 L of sap is 10^3 g

Weight % $= \dfrac{(0.0402\ mol/L)(342.3\ g/mol)}{1.0 \times 10^3\ g/L} \cdot 100\% = 1.38\%$

14.106 (a) $m = \dfrac{2.00\ g \cdot \dfrac{1\ mol\ H_2SO_4}{98.08\ g}}{0.09800\ kg\ H_2O} = 0.208\ m$

$i = \dfrac{\Delta T_{fp}}{K_{fp}m} = \dfrac{-0.796\ °C}{(-1.86\ °C/m)(0.208\ m)} = 2.06$

(b) $H^+ + HSO_4^-$

14.107 $m = \dfrac{\Delta T_{fp}}{K_{fp}i} = \dfrac{-1.28\ °C}{(-1.86\ °C/m)(2)} = 0.344\ m$

$\dfrac{0.344\ mol\ KX}{1\ kg\ H_2O} \cdot 0.100\ kg\ H_2O = 0.0344\ mol\ KX$

$\dfrac{4.00\ g\ KX}{0.344\ mol\ KX} = 116\ g/mol$

116 g/mol – 39 g/mol = 77 g/mol   The halide ion is probably Br^-

14.108 (a) Assume 100.0 g compound

$22.1\ g \cdot \dfrac{1\ mol\ B}{10.81\ g} = 2.04\ mol\ B$ $77.9\ g \cdot \dfrac{1\ mol\ F}{19.00\ g} = 4.10\ mol\ F$

$\dfrac{4.10\ mol\ F}{2.04\ mol\ B} = \dfrac{2\ mol\ F}{1\ mol\ B}$ The empirical formula is BF_2

$X_{C_6H_6} = \dfrac{P_{C_6H_6}}{P^°_{C_6H_6}} = \dfrac{94.16\ mm\ Hg}{95.26\ mm\ Hg} = 0.9885$ $10.0\ g\ C_6H_6 \cdot \dfrac{1\ mol}{78.11\ g} = 0.128\ mol\ C_6H_6$

$0.9885 = \dfrac{0.128\ mol\ C_6H_6}{0.128\ mol\ C_6H_6 + x\ mol\ solute}$

$x = 0.00150\ mol\ solute$

$\dfrac{0.146\ g\ solute}{0.00150\ mol\ solute} = 97.6\ g/mol$

$\dfrac{97.6\ g/mol}{48.81\ g/mol} = 2$ The molecular formula is $(BF_2)_2$ or B_2F_4

(b) 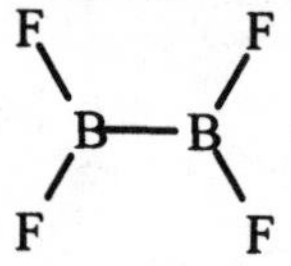 All bond angles are 120°; the boron atom is sp^2 hybridized

14.109   Compound contains 73.94% C, 8.27% H, and 17.79% Cr

$$73.94 \text{ g C} \cdot \frac{1 \text{ mol}}{12.011 \text{ g}} = 6.156 \text{ mol C} \qquad\qquad 8.27 \text{ g H} \cdot \frac{1 \text{ mol}}{1.008 \text{ g}} = 8.20 \text{ mol H}$$

$$17.79 \text{ g Cr} \cdot \frac{1 \text{ mol}}{51.996 \text{ g}} = 0.3421 \text{ mol Cr}$$

$$\frac{6.156 \text{ mol C}}{0.3421 \text{ mol Cr}} = \frac{18 \text{ mol C}}{1 \text{ mol Cr}} \qquad \frac{8.20 \text{ mol H}}{0.3421 \text{ mol Cr}} = \frac{24 \text{ mol H}}{1 \text{ mol Cr}} \qquad \text{The empirical formula is } C_{18}H_{24}Cr$$

$$n = \frac{\Pi V}{RT} = \frac{\left(3.17 \text{ mm Hg} \cdot \dfrac{1 \text{ atm}}{760 \text{ mm Hg}}\right)(0.100 \text{ L})}{(0.082057 \text{ L} \cdot \text{atm/K} \cdot \text{mol})(298.2 \text{ K})} = 1.70 \times 10^{-5} \text{ mol}$$

$$\frac{5.00 \times 10^{-3} \text{g compound}}{1.70 \times 10^{-5} \text{ mol}} = 293 \text{ g/mol}$$

The empirical formula weight is 292.4 g/mol, so the molecular formula is also $C_{18}H_{24}Cr$.

14.110   (a)   Additional $NiCl_2$ can be dissolved.

   (b)   Disturbing the solution in some way will lead to precipitation.

14.111   (a) CCl_4. Yes, both I_2 and CCl_4 are nonpolar molecules.

   (b)   Hexane is a nonpolar molecule so it will be more soluble in CCl_4 than in H_2O.

14.112   The rate at which molecules of gas enter the solution equals the rate at which they leave the solution to return to the gas phase.

14.113   10.0 g of ethylene glycol contains more moles of solute, so it has a greater influence on the vapor pressure.

14.114   (a)   Boiling point elevation is the consequence of the decrease in solvent vapor pressure, owing to the dissolution of solute.

   (b)   The ionic solute 0.10 m NH_4NO_3

14.115   (a)   The membrane surrounding the egg white

   (b)   The egg would shrink.

   (c)   [NaCl] = 1.0 M; [KNO_3] = 0.88 M   The KNO_3 solution has a higher solvent concentration, so solvent will flow from the KNO_3 solution to the NaCl solution.

14.116   See the sidebar on CD-ROM Screen 14.11.

Chapter 15
Principles of Reactivity: Chemical Kinetics

INSTRUCTOR'S NOTES

The discussion of kinetics and mechanisms has been receiving more attention lately in introductory chemistry, although there is still some argument about its value at this level. Nonetheless, we spend 3-4 lecture hours on the material. Our emphasis is on the contrast in speeds of chemical reactions and the factors that go into determining those speeds. We also discuss the idea of a rate law and the important point that it must be experimentally determined. After discussing the first order rate law in particular, we spend about one half a lecture or so on catalysis.

In talking about kinetics our preference might have been to first describe common mechanisms and then see how they are evidenced by rate laws. It would seem that students would come to a better appreciation of kinetics by taking such an approach. However, this does not seem to work in practice. The idea of a mechanism, as a hypothetical pathway for the reaction, is not an easy concept for them to grasp.

Another area of difficulty for students when studying kinetics is the contrast between the fact that the rate law is related to the mechanism but not necessarily related to the stoichiometric equation. When discussing mechanisms, we always stress this point. As in previous chapters, there are several problem-solving tips and ideas.

SUGGESTED DEMONSTRATIONS

1.   Effect of Concentration on Reaction Rate

- Figures 15.1, 15.3, and 15.4 illustrate the measurement of reaction rate and the effect of reactant concentration and temperature on the rate.

- The burning of lycopodium powder in Figure 15.6 is a good demonstration showing the effect of surface area, although it is certainly more dramatic to explode lycopodium powder as outlined in Volume 1 of *Chemical Demonstrations* by Shakhashiri (page 103).

2.   Relationships Between Concentration and Time

- Some of the examples in this chapter are based on hydrogen peroxide decomposition because we commonly do this reaction as a demonstration. The details were outlined in Chapter 4 of this *Manual*.

3.   A Microscopic View of Reactions

- Eliason, R.; McMahon, T. "Temperature effect on reaction rates," *Journal of Chemical Education* **1981** *58*, 354.

4.   Catalysts and Reaction Rate

- Summerlin, L.R.; Borgford, C.L.; Ealy, J.B. "Enzyme Kinetics: Effects of Temperature and an Inhibitor on Catalase Extracted from Potato," *Chemical Demonstrations: A Sourcebook for Teachers; 2nd Edition*, Vol. 2, p. 152.

5.   Additional Demonstrations

- In Volume 2 of *Chemical Demonstrations* by Shakhashiri the last chapter outlines many oscillating chemical reactions, which could be used as demonstrations in lectures on kinetics.

- Fortman, J.J. "The Old Nassau Demonstration: Educational and Entertaining Variations," *Journal of Chemical Education* **1992** *69*, 236.

- Steffel, M.J. "Reduction of permanganate: A kinetics demonstration for general chemistry," *ibid.* **1990** *67*, 598.

Solutions to Study Questions

15.1   The effect of these factors on reaction rates can be explained using collision theory, section 15.5.

15.2   After 2.0 hours, the $[N_2O_5]$ has dropped from 1.40 M to 0.80 M, a change of 0.60 M. According to the balanced equation, 4 mol NO_2 and 1 mol O_2 are formed for every 2 mol N_2O_5 that decompose. The decomposition of 0.60 M N_2O_5 results in the formation of 1.2 M NO_2 and 0.30 M O_2.

15.3   The reaction is second order in A and first order in B. The reaction is third order overall.

15.4   The rate will increase by a factor of 9 if the concentration of A is tripled. The rate will decrease by a factor of $^1/_4$ if the concentration of A is halved.

15.5   The rate will double.

15.6 $\ln\dfrac{[R]_t}{[R]_0} = -kt$ $[R]_t$ and $[R]_0$ are concentrations of reactant at time $t = 0$ and at a later time, t.

       k is the rate constant for the reaction.

15.7 $(^1/_2)^5 = {}^1/_{32}$ remains

15.8   The reaction is second order if a plot of 1/[reactant] versus time is linear and first order if a plot of ln[reactant] versus time is linear.

15.9

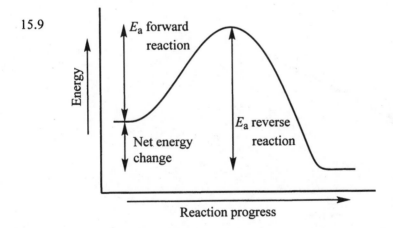

15.10 Rate constant (k), frequency factor (A), and temperature (T)

15.12 A mechanism is the sequence of bond-making and bond-breaking steps that occurs during the conversion of reactants to products.

235

15.13   Each step in a multistep-reaction sequence is an elementary step. The rate-determining step is the slow
         step that determines the rate of the reaction.

15.14   An intermediate is a species that is formed in one step of the reaction and consumed in a later step.
         Intermediates do not appear in the overall reaction equation and usually have a very fleeting existence. In
         the mechanism for the reaction $Br_2(g) + 2\ NO(g) \rightarrow 2\ BrNO(g)$, $Br_2NO(g)$ is an intermediate.

15.15   Catalysts are substances that accelerate chemical reactions but are not themselves transformed. Their
         function is to provide a different pathway with a lower activation energy for the reaction.

15.16   (a) $-\dfrac{1}{2}\left(\dfrac{\Delta[O_3]}{\Delta t}\right) = \dfrac{1}{3}\left(\dfrac{\Delta[O_2]}{\Delta t}\right)$

         (b) $-\dfrac{1}{2}\left(\dfrac{\Delta[HOF]}{\Delta t}\right) = \dfrac{1}{2}\left(\dfrac{\Delta[HF]}{\Delta t}\right) = \dfrac{\Delta[O_2]}{\Delta t}$

15.17   (a) $-\dfrac{1}{2}\left(\dfrac{\Delta[NO]}{\Delta t}\right) = -\dfrac{\Delta[Br_2]}{\Delta t} = \dfrac{1}{2}\left(\dfrac{\Delta[NOBr]}{\Delta t}\right)$

         (b) $-\dfrac{\Delta[N_2]}{\Delta t} = -\dfrac{1}{3}\left(\dfrac{\Delta[H_2]}{\Delta t}\right) = \dfrac{1}{2}\left(\dfrac{\Delta[NH_3]}{\Delta t}\right)$

15.18 $-\dfrac{\Delta[O_3]}{\Delta t} = -\dfrac{\Delta[O_2]}{\Delta t} \cdot \dfrac{2\ mol\ O_3}{3\ mol\ O_2} = -\dfrac{1.5 \times 10^{-3}\ mol/L}{s} \cdot \dfrac{2\ mol\ O_3}{3\ mol\ O_2} = -1.0 \times 10^{-3}\ mol/L \cdot s$

15.19 $\dfrac{\Delta[NH_3]}{\Delta t} = -\dfrac{\Delta[H_2]}{\Delta t} \cdot \dfrac{2\ mol\ NH_3}{3\ mol\ H_2} = \dfrac{4.5 \times 10^{-4}\ mol/L}{min} \cdot \dfrac{2\ mol\ NH_3}{3\ mol\ H_2} = 3.0 \times 10^{-4}\ mol/L \cdot min$

15.20   (a)

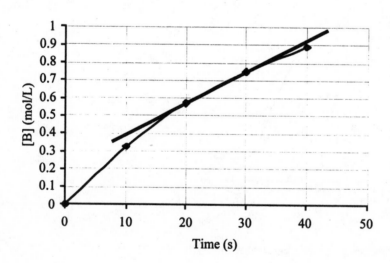

$$\frac{\Delta[B]}{\Delta t} = \frac{(0.326 - 0.000)\ mol/L}{(10.0 - 0.00)\ s} = 0.0326\ mol/L \cdot s$$

$$= \frac{(0.572 - 0.326)\ mol/L}{(20.0 - 10.0)\ s} = 0.0246\ mol/L \cdot s$$

$$= \frac{(0.750 - 0.572)\ mol/L}{(30.0 - 20.0)\ s} = 0.0178\ mol/L \cdot s$$

$$= \frac{(0.890 - 0.750)\ mol/L}{(40.0 - 30.0)\ s} = 0.0140\ mol/L \cdot s$$

The rate of change decreases from one time interval to the next due to the decrease in the amount of A remaining.

(b) A is consumed at $^1/_2$ the rate B is formed. $\dfrac{\Delta[A]}{\Delta t} = (0.0246\ mol/L \cdot s)(^1/_2) = 0.0123\ mol/L \cdot s$

(c) Instantaneous rate is determined by drawing a tangent line to the plot at [B] = 0.750 mol/L. The slope of this line is approximately 0.016 mol/L·s

15.21   (a) The curve is a decreasing exponential curve.

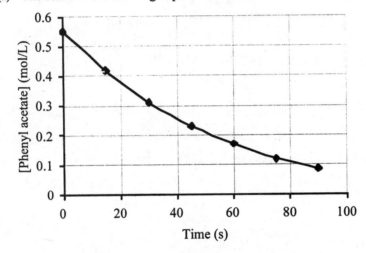

(b) $-\dfrac{\Delta[\text{phenyl acetate}]}{\Delta t} = -\dfrac{(0.31 - 0.42)\ mol/L}{(30.0 - 15.0)\ sec} = 0.0073\ mol/L \cdot sec$

$-\dfrac{\Delta[\text{phenyl acetate}]}{\Delta t} = -\dfrac{(0.085 - 0.12)\ mol/L}{(90.0 - 75.0)\ sec} = 0.0023\ mol/L \cdot sec$

The second rate is slower than the first because the rate depends on the concentration of phenyl acetate, which is smaller during the second time period.

(c) $-\dfrac{\Delta[\text{phenyl acetate}]}{\Delta t} = -\dfrac{(0.12 - 0.17)\ mol/L}{(75.0 - 60.0)\ sec} = 0.0033\ mol/L \cdot sec$

(d) Using the slope of a tangent drawn at 15 seconds, rate is approximately 0.008 mol/L·sec

15.22   (a) Rate = $k[NO_2][O_3]$

(b) If the concentration of NO_2 is tripled, the rate will triple.

(c) If the concentration of O_3 is halved, the rate will decrease by a factor of $^1/_2$.

15.23   (a) Rate = $k[NO]^2[Br_2]$

        (b) If the concentration of Br_2 is tripled, the rate will triple.

        (c) If the concentration of NO decreases by $^1/_2$, the rate will decrease by a factor of $^1/_4$.

15.24   **NOTE**: data table includes concentration data for O_2, not H_2

        (a) In the first two sets of data, the concentration of O_2 is constant while the concentration of NO is doubled. The rate increases by a factor of four on going from the first set of data to the second, so the reaction is second order in NO. Looking at the first and third data sets, [NO] is constant and $[O_2]$ doubles. The rate also doubles from the first data set to the third, so the reaction is first order in O_2.

        (b) Rate = $k[NO]^2[O_2]$

        (c) Rate $= \dfrac{1}{2}\left(\dfrac{\Delta[NO_2]}{\Delta t}\right) = \dfrac{1}{2}(2.5 \times 10^{-5}\text{ mol/L·s}) = 1.3 \times 10^{-5}\text{ mol/L·s}$

             $k = \dfrac{\text{Rate}}{[NO]^2[O_2]} = \dfrac{1.3 \times 10^{-5}\text{ mol/L·s}}{(0.010\text{ mol/L})^2(0.010\text{ mol/L})} = 13\text{ L}^2/\text{mol}^2\text{·s}$

        (d) Rate = $k[NO]^2[O_2]$ = $(13\text{ L}^2/\text{mol}^2\text{·s})(0.015\text{ mol/L})^2(0.0050\text{ mol/L}) = 1.4 \times 10^{-5}\text{ mol/L·s}$

        (e) Rate at which O_2 is reacting $= \dfrac{1.0 \times 10^{-4}\text{ mol/L}}{s} \cdot \dfrac{1\text{ mol }O_3}{2\text{ mol NO}} = 5.0 \times 10^{-5}\text{ mol/L·s}$

             Rate at which NO_2 is forming $= \dfrac{1.0 \times 10^{-4}\text{ mol/L}}{s} \cdot \dfrac{2\text{ mol }NO_2}{2\text{ mol NO}} = 1.0 \times 10^{-4}\text{ mol/L·s}$

15.25   (a) In the first two sets of data, the concentration of H_2 is constant while the concentration of NO is halved. The rate decreases by a factor of four on going from the first set of data to the second, so the reaction is second order in NO. Looking at the second and third data sets, [NO] is constant and $[H_2]$ doubles. The rate also doubles from the second data set to the third, so the reaction is first order in H_2.

        (b) Rate = $k[NO]^2[H_2]$.

        (c) Rate $= \dfrac{\Delta[N_2]}{\Delta t} = 0.136\text{ mol/L·s}$

             $k = \dfrac{\text{Rate}}{[NO]^2[H_2]} = \dfrac{0.136\text{ mol/L·s}}{(0.420\text{ mol/L})^2(0.122\text{ mol/L})} = 6.32\text{ L}^2/\text{mol}^2\cdot s$

        (d) Rate = $(6.32\text{ L}^2/\text{mol}^2\text{·s})(0.350\text{ mol/L})^2(0.205\text{ mol/L}) = 0.159\text{ mol/L·s}$

15.26   (a) In the first two data sets, [NO] is constant while $[O_2]$ doubles. The rate doubles from experiment 1 to experiment 2, so the reaction is first order in O_2. Comparing experiments 2 and 3, $[O_2]$ is constant while [NO] is halved. The rate decreases by a factor of $^1/_4$ from experiment 2 to experiment 3, so the reaction is second order in NO.

             Rate = $k[NO]^2[O_2]$

        (b) $k = \dfrac{\text{Rate}}{[NO]^2[O_2]} = \dfrac{3.4 \times 10^{-8}\text{ mol/L}\cdot h}{(3.6 \times 10^{-4}\text{ mol/L})^2(5.2 \times 10^{-3}\text{ mol/L})} = 50.\text{ L}^2/\text{mol}^2\cdot h$

        (c) Rate = $(50.\text{ L}^2/\text{mol}^2\text{·s})(1.8 \times 10^{-4}\text{ mol/L})^2(5.2 \times 10^{-3}\text{ mol/L}) = 8.5 \times 10^{-9}\text{ mol/L·h}$

15.27   (a)   In the first two data sets, [CO] is constant while [NO$_2$] is halved. The rate also halves from

experiment 1 to experiment 2, so the reaction is first order in NO$_2$. Comparing experiments 1 and 3,

[NO$_2$] is constant while [CO] doubles. The rate doubles from experiment 1 to experiment 3, so the

reaction is first order in NO.

Rate = k[CO][NO$_2$]

(b) $k = \dfrac{Rate}{[CO][NO_2]} = \dfrac{3.4 \times 10^{-8} \text{ mol/L} \cdot \text{h}}{(5.0 \times 10^{-4} \text{ mol/L})(0.36 \times 10^{-4} \text{ mol/L})} = 1.9 \text{ L/mol} \cdot \text{h}$

(c)   Rate = $(1.9. \text{ L/mol·h})(1.5 \times 10^{-3} \text{ mol/L})(0.72 \times 10^{-4} \text{ mol/L}) = 2.0 \times 10^{-7}$ mol/L·h

15.28   (a)   Comparing experiment 1 to experiment 2, [O$_2$] remains constant, [CO] doubles, and the rate increases

by a factor of four. The reaction is second order in CO ($n = 2$). Comparing experiment 1 to

experiment 3, [CO] is constant, [O$_2$] doubles, and the rate doubles. The reaction is first order in O$_2$

($m = 1$).

(b)   The reaction is second order in CO, first order in O$_2$, and third order overall.

(c) $k = \dfrac{Rate}{[CO]^2[O_2]} = \dfrac{3.68 \times 10^{-5} \text{ mol/L} \cdot \text{min}}{(0.02 \text{ mol/L})^2(0.02 \text{ mol/L})} = 5 \text{ L}^2/\text{mol}^2 \cdot \text{min}$

15.29   (a)   Comparing experiment 1 to experiment 2, [H$_2$PO$_4^-$] remains constant, [OH$^-$] doubles, and the rate

increases by a factor of four. The reaction is second order in OH$^-$. Comparing experiment 1 to

experiment 3, [OH$^-$] is constant, [H$_2$PO$_4^-$] triples, and the rate triples. The reaction is first order in

H$_2$PO$_4^-$.   Rate = k[H$_2$PO$_4^-$][OH$^-$]^2

(b) $k = \dfrac{Rate}{[H_2PO_4^-][OH^-]^2} = \dfrac{0.0020 \text{ mol/L} \cdot \text{min}}{(0.0030 \text{ mol/L})(0.00040 \text{ mol/L})^2} = 4.2 \times 10^6 \text{ L}^2/\text{mol}^2 \cdot \text{min}$

(c) $[H_2PO_4^-] = \dfrac{Rate}{k[OH^-]^2} = \dfrac{0.0020 \text{ mol/L·min}}{(4.2 \times 10^6 \text{ L}^2/\text{mol}^2 \cdot \text{min})(0.00033 \text{ mol/L})^2} = 0.0044 \text{ mol/L}$

15.30   The reaction is first order in sucrose

$\ln \dfrac{[C_{12}H_{22}O_{11}]}{[C_{12}H_{22}O_{11}]_0} = -kt$

$\ln\left(\dfrac{0.0132 \text{ M}}{0.0146 \text{ M}}\right) = -k(2.57 \text{ h})$ $k = 0.0392 \text{ h}^{-1}$

15.31 $\ln \dfrac{[N_2O_5]}{[N_2O_5]_0} = -kt$

$\ln\left(\dfrac{2.50 \text{ mg}}{2.56 \text{ mg}}\right) = -k(4.26 \text{ min})$ $k = 0.00557 \text{ min}^{-1}$

15.32 $\ln \dfrac{[SO_2Cl_2]}{[SO_2Cl_2]_0} = -kt$

$\ln\left(\dfrac{0.31 \times 10^{-3} \text{ mol/L}}{1.24 \times 10^{-3} \text{ mol/L}}\right) = -(2.8 \times 10^{-3} \text{ min}^{-1})t$ $t = 5.0 \times 10^2$ min

15.33 $\ln \dfrac{[C_3H_6]}{[C_3H_6]_0} = -kt$

$\ln\left(\dfrac{0.020\ M}{0.080\ M}\right) = -(5.4 \times 10^{-2}\ h^{-1})t$ $t = 26\ h$

15.34   The reaction is second order in ammonium cyanate

$\dfrac{1}{[NH_4NCO]} - \dfrac{1}{[NH_4NCO]_0} = kt$

$\dfrac{1}{0.180\ mol/L} - \dfrac{1}{0.229\ mol/L} = (0.0113\ L/mol\cdot min)t$ $t = 105\ min$

15.35 $\dfrac{1}{[NO_2]} - \dfrac{1}{[NO_2]_0} = kt$

$\dfrac{1}{1.50\ mol/L} - \dfrac{1}{2.00\ mol/L} = (3.40\ L/mol \cdot min)t$ $t = 0.0490\ min$

15.36   (a)   When 15% has decomposed, the fraction remaining is 85/100

$\ln\left(\dfrac{85}{100}\right) = -(1.06 \times 10^{-3}\ min^{-1})t$ $t = 153\ min$

(b) $\ln\left(\dfrac{15}{100}\right) = -(1.06 \times 10^{-3}\ min^{-1})t$ $t = 1790\ min$

15.37   When three-fourths of the sample has decomposed, the fraction remaining is $^1/_4$

$\ln\left(\dfrac{1}{4}\right) = -(2.4 \times 10^{-3}\ s^{-1})t$ $t = 580\ s$

15.38   (a) $t_{1/2} = \dfrac{0.693}{k} = \dfrac{0.693}{5.0 \times 10^{-4}\ s^{-1}} = 1400\ s$

(b) $\ln\left(\dfrac{1}{10}\right) = -(5.0 \times 10^{-4}\ s^{-1})t$ $t = 4600\ s$

15.39 $k = \dfrac{0.693}{t_{1/2}} = \dfrac{0.693}{245\ min} = 2.83 \times 10^{-3}\ min^{-1}$

$\ln\left(\dfrac{2.00 \times 10^{-4}\ mol}{3.6 \times 10^{-3}\ mol}\right) = -(2.83 \times 10^{-3}\ min^{-1})t$ $t = 1.0 \times 10^3\ min$

15.40 $\ln\left(\dfrac{x}{2.00\ g}\right) = -(40.8\ min^{-1})(0.0500\ min)$

$\ln(x) - \ln(2.00\ g) = -(40.8\ min^{-1})(0.0500\ min)$

$\ln(x) = -1.35$

$x = e^{-1.35} = 0.260\ g$ azomethane remains

$(2.00\ g - 0.260\ g) \cdot \dfrac{1\ mol\ CH_3NNCH_3}{58.08\ g} \cdot \dfrac{1\ mol\ N_2}{1\ mol\ CH_3NNCH_3} \cdot \dfrac{28.01\ g}{1\ mol\ N_2} = 0.839\ g\ N_2$

15.41 $k = \dfrac{0.693}{t_{1/2}} = \dfrac{0.693}{30.\ min} = 0.023\ min^{-1}$

$\ln\left(\dfrac{0.25\ mg}{7.50\ mg}\right) = -(0.023\ min^{-1})t$ $t = 150\ min$

15.42 $k = \dfrac{0.693}{t_{1/2}} = \dfrac{0.693}{12.70\ h} = 0.05457\ h^{-1}$

$\ln\dfrac{[^{64}Cu]}{[^{64}Cu]_0} = -(0.05457\ h^{-1})(64\ h)$

fraction remaining $= \dfrac{[^{64}Cu]}{[^{64}Cu]_0} = 0.030$

15.43 $k = \dfrac{0.693}{t_{1/2}} = \dfrac{0.693}{2.7\ days} = 0.26\ days^{-1}$

$\ln\left(\dfrac{x}{5.6\ mg}\right) = -(0.26\ days^{-1})(1.0\ day)$

$\ln(x) - \ln(5.6\ mg) = -(0.26\ days^{-1})(1.0\ day)$

$\ln(x) = 1.46$

$x = e^{1.46} = 4.3\ mg$

15.44 $\ln\left(\dfrac{25}{100}\right) = -k(72\ s)$ $k = 0.019\ s^{-1}$

$t_{1/2} = \dfrac{0.693}{k} = \dfrac{0.693}{0.019\ s^{-1}} = 36\ s$

Alternately, in a first-order reaction a sample decomposes 75% in two half-lives. $t_{1/2} = 72\ s \cdot {}^1/_2 = 36\ s$

15.45 $k = \dfrac{0.693}{t_{1/2}} = \dfrac{0.693}{2.5 \times 10^3\ min} = 2.8 \times 10^{-4}\ min^{-1}$

$\ln\dfrac{[SO_2Cl_2]}{[SO_2Cl_2]_0} = -(2.8 \times 10^{-4}\ min^{-1})(750\ min)$

fraction remaining $= \dfrac{[SO_2Cl_2]}{[SO_2Cl_2]_0} = 0.81$

15.46   (a)   The plot of ln[sucrose] versus time is linear so the reaction is first order in sucrose.

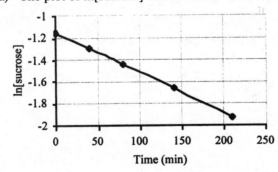

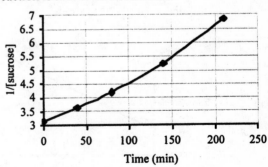

(b) Rate = $k[C_{12}H_{11}O_{22}]$

$$\ln\left(\frac{0.274 \text{ mol/L}}{0.316 \text{ mol/L}}\right) = -k(39 \text{ min}) \qquad\qquad k = 0.0037 \text{ min}^{-1}$$

(c) Using the ln[sucrose] versus time plot, ln[sucrose] = −1.79 when t = 175

$$[C_{12}H_{11}O_{22}] = e^{-1.79} = 0.167 \text{ mol/L}$$

15.47   The plot of ln[phenyl acetate] versus time is linear, so the reaction is first order in phenyl acetate.

$$k = -\text{slope} = -(-0.0207 \text{ min}^{-1}) = 0.0207 \text{ min}^{-1}$$

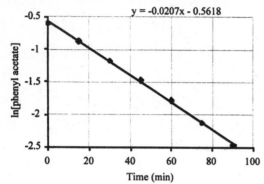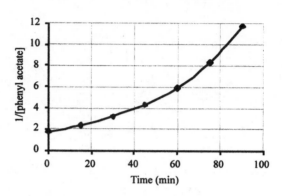

15.48   The plot of ln[N$_2$O] versus time is linear. $k = -\text{slope} = -(-0.0128 \text{ min}^{-1}) = 0.0128 \text{ min}^{-1}$

Rate = $k[N_2O] = (0.0128 \text{ min}^{-1})(0.035 \text{ mol/L}) = 4.5 \times 10^{-4}$ mol/L·min

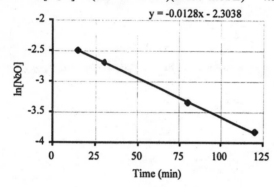

15.49   The plot of 1/[NH$_3$] versus time is linear, indicating that the reaction is second-order in [NH$_3$]. The slope of the line = k = 9220 L/mol·h.

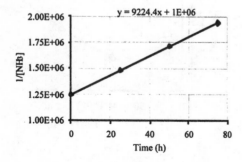

15.50   The reaction is second order in NO_2 Rate $= k[NO_2]^2$

       $k =$ slope $= 1.1$ L/mol·s

15.51   The plot of ln[HOF] versus time is linear, indicating that the reaction is first order in HOF.

       Rate $= k$[HOF] $k = -$slope $= -(-0.025$ min$^{-1}) = 0.025$ min^{-1}

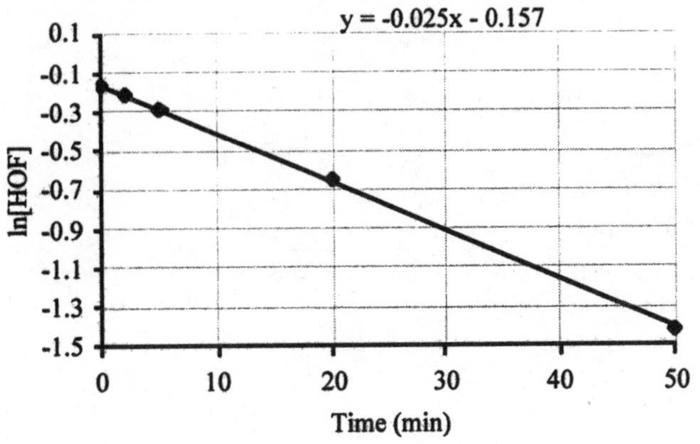

$$y = -0.025x - 0.157$$

15.52   Rate $= (0.04$ L/mol·s$)[C_2F_4]^2$

15.53   (a) The plot of $1/[C_4H_6]$ versus time is linear, indicating that the reaction is second order in C_4H_6.

       (b) $k =$ slope $= 0.0583$ L/mol·s

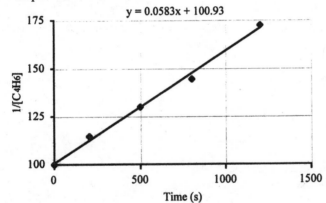

$$y = 0.0583x + 100.93$$

15.54 $\ln\dfrac{k_2}{k_1} = -\dfrac{E_a}{R}\left(\dfrac{1}{T_2} - \dfrac{1}{T_1}\right)$

       $\ln\left(\dfrac{1.5 \times 10^{-3}\text{ s}^{-1}}{3.46 \times 10^{-5}\text{ s}^{-1}}\right) = -\dfrac{E_a}{8.3145 \times 10^{-3}\text{ kJ/K·mol}}\left(\dfrac{1}{328\text{ K}} - \dfrac{1}{298\text{ K}}\right)$

       $E_a = 102$ kJ/mol

15.55 $\ln \dfrac{k_2}{k_1} = -\dfrac{E_a}{R}\left(\dfrac{1}{T_2} - \dfrac{1}{T_1}\right)$

$\ln\left(\dfrac{3k_1}{k_1}\right) = -\dfrac{E_a}{8.3145 \times 10^{-3} \text{ kJ/K·mol}}\left(\dfrac{1}{310.\ \text{K}} - \dfrac{1}{300.\ \text{K}}\right)$

$E_a = 85 \text{ kJ/mol}$

15.56 $\ln \dfrac{k_2}{k_1} = -\dfrac{E_a}{R}\left(\dfrac{1}{T_2} - \dfrac{1}{T_1}\right)$

$\ln\dfrac{k_2}{0.0315 \text{ s}^{-1}} = -\dfrac{260 \text{ kJ/mol}}{8.3145 \times 10^{-3} \text{ kJ/K·mol}}\left(\dfrac{1}{850 \text{ K}} - \dfrac{1}{800 \text{ K}}\right)$

$\ln(k_2) - \ln(0.0315 \text{ s}^{-1}) = -\dfrac{260 \text{ kJ/mol}}{8.3145 \times 10^{-3} \text{ kJ/K·mol}}\left(\dfrac{1}{850 \text{ K}} - \dfrac{1}{800 \text{ K}}\right)$

$k_2 = 0.314 \text{ s}^{-1}$

15.57 $\ln \dfrac{k_2}{k_1} = -\dfrac{E_a}{R}\left(\dfrac{1}{T_2} - \dfrac{1}{T_1}\right)$

$\ln\left(\dfrac{1.02 \times 10^{-3}}{1.10 \times 10^{-4}}\right) = -\dfrac{E_a}{8.3145 \times 10^{-3} \text{ kJ/mol·K}}\left(\dfrac{1}{783 \text{ K}} - \dfrac{1}{743 \text{ K}}\right)$

$E_a = 270 \text{ kJ/mol}$

15.58

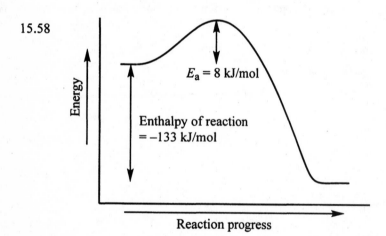

15.59   (a) The reaction is endothermic

(b) Yes, the reaction occurs in two steps

15.60   (a) Rate = k[NO][NO$_3$]

(b) Rate = k[Cl][H$_2$]

(c) Rate = k[(CH$_3$)$_3$CBr]

15.61   (a) Rate = k[Cl][ICl]

(b) Rate = k[O][O$_3$]

(c) Rate = k[NO$_2$]^2

15.62   (a) The second step (the slow step) is rate-determining

         (b) Rate = $k[O_3][O]$

15.63   (a) $NO_2(g) + \cancel{NO_2(g)} \rightarrow NO(g) + \cancel{NO_3(g)}$

             $\cancel{NO_3(g)} + CO(g) \rightarrow \cancel{NO_2(g)} + CO_2(g)$

             ——————————————————

             $NO_2(g) + CO(g) \rightarrow NO(g) + CO_2(g)$

         (b) Both steps are bimolecular

         (c) Rate = $k[NO_2]^2$

         (d) $NO_3(g)$ is an intermediate

15.64   (a) $H_2O_2(aq) + I^-(aq) \rightarrow H_2O(\ell) + \cancel{OI^-(aq)}$

             $H^+(aq) + \cancel{OI^-(aq)} \rightarrow \cancel{HOI(aq)}$

             $\cancel{HOI(aq)} + H^+(aq) + I^-(aq) \rightarrow I_2(aq) + H_2O(\ell)$

             ——————————————————————————

             $H_2O_2(aq) + 2\ I^-(aq) + 2\ H^+(aq) \rightarrow I_2(aq) + 2\ H_2O(\ell)$

         (b) Step 1 and Step 2 are bimolecular, Step 3 is termolecular.

         (c) rate = $k[H_2O_2][I^-]$

         (d) $OI^-(aq)$ and $HOI(aq)$ are intermediates.

15.65   (a) $CH_3OH + H^+ + Br^- \rightarrow CH_3Br + H_2O$

         (b)

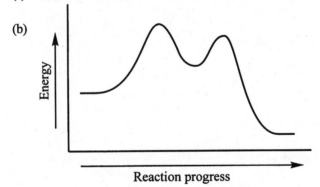

         (c) Using the rate-determining step, the rate law is $-\dfrac{\Delta[CH_3OH]}{\Delta t} = k_2[CH_3OH_2^+][Br^-]$.

             However, this rate law contains an intermediate, $CH_3OH_2^+$

             Rate of production of $CH_3OH_2^+ = k_1[CH_3OH][H^+]$

             $-\dfrac{\Delta[CH_3OH]}{\Delta t} = k_2\{k_1[CH_3OH][H^+]\}[Br^-] = k[CH_3OH][H^+][Br^-]$ $(k = k_1 \cdot k_2)$

15.66   (a)   Reactants: $NO_2(g)$, $CO(g)$ Products: $NO(g)$, $CO_2(g)$ Intermediate: NO_3

         (b)

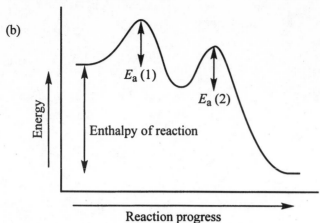

15.67   (a) $(CH_3)_3CBr + H_2O \rightarrow (CH_3)_3COH + HBr$

         (b)   Step 1, the slow step, is rate-determining.

         (c)   Rate $= k[(CH_3)_3CBr]$

15.68   To prove a second-order rate dependence, plot $1/[OH^-]$ versus time. If the plot produces a straight line, the reaction is second order in OH^-.

15.69   (a)   False. The reaction might occur in a single step, but this does not have to be true.

         (b)   True

         (c)   False. Raising the temperature increases the value of k.

         (d)   False. Temperature has no effect on the value of E_a.

         (e)   False. If the concentrations of both reactants are doubled the rate will increase by a factor of four.

         (f)   True

15.70   (a)   Incorrect. Reactions are faster at a higher temperature because the fraction of molecules with higher energies increases.

         (b)   Correct

         (c)   Correct

         (d)   Incorrect. The function of a catalyst is to provide a different pathway with a lower activation energy for the reaction.

15.71   (a)   decrease   (d)   no change

         (b)   increase   (e)   no change

         (c)   no change   (f)   no change (**NOTE**: should read "the half-life of cyclopropane")

15.72   (a) Comparing experiment 1 to experiment 2, $[H_2]$ remains constant, $[N_2]$ doubles, and the rate increases by a factor of four. The reaction is second order in N_2. Comparing experiment 1 to experiment 3, $[N_2]$ is constant, $[H_2]$ doubles, and the rate increases by a factor of eight. The reaction is third order in H_2.

$$\text{Rate} = k[N_2]^2[H_2]^3$$

      (b) $k = \dfrac{\text{Rate}}{[N_2]^2[H_2]^3} = \dfrac{4.21 \times 10^{-5}\ \text{mol/L·min}}{(0.03\ \text{mol/L})^2(0.01\ \text{mol/L})^3} = 5 \times 10^4\ \text{L}^4/\text{mol}^4\text{·min}$

      (c) third order

      (d) fifth order

15.73   (a) $\text{Rate} = k[NH_3]$

      (b) $\ln\left(\dfrac{0.26\ \text{mol/L}}{0.67\ \text{mol/L}}\right) = -k(19\ \text{s})$ $k = 0.050\ \text{s}^{-1}$

      (c) $t_{1/2} = \dfrac{0.693}{k} = \dfrac{0.693}{0.050\ \text{s}^{-1}} = 14\ \text{s}$

15.74   (a) Comparing experiment 1 to experiment 2, $[Br_2]$ remains constant, $[NO]$ increases by a factor of four, and the rate increases by a factor of sixteen. The reaction is second order in NO.

      (b) Comparing experiment 1 to experiment 3, $[NO]$ is constant, $[Br_2]$ increases by a factor of 2.5, and the rate increases by a factor of 2.5. The reaction is first order in Br_2.

      (c) third order

15.75   (a) $\text{Rate} = k[CO_2]$

      (b) $\ln\left(\dfrac{0.27\ \text{mol/L}}{0.38\ \text{mol/L}}\right) = -k(12\ \text{s})$ $k = 0.028\ \text{s}^{-1}$

      (c) $t_{1/2} = \dfrac{0.693}{k} = \dfrac{0.693}{0.028\ \text{s}^{-1}} = 24\ \text{s}$

15.76

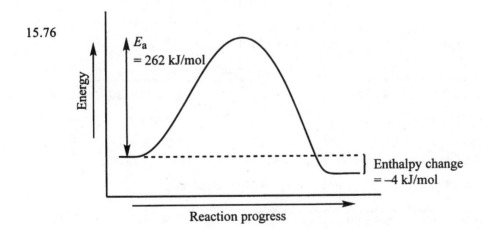

15.77   (a) The reaction is first order in CH_3NC. $\text{Rate} = k[CH_3NC]$

      (b) $\ln[CH_3NC]_t = \ln[CH_3NC]_0 - kt$

(c) Estimating slope from the graph, $k = -\text{slope} = -(-2 \times 10^{-4} \text{ s}^{-1}) = 2 \times 10^{-4} \text{ s}^{-1}$

(d) $t_{1/2} = \dfrac{0.693}{k} = \dfrac{0.693}{2 \times 10^{-4} \text{ s}^{-1}} = 3 \times 10^{3} \text{ s}$

(e) $[CH_3NC]_0 = e^{-4.1} = 0.0166 \text{ mol/L}$

$\ln\dfrac{[CH_3NC]}{0.0166 \text{ mol/L}} = -(2 \times 10^{-4} \text{ s}^{-1})(10,000 \text{ s})$

$\ln[CH_3NC] - \ln(0.0166 \text{ mol/L}) = -(2 \times 10^{-4} \text{ s}^{-1})(10,000 \text{ s})$

$[CH_3NC] = 0.002 \text{ mol/L}$

15.78 (a) The reaction is second order in C_2F_4. Rate $= k[C_2F_4]^2$

(b) $\dfrac{1}{0.080 \text{ M}} - \dfrac{1}{0.100 \text{ M}} = k(56 \text{ s})$ \hspace{1cm} $k = 0.045 \text{ s}^{-1}$

(c) $\dfrac{1}{[C_2F_4]} - \dfrac{1}{0.100 \text{ M}} = (0.045 \text{ s}^{-1})(600 \text{ s})$ \hspace{1cm} $[C_2F_4] = 0.03 \text{ M}$

(d) $\dfrac{1}{0.010} - \dfrac{1}{0.100 \text{ M}} = (0.045 \text{ s}^{-1})t$ \hspace{1cm} $t = 2000 \text{ s}$

15.79 (a) Comparing experiment 1 to experiment 2, [CO] remains constant, [NO$_2$] doubles, and the rate doubles. The reaction is first order in NO$_2$. Comparing experiment 1 to experiment 4, [NO$_2$] is constant, [CO] doubles, and the rate doubles. The reaction is first order in CO. Rate $= k[CO][NO_2]$

(b) The reaction is first order in NO$_2$ and first order in CO.

(c) $k = \dfrac{\text{Rate}}{[CO][NO_2]} = \dfrac{3.4 \times 10^{-8} \text{ mol/L·h}}{(5.1 \times 10^{-4} \text{ mol/L})(0.35 \times 10^{-4} \text{ mol/L})} = 1.9 \text{ L/mol·h}$

15.80 (a) Plot 1/[NH$_4$NCO] versus time and ln[NH$_4$NCO] versus time:

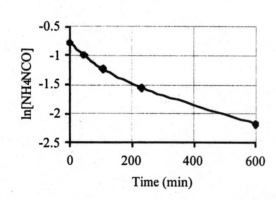 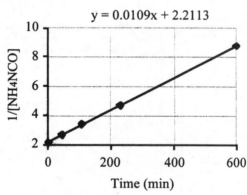

The plot of 1/[NH$_4$NCO] versus time is linear. The reaction is second-order in NH$_4$NCO.

(b) From the slope of the 1/[NH$_4$NCO] versus time plot, $k = 0.0109$ L/mol·min.

(c) $t_{1/2} = \dfrac{1}{[NH_4NCO]_0 k} = \dfrac{1}{(0.458 \text{ mol/L})(0.0109 \text{ L/mol·min})} = 200. \text{ min}$

(d) $\dfrac{1}{[NH_4NCO]} - \dfrac{1}{0.458 \text{ mol/L}} = (0.0109 \text{ L/mol·min})(720 \text{ min})$

$[NH_4NCO] = 0.0997 \text{ mol/L}$

15.81 (a) $k = \dfrac{0.693}{t_{1/2}} = \dfrac{0.693}{3.9\ h} = 0.18\ h^{-1}$

$\ln\left(\dfrac{x}{1.50\ mg}\right) = -(0.18\ h^{-1})(5.25\ h)$

$\ln(x) - \ln(1.50\ mg) = -(0.18\ h^{-1})(5.25\ h)$

$x = 0.59\ mg$

(b) $\ln\left(\dfrac{2.50 \times 10^{-6}\ mg}{1.50\ mg}\right) = -(0.18\ h^{-1})t$ $\qquad\qquad t = 75\ h$

15.82 Mechanism 2: Rate $= k[NO_2][NO_2] = k[NO_2]^2$

The rate equation derived from Mechanism 2 matches the experimentally observed rate equation. Also, the two steps in Mechanism 2 add up to the overall reaction.

15.83 $\cancel{Cl} + O_3 \rightarrow \cancel{ClO} + O_2$

$\cancel{ClO} + \cancel{O} \rightarrow \cancel{Cl} + O_2$

$O_3 \rightarrow \cancel{O} + O_2$

_____

$2\ O_3 \rightarrow 3\ O_2$

The overall process consumes two moles of ozone, and since the Cl atoms are not consumed in the process (Cl is a catalyst), it can be repeated many times. ClO is an intermediate.

15.84 (a) In experiments 1 and 2, $[F_2]$ and $[NO_2F]$ are constant while the concentration of NO_2 doubles. The rate also doubles, so the reaction is first order in NO_2. In experiments 3 and 4, $[F_2]$ doubles while $[NO_2F]$ and $[NO_2]$ remain constant. The rate also doubles, so the reaction is first order in F_2. Finally, in experiments 5 and 6 $[F_2]$ and $[NO_2]$ remain constant while $[NO_2F]$ doubles. The rate remains constant, so the reaction is zero order in NO_2F. Rate $= k[F_2][NO_2]$

(b) The reaction is first order in F_2, first order in NO_2, and zero order in NO_2F.

(c) $k = \dfrac{2 \times 10^{-4}\ mol/L \cdot s}{(0.001\ mol/L)(0.005\ mol/L)} = 40\ L/mol \cdot s$

15.85 (a) True

(b) True

(c) False. As a reaction proceeds the reactant concentration decreases and rate decreases.

(d) False. It is possible to have a one step mechanism for a third order reaction if the slow, rate-determining step is termolecular.

15.86 $\ln\left(\dfrac{0.8}{1.0}\right) = -k(6.0 \text{ h})$

$k = 0.037 \text{ h}^{-1}$

$t_{1/2} = \dfrac{\ln 2}{k} = \dfrac{0.693}{0.037 \text{ h}^{-1}} = 19 \text{ hours}$

15.87   Plot $1/T$ versus $\ln k$

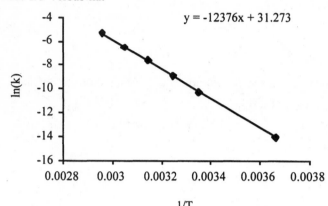

$y = -12376x + 31.273$

slope $= -12400 = -\dfrac{E_a}{R} = -\dfrac{E_a}{8.3145 \times 10^{-3} \text{ kJ/K·mol}}$

$E_a = 103 \text{ kJ/mol}$

15.88   (a) $k = \dfrac{\ln 2}{t_{1/2}} = \dfrac{0.693}{25.0 \text{ min}} = 0.0277 \text{ min}^{-1}$

$\ln\dfrac{[CH_3OCH_3]}{8.00 \text{ g}} = -(0.0277 \text{ min}^{-1})(125 \text{ min})$

$[CH_3OCH_3]$ after 125 min $= 0.251$ g $[CH_3OCH_3]$ after 145 min $= 0.144$ g

(b) $\ln\left(\dfrac{2.25 \text{ ng}}{7.60 \text{ ng}}\right) = -(0.0277 \text{ min}^{-1})t$ $t = 43.9 \text{ min}$

(c) $\ln\dfrac{[CH_3OCH_3]}{[CH_3OCH_3]_0} = -(0.0277 \text{ min}^{-1})(150 \text{ min})$

fraction remaining $= \dfrac{[CH_3OCH_3]}{[CH_3OCH_3]_0} = 0.016$

15.89   (a)   When $^3/_4$ of the PH_3 has decomposed, $^1/_4$ remains and two half-lives have passed. $2 \times 37.9 \text{ s} = 75.8 \text{ s}$

(b) $k = \dfrac{0.693}{t_{1/2}} = \dfrac{0.693}{37.9 \text{ s}} = 0.0183 \text{ s}^{-1}$

$\ln\dfrac{[PH_3]}{[PH_3]_0} = -(0.0183 \text{ s}^{-1})(1 \text{ min})\left(\dfrac{60 \text{ s}}{1 \text{ min}}\right)$

fraction remaining $= \dfrac{[PH_3]}{[PH_3]_0} = 0.33$

15.90   (a) $2\,NO(g) + Br_2(g) \rightarrow 2\,BrNO(g)$

(b)   Mechanism 1:   termolecular

Mechanism 2:   Step 1: bimolecular

Step 2: bimolecular

Mechanism 3:   Step 1: bimolecular

Step 2: bimolecular

(c)   Mechanism 2: $Br_2NO(g)$ is an intermediate

Mechanism 3 $N_2O_2(g)$ is an intermediate

(d)   Assuming step 1 in each mechanism is the slow step, the rate equations will all differ. Mechanism 1 would be second order in NO and first order in Br_2. Mechanism 2 would be first order in both NO and Br_2. Finally, Mechanism 3 would be second order in NO and zero order in Br_2.

15.91 $k = \dfrac{0.693}{8.04\ days} = 0.0862\ days^{-1}$

$\ln\left(\dfrac{x}{25.0\ mg}\right) = -(0.0862\ days^{-1})(31\ days)$

$x = 1.7\ mg$

15.92   The steps in the mechanism add up to give the overall equation.

Step 2 is rate-determining: $-\dfrac{\Delta[O_3]}{\Delta t} = k[O_3][O]$ However, O is an intermediate

Step 1: $K_1 = \dfrac{[O_2][O]}{[O_3]}$ $[O] = \dfrac{K_1[O_3]}{[O_2]}$

Substitute into the rate equation: $-\dfrac{\Delta[O_3]}{\Delta t} = k[O_3]\left(\dfrac{K_1[O_3]}{[O_2]}\right) = kK_1[O_3]^2/[O_2]$

The mechanism agrees with the experimental rate law.

15.93   The slowest reaction has the smallest k (d) $Cl + CH_2FCl \rightarrow HCl + CHFCl$

The fastest reaction has the largest k (c) $Cl + C_3H_8 \rightarrow HCl + C_3H_7$

15.94   The finely divided rhodium will have a significantly greater surface area than the small block of metal, which creates a huge increase in the number of reaction sites and vastly increases the reaction rate.

15.95   Accounting for the edge and corner cubes, there are 488 cubes with at least one surface on the outside surface of the 10. cm by 10. cm cube (48.8%). Splitting the cubes into eight piles of 125 blocks results in 784 blocks with at least one surface on the outside surface of the smaller cubes (78.4%). This model demonstrates that the surface area for a finely divided substance is much greater than that for a large lump of substance having the same mass.

15.96   Assume that you begin with labeled oxygen in methanol, $CH_3^{18}OH$. If we represent the labeled oxygen

with a *, you can see from the equation below that labeled oxygen (in the water) results if the O originated

from the methanol.

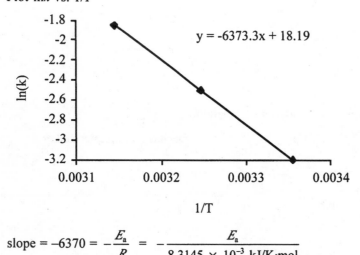

15.97   (a)   There are three steps in the mechanism

(b)   The slowest step in the reaction has the largest activation energy. Steps 1 and 2 have approximately

equal (and large) activation energies

(c)   The overall reaction is exothermic

15.98   Plot $\ln k$ vs. $1/T$

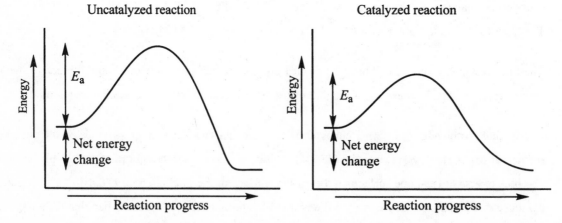

$$\text{slope} = -6370 = -\frac{E_a}{R} = -\frac{E_a}{8.3145 \times 10^{-3} \text{ kJ/K·mol}} \qquad E_a = 53.0 \text{ kJ/mol}$$

15.99

Uncatalyzed reaction

Catalyzed reaction

The activation energy in the catalyzed reaction is less than the activation energy in the uncatalyzed reaction.

The net energy change is the same in both reactions.

15.100 $\ln \dfrac{k_2}{k_1} = -\dfrac{E_a}{R}\left(\dfrac{1}{T_2} - \dfrac{1}{T_1}\right)$

$\ln\left(\dfrac{k_2}{0.0900 \text{ min}^{-1}}\right) = -\dfrac{103 \text{ kJ/mol}}{8.3145 \times 10^{-3} \text{ kJ/K·mol}}\left(\dfrac{1}{318.0 \text{ K}} - \dfrac{1}{328.0 \text{ K}}\right)$

$k_2 = 0.0274 \text{ min}^{-1}$

15.101 Recognizing that $\dfrac{t_{90}}{t_{100}} = \dfrac{k_{100}}{k_{90}}$:

$\ln \dfrac{k_{100}}{k_{90}} = \ln \dfrac{t_{90}}{t_{100}} = -\dfrac{E_a}{R}\left(\dfrac{1}{T_2} - \dfrac{1}{T_1}\right)$

$\ln \dfrac{t_{90}}{t_{100}} = -\dfrac{52.0 \text{ kJ/mol}}{8.3145 \times 10^{-3} \text{ kJ/K·mol}}\left(\dfrac{1}{373 \text{ K}} - \dfrac{1}{363 \text{ K}}\right)$

$\dfrac{t_{90}}{t_{100}} = 1.59$

$t_{90} = (1.59)(3 \text{ min}) = 4.76 \text{ min}$

15.102 Overall reaction: $HA + X \rightarrow A^- + \text{products}$

Step 3 is rate-determining: rate = $k[XH^+]$ XH^+ is an intermediate

Step 1: $K_1 = \dfrac{[H^+][A^-]}{[HA]}$ $[H^+] = \dfrac{K_1[HA]}{[A^-]}$

Step 2: $K_2 = \dfrac{[XH^+]}{[X][H^+]}$ $[XH^+] = K_2[X][H^+]$

Substitute into rate equation: rate = $k[XH^+] = k\big(K_2[X]\big)\left(\dfrac{K_1[HA]}{[A^-]}\right) = kK_1K_2 \dfrac{[X][HA]}{[A^-]}$

The reaction is first order with respect to HA

Doubling the HA concentration would double the rate

15.103 After 30 min (one half-life) $P_{HOF} = 50.0 \text{ mm Hg}$, $P_{HF} = P_{HOF} = 50.0 \text{ mm Hg}$, $P_{O_2} = \frac{1}{2} P_{HF} = 25.0 \text{ mm Hg}$

$P_{total} = 50.0 \text{ mm Hg} + 50.0 \text{ mm Hg} + 25.0 \text{ mm Hg} = 125.0 \text{ mm Hg}$

To calculate the total pressure after 45 min, use the integrated first-order rate law:

$k = \dfrac{0.693}{t_{1/2}} = \dfrac{0.693}{30 \text{ min}} = 0.0231 \text{ min}^{-1}$

$\ln\left(\dfrac{x}{100. \text{ mm Hg}}\right) = -(0.0231 \text{ min}^{-1})(45 \text{ min})$

$\ln(x) - \ln(100. \text{ mm Hg}) = -(0.0231 \text{ min}^{-1})(45 \text{ min})$

$x = 35.4 \text{ mm Hg}$

$P_{HOF} = 35.4 \text{ mm Hg}$, $P_{HF} = P_{HOF}$ consumed = $100. - 35.4 \text{ mm Hg} = 65 \text{ mm Hg}$,

$P_{O_2} = \frac{1}{2} P_{HF} = 32 \text{ mm Hg}$

$P_{total} = 132 \text{ mm Hg}$

15.104   After 245 minutes (one half-life) $P_{SO_2Cl_2}$ = 13 mm Hg, P_{SO_2} = 13 mm Hg, P_{Cl_2} = 13 mm Hg

   P_{total} = 38 mm Hg

   To calculate the total pressure after 12 hours (720 min), use the integrated first-order rate law:

   $$k = \frac{0.693}{t_{1/2}} = \frac{0.693}{245 \text{ min}} = 0.00283 \text{ min}^{-1}$$

   $$\ln\left(\frac{x}{25 \text{ mm Hg}}\right) = -(0.00283 \text{ min}^{-1})(720 \text{ minutes})$$

   $$\ln(x) - \ln(25 \text{ mm Hg}) = -(0.00283 \text{ min}^{-1})(720 \text{ minutes})$$

   $$x = 3.3 \text{ mm Hg}$$

   $P_{SO_2Cl_2}$ = 3.3 mm Hg, P_{SO_2} = $P_{SO_2Cl_2}$ consumed = 25 – 3.3 = 22 mm Hg, P_{Cl_2} = P_{SO_2} = 22 mm Hg

   P_{total} = 47 mm Hg

15.105   (a)   The slow step is unimolecular and the fast step is bimolecular

   (b)   Rate = k[Ni(CO)$_4$]   Yes, this rate law matches the stoichiometry of the slow step in the mechanism.

   (c) $\ln\dfrac{[\text{Ni(CO)}_4]}{[\text{Ni(CO)}_4]_0} = -kt$

   $$\ln\frac{[\text{Ni(CO)}_4]}{0.025 \text{ mol/L}} = -(9.3 \times 10^{-3} \text{ s}^{-1})(5.0 \text{ min})\left(\frac{60 \text{ s}}{1 \text{ min}}\right)$$

   $$\ln[\text{Ni(CO)}_4] - \ln(0.025 \text{ mol/L}) = -(9.3 \times 10^{-3} \text{ s}^{-1})(5.0 \text{ min})\left(\frac{60 \text{ s}}{1 \text{ min}}\right)$$

   $$[\text{Ni(CO)}_4] = 0.0015 \text{ mol/L}$$

   [Ni(CO)$_3$L] = [Ni(CO)$_4$] consumed = 0.025 mol/L – 0.0015 mol/L = 0.023 M

15.106   (a)   The average rate is calculated over a period of time, whereas the instantaneous rate is the rate of reaction at some instant in time.

   (b)   The reaction rate decreases with time as the dye concentration decreases.

   (c)   See (b) above.

15.107   (a)   An increase in HCl concentration increases the reaction rate.

   (b)   Initial rate and concentration are directly related.

15.108   (a)   Chemists use initial rates because the presence of products can affect the mechanism of the reaction.

   (b)   0.648 mol/L·min

15.109   The first-order integrated rate equation.

15.110   3270 min represents 5 half-lives, so $^1/_{32}$ is the fraction remaining. The concentration will be 6.3×10^{-4} M. After 3924 min, the fraction remaining is $^1/_{64}$ because 6 half-lives have elapsed. The concentration at this point is 3.1×10^{-4} M.

15.111 (a) Molecules must collide with enough energy to overcome the activation energy and in the correct orientation.

(b) In animation 2 the molecules are moving faster, so they are at a higher temperature.

(c) Less sensitive. The O_3 and NO must collide with NO in the correct orientation. The O_3 and N_2 collision does not depend as much on orientation because N_2 is a homonuclear diatomic molecule.

15.112 One mechanism is a bimolecular substitution reaction. The reaction passes through the transition state as an incoming ion displaces an atom attached to the C atom. In the other mechanism a high energy intermediate is formed, and the reaction has two transition states.

15.113 When two molecules react in an elementary step, it is bimolecular.

15.114 (a) An overall reaction can be the result of a sequence of two or more elementary reactions or steps. The net result of these elementary steps is the overall reaction.

(b) The stoichiometric coefficient of a reactant in an elementary step is the order of the reaction for that reactant in that step.

(c) Rate = $k[NO_3][CO]$

(d) No. Only in the two-step mechanism is there O atom exchange between NO_2 molecules. If CO reacts directly with NO_2, the CO_2 can have either ^{16}O or ^{18}O, and the product NO molecules will be either $N^{16}O$ or $N^{18}O$.

15.115 (a) I^- is regenerated during the second step in the mechanism

(b) The activation energy is smaller for the catalyzed reaction.

Chapter 16
Principles of Reactivity: Chemical Equilibria

INSTRUCTOR'S NOTES

Introductory courses have always been the point at which students began their study of chemical equilibria, so Chapters 16-18 are quite important. Chapter 16 covers the most basic aspects of equilibria, and we usually spend about 3 lecture hours on the material.

One somewhat unusual aspect of this book is the graphical presentation of equilibria. We have found this a useful approach, since the students tie this in with previous discussions of phase equilibria and because they can readily see that there are many combinations of concentrations that can define an equilibrium system. Further, it is easy to see when a system is or is not at equilibrium.

You will notice that we have not restricted ourselves to gas phase equilibrium systems here but have introduced a few simple systems in aqueous solution. This was done deliberately so that students see that the principles apply to all types of chemical systems.

SUGGESTED DEMONSTRATIONS

1.   The Nature of the Equilibrium State

   •   We have demonstrated the CO_2/$Ca(OH)_2$ system shown in the Chapter Focus in class with reasonable success. (This is taken from Volume 1 of *Chemical Demonstrations* by Shakhashiri, page 329.)

   •   The use of the Fe^{3+}/SCN^- system in Figure 16.3 was done to tie the book to the classical laboratory experiment on this equilibrium system.

2.   Disturbing a Chemical Equilibrium: Le Chatelier's Principle

   •   The equilibrium system between $[Co(H_2O)_6]^{2+}$ and $[CoCl_4]^{2-}$ is an effective demonstration. See L. R. Summerlin, J. L. Ealy, Jr. *Chemical Demonstrations: A Sourcebook for Teachers, 2nd Edition*, Vol. 1: "Effects of Temperature Change on Equilibrium: Cobalt Complex." Also in this book: "Equilibrium and Le Chatelier's Principle" and "Effect of Concentration on Equilibrium: Cobalt Complex."

   •   A simple demonstration which relates an equilibrium shift to a change in pressure is the effect of pressure on the melting point of ice. (Ellis, A. B.; Geselbracht, M. J.; Johnson, B. J.; Lisensky, G. C; Robinson, W. R. *Teaching General Chemistry: A Materials Science Companion*; American Chemical Society: Washington, D.C., 1993, p. 279.)

   •   The illustration of the NO_2/N_2O_4 equilibrium system in Figure 16.6 is simple to perform. Nitrogen dioxide, generated in the copper/nitric acid reaction, can be sealed into flasks. To see a distinct color difference it is necessary to have as large a temperature difference as possible.

Solutions to Study Questions

16.1   (a) False. The magnitude of the equilibrium constant is always dependent on temperature.

   (b) True

   (c) The equilibrium constant for a reaction is the reciprocal of the value of K for its reverse.

   (d) True

   (e) True

16.2 $PbCl_2$ has a larger K than PbF_2 so solutions of $PbCl_2$ have a greater concentration of Pb^{2+}.

16.3   Heat energy will be consumed when the temperature is raised, so the equilibrium will shift to form more product (and the value of K will change). $CaCO_3$ does not appear in the equilibrium expression so adding more of the solid has no effect on the equilibrium position. If additional CO_2 is added to the flask the equilibrium will shift to consume the added product, forming more reactant.

16.4   (a) Heat energy will be generated when the temperature is lowered, and the equilibrium will shift to form more product (and the value of K will change).

   (b) When the volume of the reaction flask is increased, the equilibrium will shift to increase the total number of moles of gas, to form more reactants.

16.5   When $Q < K$ the reaction proceeds to form more product. A will continue to be consumed to form B.

16.6   (a) product-favored $K \gg 1$

   (b) reactant favored $K \ll 1$

   (c) product-favored $K \gg 1$

16.7   (d) Solids do not appear in equilibrium constant expressions.

16.8   (a) $K = \dfrac{[H_2O]^2[O_2]}{[H_2O_2]^2}$ $K_p = \dfrac{P^2_{H_2O}P_{O_2}}{P^2_{H_2O_2}}$

   (b) $K = \dfrac{[CO_2]}{[CO][O_2]^{1/2}}$ $K_p = \dfrac{P_{CO_2}}{P_{CO}P^{1/2}_{O_2}}$

   (c) $K = \dfrac{[CO]^2}{[CO_2]}$ $K_p = \dfrac{P^2_{CO}}{P_{CO_2}}$

   (d) $K = \dfrac{[CO_2]}{[CO]}$ $K_p = \dfrac{P_{CO_2}}{P_{CO}}$

16.9   (a) $K = \dfrac{[O_3]^2}{[O_2]^3}$ $\qquad\qquad\qquad$ $K_p = \dfrac{P^2_{O_3}}{P^3_{O_2}}$

   (b) $K = \dfrac{[Fe(CO)_5]}{[CO]^5}$ $\qquad\qquad$ $K_p = \dfrac{P_{Fe(CO)_5}}{P^5_{CO}}$

   (c) $K = [NH_3]^2[CO_2][H_2O]$ $\qquad$ $K_p = P^2_{NH_3} P_{CO_2} P_{H_2O}$

   (d) $K = [Ag^+]^2[SO_4{}^{2-}]$

16.10 $Q = \dfrac{[I]^2}{[I_2]} = \dfrac{(2.0 \times 10^{-8})^2}{0.020} = 2.0 \times 10^{-14}$

   $Q < K$ The reaction is not at equilibrium. The reaction will proceed to the right, to form more products.

16.11 $[NO_2] = \dfrac{2.0 \times 10^{-3}\ mol}{10.\ L} = 2.0 \times 10^{-4}\ mol/L$ $\qquad$ $[N_2O_4] = \dfrac{1.5 \times 10^{-3}\ mol}{10.\ L} = 1.5 \times 10^{-4}\ mol/L$

   $Q = \dfrac{[N_2O_4]}{[NO_2]^2} = \dfrac{1.5 \times 10^{-4}}{(2.0 \times 10^{-4})^2} = 3800$

   $Q > K$ The reaction is not at equilibrium. The concentration of NO_2 will increase as the system proceeds to equilibrium.

16.12 $Q = \dfrac{[SO_3]^2}{[SO_2]^2[O_2]} = \dfrac{(6.9 \times 10^{-3})^2}{(5.0 \times 10^{-3})^2(1.9 \times 10^{-3})} = 1.0 \times 10^3$

   $Q > K$ The reaction is not at equilibrium. The reaction will proceed to the left, to form more reactants.

16.13 $Q = \dfrac{[NO]^2[Cl_2]}{[NOCl]^2} = \dfrac{(2.5 \times 10^{-3})^2(2.0 \times 10^{-3})}{(5.0 \times 10^{-3})^2} = 5.0 \times 10^{-4}$

   $Q < K$ The reaction is not at equilibrium. The reaction will proceed to the right, to form more products.

16.14 $K = \dfrac{[PCl_3][Cl_2]}{[PCl_5]} = \dfrac{(1.3 \times 10^{-2})(3.9 \times 10^{-3})}{4.2 \times 10^{-5}} = 1.2$

16.15 $K = \dfrac{[SO_3]^2}{[SO_2]^2[O_2]} = \dfrac{(4.13 \times 10^{-3})^2}{(3.77 \times 10^{-3})^2(4.30 \times 10^{-3})} = 279$

16.16 $[CO] = \dfrac{0.10\ mol}{2.0\ L} = 0.050\ mol/L$ $\qquad\qquad$ $[CO_2] = \dfrac{0.20\ mol}{2.0\ L} = 0.10\ mol/L$

   (a) $K = \dfrac{[CO]^2}{[CO_2]} = \dfrac{(0.050)^2}{0.10} = 0.025$

   (b) Only the amount of C has changed, and solids do not appear in equilibrium constant expressions.

   $K = 0.025$

   (c) The value of K is independent of the quantity of solid present.

16.17   (a) $K = \dfrac{[H_2O][CO]}{[H_2][CO_2]} = \dfrac{(0.11)(0.11)}{(0.087)(0.087)} = 1.6$

$\qquad\qquad\qquad\qquad\qquad\qquad\qquad$

(b)

	H_2	+	CO_2	$\rightleftharpoons$	H_2O	+	CO
Initial (M)	0.050 mol/2.0 L		0.050 mol/2.0 L		0		0
	= 0.025 M		= 0.025 M				
Change (M)	$-x$		$-x$		$+x$		$+x$
Equilibrium (M)	$0.025 - x$		$0.025 - x$		x		x

$$K = 1.6 = \frac{(x)(x)}{(0.025 - x)(0.025 - x)} = \frac{x^2}{(0.025 - x)^2}$$

$$\sqrt{1.6} = \sqrt{\frac{x^2}{(0.025 - x)^2}} = \frac{x}{0.025 - x}$$

$x = 0.014$ mol/L

$$\frac{0.014 \text{ mol}}{1 \text{ L}} \cdot 2.0 \text{ L} = 0.028 \text{ mol } H_2O = 0.028 \text{ mol CO}$$

16.18

	CO	+	Cl_2	$\rightleftharpoons$	$COCl_2$
Initial (M)	0.0102		0.00609		0
Change (M)	-0.00308		-0.00308		$+0.00308$
Equilibrium (M)	0.0071		0.00301		0.00308

$$K = \frac{(0.00308)}{(0.00301)(0.0071)} = 140$$

16.19 $[SO_3] = \dfrac{3.00 \text{ mol}}{8.00 \text{ L}} = 0.375$ M $[O_2] = \dfrac{0.58 \text{ mol}}{8.00 \text{ L}} = 0.073$ M

	$2 SO_3$	$\rightleftharpoons$	$2 SO_2$	+	O_2
Initial (M)	0.375		0		0
Change (M)	$-2(0.073)$		$+2(0.073)$		$+0.073$
Equilibrium (M)	0.230		0.15		0.073

$$K = \frac{(0.15)^2(0.073)}{(0.230)^2} = 0.029$$

16.20 $[butane] = \dfrac{0.017 \text{ mol}}{0.50 \text{ L}} = 0.034$ M

	butane	$\rightleftharpoons$	isobutane
Initial (M)	0.034		0
Change (M)	$-x$		$+x$
Equilibrium (M)	$0.034 - x$		x

$$K = 2.5 = \frac{x}{0.034 - x}$$

$[isobutane] = x = 0.024$ M

$[butane] = 0.034$ M $- x = 0.010$ M

16.21 $[C_6H_{12}] = \dfrac{0.45\ mol}{2.8\ L} = 0.016\ M$

	$[C_6H_{12}]$	$\rightleftharpoons$	$[C_5H_9CH_3]$
Initial (M)	0.016		0
Change (M)	$-x$		$+x$
Equilibrium (M)	$0.016 - x$		x

$K = 0.12 = \dfrac{[C_5H_9CH_3]}{[C_6H_{12}]} = \dfrac{x}{0.016 - x}$

$[C_5H_9CH_3] = x = 1.7 \times 10^{-3}\ M$

$[C_6H_{12}] = 0.016 - x = 0.014$

16.22 $[I_2] = \dfrac{0.105\ mol}{12.3\ L} = 0.00854\ M$

	I_2	$\rightleftharpoons$	$2\ I$
Initial (M)	0.00845		0
Change (M)	$-x$		$+2x$
Equilibrium (M)	$0.00845 - x$		$2x$

$K = 3.76 \times 10^{-3} = \dfrac{(2x)^2}{0.00845 - x}$

$0 = 4x^2 + 3.76 \times 10^{-3}\,x - (3.76 \times 10^{-3})(0.00845)$

Solve using the quadratic equation. $x = 0.00240$ and -0.00334

$[I_2] = 0.00845 - x = 0.00614\ M$

$[I] = 2x = 0.00480\ M$

16.23 $[N_2O_4] = \dfrac{15.6\ g}{5.00\ L} \cdot \dfrac{1\ mol\ N_2O_4}{92.01\ g} = 0.0339\ M$

	N_2O_4	$\rightleftharpoons$	$2\ NO_2$
Initial (M)	0.0339		0
Change (M)	$-x$		$+2x$
Equilibrium (M)	$0.0339 - x$		$2x$

$K = \dfrac{[NO_2]^2}{[N_2O_4]} = 5.88 \times 10^{-3} = \dfrac{(2x)^2}{0.0339 - x}$

$0 = 4x^2 - 5.88 \times 10^{-3}(0.0339 - x)$

Solve using the quadratic equation. $x = 0.00636$ and -0.00783

(a) Moles NO_2 at equilibrium $= 2(0.00636\ mol/L)(5.00\ L) = 0.0636$ moles NO_2

(b) % N_2O_4 dissociated $= \dfrac{0.00636\ M}{0.0339\ M} \cdot 100\% = 18.8\%$

16.24 $[COBr_2] = \dfrac{0.500 \text{ mol}}{2.00 \text{ L}} = 0.250 \text{ M}$

	$COBr_2$ $\rightleftharpoons$	CO	$+$	Br_2
Initial (M)	0.250	0		0
Change (M)	$-x$	$+x$		$+x$
Equilibrium (M)	$0.250 - x$	x		x

$K = 0.190 = \dfrac{(x)(x)}{0.250 - x}$

$0 = x^2 - 0.190(0.250 - x)$

Solve using the quadratic equation. $x = 0.143$ and -0.333

$[COBr_2] = 0.250 - x = 0.107 \text{ M}$ $[CO] = [Br_2] = 0.143 \text{ M}$

% $COBr_2$ decomposed $= \dfrac{0.143 \text{ M}}{0.250 \text{ M}} \cdot 100\% = 57.1\%$

16.25 $[I_2(aq)] = \dfrac{0.0340 \text{ g}}{0.1000 \text{ L}} \cdot \dfrac{1 \text{ mol } I_2}{253.8 \text{ g}} = 0.00134 \text{ M}$

	$I_2(aq)$ $\rightleftharpoons$	$I_2(CCl_4)$
Initial (M)	0.00134	0
Change (M)	$-x$	$+x$
Equilibrium (M)	$0.00134 - x$	x

$K = 85.0 = \dfrac{x}{0.00134 - x}$

$x = 0.00132$

$[I_2(aq)] = 0.00134 - x = 2 \times 10^{-5} \text{ M}$

amount of I_2 remaining in water $= (2 \times 10^{-5} \text{ mol/L})(0.1000 \text{ L})(253.8 \text{ g/mol}) = 4 \times 10^{-4} \text{ g}$

16.26   The second equation has been multiplied by 2

(b) $K_2 = K_1^2$

16.27   The second equation has been reversed and multiplied by $^1/_2$

(a) $K_2 = 1/(K_1)^{1/2}$

16.28   The second equation has been reversed and multiplied by 2

(e) $K_2 = 1/K_1^2$

16.29   The second equation has been reversed and multiplied by 2

$K_{new} = 1/K^2 = 1/(6.66 \times 10^{-12})^2 = 2.25 \times 10^{22}$

16.30 $SnO_2(s) + 2 H_2(g) \rightleftharpoons Sn(s) + 2 H_2O(g)$ $K = 8.12$

       $2 H_2O(g) + 2 CO(g) \rightleftharpoons 2 H_2(g) + 2 CO_2(g)$ $K = 1/(0.771)^2$

       $SnO_2(s) + 2 CO(g) \rightleftharpoons Sn(s) + 2 CO_2(g)$ $K_{net} = (8.12)/(0.771)^2 = 13.7$

16.31 $H_2O(g) + CO(g) \rightleftharpoons H_2(g) + CO_2(g)$ $K = 1.6$

       $Fe(s) + CO_2(g) \rightleftharpoons FeO(s) + CO(g)$ $K = 1/(0.67)$

       $Fe(s) + H_2O(g) \rightleftharpoons FeO(s) + H_2(g)$ $K_{net} = (1.6)/(0.67) = 2.4$

16.32 $N_2O_3(g) \rightleftharpoons NO(g) + NO_2(g)$

    (a)   Adding more $N_2O_3(g)$ will shift the equilibrium to the right

    (b)   Adding more $NO_2(g)$ will shift the equilibrium to the left

    (c)   Increasing the volume of the reaction flask will shift the equilibrium to the right

    (d)   Lowering the temperature will shift the equilibrium to the left

16.33 $2 NOBr(g) \rightleftharpoons 2 NO(g) + Br_2(g)$

    (a)   Adding more $Br_2(g)$ will shift the equilibrium to the left

    (b)   Removing some $NOBr(g)$ will shift the equilibrium to the left

    (c)   Decreasing the temperature will shift the equilibrium to the left

    (d)   Increasing the container volume will shift the equilibrium to the right

16.34   (a)

	butane $\rightleftharpoons$	isobutane
Initial (M)	1.0	2.5
Concentration immediately on adding isobutane (M)	1.0	2.5 + 0.50
Change in concentration to reestablish equilibrium (M)	+x	−x
Equilibrium (M)	1.0 + x	3.0 − x

$K = 2.5 = \dfrac{3.0 - x}{1.0 + x}$ $x = 0.14$

[butane] = 1.0 + x = 1.1 M   [isobutane] = 3.0 − x = 2.9 M

(b)

	butane $\rightleftharpoons$	isobutane
Initial (M)	1.0	2.5
Concentration immediately on adding isobutane (M)	1.0 + 0.50	2.5
Change in concentration to reestablish equilibrium (M)	−x	+x
Equilibrium (M)	1.5 − x	2.5 + x

$K = 2.5 = \dfrac{2.5 + x}{1.5 - x}$ $x = 0.36$

[butane] = 1.5 − x = 1.1 M   [isobutane] = 2.5 + x = 2.9 M

16.35   When the temperature is raised, the reaction adjusts to the added heat by consuming reactants and forming more products. The equilibrium shifts to the right. Adding NH_4HS, a solid, will have no effect on the equilibrium. Adding $NH_3(g)$, a product, will shift the equilibrium to the left. Removing H_2S, a product, will shift the reaction to the right, increasing the NH_3 pressure.

16.36 $[Br_2] = \dfrac{0.086\,mol}{1.26\,L} = 0.068\,M$ 3.7% of $[Br_2] = (0.068\,M)(0.037) = 0.0025\,M$

	Br_2	$\rightleftharpoons$	2 Br
Initial (M)	0.068		0
Change (M)	-0.0025		$+2(0.0025)$
Equilibrium (M)	0.066		0.0051

$K = \dfrac{[Br]^2}{[Br_2]} = \dfrac{(0.0051)^2}{0.066} = 3.9 \times 10^{-4}$

16.37   (a)   The equation has been multiplied by $\frac{1}{2}$

$K_{new} = K^{1/2} = (1.7 \times 10^{-3})^{1/2} = 0.041$

(b)   The equation has been reversed

$K_{new} = 1/K = 1/(1.7 \times 10^{-3}) = 590$

16.38   The equation has been reversed

$K_p(\text{dissociation}) = 1/[K_p(\text{formation})] = 1/(6.5 \times 10^{11}) = 1.5 \times 10^{-12}$

16.39 $K = \dfrac{[CH_4][CCl_4]}{[CH_2Cl_2]^2}$

$1.05 = \dfrac{0.0163[CCl_4]}{(0.0206)^2}$

$[CCl_4] = 0.0273\,M$

16.40

	CS_2	+ 3 Cl_2	$\rightleftharpoons$	S_2Cl_2	+ CCl_4
Initial (M)	1.2	3.6		0	0
Change (M)	-0.90	$-3(0.90)$		$+0.90$	$+0.90$
Equilibrium (M)	0.3	0.9		0.90	0.90

$K = \dfrac{[CCl_4][S_2Cl_2]}{[CS_2][Cl_2]^3} = \dfrac{(0.90)(0.90)}{(0.3)(0.9)^3} = 4$

16.41

	H$_2$	+	I$_2$	$\rightleftharpoons$	2 HI
Initial (M)	0.0088		0.0088		0
Change (M)	$-(0.786)(0.0088)$		$-(0.786)(0.0088)$		$+2(0.786)(0.0088)$
Equilibrium (M)	0.0019		0.0019		0.014

$$K = \frac{[HI]^2}{[H_2][I_2]} = \frac{(0.014)^2}{(0.0019)(0.0019)} = 54$$

16.42 (a) [B] will immediately increase, and the blue color will become darker.

(b) The reaction equilibrium will shift to the side with fewer molecules (because the flask size has been halved). Thus, it will shift toward the blue molecules, and the blue color will become even more pronounced.

16.43 Assume volume is 1.00 L

$$Q = \frac{[isobutane]}{[butane]} = \frac{1.25}{1.75} = 0.714 \quad Q \text{ is less than } K, \text{ so the system shifts to form more isobutane.}$$

	butane	$\rightleftharpoons$	isobutane
Initial (M)	1.75		1.25
Change (M)	$-x$		$+x$
Equilibrium (M)	$1.75 - x$		$1.25 + x$

$$K = 2.5 = \frac{[isobutane]}{[butane]} = \frac{1.25 + x}{1.75 - x} \qquad x = 0.89$$

$[butane] = 1.75 - x = 0.86 \text{ M} \qquad [isobutane] = 1.25 + x = 2.14 \text{ M}$

16.44 (a) $Q = \dfrac{[NO]^2}{[N_2][O_2]} = \dfrac{(0.0042)^2}{(0.25)(0.25)} = 2.8 \times 10^{-4} \qquad Q < K, \text{ so the system is not at equilibrium.}$

(b) $Q < K$; the reaction proceeds to the right.

(c)

	N$_2$	+	O$_2$	$\rightleftharpoons$	2 NO
Initial (M)	0.25		0.25		0.0042
Change (M)	$-x$		$-x$		$+2x$
Equilibrium (M)	$0.25 - x$		$0.25 - x$		$0.0042 + 2x$

$$K = 1.7 \times 10^{-3} = \frac{[NO]^2}{[N_2][O_2]} = \frac{(0.0042 + 2x)^2}{(0.25 - x)^2}$$

Take the square root of both sides of the equation and solve for x

$x = 0.0030$

$[N_2] = [O_2] = 0.25 - x = 0.25 \text{ M}$

$[NO] = 0.0042 + 2x = 0.0102 \text{ M}$

16.45   The second equation has been reversed and multiplied by 2

(c) $K_2 = 1/K_1^2$

16.46 $3.00 \text{ g} \cdot \dfrac{1 \text{ mol } SO_2}{64.06 \text{ g}} \cdot \dfrac{1 \text{ mol } O_2}{2 \text{ mol } SO_2} \cdot \dfrac{32.00 \text{ g}}{1 \text{ mol } O_2} = 0.749 \text{ g } O_2 \text{ required}$ SO_2 is the limiting reactant

Assume that the reaction proceeds completely to the right (because K is large).

$3.00 \text{ g} \cdot \dfrac{1 \text{ mol } SO_2}{64.06 \text{ g}} \cdot \dfrac{2 \text{ mol } SO_3}{2 \text{ mol } SO_2} \cdot \dfrac{80.06 \text{ g}}{1 \text{ mol } SO_3} = 3.75 \text{ g } SO_3 \text{ produced}$

Because the value of K is not infinite, however, we know the reaction does not proceed completely to the right, so (c) 3.61 g is the only reasonable answer.

16.47   (a)   no change

(b)   shifts left

(c)   no change

(d)   shifts right

(e)   shifts right

16.48   (a)   The addition of CO(g), a product, will shift the equilibrium to the left.

(b) $[COBr_2] = \dfrac{0.500 \text{ mol}}{2.00 \text{ L}} = 0.250 \text{ M}$ $[CO] = \dfrac{2.00 \text{ mol}}{2.00 \text{ L}} = 1.00 \text{ M}$

	COBr$_2$ $\rightleftharpoons$	CO	+	Br$_2$
Initial (M) (values from 16.24)	0.107	0.143		0.143
Concentration on adding CO (M)	0.107	0.143 + 1.00		0.143
Change to reestablish equilibrium (M)	+x	−x		−x
Equilibrium (M)	0.107 + x	1.143 − x		0.143 − x

$K = 0.190 = \dfrac{(1.143 - x)(0.143 - x)}{0.107 + x}$

$0 = x^2 - 1.48x + 0.143$

Solve using the quadratic equation. $x = 1.37$ and 0.104

$[COBr_2] = 0.107 + x = 0.211 \text{ M}$

$[CO] = 1.143 - x = 1.039$

$[Br_2] = 0.143 - x = 0.039$

(c)   The COBr$_2$ was 57.1% decomposed before the addition of CO(g).

$\dfrac{0.250 \text{ M} - 0.211 \text{ M}}{0.250 \text{ M}} \cdot 100\% = 16\%$

Adding CO(g) has decreased the amount of COBr$_2$ decomposed.

16.49   The reaction is endothermic. Adding heat shifts an equilibrium in the endothermic direction.

16.50   Adding Cl_2, a product, will shift the equilibrium to the left.

$$[PCl_5] = \frac{3.120 \text{ g}}{1.00 \text{ L}} \cdot \frac{1 \text{ mol}}{208.24 \text{ g}} = 0.0150 \text{ M} \qquad [PCl_3] = \frac{3.845 \text{ g}}{1.00 \text{ L}} \cdot \frac{1 \text{ mol}}{137.33 \text{ g}} = 0.0280 \text{ M}$$

$$[Cl_2] = \frac{1.787 \text{ g}}{1.00 \text{ L}} \cdot \frac{1 \text{ mol}}{70.905 \text{ g}} = 0.0252 \text{ M} \qquad K = \frac{[PCl_3][Cl_2]}{[PCl_5]} = \frac{(0.0280)(0.0252)}{0.0150} = 0.0471$$

$$[Cl_2](\text{added}) = \frac{1.418 \text{ g}}{1.00 \text{ L}} \cdot \frac{1 \text{ mol}}{70.905 \text{ g}} = 0.0200 \text{ M}$$

	$PCl_5 \rightleftharpoons$	$PCl_3 +$	Cl_2
Initial (M)	0.0150	0.0280	0.0252
Concentration on adding Cl_2 (M)	0.0150	0.0280	0.0252 + 0.0200
Change to reestablish equilibrium (M)	$+x$	$-x$	$-x$
Equilibrium (M)	$0.0150 + x$	$0.0280 - x$	$0.0452 - x$

$$K = 0.0471 = \frac{(0.0280 - x)(0.0452 - x)}{0.0150 + x}$$

$$0 = x^2 - 0.1203x + 0.00559$$

Solve using the quadratic equation. $x = 0.115$ and 0.00485

$[PCl_5] = 0.0150 + x = 0.0199 \text{ M}$

$[PCl_3] = 0.0280 - x = 0.0232 \text{ M}$

$[Cl_2] = 0.0452 - x = 0.0404 \text{ M}$

16.51

	$2 SO_2$	$+$	O_2	$\rightleftharpoons$	$2 SO_3$
Initial (M)	0		0		x
Change (M)	+2(2.0)		+2.0		−2(2.0)
Equilibrium (M)	4.0		2.0		$x - 4.0$

$$K = 4.5 = \frac{(x - 4.0)^2}{(4.0)^2(2.0)}$$

Take the square root of both sides of the equation and solve for x

$x = [SO_3] = 16 \text{ M}$

$(16 \text{ mol/L})(1.00 \text{ L})(80.1 \text{ g/mol}) = 1300 \text{ g } SO_3$

16.52 $K_p = P_{NH_3}P_{H_2S} = 0.11$

$P_{NH_3} = P_{H_2S}$, so $K_p = 0.11 = P_{NH_3}{}^2 = P_{H_2S}{}^2$

$P_{NH_3} = P_{H_2S} = 0.33 \text{ atm}$

$P_{total} = 0.33 \text{ atm} + 0.33 \text{ atm} = 0.66 \text{ atm}$

16.53 $P_{total} = 705 \text{ mm Hg} \cdot \dfrac{1 \text{ atm}}{760 \text{ mm Hg}} = 0.928 \text{ atm} = P_{NH_3} + P_{HI}$

$P_{NH_3} = P_{HI} = \frac{1}{2}(0.928 \text{ atm}) = 0.464 \text{ atm}$

$K_P = (0.464 \text{ atm})^2 = 0.215$

16.54 $P_{total} = 0.116 \text{ atm} = (2 \times P_{NH_3}) + P_{CO_2}$

$P_{NH_3} = 2 \times P_{CO_2}$, so $P_{CO_2} = \frac{1}{3} P_{total} = 0.0387 \text{ atm}$ and $P_{NH_3} = 0.0774 \text{ atm}$

$K_p = (P_{NH_3})^2 P_{CO2} = (0.0774)^2(0.0387) = 2.31 \times 10^{-4}$

16.55 $K = 0.15 = \dfrac{P_{NO_2}{}^2}{0.85 \text{ atm}}$

$P_{NO_2} = 0.36 \text{ atm}$

$P_{total} = 0.36 \text{ atm} + 0.85 \text{ atm} = 1.21 \text{ atm}$

16.56 (a)

	$2 \text{ CH}_3\text{CO}_2\text{H} \rightleftharpoons$	$(\text{CH}_3\text{CO}_2\text{H})_2$
Initial (M)	5.4×10^{-4}	0
Change (M)	$-2x$	$+x$
Equilibrium (M)	$5.4 \times 10^{-4} - 2x$	x

$K = 3.2 \times 10^4 = \dfrac{x}{(5.4 \times 10^{-4} - 2x)^2}$

$0 = 1.3 \times 10^5 x^2 - 70.x + 9.3 \times 10^{-3}$

Solve using the quadratic equation. $x = 3.2 \times 10^{-4}$ and 2.3×10^{-4}

$\dfrac{2(2.3 \times 10^{-4} \text{ M})}{5.4 \times 10^{-4} \text{ M}} \cdot 100\% = 84\%$

(b) Increasing the temperature will shift the equilibrium to the left.

16.57

	$2 \text{ NH}_3 \rightleftharpoons$	N_2 +	3 H_2
Initial (M)	1.80	0	0
Change (M)	$-2x$	$+x$	$+3x$
Equilibrium (M)	$1.80 - 2x$	x	$3x$

$K = 6.3 = \dfrac{[\text{N}_2][\text{H}_2]^3}{[\text{NH}_3]^2} = \dfrac{(x)(3x)^3}{(1.80 - 2x)^2} = \dfrac{27x^4}{(1.80 - 2x)^2}$

Take the square root of both sides of the equation and simplify.

$0 = 5.20x^2 + 5.02x - 4.52$

Solve using the quadratic equation. $x = 0.567$ and -1.53

$[\text{NH}_3] = 1.80 - 2x = 0.67 \text{ M}$ $\qquad [\text{N}_2] = x = 0.567 \text{ M}$

$[\text{H}_2] = 3x = 1.70 \text{ M}$

$P_{total} = \dfrac{n}{V} RT = [(0.57 + 1.70 + 0.67) \text{ mol/L}](0.082057 \text{ L} \cdot \text{atm/K} \cdot \text{mol})(723 \text{ K}) = 175 \text{ atm}$

16.58 $P_{total} = P_{NO_2} + P_{N_2O_4}$ $P_{N_2O_4} = 1.5 - P_{NO_2}$

$$K_p = 6.75 = \frac{1.5 - P_{NO_2}}{P_{N_2O_4}^2}$$

$$0 = 6.75 P_{NO_2}^2 + P_{NO_2} - 1.5$$

Solve using the quadratic equation. $P_{NO_2} = 0.40$ atm $P_{N_2O_4} = 1.5 - P_{NO_2} = 1.1$ atm

16.59   (a) $K_c = 1.8 \times 10^{-4} = [NH_3][H_2S]$

$[NH_3] = [H_2S]$, so $K = [NH_3]^2 = [H_2S]^2$

$[NH_3] = [H_2S] = (1.8 \times 10^{-4})^{1/2} = 0.013$ M

(b)   NH₄HS $\rightleftharpoons$ NH₃ + H₂S

	NH₄HS $\rightleftharpoons$	NH₃	+	H₂S
Initial (M)		0.020		0
Change (M)		+x		+x
Equilibrium (M)		0.020 + x		x

$K_c = 1.8 \times 10^{-4} = [NH_3][H_2S] = (0.020\ M + x)x$

$x = [H_2S] = 0.0067$ M

$[NH_3] = 0.020 + x = 0.027$ M

16.60   This is a dynamic equilibrium. Initially, the rate of evaporation is greater than the rate of condensation. At equilibrium, the two rates are equal.

16.61   The system is not at equilibrium because it continues to gain heat from the surroundings. The temperature of the water/ice mixture will remain at 0 °C until all the ice is melted, then the temperature will rise as more heat is gained. Only if the beaker of water/ice were moved to a perfectly insulated compartment, also at 0 °C, would it attain equilibrium at 0 °C. In this case, it would be a dynamic equilibrium with water molecules moving from the solid to the liquid phase and from the liquid to the solid phase. The quantity of ice would not change. If a D₂O ice cube was added to some H₂O(ℓ), an equilibrium would be obtained. The amount of D₂O in the liquid phase would increase due to the continuing molecular exchange. The water could then be sampled for the presence of D₂O.

16.62   (a) $Q = \dfrac{[O_2][NO_2]}{[O_3][NO]} = \dfrac{(8.2 \times 10^{-3})(2.5 \times 10^{-4})}{(1.0 \times 10^{-6})(1.0 \times 10^{-5})} = 2.1 \times 10^5$

$Q < K$ so the reaction will proceed to the right to reach equilibrium

(b) $\Delta H° = \Delta H_f°[NO_2(g)] - (\Delta H_f°[O_3(g)] + \Delta H_f°[NO(g)])$

$\Delta H° = 1\ mol \cdot 33.1\ kJ/mol - (1\ mol \cdot 142.67\ kJ/mol + 1\ mol \cdot 90.29\ kJ/mol)$

$\Delta H° = -199.9$ kJ

Increasing the temperature will shift the equilibrium to the left. The concentrations of the products will decrease.

16.63 $P_{total} = 1.50$ atm $= P_{NO_2} + P_{N_2O_4}$ $\qquad\qquad$ $P_{N_2O_4} = 1.50 - P_{NO_2}$

$$K_p = 0.148 = \frac{P_{NO_2}{}^2}{1.50 - P_{NO_2}}$$

Solve using the quadratic equation. $P_{NO_2} = 0.403$ atm $\qquad$ $P_{N_2O_4} = 1.50 - P_{NO_2} = 1.10$ atm

$$P_{N_2O_4}(\text{initial}) = 1.10 \text{ atm} + (0.403 \text{ atm})\left(\frac{1 \text{ mol } N_2O_4}{2 \text{ mol } NO_2}\right) = 1.30 \text{ atm}$$

$$\text{fraction dissociated} = \frac{1.30 \text{ atm} - 1.10 \text{ atm}}{1.30 \text{ atm}} = 0.15$$

If the total pressure falls to 1.00 atm:

$$K_p = \frac{P_{NO_2}{}^2}{P_{N_2O_4}} = 0.148 = \frac{P_{NO_2}{}^2}{1.00 - P_{NO_2}}$$

Solve using the quadratic equation. $P_{NO_2} = 0.318$ atm $\qquad$ $P_{N_2O_4} = 1.00 - P_{NO_2} = 0.682$ atm

$$P_{N_2O_4}(\text{initial}) = 0.682 \text{ atm} + (0.318 \text{ atm})\left(\frac{1 \text{ mol } N_2O_4}{2 \text{ mol } NO_2}\right) = 0.841 \text{ atm}$$

$$\text{fraction dissociated} = \frac{0.841 \text{ atm} - 0.682 \text{ atm}}{0.841 \text{ atm}} = 0.189$$

If pressure decreases, the equilibrium will shift to the right, increasing the fraction of N_2O_4 dissociated.

16.64   (a) $P_{total} = 0.200$ atm $= P_{CO} + P_{CO_2}$

$P_{CO} = P_{CO_2} = {}^1\!/_2(0.200 \text{ atm}) = 0.100$ atm

$K_p = (0.100 \text{ atm})^3(0.100 \text{ atm})^3 = 1.00 \times 10^{-6}$

(b) $n_{CO} = \dfrac{PV}{RT} = \dfrac{(0.100 \text{ atm})(10.0 \text{ L})}{(0.082057 \text{ L} \cdot \text{atm/K} \cdot \text{mol})(373 \text{ K})} = 0.0327$ mol CO

$0.0327 \text{ mol CO} \cdot \dfrac{1 \text{ mol La}_2(C_2O_4)_3}{3 \text{ mol CO}} = 0.0109 \text{ mol La}_2(C_2O_4)_3$

$(0.100 \text{ mol} - 0.0109 \text{ mol}) = 0.089 \text{ mol La}_2(C_2O_4)_3$ remains

16.65   (a)   The flask containing the complex with the largest K for the dissociation reaction, $(H_3N)B(CH_3)_3$, will have the largest partial pressure of $B(CH_3)_3$.

(b) $P_{(NH_3)B(CH_3)_3} = \dfrac{nRT}{V} = \dfrac{(0.010 \text{ mol})(0.082057 \text{ L} \cdot \text{atm/K} \cdot \text{mol})(373 \text{ K})}{0.100 \text{ L}} = 3.1$ atm

	$(NH_3)B(CH_3)_3$	$\rightleftharpoons$	$B(CH_3)_3$	+	NH_3
Initial (atm)	3.1		0		0
Change (atm)	$-x$		$+x$		$+x$
Equilibrium (atm)	$3.1 - x$		x		x

$$K_p = 4.62 = \frac{(x)(x)}{3.1 - x}$$

Solve using the quadratic equation. $x = 2.1$ and -6.7

$P_{B(CH_3)_3} = P_{NH_3} = x = 2.1$ atm $\qquad$ $P_{(NH_3)B(CH_3)_3} = 3.1 - x = 1.0$ atm

$P_{total} = 2.1 \text{ atm} + 2.1 \text{ atm} + 1.0 \text{ atm} = 5.2 \text{ atm}$ $\qquad$ % dissociation $= \dfrac{2.1 \text{ atm}}{3.1 \text{ atm}} \cdot 100\% = 69\%$

16.66 $[SO_2Cl_2] = \dfrac{6.70 \text{ g } SO_2Cl_2}{1.00 \text{ L}} \cdot \dfrac{1 \text{ mol } SO_2Cl_2}{135.0 \text{ g}} = 0.0496 \text{ M}$

(a) $K = 0.045 = \dfrac{x^2}{0.0496 - x}$

Solve using the quadratic equation. $x = 0.030$

$[SO_2Cl_2] = 0.0496 - x = 0.020 \text{ M}$

$[SO_2] = [Cl_2] = x = 0.030 \text{ M}$

fraction dissociated $= \dfrac{0.030}{0.0496} = 0.60$

(b) $[Cl_2] = \dfrac{n}{V} = \dfrac{P}{RT} = \dfrac{1.00 \text{ atm}}{(0.082057 \text{ L} \cdot \text{atm/K} \cdot \text{mol})(648 \text{ K})} = 0.0188 \text{ M}$

$K = 0.045 = \dfrac{x(0.0188 + x)}{0.0496 - x}$

Solve using the quadratic equation. $x = 0.025$

$[SO_2Cl_2] = 0.0496 - x = 0.025 \text{ M}$

$[SO_2] = x = 0.025 \text{ M}$

$[Cl_2] = 0.0188 + x = 0.044 \text{ M}$

fraction dissociated $= \dfrac{0.025}{0.0496} = 0.50$

(c)   Le Chatelier's principle predicts that the addition of $Cl_2(g)$ would shift the equilibrium to the left, preserving more SO_2Cl_2, a prediction that is confirmed by these calculations.

16.67 $K_p = P_{CO_2} = 3.87 \text{ atm}$

$n_{CO_2} = \dfrac{PV}{RT} = \dfrac{(3.87 \text{ atm})(5.00 \text{ L})}{(0.082057 \text{ L} \cdot \text{atm/K} \cdot \text{mol})(1273 \text{ K})} = 0.185 \text{ mol } CO_2$

$0.0185 \text{ mol} \cdot \dfrac{1 \text{ mol } CaCO_3}{1 \text{ mol } CO_2} \cdot \dfrac{100.1 \text{ g}}{1 \text{ mol } CaCO_3} = 18.5 \text{ g } CaCO_3$

16.68 $K = \dfrac{[HbCO]P_{O_2}}{[HbO_2]P_{CO}}$

$2.0 \times 10^2 = (1)\dfrac{0.20 \text{ atm}}{P_{CO}}$

$P_{CO} = 0.0010 \text{ atm}$

16.69   Calculate the more convenient K_c value:

$K_p = K_c(RT)^{\Delta n} = 1.2 \times 10^{-10} = K_c[(0.082057 \text{ L} \cdot \text{atm/K} \cdot \text{mol})(1800 \text{ K})]^1$

$K_c = 8.12 \times 10^{-13}$

Assume that x mol O_2 dissociates and that $2x$ mol O is present at equilibrium:

$K_c = \dfrac{[O]^2}{[O_2]} = 8.12 \times 10^{-13} = \dfrac{(2x)^2}{(1.0 \text{ mol/10. L}) - x}$

K_c is very small, so assume x is very small when compared to $[O_2]_{initial}$

$x = 1.4 \times 10^{-7}$ $[O] = 2x = 2.8 \times 10^{-7}$ M

$\dfrac{2.8 \times 10^{-7} \text{ mol}}{L} \cdot 10 \text{ L} \cdot \dfrac{6.02 \times 10^{23} \text{ atoms}}{1 \text{ mol}} = 1.7 \times 10^{18}$ O atoms

16.70 $190 \text{ mm Hg} \cdot \dfrac{1 \text{ atm}}{760 \text{ mm Hg}} = 0.25$ atm

$$\text{NOBr} \rightleftharpoons \text{NO} \quad + \quad {}^1\!/_2 \text{ Br}_2$$

	NOBr	NO	½ Br₂
Initial (atm)	x	0	0
Equilibrium (atm)	$0.66x$	$0.34x$	$0.17x$

$P_{total} = 0.25 \text{ atm} = 0.66x + 0.34x + 0.17x$

$x = 0.21$ atm

$P_{NOBr} = 0.66x = 0.14$ atm $P_{NO} = 0.34x = 0.073$ atm $P_{Br_2} = 0.17x = 0.036$ atm

$K_p = \dfrac{P_{NO} P_{Br_2}{}^{1/2}}{P_{NOBr}} = \dfrac{(0.073)(0.036)^{1/2}}{0.14} = 0.098$

16.71   Any elementary chemical step can occur both in the forward and reverse directions. Solid lead chloride forms when solutions containing lead ions and chloride ions are mixed, and a solution containing lead ions and chloride ions forms when pure lead chloride is placed in water and heated.

16.72   Adding SCN^- ion shifts the equilibrium to the right, increasing the concentration of the red $Fe(H_2O)_5(SCN)^{2+}$ ion. The color of the solution should become more red, as observed.

16.73   (a) $[Fe^{3+}]$ does not go to zero. $K = \dfrac{[FeSCN^{2+}]}{[Fe^{3+}][SCN^-]} = \dfrac{2.060 \times 10^{-3}}{(2.939 \times 10^{-3})(4.939 \times 10^{-3})} = 142$

(b) $[Fe^{3+}] = [SCN^-]$ at equilibrium, and these ions have the largest concentration

(c) At equilibrium, $[Fe^{3+}] = 2.64 \times 10^{-3}$ M, $[SCN^-] = 3.64 \times 10^{-3}$ M, $[FeSCN^{2+}] = 1.36 \times 10^{-3}$ M

16.74   (a) K = 4.5

(b) K = 2.3

(c) K = 6.0

(d) K = 5.6

Chapter 17
Principles of Reactivity: Chemistry of Acids and Bases

INSTRUCTOR'S NOTES

For this edition, the three chapters on aqueous equilibria have been reorganized into two chapters, Chapter 17 (Chemistry of Acids and Bases) and Chapter 18 (Other Aspects of Aqueous Equilibria). Chapter 17 now introduces acid-base theories, applies the concepts of equilibria to acids and bases in aqueous solution, and covers acid-base reactions. The common ion effect, buffer solutions, acid-base titrations, and the solubility of salts are topics covered in Chapter 18.

We cover aqueous equilibria in the second semester of our course. Approximately 9 lectures are devoted to the entire subject of equilibrium (Chapters 16-18). We do not give much coverage to polyprotic acids or to equilibria involving complex ions. Lewis acid/base concepts are mentioned briefly.

One aspect of the lectures on Chapter 17 that we especially emphasize is the concept of conjugate acids and bases and relative acid and base strengths. In lecture we perform some acid-base reactions to build a portion of Table 17.3, the chart of relative strengths of acids and bases.

As we are all aware students have some difficulty with the general topic of aqueous equilibria. The successful student is generally one who takes the time to work through as many examples, exercises, and study questions as possible. Therefore, it is useful to assign as many homework problems as possible and point out extra work that may be done. The *Study Guide* that accompanies this text is especially useful for the students studying these chapters.

SUGGESTED DEMONSTRATIONS

1.   Acids, Bases, and Arrhenius
   * Acid-base chemistry can be introduced by performing a reaction such as HCO_3^- or CO_3^{2-} plus acid. For example, show the reaction of an Alka-Seltzer tablet with acid in a petri dish on an overhead projector.
   * Volume 3 of the *Chemical Demonstrations* series by Shakhashiri contains a useful discussion of acid-base chemistry along with 32 demonstrations for this topic. In addition, the videotape, which was prepared by Shakhashiri and which accompanies this text, shows some useful demonstrations.
   * Another source of acid-base demonstrations is L. R. Summerlin and J. L. Ealy, Jr.: *Chemical Demonstrations: A Sourcebook for Teachers, 2nd Edition*, Volume 1, American Chemical Society, 1988.

2.   The Brønsted Concept of Acids and Bases

- The concept of strong and weak acids and bases is a topic introduced early in these lectures. Although the demonstration was done for Chapter 5, we like to show again how conductivity differs for aqueous solutions of strong and weak acids and bases.

3.   Water and the pH Scale

- To demonstrate pH in a large classroom we use a variety of solutions in petri dishes on the overhead projector, adding universal indicator to each one. To show acidic pH's we have used the following: dilute HCl; an aqueous Cu^{2+} or Al^{3+} solution; NH_4Cl; Dry Ice; CO_2 from exhaled breath. For pH's on the basic side: sodium acetate; sodium carbonate; NH_3; dilute NaOH.

4.   The Lewis Concept of Acids and Bases

- The concept of amphoterism is effectively demonstrated by the procedure shown in Figure 17.8. Either $Al(OH)_3$ or $Zn(OH)_2$ works well.

- We find the reaction depicted in Figure 17.7 to be particularly useful to demonstrate.

- Many metal ion/Lewis base complexes can be illustrated in lecture. One of the simplest is the formation of $[Cu(NH_3)_4]^{2+}$, but others would include Prussian blue $[Fe(CN)_6^{4-} + Fe^{3+}]$, the deep red iron(III)-thiocyanate complex, or Ni^{2+} and dimethylglyoxime. Conditions for forming these and other complexes may be found in any qualitative analysis book.

Solutions to Study Questions

17.1   Water can both accept a proton (Brønsted base) and donate a lone pair of electrons (Lewis base). Water can donate a proton (Brønsted acid) but it cannot accept a lone pair of electrons (Lewis acid).

17.2   A species that can behave as an acid or a base. Many metal hydroxides are amphoteric. They act as a Lewis acid when accepting a lone pair of electrons from OH^- to form a water-soluble ion, and as a Brønsted base when reacting with a Brønsted acid to form water.

17.3   The polar $Ni—OH_2$ bonds result in polarized O—H bonds, and the H^+ ion can be removed by H_2O in the reaction of $Ni(H_2O)_6^{2+}$ with H_2O. See page 727.

$$Ni(H_2O)_6^{2+}(aq) + H_2O(\ell) \rightleftharpoons Ni(H_2O)_5(OH)^+(aq) + H_3O^+(aq)$$

17.4   Measure the pH of 0.1 M solutions of the three bases. The solution containing the strongest base will have the largest pH. The solution containing the weakest base will have the lowest pH.

17.5   (a) The increasing acidity as Cl atoms replace H atoms is due to the inductive effect of the Cl atoms. See page 727.

(b) The strongest acid (Cl_3CCO_2H) will have the lowest pH, and the weakest acid (CH_3CO_2H) will have the highest pH.

17.6 H_2SeO_4 should be the stronger acid. In oxoacids, the acid with more oxygen atoms leads to a stronger inductive effect. See page 725. Measure the pH of 0.1 M solutions of the two acids. The solution containing the stronger acid will have the lower pH.

17.7   (a) $HClO_4 + H_2SO_4 \rightarrow ClO_4^- + H_3SO_4^+$

(b) $\overset{\displaystyle :O:}{\underset{\displaystyle :O:}{HO—\overset{||}{\underset{||}{S}}—OH}}$ Sulfuric acid has lone pairs of electrons on all four oxygen atoms that allow it

to act as a proton acceptor (a Brønsted base) or a lone pair donor (a Lewis base).

17.8   Dissolved carbon dioxide gas or dissolved metal ions can cause bottled water to be slightly acidic.

17.9   The possible cation-anion combinations are NaCl (neutral), NaOH (basic), NH_4Cl (acidic), NH_4OH (basic), HCl (acidic), and H_2O (neutral).

A = H^+ solution; B = NH_4^+ solution, C = Na^+ solution, Y = Cl^- solution, Z = OH^- solution

275

17.10   (a) CN^- cyanide ion

        (b) SO_4^{2-} sulfate ion

        (c) F^- fluoride ion

17.11   (a) NH_4^+ ammonium ion

        (b) H_2CO_3 carbonic acid

        (c) HBr hydrobromic acid

17.12   (a) HNO_3 + H_2O → H_3O^+ + NO_3^-

             acid A   base B   conjugate acid of B   conjugate base of A

        (b) HSO_4^- + H_2O → H_3O^+ + SO_4^{2-}

             acid A   base B   conjugate acid of B   conjugate base of A

        (c) H_3O^+ + F^- →   HF   + H_2O

             acid A   base B   conjugate acid of B   conjugate base of A

17.13   (a) $HClO_4$ + H_2O → H_3O^+ + ClO_4^-

             acid A   base B   conjugate acid of B   conjugate base of A

        (b) NH_4^+ + H_2O → NH_3 + H_3O^+

             acid A   base B   conjugate base of A   conjugate acid of B

        (c) HCO_3^- + OH^- → CO_3^{2-} + H_2O

             acid A   base B   conjugate base of A   conjugate acid of B

17.14   Brønsted acid: $HC_2O_4^-(aq) + H_2O(\ell) \rightleftarrows H_3O^+(aq) + C_2O_4^{2-}(aq)$

        Brønsted base: $HC_2O_4^-(aq) + H_2O(\ell) \rightleftarrows H_2C_2O_4(aq) + OH^-(aq)$

17.15   Brønsted acid: $HPO_4^{2-}(aq) + H_2O(\ell) \rightleftarrows H_3O^+(aq) + PO_4^{3-}(aq)$

        Brønsted base: $HPO_4^{2-}(aq) + H_2O(\ell) \rightleftarrows OH^-(aq) + H_2PO_4^-(aq)$

17.16

	Brønsted acid	Brønsted base	conjugate base	conjugate acid
(a)	HCO_2H	H_2O	HCO_2^-	H_3O^+
(b)	H_2S	NH_3	HS^-	NH_4^+
(c)	HSO_4^-	OH^-	SO_4^{2-}	H_2O

17.17

	Brønsted acid	Brønsted base	conjugate base	conjugate acid
(a)	CH_3CO_2H	C_5H_5N	$CH_3CO_2^-$	$C_5H_5NH^+$
(b)	HSO_4^-	N_2H_4	SO_4^{2-}	$N_2H_5^+$
(c)	$[Al(H_2O)_6]^{3+}$	OH^-	$[Al(H_2O)_5(OH)]^{2+}$	H_2O

17.18 $[H_3O^+] = 10^{-pH} = 10^{-3.75} = 1.8 \times 10^{-4}$ M   The solution is acidic (pH < 7)

276

17.19 $[H_3O^+] = 10^{-pH} = 10^{-10.52} = 2.0 \times 10^{-11}$ M

   $[OH^-] = \dfrac{K_w}{[H_3O^+]} = \dfrac{1.0 \times 10^{-14}}{3.0 \times 10^{-11}} = 3.3 \times 10^{-4}$ M   The solution is basic (pH > 7)

17.20   HCl is a strong acid so $[H_3O^+] = [HCl] = 0.0075$ M $pH = -\log[H_3O^+] = -\log(0.0075) = 2.12$

   $[OH^-] = \dfrac{K_w}{[H_3O^+]} = \dfrac{1.0 \times 10^{-14}}{0.0075} = 1.3 \times 10^{-12}$ M

17.21   KOH is a strong base so $[OH^-] = [KOH] = 1.2 \times 10^{-4}$

   $[H_3O^+] = \dfrac{K_w}{[OH^-]} = \dfrac{1.0 \times 10^{-14}}{1.2 \times 10^{-4}} = 8.3 \times 10^{-11}$ M $pH = -\log[H_3O^+] = -\log(8.3 \times 10^{-11}) = 10.08$

17.22 $Ba(OH)_2 \rightarrow Ba^{2+} + 2\ OH^-$ $[OH^-] = 2 \times [Ba(OH)_2] = 0.0030$ M

   $[H_3O^+] = \dfrac{K_w}{[OH^-]} = \dfrac{1.0 \times 10^{-14}}{0.0030} = 3.3 \times 10^{-12}$ M $pH = -\log[H_3O^+] = -\log(3.3 \times 10^{-12}) = 11.48$

17.23   pOH = 14.00 − pH = 3.34

   $[OH^-] = 10^{-pOH} = 10^{-3.34} = 4.6 \times 10^{-4}$ M

   $\dfrac{4.6 \times 10^{-4}\ \text{mol OH}^-}{1\ \text{L}} \cdot 0.125\ \text{L} \cdot \dfrac{1\ \text{mol Ba(OH)}_2}{2\ \text{mol OH}^-} \cdot \dfrac{171.3\ \text{g}}{1\ \text{mol}} = 4.9 \times 10^{-3}$ g

17.24   (a)   The strongest acid is HCO_2H (largest K_a) and the weakest acid is C_6H_5OH (smallest K_a).

   (b)   The strongest acid (HCO_2H) has the weakest conjugate base.

   (c)   The weakest acid (C_6H_5OH) has the strongest conjugate base.

17.25   (a)   The strongest acid is HF (largest K_a) and the weakest acid is HPO_4^{2-} (smallest K_a).

   (b) F^-

   (c)   The strongest acid (HF) has the weakest conjugate base.

   (d)   The weakest acid (HPO_4^{2-}) has the strongest conjugate base.

17.26   (c)   HClO is the weakest acid of the three, so it has the strongest conjugate base.

17.27   (c) SO_4^{2-} is the weakest base of the three, so it has the strongest conjugate acid.

17.28   Potassium carbonate is soluble in water, producing $K^+(aq)$ and $CO_3^{2-}(aq)$

   $CO_3^{2-}(aq) + H_2O(\ell) \rightleftharpoons HCO_3^-(aq) + OH^-(aq)$

17.29   Ammonium bromide is soluble in water, producing $Br^-(aq)$ and $NH_4^+(aq)$.

   $NH_4^+(aq) + H_2O(\ell) \rightleftharpoons H_3O^+(aq) + NH_3(aq)$

17.30 Na^+, $CH_3CO_2^-$, and Cl^- are neutral ions. S^{2-}, PO_4^{3-}, and F^- are basic ions. $H_2PO_4^-$ and Al^{3+} are acidic ions. According to Table 17.3, S^{2-} is most basic. A solution of (a) Na_2S will have the highest pH. According to Table 17.3, $Al(H_2O)_6^{3+}$ is most acidic. A solution of (f) $AlCl_3$ will have the lowest pH.

17.31   (a) $NaNO_3$ Neutral. Neither ion affects the pH of the solution.

         (b) $NaC_7H_5O_2$ Basic. Na^+ has no effect on pH, but $C_7H_5O_2^-$, the conjugate base of the weak acid $HC_7H_5O_2$, makes the solution basic.

         (c) Na_2HPO_4 Basic. Na^+ has no effect on pH, but HPO_4^{2-}, the conjugate base of the weak acid $H_2PO_4^-$, makes the solution basic.

17.32 $pK_a = -\log(K_a) = -\log(6.5 \times 10^{-5}) = 4.19$

17.33 $pK_a = -\log(K_a) = -\log(2.4 \times 10^{-11}) = 10.62$

17.34 $K_a = 10^{-pK_a} = 10^{-9.53} = 3.0 \times 10^{-10}$ The acid is weaker than $Fe(H_2O)_6^{2+}$ and stronger than HCO_3^-

17.35 $K_a = 10^{-pK_a} = 10^{-8.95} = 1.1 \times 10^{-9}$ The acid is weaker than $Co(H_2O)_6^{2+}$ and stronger than $B(OH)_3H_2O$

17.36   The acid with the smaller pK_a has the larger K_a. (b) 2-chlorobenzoic acid is the stronger acid

17.37   Acetic acid $pK_a = -\log(1.8 \times 10^{-5}) = 4.74$

         The acid with the smaller pK_a has the larger K_a. (b) chloroacetic acid is the stronger acid

17.38 $K_b = \dfrac{K_w}{K_a} = \dfrac{1.0 \times 10^{-14}}{1.36 \times 10^{-3}} = 7.4 \times 10^{-12}$

17.39 $K_a = \dfrac{K_w}{K_b} = \dfrac{1.0 \times 10^{-14}}{1.5 \times 10^{-9}} = 6.7 \times 10^{-6}$

17.40 $K_a = 10^{-pK_a} = 10^{-9.80} = 1.6 \times 10^{-10}$ $K_b = \dfrac{K_w}{K_a} = \dfrac{1.0 \times 10^{-14}}{1.6 \times 10^{-10}} = 6.3 \times 10^{-5}$

17.41 $K_a = 10^{-pK_a} = 10^{-3.95} = 1.1 \times 10^{-4}$ $K_b = \dfrac{K_w}{K_a} = \dfrac{1.0 \times 10^{-14}}{1.1 \times 10^{-4}} = 8.9 \times 10^{-11}$

17.42 $CH_3CO_2H(aq) + HCO_3^-(aq) \rightleftharpoons CH_3CO_2^-(aq) + H_2CO_3(aq)$

         $K_a(CH_3CO_2H) > K_a(H_2CO_3)$ The equilibrium will lie predominantly to the right.

17.43 $NH_4^+(aq) + H_2PO_4^-(aq) \rightleftharpoons NH_3(aq) + H_3PO_4(aq)$

         $K_a(H_3PO_4) > K_a(NH_4^+)$ The equilibrium will lie predominantly to the left.

17.44   (a) HBr is a stronger acid than NH_4^+, so the equilibrium lies predominantly to the left.

(b) CH_3CO_2H is a stronger acid than HPO_4^{2-}, so the equilibrium lies predominantly to the left.

(c) $Fe(H_2O)_6^{3+}$ is a stronger acid than H_2CO_3, so the equilibrium lies predominantly to the right.

17.45   (a) H_2S is a stronger acid than HCO_3^-, so the equilibrium lies predominantly to the right.

(b) HSO_4^- is a stronger acid than HCN, so the equilibrium lies predominantly to the left.

(c) HSO_4^- is a stronger acid than CH_3CO_2H, so the equilibrium lies predominantly to the left.

17.46   (a) $OH^-(aq) + HPO_4^{2-}(aq) \rightleftharpoons H_2O(\ell) + PO_4^{3-}(aq)$

(b) The resulting solution should be basic because the significant species remaining in solution upon completion of the reaction is PO_4^{3-}, the conjugate base of a weak acid.

17.47   (a) $H_3O^+(aq) + OCl^-(aq) \rightleftharpoons H_2O(\ell) + HOCl(aq)$

(b) The resulting solution should be acidic because the significant species remaining in solution upon completion of the reaction is HOCl, a weak acid.

17.48   (a) $CH_3CO_2H(aq) + HPO_4^{2-}(aq) \rightleftharpoons CH_3CO_2^-(aq) + H_2PO_4^-(aq)$

(b) CH_3CO_2H is a stronger acid than $H_2PO_4^-$. The equilibrium will lie predominantly to the right. $K_a(H_2PO_4^-) > K_b(CH_3CO_2^-)$ The solution will be slightly acidic.

17.49   (a) $NH_3(aq) + H_2PO_4^-(aq) \rightleftharpoons NH_4^+(aq) + HPO_4^{2-}(aq)$

(b) $H_2PO_4^-$ is a stronger acid than NH_4^+. The equilibrium will lie predominantly to the right. $K_b(HPO_4^{2-}) > K_a(NH_4^+)$ The solution will be slightly basic.

17.50   (a) $[H_3O^+] = 10^{-pH} = 10^{-2.67} = 0.0021$ M

(b)

	HOCN + H$_2$O $\rightleftharpoons$ OCN$^-$	+	H$_3$O$^+$
Initial (M)	0.015	0	0
Change (M)	−0.0021	+0.0021	+0.0021
Equilibrium (M)	0.013	0.0021	0.0021

$$K_a = \frac{[OCN^-][H_3O^+]}{[HOCN]} = \frac{(0.0021)(0.0021)}{0.013} = 3.6 \times 10^{-4}$$

17.51 $[ClCH_2CO_2^-] = [H_3O^+] = 10^{-pH} = 10^{-1.95} = 0.011$ M

$$ClCH_2CO_2H + H_2O \rightleftharpoons ClCH_2CO_2^- + H_3O^+$$

Initial (M)	0.10	0	0
Change (M)	−0.011	+0.011	+0.011
Equilibrium (M)	0.09	0.011	0.011

$$K_a = \frac{[ClCH_2CO_2^-][H_3O^+]}{[ClCH_2CO_2H]} = \frac{(0.011)(0.011)}{0.09} = 1 \times 10^{-3}$$

17.52 $pOH = 14.00 - pH = 4.89$

$[H_3NOH^+] = [OH^-] = 10^{-pOH} = 10^{-4.89} = 1.3 \times 10^{-5}$ M

$$K_b = \frac{[H_3NOH^+][OH^-]}{[H_2NOH]} = \frac{(1.3 \times 10^{-5})(1.3 \times 10^{-5})}{0.025 - 1.3 \times 10^{-5}} = 6.6 \times 10^{-9}$$

17.53 $pOH = 14.00 - pH = 2.30$

$[CH_3NH_3^+] = [OH^-] = 10^{-pOH} = 10^{-2.30} = 0.0050$ M

$$K_b = \frac{[CH_3NH_3^+][OH^-]}{[CH_3NH_2]} = \frac{(0.0050)(0.0050)}{0.065 - 0.0050} = 4.2 \times 10^{-4}$$

17.54 (a) $[H_3O^+] = 10^{-pH} = 10^{-3.80} = 1.6 \times 10^{-4}$ M

$$K_a = \frac{[A^-][H_3O^+]}{[HA]} = \frac{(1.6 \times 10^{-4})(1.6 \times 10^{-4})}{2.5 \times 10^{-3} - 1.6 \times 10^{-4}} = 1.1 \times 10^{-5} \qquad \text{The acid is moderately weak}$$

17.55 (a) $[H_3O^+] = 10^{-pH} = 10^{-10.09} = 8.1 \times 10^{-11}$ M

$$[OH^-] = \frac{K_w}{[H_3O^+]} = 1.2 \times 10^{-4} \text{ M}$$

(b) $K_b = \dfrac{(1.2 \times 10^{-4})(1.2 \times 10^{-4})}{0.015 - 1.2 \times 10^{-4}} = 1.0 \times 10^{-6}$ \qquad The base is moderately weak.

17.56

$$CH_3CO_2H + H_2O \rightleftharpoons CH_3CO_2^- + H_3O^+$$

Initial (M)	0.20	0	0
Change (M)	−x	+x	+x
Equilibrium (M)	0.20 − x	x	x

$$K_a = 1.8 \times 10^{-5} = \frac{[CH_3CO_2^-][H_3O^+]}{[CH_3CO_2H]} = \frac{x^2}{0.20 - x} \qquad \text{Assume that } x \text{ is much smaller than 0.20}$$

$$1.8 \times 10^{-5} = \frac{x^2}{0.20}$$

$x = [CH_3CO_2^-] = [H_3O^+] = 1.9 \times 10^{-3}$ M $\qquad\qquad [CH_3CO_2H] = 0.20$ M

17.57

	$HA + H_2O \rightleftharpoons$		A^-	$+$	H_3O^+
Initial (M)	0.040		0		0
Change (M)	$-x$		$+x$		$+x$
Equilibrium (M)	$0.040 - x$		x		x

$$K_a = 4.0 \times 10^{-9} = \frac{[A^-][H_3O^+]}{[HA]} = \frac{x^2}{0.040 - x}$$ Assume that x is much smaller than 0.040

$$4.0 \times 10^{-9} = \frac{x^2}{0.040}$$

$x = [A^-] = [H_3O^+] = 1.3 \times 10^{-5}$ M $[HA] = 0.040$ M

17.58

	$HCN + H_2O \rightleftharpoons$		CN^-	$+$	H_3O^+
Initial (M)	0.025		0		0
Change (M)	$-x$		$+x$		$+x$
Equilibrium (M)	$0.025 - x$		x		x

$$K_a = 4.0 \times 10^{-10} = \frac{[CN^-][H_3O^+]}{[HCN]} = \frac{x^2}{0.025 - x}$$ Assume that x is much smaller than 0.025

$$4.0 \times 10^{-10} = \frac{x^2}{0.025}$$

$x = [CN^-] = [H_3O^+] = 3.2 \times 10^{-6}$ M $[HCN] = 0.025$ M $pH = -\log[H_3O^+] = 5.50$

17.59 $\dfrac{0.195 \text{ g}}{0.125 \text{ L}} \cdot \dfrac{1 \text{ mol}}{94.11 \text{ g}} = 0.0166$ M C_6H_5OH

	$C_6H_5OH + H_2O \rightleftharpoons$		$C_6H_5O^-$	$+$	H_3O^+
Initial (M)	0.0166		0		0
Change (M)	$-x$		$+x$		$+x$
Equilibrium (M)	$0.0166 - x$		x		x

$$K_a = 1.3 \times 10^{-10} = \frac{[C_6H_5O^-][H_3O^+]}{[C_6H_5OH]} = \frac{x^2}{0.0166 - x}$$ Assume x is much smaller than 0.0166

$$1.3 \times 10^{-10} = \frac{x^2}{0.0166}$$

$x = [H_3O^+] = 1.5 \times 10^{-6}$ M $pH = -\log[H_3O^+] = 5.83$

17.60 $NH_3(aq) + H_2O(\ell) \rightleftharpoons NH_4^+(aq) + OH^-(aq)$

$$K_b = 1.8 \times 10^{-5} = \frac{[NH_4^+][OH^-]}{[NH_3]} = \frac{x^2}{0.15 - x}$$ Assume x is much smaller than 0.15

$$1.8 \times 10^{-5} = \frac{x^2}{0.15}$$

$x = [NH_4^+] = [OH^-] = 0.0016$ M $[NH_3] = 0.15$ M

$pOH = -\log[OH^-] = 2.78$ $pH = 14.00 - pOH = 11.22$

17.61 $B(aq) + H_2O(\ell) \rightleftharpoons BH^+(aq) + OH^-(aq)$

$K_b = 5.0 \times 10^{-4} = \dfrac{[BH^+][OH^-]}{[B]} = \dfrac{x^2}{0.15 - x}$

The assumption $x \ll [B]_{initial}$ is not valid. Solve using the quadratic equation.

$x = [BH^+] = [OH^-] = 8.4 \times 10^{-3}$ M $[B] = 0.15 - x = 0.14$ M

17.62 $K_b = 4.2 \times 10^{-4} = \dfrac{[CH_3NH_3^+][OH^-]}{[CH_3NH_2]} = \dfrac{x^2}{0.25 - x}$ Assume x is much smaller than 0.25

$4.2 \times 10^{-4} = \dfrac{x^2}{0.25}$

$x = [OH^-] = 0.010$ M $pOH = -\log[OH^-] = 1.99$ $pH = 14.00 - pOH = 12.01$

17.63 $K_b = 4.0 \times 10^{-10} = \dfrac{[C_6H_5NH_3^+][OH^-]}{[C_6H_5NH_2]} = \dfrac{x^2}{0.12 - x} \approx \dfrac{x^2}{0.12}$

$x = [OH^-] = 6.9 \times 10^{-6}$ M $pOH = -\log[OH^-] = 5.16$ $pH = 14.00 - pOH = 8.84$

17.64 $HF(aq) + H_2O(\ell) \rightleftharpoons H_3O^+(aq) + F^-(aq)$

$K_a = 7.2 \times 10^{-4} = \dfrac{[F^-][H_3O^+]}{[HF]} = \dfrac{x^2}{0.0010 - x}$

The assumption $x \ll [HF]_{initial}$ is not valid. Solve using the quadratic equation.

$x = [H_3O^+] = 5.6 \times 10^{-4}$ M $pH = -\log[H_3O^+] = 3.25$

17.65 $HF(aq) + H_2O(\ell) \rightleftharpoons H_3O^+(aq) + F^-(aq)$

$[F^-] = [H_3O^+] = 10^{-pH} = 10^{-2.30} = 0.0050$ M

$K_a = 7.2 \times 10^{-4} = \dfrac{[F^-][H_3O^+]}{[HF]} = \dfrac{(0.0050)^2}{x}$

$x = [HF] = 0.035$ M

$[HF]_{initial} = 0.035$ M $+ 0.0050$ M $= 0.040$ M

17.66 $NH_4^+(aq) + H_2O(\ell) \rightleftharpoons NH_3(aq) + H_3O^+(aq)$ $K_a = \dfrac{K_w}{K_b} = \dfrac{1.0 \times 10^{-14}}{1.8 \times 10^{-5}} = 5.6 \times 10^{-10}$

$5.6 \times 10^{-10} = \dfrac{[NH_3][H_3O^+]}{[NH_4^+]} = \dfrac{x^2}{0.20 - x} \approx \dfrac{x^2}{0.20}$

$x = [H_3O^+] = 1.1 \times 10^{-5}$ M $pH = -\log[H_3O^+] = 4.98$

17.67 $HCO_2^-(aq) + H_2O(\ell) \rightleftharpoons HCO_2H(aq) + OH^-(aq)$ $K_b = \dfrac{K_w}{K_a} = \dfrac{1.0 \times 10^{-14}}{1.8 \times 10^{-4}} = 5.6 \times 10^{-11}$

$5.6 \times 10^{-11} = \dfrac{[HCO_2H][OH^-]}{[HCO_2^-]} = \dfrac{x^2}{0.015 - x} \approx \dfrac{x^2}{0.015}$

$x = [OH^-] = 9.1 \times 10^{-7}$ M $[H_3O^+] = \dfrac{K_w}{[OH^-]} = 1.1 \times 10^{-8}$ M $pH = -\log[H_3O^+] = 7.96$

17.68 $[CN^-]_{initial} = \dfrac{10.8\ g}{0.500\ L} \cdot \dfrac{1\ mol\ NaCN}{49.01\ g} = 0.441\ M$

$CN^-(aq) + H_2O(\ell) \rightleftharpoons HCN(aq) + OH^-(aq)$ $K_b = \dfrac{K_w}{K_a} = \dfrac{1.0 \times 10^{-14}}{4.0 \times 10^{-10}} = 2.5 \times 10^{-5}$

$2.5 \times 10^{-5} = \dfrac{[HCN][OH^-]}{[CN^-]} = \dfrac{x^2}{0.441 - x} \approx \dfrac{x^2}{0.441}$

$x = [HCN] = [OH^-] = 0.0033\ M$ $[H_3O^+] = \dfrac{K_w}{[OH^-]} = 3.0 \times 10^{-12}$ $[CN^-] = [Na^+] = 0.441\ M$

17.69 $CH_3CH_2CO_2^-(aq) + H_2O(\ell) \rightleftharpoons CH_3CH_2CO_2H(aq) + OH^-(aq)$ $K_b = \dfrac{1.0 \times 10^{-14}}{1.3 \times 10^{-5}} = 7.7 \times 10^{-10}$

$7.7 \times 10^{-10} = \dfrac{[CH_3CH_2CO_2H][OH^-]}{[CH_3CH_2CO_2^-]} = \dfrac{x^2}{0.10 - x} \approx \dfrac{x^2}{0.10}$

$x = [CH_3CH_2CO_2H] = [OH^-] = 8.8 \times 10^{-6}\ M$

$pOH = -\log[OH^-] = 5.06$ $pH = 14.00 - pOH = 8.94$ $[H_3O^+] = 10^{-pH} = 1.1 \times 10^{-9}\ M$

17.70 $CH_3CO_2H(aq) + OH^-(aq) \rightarrow CH_3CO_2^-(aq) + H_2O(\ell)$

$(0.0220\ L\ CH_3CO_2H)(0.15\ mol/L) = 0.0033\ mol\ CH_3CO_2H$

$(0.0220\ L\ NaOH)(0.15\ mol/L) = 0.0033\ mol\ NaOH$

$0.0033\ mol\ CH_3CO_2H \cdot \dfrac{1\ mol\ CH_3CO_2^-}{1\ mol\ CH_3CO_2H} = 0.0033\ mol\ CH_3CO_2^-$

$[CH_3CO_2^-] = \dfrac{0.0033\ mol}{(0.0220 + 0.0220)\ L} = 0.075\ M$

$CH_3CO_2^-(aq) + H_2O(\ell) \rightleftharpoons CH_3CO_2H(aq) + OH^-(aq)$

$K_b = 5.6 \times 10^{-10} = \dfrac{[CH_3CO_2H][OH^-]}{[CH_3CO_2^-]} = \dfrac{x^2}{0.075 - x} \approx \dfrac{x^2}{0.075}$

$x = [OH^-] = 6.5 \times 10^{-6}\ M$ $[H_3O^+] = \dfrac{K_w}{[OH^-]} = 1.5 \times 10^{-9}$ $pH = -\log[H_3O^+] = 8.81$

17.71 $NH_3(aq) + H_3O^+(aq) \rightarrow NH_4^+(aq) + H_2O(\ell)$

$(0.0500\ L\ NH_3)(0.40\ mol/L) = 0.020\ mol\ NH_3$

$(0.0500\ L\ HCl)(0.40\ mol/L) = 0.020\ mol\ HCl$

$0.020\ mol\ NH_3 \cdot \dfrac{1\ mol\ NH_4^+}{1\ mol\ NH_3} = 0.020\ mol\ NH_4^+$

$[NH_4^+] = \dfrac{0.020\ mol}{(0.0500 + 0.0500)\ L} = 0.20\ M$

$NH_4^+(aq) + H_2O(\ell) \rightleftharpoons NH_3(aq) + H_3O^+(aq)$

$K_a = 5.6 \times 10^{-10} = \dfrac{[NH_3][H_3O^+]}{[NH_4^+]} = \dfrac{x^2}{0.20 - x} \approx \dfrac{x^2}{0.20}$

$x = [H_3O^+] = 1.1 \times 10^{-5}\ M$ $pH = -\log[H_3O^+] = 4.98$

17.72 (a) $pH > 7$ The predominant ion in solution will be $CH_3CO_2^-$, a weak base.

(b) $pH < 7$ The predominant ion in solution will be NH_4^+, a weak acid.

(c) $pH = 7$ Equimolar amounts of strong acid and strong base result in a neutral solution.

17.73 (a) $pH = 7$ Equimolar amounts of strong acid and strong base result in a neutral solution.

(b) $pH > 7$ The predominant ion in solution will be HCO_2^-, a weak base.

(c) $pH > 7$ The predominant ion in solution will be $C_2O_4^{2-}$, a weak base.

17.72 The pH of the solution is determined by the first ionization of the acid.

$$H_2SO_3(aq) + H_2O(\ell) \rightleftharpoons HSO_3^-(aq) + H_3O^+(aq) \qquad\qquad K_{a1} = 1.2 \times 10^{-2}$$

(a) $1.2 \times 10^{-2} = \dfrac{[HSO_3^-][H_3O^+]}{[H_2SO_3]} = \dfrac{x^2}{0.45 - x}$

The approximation $x \ll 0.45$ is not valid. Solve using the quadratic equation.

$x = [H_3O^+] = 0.0677\ M$ $\qquad\qquad$ $pH = -\log[H_3O^+] = 1.17$

(b) $[SO_3^{2-}] = K_{a2} = 6.2 \times 10^{-8}\ M$

17.75 The pH of the solution is determined by the first ionization of the acid.

$$C_6H_8O_6(aq) + H_2O(\ell) \rightleftharpoons C_6H_7O_6^-(aq) + H_3O^+(aq)$$

$\dfrac{0.0050\ g}{0.0010\ L} \cdot \dfrac{1\ mol}{176\ g} = 0.028\ M$

$K_{a1} = 6.8 \times 10^{-5} = \dfrac{[C_6H_7O_6^-][H_3O^+]}{[C_6H_8O_6]} = \dfrac{x^2}{0.028 - x} \approx \dfrac{x^2}{0.028}$

$x = [H_3O^+] = 1.4 \times 10^{-3}\ M$ $\qquad\qquad$ $pH = -\log[H_3O^+] = 2.86$

17.76 The pH of the solution is determined by the first ionization of the base.

$$N_2H_4(aq) + H_2O(\ell) \rightleftharpoons N_2H_5^+(aq) + OH^-(aq)$$

(a) $K_{b1} = 8.5 \times 10^{-7} = \dfrac{[N_2H_5^+][OH^-]}{[N_2H_4]} = \dfrac{x^2}{0.010 - x} \approx \dfrac{x^2}{0.010}$

$x = [N_2H_5^+] = [OH^-] = 9.2 \times 10^{-5}\ M$ $\qquad\qquad$ $[N_2H_6^{2+}] = K_{b2} = 8.9 \times 10^{-16}$

(b) $pOH = -\log[OH^-] = 4.04$ $\qquad$ $pH = 14.00 - pOH = 9.96$

17.77 The pH of the solution is determined by the first ionization.

$$H_2NCH_2CH_2NH_2(aq) + H_2O(\ell) \rightleftharpoons H_2NCH_2CH_2NH_3^+(aq) + OH^-(aq)$$

$K_{b1} = 8.5 \times 10^{-5} = \dfrac{[H_2NCH_2CH_2NH_3^+][OH^-]}{[H_2NCH_2CH_2NH_2]} = \dfrac{x^2}{0.15 - x} \approx \dfrac{x^2}{0.15}$

$x = [OH^-] = 3.6 \times 10^{-3}\ M$ $\qquad\qquad$ $[H_3NCH_2CH_2NH_3^{2+}] = K_{b2} = 2.7 \times 10^{-8}\ M$

17.78 (a) H_2NOH is a Lewis base

(b) Fe^{2+} is a Lewis acid

(c) CH_3NH_2 is a Lewis base

17.79   (a) BCl_3 is a Lewis acid.

      (b) H_2NNH_2 is a Lewis base.

      (c) Ag^+ is a Lewis acid, NH_3 is a Lewis base

17.80 $:C{\equiv}O:$ is a Lewis base in its complexes with Fe, Ni, and other transition metals.

17.81 BH_3 is a Lewis acid

17.82   HOCN should be a stronger acid than HCN because the H atom in HOCN is attached to a highly electronegative O atom. This induces a positive charge on the H atom, making it more readily removed by an interaction with water.

17.83   The ion with the more highly charged metal ion, $V(H_2O)_6^{3+}$, should be the stronger acid.

17.84   The S atom is surrounded by four highly electronegative O atoms. The inductive effect of these atoms induces a positive charge on the H atom, making it susceptible to removal by water.

17.85   Ethylenediamine can act as a proton acceptor (Brønsted base) and an electron pair donor (Lewis base).

17.86 $[HC_9H_7O_4] = \dfrac{2(0.325\ g)}{0.225\ L} \cdot \dfrac{1\ mol}{180.2\ g} = 0.0160\ M$

$K_a = 3.27 \times 10^{-4} = \dfrac{[C_9H_7O_4^-][H_3O^+]}{[HC_9H_7O_4]} = \dfrac{x^2}{0.0160 - x}$

The assumption $x \ll 0.160$ is not valid. Solve using the quadratic equation.

$x = [H_3O^+] = 2.13 \times 10^{-3}\ M$ $pH = -\log[H_3O^+] = 2.671$

17.87   (a) NH_4^+ might lead to an acidic solution, CO_3^{2-} and S^{2-} might lead to a basic solution in water

      (b) Br^- and ClO_4^- have no effect on the pH of a solution.

      (c) S^{2-} is the strongest base.

      (d) $CO_3^{2-}(aq) + H_2O(\ell) \rightleftharpoons HCO_3^-(aq) + OH^-(aq)$

          $S^{2-}(aq) + H_2O(\ell) \rightleftharpoons HS^-(aq) + OH^-(aq)$

17.88   Benzoic acid is the weaker acid so its solution will have the higher pH.

17.89   (a) $(CH_3)_3NH^+ < ClC_6H_4CO_2H < BrCH_2CO_2H$

          —increasing acid strength$\rightarrow$

      (b) $BrCH_2CO_2H < ClC_6H_4CO_2H < (CH_3)_3NH^+$

          —increasing pH$\rightarrow$

17.90 $H_2S(aq) + CH_3CO_2^-(aq) \rightleftharpoons HS^-(aq) + CH_3CO_2H(aq)$

CH_3CO_2H is a stronger acid than H_2S so the equilibrium will lie predominantly towards reactants.

17.91   (a) HCO_3^- is a weaker acid than HSO_4^-, so the equilibrium lies predominantly to the left.

         (c) HSO_4^- is a stronger acid than CH_3CO_2H, so the equilibrium lies predominantly to the right.

         (d) $Co(H_2O)_6^{2+}$ is a weaker acid than CH_3CO_2H, so the equilibrium lies predominantly to the left.

17.92 $K_a = 1.3 \times 10^{-3} = \dfrac{[X^-][H_3O^+]}{[HX]} = \dfrac{x^2}{0.010 - x}$

The assumption $x << 0.010$ is not valid. Solve using the quadratic equation.

$x = [H_3O^+] = 3.0 \times 10^{-3}$ M $[HX] = 0.010 - x = 0.007$ M $pH = -\log[H_3O^+] = 2.52$

17.93 $[OH^-] = \dfrac{0.50 \text{ g}}{1.0 \text{ L}} \cdot \dfrac{1 \text{ mol Ca(OH)}_2}{74.1 \text{ g}} \cdot \dfrac{2 \text{ mol OH}^-}{1 \text{ mol Ca(OH)}_2} = 0.013$ M

$pOH = -\log[OH^-] = 1.87$ $pH = 14.00 - pOH = 12.13$

17.94 $[H_3O^+] = 10^{-pH} = 10^{-3.44} = 3.6 \times 10^{-4}$ M

$K_a = \dfrac{[H_3O^+]^2}{[m\text{-nitrophenol}]} = \dfrac{(3.6 \times 10^{-4})^2}{0.010 - 3.6 \times 10^{-4}} = 1.4 \times 10^{-5}$ $pK_a = -\log(K_a) = 4.86$

17.95   (a) $K_b = \dfrac{K_w}{K_a} = \dfrac{1.0 \times 10^{-14}}{2.3 \times 10^{-11}} = 4.3 \times 10^{-4}$

         (b)   The acid is placed directly below $Ni(H_2O)_6^{2+}$. HPO_4^{2-} is a weaker acid than $C_4H_9NH_3^+$. PO_4^{3-} is a stronger base than $C_4H_9NH_2$.

         (c) $K_a = 2.3 \times 10^{-11} = \dfrac{[C_4H_9NH_2][H_3O^+]}{[C_4H_9NH_3^+]} = \dfrac{x^2}{0.015 - x} \approx \dfrac{x^2}{0.015}$

             $x = [H_3O^+] = 5.9 \times 10^{-7}$ M $pH = -\log[H_3O^+] = 6.23$

17.96 $K_a = 10^{-pK_a} = 10^{-8.85} = 1.4 \times 10^{-9}$

$HC_{13}H_{20}N_2O_2^+(aq) + H_2O(\ell) \rightleftharpoons H_3O^+(aq) + C_{13}H_{20}N_2O_2(aq)$

$1.4 \times 10^{-9} = \dfrac{[C_{13}H_{20}N_2O_2][H_3O^+]}{[HC_{13}H_{20}N_2O_2^+]} = \dfrac{x^2}{0.0015 - x} \approx \dfrac{x^2}{0.0015}$

$x = [H_3O^+] = 1.4 \times 10^{-6}$ M $pH = -\log[H_3O^+] = 5.84$

17.97 $K_a = 10^{-pK_a} = 10^{-4.60} = 2.5 \times 10^{-5}$

$C_6H_5NH_3^+(aq) + H_2O(\ell) \rightleftharpoons H_3O^+(aq) + C_6H_5NH_2(aq)$

$2.5 \times 10^{-5} = \dfrac{[C_6H_5NH_2][H_3O^+]}{[C_6H_5NH_3^+]} = \dfrac{x^2}{0.080 - x} \approx \dfrac{x^2}{0.080}$

$x = [H_3O^+] = 0.0014$ M $pH = -\log[H_3O^+] = 2.85$

17.98   (a) The ethylamine solution will have a higher pH because it is a stronger base (larger K_b value).

   (b) $K_b = 4.3 \times 10^{-4} = \dfrac{[CH_3CH_2NH_3^+][OH^-]}{[CH_3CH_2NH_2]} = \dfrac{x^2}{0.10 - x} \approx \dfrac{x^2}{0.10}$

   $x = [OH^-] = 0.0066\ M$ \qquad $pOH = -\log[OH^-] = 2.18$ \qquad $pH = 14.00 - pOH = 11.82$

17.99 $ClCH_2CO_2H(aq) + H_2O(\ell) \rightleftharpoons ClCH_2CO_2^-(aq) + H_3O^+(aq)$

   $[ClCH_2CO_2H] = \dfrac{0.0945\ g}{0.125\ L} \cdot \dfrac{1\ mol}{94.50\ g} = 0.00800\ M$

   $K_a = 1.40 \times 10^{-3} = \dfrac{[ClCH_2CO_2^-][H_3O^+]}{[ClCH_2CO_2H]} = \dfrac{x^2}{0.00800 - x}$

   The approximation $x \ll 0.00800$ is not valid. Solve using the quadratic equation.

   $x = [H_3O^+] = 2.72 \times 10^{-3}\ M$ \qquad $pH = -\log[H_3O^+] = 2.566$

17.100 $C_5H_5NH^+(aq) + H_2O(\ell) \rightleftharpoons H_3O^+(aq) + C_5H_5N(aq)$

   $K_b(C_5H_5N) = 1.5 \times 10^{-9}$ \qquad $K_a(C_5H_5NH^+) = \dfrac{K_w}{K_b} = 6.7 \times 10^{-6}$

   $K_a = 6.7 \times 10^{-6} = \dfrac{[C_5H_5N][H_3O^+]}{[C_5H_5NH^+]} = \dfrac{x^2}{0.025 - x} \approx \dfrac{x^2}{0.025}$

   $x = [H_3O^+] = 4.1 \times 10^{-4}\ M$ \qquad $pH = -\log[H_3O^+] = 3.39$

17.101 $C_7H_4NO_3S^-(aq) + H_2O(\ell) \rightleftharpoons HC_7H_4NO_3S(aq) + OH^-(aq)$

   $K_a = 10^{-pK_a} = 10^{-2.32} = 4.8 \times 10^{-3}$ \qquad $K_b = \dfrac{K_w}{K_a} = 2.1 \times 10^{-12}$

   $2.1 \times 10^{-12} = \dfrac{[HC_7H_4NO_3S][OH^-]}{[C_7H_4NO_3S^-]} = \dfrac{x^2}{0.10 - x} \approx \dfrac{x^2}{0.10}$

   $x = [OH^-] = 4.6 \times 10^{-7}\ M$ \qquad $pOH = -\log[OH^-] = 6.34$ \qquad $pH = 14.00 - pOH = 7.66$

17.102   (a) pH < 7 HSO_4^- is weak acid \qquad (f) pH = 7 Both are neutral ions

   (b) pH < 7 NH_4^+ is a weak acid \qquad (g) pH > 7 HPO_4^- is a weak base

   (c) pH = 7 Both are neutral ions \qquad (h) pH = 7 Both are neutral ions

   (d) pH > 7 CO_3^{2-} is a weak base \qquad (i) pH < 7 $Fe(H_2O)_6^{3+}$ is a weak acid

   (e) pH > 7 $K_b(S^{2-}) > K_a(NH_4^+)$

17.103   (i)   (d) 0.1 M CH_3CO_2H and (e) 0.1 M NH_4Cl are acidic solutions

   (ii) (a) 0.1 M NH_3, (b) 0.1 M Na_2CO_3, and (f) 0.1 M $NaCH_3CO_2$ are basic solutions

   (iii) (d) CH_3CO_2H is a stronger acid than NH_4^+

17.104 $HCl < NH_4Cl < NaCl < NaCH_3CO_2 < KOH$

   —increasing pH→

17.105 $[C_6H_4NO_2^+] = [H_3O^+] = 10^{-pH} = 10^{-2.70} = 2.0 \times 10^{-3}$ M

$$[C_6H_5NO_2] = \frac{1.0 \text{ g}}{0.060 \text{ L}} \cdot \frac{1 \text{ mol}}{123.1 \text{ g}} = 0.14 \text{ M}$$

$$K_a = \frac{[C_6H_4NO_2^+][H_3O^+]}{[C_6H_5NO_2]} = \frac{(2.0 \times 10^{-3})^2}{0.14 - 2.0 \times 10^{-3}} = 3.0 \times 10^{-5}$$

17.106 $K_{net} = K_{a1}K_{a2} = (5.9 \times 10^{-2})(6.4 \times 10^{-5}) = 3.8 \times 10^{-6}$

17.107   The pH of the solution is determined by the first ionization of the base.

$$K_{b1} = 7.0 \times 10^{-7} = \frac{[NicH^+][OH^-]}{[Nic]} = \frac{x^2}{0.020 - x} \approx \frac{x^2}{0.020}$$

$x = [OH^-] = 1.2 \times 10^{-4}$ M $pOH = -\log[OH^-] = 3.93$ $pH = 14.00 - pOH = 10.07$

17.108   (a)   The $CH_3C_5H_4NH^+$ solution would have the highest pH (smallest K_a value, weakest conjugate acid). The $NO_2C_5H_4NH^+$ solution would have the lowest pH (largest K_a value, strongest conjugate acid).

(b)   The strongest conjugate acid ($NO_2C_5H_4NH^+$) has the weakest Brønsted base ($NO_2C_5H_4N$). The weakest conjugate acid ($CH_3C_5H_4NH^+$) has the strongest Brønsted base ($CH_3C_5H_4N$).

17.109 $HCO_2H(aq) + H_2O(\ell) \rightleftharpoons HCO_2^-(aq) + H_3O^+(aq)$ $K_a = 1.8 \times 10^{-4}$

$OH^-(aq) + H_3O^+(aq) \rightleftharpoons 2 H_2O(\ell)$ $K = 1/K_w$

$HCO_2H(aq) + OH^-(aq) \rightleftharpoons H_2O(\ell) + HCO_2^-(aq)$ $K = (1.8 \times 10^{-4})/K_w = 1.8 \times 10^{10}$

17.110 $NH_3(aq) + H_2O(\ell) \rightleftharpoons NH_4^+(aq) + OH^-(aq)$ $K_b = 1.8 \times 10^{-5}$

$OH^-(aq) + H_3O^+(aq) \rightleftharpoons 2 H_2O(\ell)$ $K = 1/K_w$

$NH_3(aq) + H_3O^+(aq) \rightleftharpoons H_2O(\ell) + NH_4^+(aq)$ $K = (1.8 \times 10^{-5})/K_w = 1.8 \times 10^9$

17.111   (a) $NH_4^+(aq) + H_2O(\ell) \rightleftharpoons NH_3(aq) + H_3O^+(aq)$ $K_1 = K_w/K_b$

$CN^-(aq) + H_2O(\ell) \rightleftharpoons HCN(aq) + OH^-(aq)$ $K_2 = K_w/K_a$

$H_3O^+(aq) + OH^-(aq) \rightleftharpoons 2 H_2O(\ell)$ $K_3 = 1/K_w$

$NH_4^+(aq) + CN^-(aq) \rightleftharpoons NH_3(aq) + HCN(aq)$ $K_{total} = K_1K_2K_3 = \dfrac{K_w}{K_aK_b}$

(b)   From the ionization of the ammonium ion we can write the equation

$$[H_3O^+] = \frac{K_a[NH_4^+]}{[NH_3]} = \frac{\frac{K_w}{K_b}[NH_4^+]}{[NH_3]}$$

From the ionization of HCN we can write the equation $[H_3O^+] = \dfrac{K_a[HCN]}{[CN^-]}$

Combine these two equations into an expression for $[H_3O^+]^2$:

$$[H_3O^+]^2 = \frac{\dfrac{K_w}{K_b}[NH_4^+]}{[NH_3]} \cdot \frac{K_a[HCN]}{[CN^-]}$$

In any solution of NH_4CN, $[NH_4^+] = [CN^-]$ and $[HCN] = [NH_3]$. The equation for $[H_3O^+]^2$ can be simplified to

$$[H_3O^+]^2 = \frac{K_w K_a}{K_b} \text{ and } [H_3O^+] = \sqrt{\frac{K_w K_a}{K_b}}$$

(c) $[H_3O^+] = \sqrt{\dfrac{K_w K_a}{K_b}} = \sqrt{\dfrac{(1.0 \times 10^{-14})(4.0 \times 10^{-10})}{1.8 \times 10^{-5}}} = 4.7 \times 10^{-10}$ M

$pH = -\log[H_3O^+] = 9.33$

17.112 (a) Acid strength increases as pK_a decreases, so chloroacetic acid is the strongest acid.

(b) The strongest conjugate base will come from the weakest acid, the benzylammonium ion.

(c) benzylammonium ion < conjugate acid of cocaine < benzoic acid < thioacetic acid < chloroacetic acid

17.113 $[A]_1$ = initial concentration of weak acid in original solution

$[A]_2$ = initial concentration of weak acid in diluted solution

$[H_3O^+]_1$ = equilibrium hydronium ion concentration in original solution

$[H_3O^+]_2$ = equilibrium hydronium ion concentration in diluted solution

If the fraction ionized doubles, then $[H_3O^+]_2 = 2 \cdot [H_3O^+]_1$

Because $K \approx \dfrac{[H_3O^+]^2}{[HA]_{initial}}$

$$\frac{[H_3O^+]_1^2}{[A]_1} = \frac{[H_3O^+]_2^2}{[A]_2}$$

$$\frac{[H_3O^+]_1^2}{[A]_1} = \frac{(2 \cdot [H_3O^+]_1)^2}{[A]_2}$$

$$\frac{[A]_2}{[A]_1} = 4$$

In order to double the percent ionization of the acid, you must dilute 100 mL of solution to 400 mL.

17.114 (a) BF_3 is a Lewis acid, $(CH_3)_2O$ is a Lewis base

(b) $P_{(CH_3)_2OBF_3} = \dfrac{nRT}{V} = \dfrac{\left(0.100 \text{ g} \cdot \dfrac{1 \text{ mol}}{113.9 \text{ g}}\right)(0.082057 \text{ L} \cdot \text{atm/K} \cdot \text{mol})(298 \text{ K})}{0.565 \text{ L}} = 0.0380$ atm

$K_P = 0.17 = \dfrac{P_{BF_3}P_{(CH_3)_2O}}{P_{(CH_3)_2OBF_3}} = \dfrac{x^2}{0.0380 - x}$

Solve using the quadratic equation

$x = P_{BF_3} = P_{(CH_3)_2O} = 0.032$ atm $P_{(CH_3)_2OBF_3} = 0.0380 - x = 0.006$ atm

$P_{total} = 0.032 \text{ atm} + 0.032 \text{ atm} + 0.006 \text{ atm} = 0.0700$ atm

17.115 (a)

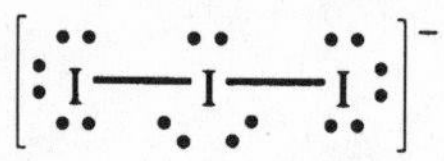

$$\left[:\ddot{I}—\ddot{I}—\ddot{I}: \right]^{-}$$

(b) $I^-(aq)$ + $I_2(aq)$ → $I_3^-(aq)$

Lewis base   Lewis acid

17.116 $H_2NC_6H_4SO_3^-(aq) + H_2O(\ell) \rightleftharpoons H_2NC_6H_4SO_3H(aq) + OH^-(aq)$

$K_a = 10^{-pK_a} = 10^{-3.23} = 5.9 \times 10^{-4}$ $K_b = \dfrac{K_w}{K_a} = 1.7 \times 10^{-11}$

$\dfrac{1.25\ g}{0.125\ L} \cdot \dfrac{1\ mol}{195.2\ g} = 0.0512\ M$

$1.7 \times 10^{-11} = \dfrac{x^2}{0.0512 - x} \approx \dfrac{x^2}{0.0512}$

$x = [OH^-] = 9.3 \times 10^{-7}\ M$ $pOH = -\log[OH^-] = 6.03$ $pH = 14.00 - pH = 7.97$

17.117 (a) 5.75×10^{-14}

(b) $[H_3O^+] = (K_w)^{1/2} = 2.40 \times 10^{-7}\ M$ $pH = 6.62$

(c) smaller

(d) At 5 °C, neutral pH is 7.35 so a solution with pH 7.00 is acidic.

17.118 (a) $HF(aq) + NO_2^-(aq) \rightleftharpoons F^-(aq) + HNO_2(aq)$

HF is slightly stronger than HNO_2 (NO_2^- is a stronger base than F^-) so the reaction is slightly product-favored.

(b) HCO_2^- is a stronger base than NO_2^-.

(c) HF is a much stronger acid than NH_4^+. The reaction will be product-favored.

17.119 (a) 4.78 As [NH_4Cl] increases, pH decreases. When [NH_4Cl] doubles, the pH decreases by 0.15.

(b) pH increases. Na^+ is a neutral cation that does not affect pH. NH_4^+ is an acidic cation.

(c) A C_5H_5NHCl solution has the lowest pH and a NaCN solution has the highest pH.

Chapter 18
Principles of Reactivity:
Other Aspects of Aqueous Equilibria

INSTRUCTOR'S NOTES

As described in the previous chapter, this chapter combines the common ion effect, buffers, acid-base titrations, and the solubility of ionic compounds. It is an extension of the concepts introduced in Chapter 17. As noted there we usually plan on about 9 lectures for all of the material on aqueous equilibria, with about five of those assigned to this chapter.

SUGGESTED DEMONSTRATIONS

1.   The Common Ion Effect

   - See "Effect of Acetate Ion on the Acidity of Acetic Acid: Common Ion Effect" in the third volume of *Chemical Demonstrations* by Shakhashiri.

2.   Buffer Solutions

   - "Buffering Action and Capacity" in the third volume of *Chemical Demonstrations* by Shakhashiri.

3.   The Solubility Product constant, K_{sp}

   - There are many demonstrations that can be done for this topic. To begin the lectures, we bring some mineral samples to class to show how many common minerals are really insoluble salts whose behavior in water can be treated by the methods of this chapter.

   - Volume 1 of the demonstration books by Shakhashiri contains a number of demonstrations involving insoluble salts. (Many also involve the dissolution of precipitates using complex ion formation.)

4.   Solubility and the Common Ion Effect

   - The photograph in Figure 18.11 that illustrates the common ion effect was not difficult to set up. Silver acetate was freshly precipitated. After washing with water, distilled water was added, the mixture was shaken vigorously, and the test tube was allowed to stand for some time. On adding $AgNO_3$, more silver acetate is clearly precipitated.

5.   Solubility, Ion Separations, and Qualitative Analysis

   - See Chirpich, T. P. "A simple vivid demonstration of selective precipitation," *Journal of Chemical Education* **1988**, *65*, 359.

Solutions to Study Questions

18.1   Test the pH of the solution. If the pH is less than 7, some acid remains.

18.2   (a) pH < 7 The solution will contain the conjugate acid of the weak base.

(b) pH = 7 The solution will contain neutral ions.

(c) pH > 7 The solution will contain the conjugate base of the weak acid.

18.3   The strong acid (H_3O^+) is consumed completely in a reaction with the weak base present in the buffer.

$$H_3O^+(aq) + NH_3(aq) \rightarrow NH_4^+(aq) + H_2O(\ell)$$

18.4   The pH changes over a large value at the equivalence point. Therefore, we only need a dye that changes color somewhere in the pH range of the equivalence point.

18.5   See Figure 18.4 (page 751) and Figure 18.7 (page 757).

18.6   The strong base (OH^-) is consumed completely in a reaction with the weak acid present in the buffer.

$$OH^-(aq) + CH_3CO_2H(aq) \rightarrow CH_3CO_2^-(aq) + H_2O(\ell)$$

18.7 $$pH = pK_a + \log\frac{[\text{conjugate base}]}{[\text{acid}]}$$

(a) If K_a increases, pK_a decreases. Therefore, the pH should decrease.

(b) If [acid] decreases, the ratio [conjugate base]/[acid] will increase. The log term will increase, so the pH should increase. (In order words, as the conjugate base concentration increases, the solution will become more basic, and the pH increases.)

18.8   Solids to not appear in equilibrium constant expressions. Solid concentration is not changed either by reaction or by addition or removal of some solid.

18.9   The expression for the reaction quotient is the same as the expression used for the equilibrium constant. $Q = [Ag^+][Cl^-]$ $K_{sp} = [Ag^+][Cl^-]$ However, the concentrations used in the reaction quotient expression may or may not be those at equilibrium.

18.10   (a) $BaCrO_4(s) \rightleftharpoons Ba^{2+}(aq) + CrO_4^{2-}(aq)$ $K_{sp} = 1.2 \times 10^{-10}$

$AgBr(s) \rightleftharpoons Ag^+(aq) + Br^-(aq)$ $K_{sp} = 5.4 \times 10^{-13}$

(b) $K_{sp}(BaCrO_4) = [Ba^{2+}][CrO_4^{2-}]$ $K_{sp}(AgBr) = [Ag^+][Br^-]$

18.11   A saturated solution of CaF_2 is one in which no additional solid dissolves. The concentrations of Ca^{2+} and F^- will not increase further, and any additional solid added will simply remain as a solid at the bottom of the beaker. $Q = K_{sp}$ An unsaturated solution is one with concentrations of Ca^{2+} and F^- that are less than that of a saturated solution. $Q < K_{sp}$ A supersaturated solution is one in which there is more dissolved CaF_2 than the amount in a saturated solution. $Q > K_{sp}$

18.12   The common ion effect is the addition of an ion common to an equilibrium system. For example, adding NaOH to a saturated solution of $Fe(OH)_2$ will decrease the solubility of the solid by shifting the equilibrium back towards $Fe(OH)_2$ formation.

18.13   When Ag_3PO_4 dissolves slightly, it produces a small concentration of PO_4^{3-} ion. The phosphate ion is a strong base and readily hydrolyzes to HPO_4^{2-}. As this removes PO_4^{3-} from the equilibrium with Ag_3PO_4, the equilibrium shifts to the right, $Ag_3PO_4(s) \rightleftarrows 3\,Ag^+(aq) + PO_4^{3-}(aq)$ and Ag_3PO_4 dissolves to a greater extent than expected from the K_{sp} value.

18.14   Silver ion reacts with ammonia to form the soluble complex ion, $Ag(NH_3)_2^+(aq)$. This shifts the solubility equilibrium to the right, dissolving AgCl.

18.15   When you breathe into a paper bag, the CO_2 you exhale is recycled. This raises the blood CO_2 level and causes the equilibrium $H_2CO_3(aq) + H_2O(\ell) \rightleftarrows H_3O^+(aq) + HCO_3^-(aq)$ to shift to the right, thus raising the hydronium ion concentration and decreasing blood pH.

18.16   The Fe^{2+} ions can be precipitated as solid $Fe(OH)_2$ by the addition of KOH. The KOH will not react with Na^+ ions. The solid can then be separated by carefully pouring the solution containing Na^+ ions into another test tube.

18.17   (a) $NaBr(aq) + AgNO_3(aq) \rightarrow AgBr(s) + NaNO_3(aq)$

         (b) $2\,KCl(aq) + Pb(NO_3)_2(aq) \rightarrow PbCl_2(s) + 2\,KNO_3(aq)$

         (c) No precipitate forms.

18.18   (a) pH decreases (NH_4^+ is a weak acid)

         (b) pH increases ($CH_3CO_2^-$ is a weak base)

         (c) no change (NaCl is a neutral salt)

18.19   (a) pH increases ($C_2O_4^{2-}$ is a weak base)

         (b) pH decreases slightly (NH_4^+, a weak acid, is being added to a solution containing a strong acid)

         (c) no change (NaCl is a neutral salt)

18.20 $NH_4^+(aq) + H_2O(\ell) \rightleftharpoons H_3O^+(aq) + NH_3(aq)$

$$K_a = 5.6 \times 10^{-10} = \frac{[H_3O^+][NH_3]}{[NH_4^+]} = \frac{(x)(0.20 + x)}{(0.20 - x)} \approx \frac{(x)(0.20)}{0.20}$$

$x = [H_3O^+] = 5.6 \times 10^{-10} \ M$ $pH = -\log[H_3O^+] = 9.25$

18.21 $[CH_3CO_2^-] = \dfrac{1.56 \ g \ NaCH_3CO_2}{0.1000 \ L} \cdot \dfrac{1 \ mol}{82.03 \ g} = 0.190 \ M$

$$K_a = 1.8 \times 10^{-5} = \frac{[H_3O^+][CH_3CO_2^-]}{[CH_3CO_2H]} = \frac{(x)(0.190 + x)}{(0.15 - x)} \approx \frac{(x)(0.190)}{0.15}$$

$x = [H_3O^+] = 1.4 \times 10^{-5} \ M$ $pH = -\log[H_3O^+] = 4.85$

18.22 $C_6H_5CO_2H(aq) + OH^-(aq) \rightarrow C_6H_5CO_2^-(aq) + H_2O(\ell)$

$(0.0300 \ L \ KOH)(0.015 \ mol/L) = 4.5 \times 10^{-4} \ mol \ KOH$

$(0.0500 \ L \ C_6H_5CO_2H)(0.015 \ mol/L) = 7.5 \times 10^{-4} \ mol \ C_6H_5CO_2H$

$4.5 \times 10^{-4} \ mol \ NaOH \cdot \dfrac{1 \ mol \ C_6H_5CO_2^-}{1 \ mol \ NaOH} = 4.5 \times 10^{-4} \ mol \ C_6H_5CO_2^- \ produced$

$4.5 \times 10^{-4} \ mol \ NaOH \cdot \dfrac{1 \ mol \ C_6H_5CO_2H}{1 \ mol \ NaOH} = 4.5 \times 10^{-4} \ mol \ C_6H_5CO_2H \ consumed$

$7.5 \times 10^{-4} \ mol \ C_6H_5CO_2H - 4.5 \times 10^{-4} \ mol \ consumed = 3.0 \times 10^{-4} \ mol \ C_6H_5CO_2H \ remaining$

$[C_6H_5CO_2H] = \dfrac{3.0 \times 10^{-4} \ mol}{0.0800 \ L} = 0.0038 \ M$ $[C_6H_5CO_2^-] = \dfrac{4.5 \times 10^{-4} \ mol}{0.0800 \ L} = 0.0056 \ M$

$C_6H_5CO_2H(aq) + H_2O(\ell) \rightleftharpoons H_3O^+(aq) + C_6H_5CO_2^-(aq)$

$$K_a = 6.3 \times 10^{-5} = \frac{[H_3O^+][C_6H_5CO_2^-]}{[C_6H_5CO_2H]} = \frac{(x)(0.0056 + x)}{(0.0038 - x)} \approx \frac{(x)(0.0056)}{0.0038}$$

$x = [H_3O^+] = 4.2 \times 10^{-5} \ M$ $pH = -\log[H_3O^+] = 4.38$

18.23 $NH_3(aq) + H_3O^+(aq) \rightarrow NH_4^+(aq) + H_2O(\ell)$

$(0.0250 \ L \ HCl)(0.12 \ mol/L) = 0.0030 \ mol \ HCl$

$(0.0250 \ L \ NH_3)(0.43 \ mol/L) = 0.011 \ mol \ NH_3$

$0.0030 \ mol \ HCl \cdot \dfrac{1 \ mol \ NH_4^+}{1 \ mol \ HCl} = 0.0030 \ mol \ NH_4^+ \ produced$

$0.0030 \ mol \ HCl \cdot \dfrac{1 \ mol \ NH_3}{1 \ mol \ HCl} = 0.0030 \ mol \ NH_3 \ consumed$

$0.011 \ mol \ NH_3 - 0.0030 \ mol \ consumed = 0.008 \ mol \ NH_3 \ remaining$

$[NH_3] = \dfrac{0.008 \ mol}{0.0500 \ L} = 0.2 \ M$ $[NH_4^+] = \dfrac{0.0030 \ mol}{0.0500 \ L} = 0.060 \ M$

$NH_4^+(aq) + H_2O(\ell) \rightleftharpoons H_3O^+(aq) + NH_3(aq)$

$$K_a = 5.6 \times 10^{-10} = \frac{[H_3O^+][NH_3]}{[NH_4^+]} = \frac{(x)(0.2 + x)}{(0.060 - x)} \approx \frac{(x)(0.2)}{0.060}$$

$x = [H_3O^+] = 2 \times 10^{-10} \ M$ $pH = -\log[H_3O^+] = 9.7$

18.24 $NH_4^+(aq) + H_2O(\ell) \rightleftharpoons H_3O^+(aq) + NH_3(aq)$

$$[NH_4^+] = \frac{2.2 \text{ g } NH_4Cl}{0.25 \text{ L}} \cdot \frac{1 \text{ mol}}{53.5 \text{ g}} = 0.16 \text{ M}$$

$$K_a = 5.6 \times 10^{-10} = \frac{[H_3O^+][NH_3]}{[NH_4^+]} = \frac{(x)(0.12 + x)}{(0.16 - x)} \approx \frac{(x)(0.12)}{0.16}$$

$x = [H_3O^+] = 7.7 \times 10^{-10} \text{ M}$ \qquad\qquad $pH = -\log[H_3O^+] = 9.11$

The buffer solution has a lower pH than the original NH_3 solution (pH = 11.17) because a weak acid (NH_4^+)
was added to the ammonia solution.

18.25   (a) $CH_3CHOHCO_2H(aq) + H_2O(\ell) \rightleftharpoons H_3O^+(aq) + CH_3CHOHCO_2^-(aq)$

$$\frac{2.75 \text{ g } NaCH_3CHOHCO_2}{0.500 \text{ L}} \cdot \frac{1 \text{ mol}}{112.1 \text{ g}} = 0.0491 \text{ M}$$

$$K_a = 1.4 \times 10^{-4} = \frac{[H_3O^+][CH_3CHOHCO_2^-]}{[CH_3CHOHCO_2H]} = \frac{(x)(0.0491 + x)}{(0.100 - x)} \approx \frac{(x)(0.0491)}{0.100}$$

$x = [H_3O^+] = 2.9 \times 10^{-4} \text{ M}$ \qquad\qquad $pH = -\log[H_3O^+] = 3.54$

(b)   The buffer solution has a higher pH than the original lactic acid solution (pH = 2.43) because a weak
base ($CH_3CHOHCO_2^-$) was added to the lactic acid solution.

18.26 $[H_3O^+] = 10^{-pH} = 10^{-4.50} = 3.2 \times 10^{-5} \text{ M}$

$$K_a = 1.8 \times 10^{-5} = \frac{[H_3O^+][CH_3CO_2^-]}{[CH_3CO_2H]} = \frac{(3.2 \times 10^{-5})(x)}{(0.10)}$$

$x = [CH_3CO_2^-] = 0.057 \text{ M}$

$$\frac{0.057 \text{ mol}}{1.0 \text{ L}} \cdot \frac{1 \text{ mol } NaCH_3CO_2}{1 \text{ mol } CH_3CO_2^-} \cdot 1.00 \text{ L} \cdot \frac{82.0 \text{ g}}{1 \text{ mol } NaCH_3CO_2} = 4.7 \text{ g}$$

18.27 $[H_3O^+] = 10^{-pH} = 10^{-9.00} = 1.0 \times 10^{-9}$

$$K_a = 5.6 \times 10^{-10} = \frac{[H_3O^+][NH_3]}{[NH_4^+]} = \frac{(1.0 \times 10^{-9})(0.10)}{x}$$

$x = [NH_4^+] = 0.18 \text{ M}$

$$\frac{0.18 \text{ mol}}{1.0 \text{ L}} \cdot \frac{1 \text{ mol } NH_4Cl}{1 \text{ mol } NH_4^+} \cdot 0.500 \text{ L} \cdot \frac{53.5 \text{ g}}{1 \text{ mol } NH_4Cl} = 4.8 \text{ g } NH_4Cl$$

18.28 $pK_a = -\log(K_a) = -\log(1.8 \times 10^{-5}) = 4.74$

$$pH = pK_a + \log\frac{[CH_3CO_2^-]}{[CH_3CO_2H]} = 4.74 + \log\frac{0.075}{0.050} = 4.92$$

18.29 $pK_a = -\log(K_a) = -\log(5.6 \times 10^{-10}) = 9.25$

$$pH = pK_a + \log\frac{[NH_3]}{[NH_4^+]} = 9.25 + \log\frac{0.045}{0.050} = 9.21$$

18.30   (a) $pK_a = -\log(K_a) = -\log(1.8 \times 10^{-4}) = 3.74$

$$pH = pK_a + \log\frac{[HCO_2^-]}{[HCO_2H]} = 3.74 + \log\frac{0.035}{0.050} = 3.59$$

(b) $pH = 4.09 = 3.74 + \log\dfrac{[HCO_2^-]}{[HCO_2H]}$

$0.35 = \log\dfrac{[HCO_2^-]}{[HCO_2H]}$

$-0.35 = \log\dfrac{[HCO_2H]}{[HCO_2^-]}$

$\dfrac{[HCO_2H]}{[HCO_2^-]} = 10^{-0.35} = 0.45$

18.31   (a) $pK_a = -\log(6.2 \times 10^{-8}) = 7.21$

$5.677\ g \cdot \dfrac{1\ mol}{141.96\ g} = 0.03999\ mol\ Na_2HPO_4 \qquad 1.360\ g \cdot \dfrac{1\ mol}{136.08\ g} = 0.009994\ mol\ KH_2PO_4$

$$pH = pK_a + \log\frac{[HPO_4^{2-}]}{[H_2PO_4^-]} = 7.21 + \log\left(\frac{0.03999\ mol}{0.009994\ mol}\right) = 7.81$$

(b) $pH = 7.31 = 7.21 + \log\dfrac{[HPO_4^{2-}]}{[H_2PO_4^-]}$

$0.10 = \log\dfrac{[HPO_4^{2-}]}{[H_2PO_4^-]}$

$\dfrac{[HPO_4^{2-}]}{[H_2PO_4^-]} = 1.3 = \dfrac{0.03999\ mol}{x} \qquad\qquad x = 0.032\ mol\ H_2PO_4^-$

$0.032\ mol \cdot \dfrac{1\ mol\ KH_2PO_4}{1\ mol\ H_2PO_4^-} \cdot \dfrac{136.1\ g}{1\ mol} = 4.3\ g$

mass of KH_2PO_4 to add = 4.3 g total − 1.360 g in buffer = 2.9 g

18.32   (a) HCl and NaCl   not a buffer

(b) NH_3 and NH_4Cl $pK_a(NH_4^+) = 9.25$

(c) CH_3CO_2H and $NaCH_3CO_2$ $pK_a(CH_3CO_2H) = 4.74$

The best choice here is (b), the NH_3/NH_4Cl buffer

18.33   (a) H_3PO_4/NaH_2PO_4 $pK_a(H_3PO_4) = 2.12$

(b) NaH_2PO_4/Na_2HPO_4 $pK_a(H_2PO_4^-) = 7.21$

(c) Na_2HPO_4/Na_3PO_4 $pK_a(HPO_4^{2-}) = 12.44$

The best choice here is (b), the NaH_2PO_4/Na_2HPO_4 buffer.

18.34   (a) $[CH_3CO_2^-] = \dfrac{4.95\ g}{0.250\ L} \cdot \dfrac{1\ mol}{82.03\ g} = 0.241\ M$

$$pH = pK_a + \log\frac{[CH_3CO_2^-]}{[CH_3CO_2H]} = -\log(1.8 \times 10^{-5}) + \log\left(\frac{0.241}{0.150}\right) = 4.95$$

(b) $OH^-(aq) + CH_3CO_2H(aq) \rightarrow H_2O(\ell) + CH_3CO_2^-(aq)$

$$0.082 \text{ g} \cdot \frac{1 \text{ mol NaOH}}{40.0 \text{ g}} = 0.0021 \text{ mol NaOH added to buffer}$$

$$\frac{0.241 \text{ mol}}{1.00 \text{ L}} \cdot 0.100 \text{ L} = 0.0241 \text{ mol } CH_3CO_2^- \text{ before NaOH addition}$$

$$\frac{0.150 \text{ mol}}{1.00 \text{ L}} \cdot 0.100 \text{ L} = 0.0150 \text{ mol } CH_3CO_2H \text{ before NaOH addition}$$

	CH_3CO_2H	$CH_3CO_2^-$
Initial (mol)	0.0150	0.0241
Change (mol)	−0.0021	+0.0021
Equilibrium (mol)	0.0129	0.0262

$$[H_3O^+] = \frac{[CH_3CO_2H]}{[CH_3CO_2^-]} \cdot K_a \approx \left(\frac{0.0129}{0.0262}\right)(1.8 \times 10^{-5}) = 8.9 \times 10^{-6} \text{ M}$$

$$pH = -\log[H_3O^+] = 5.05$$

18.35 $[H_2PO_4^-] = [HPO_4^{2-}]$ so $[H_3O^+] = K_a = 6.2 \times 10^{-8}$ $pH = -\log[H_3O^+] = 7.21$

$$[NaOH] = \frac{0.425 \text{ g}}{2.00 \text{ L}} \cdot \frac{1 \text{ mol}}{40.00 \text{ g}} = 0.00531 \text{ M}$$

	$H_2PO_4^-$	HPO_4^{2-}
Initial (M)	0.132	0.132
Change (M)	−0.00531	+0.00531
Equilibrium (M)	0.127	0.137

$$[H_3O^+] = \frac{[H_2PO_4^-]}{[HPO_4^{2-}]} K_a \approx \left(\frac{0.127}{0.137}\right)(6.2 \times 10^{-8}) = 5.7 \times 10^{-8} \text{ M}$$

$$pH = -\log[H_3O^+] = 7.24$$

18.36 (a) $[NH_4^+] = \dfrac{0.125 \text{ mol}}{0.500 \text{ L}} = 0.250 \text{ M}$

$$pH = pK_a + \log\frac{[NH_3]}{[NH_4^+]} = -\log(5.6 \times 10^{-10}) + \log\left(\frac{0.500}{0.250}\right) = 9.55$$

(b) $[HCl] = \dfrac{0.0100 \text{ mol}}{0.500 \text{ L}} = 0.0200 \text{ M}$

	NH_4^+	NH_3
Initial (M)	0.250	0.500
Change (M)	+0.0200	−0.0200
Equilibrium (M)	0.270	0.480

$$pH = pK_a + \log\frac{[NH_3]}{[NH_4^+]} = -\log(5.6 \times 10^{-10}) + \log\left(\frac{0.480}{0.270}\right) = 9.50$$

18.37 $pH = pK_a + \log\dfrac{[NH_3]}{[NH_4{}^+]} = -\log(5.6 \times 10^{-10}) + \log\left(\dfrac{0.169}{0.183}\right) = 9.22$

(0.0200 L NaOH)(0.100 mol/L) = 0.00200 mol NaOH

(0.0800 L NH₃)(0.169 mol/L) = 0.0135 mol NH₃

(0.0800 L NH₄⁺)(0.183 mol/L) = 0.0146 mol NH₄⁺

Total volume = 0.0200 L + 0.0800 L = 0.100 L

	NH₄⁺	NH₃
Initial (mol)	0.0146	0.0135
Change (mol)	−0.00200	+0.00200
Equilibrium (mol)	0.0126	0.0155

$pH = pK_a + \log\dfrac{[NH_3]}{[NH_4{}^+]} = -\log(5.6 \times 10^{-10}) + \log\left(\dfrac{0.0155 \text{ mol}}{0.0126 \text{ mol}}\right) = 9.34$

The change in pH is 9.34 − 9.22 = 0.12

18.38   (a) $[C_6H_5OH] = \dfrac{0.515 \text{ g}}{0.125 \text{ L}} \cdot \dfrac{1 \text{ mol}}{94.11 \text{ g}} = 0.0438 \text{ M}$

$K_a = 1.3 \times 10^{-10} = \dfrac{[C_6H_5O^-][H_3O^+]}{[C_6H_5OH]} = \dfrac{x^2}{0.0438 - x} \approx \dfrac{x^2}{0.0438}$

$x = [H_3O^+] = 2.4 \times 10^{-6} \text{ M}$ $pH = -\log[H_3O^+] = 5.62$

(b)

	C₆H₅OH	OH⁻	→	C₆H₅O⁻	+ H₂O
Initial (mol)	0.00547	0.00547		0	
Change (mol)	−0.00547	−0.00547		+0.00547	
After reaction (mol)	0	0		0.00547	

Total volume = 0.125 L + (0.00547 mol NaOH)(1 L/0.123 mol) = 0.169 L

$C_6H_5O^-(aq) + H_2O(\ell) \rightleftharpoons C_6H_6OH(aq) + OH^-(aq)$

$[C_6H_5O^-] = \dfrac{0.00547 \text{ mol}}{0.169 \text{ L}} = 0.0323 \text{ M}$

$K_b = \dfrac{K_w}{K_a} = 7.7 \times 10^{-5} = \dfrac{[C_6H_5OH][OH^-]}{[C_6H_5O^-]} = \dfrac{x^2}{0.0323 - x}$

Solve using the quadratic equation. $x = 0.0015 \text{ M} = [OH^-]$ $[H_3O^+] = \dfrac{K_w}{[OH^-]} = 6.5 \times 10^{-12} \text{ M}$

$[Na^+] = 0.0323 \text{ M}$ $[C_6H_5O^-] = 0.323 - x = 0.0307 \text{ M}$

(c) $pH = -\log[H_3O^+] = 11.19$

18.39   (a) $[C_6H_5CO_2H] = \dfrac{0.235 \text{ g } C_6H_5CO_2H}{0.100 \text{ L}} \cdot \dfrac{1 \text{ mol}}{122.1 \text{ g}} = 0.0192 \text{ M}$

$K_a = 6.3 \times 10^{-5} = \dfrac{[C_6H_5CO_2^-][H_3O^+]}{[C_6H_5CO_2H]} = \dfrac{x^2}{0.0192 - x} \approx \dfrac{x^2}{0.0192}$

$x = [H_3O^+] = 0.0011 \text{ M}$ $\qquad\qquad\qquad$ $pH = -\log[H_3O^+] = 2.96$

(b) $\qquad\qquad\qquad\qquad$ $C_6H_5CO_2H \ + \ OH^- \ \rightarrow \ C_6H_5CO_2^- \ + H_2O$

Initial (mol)	0.00192	0.00192	0
Change (mol)	–0.00192	–0.00192	+0.00192
After reaction (mol)	0	0	0.00192

Total volume = 0.100 L + (0.00192 mol NaOH)(1 L/0.108 mol) = 0.118 L

$C_6H_5CO_2^-(aq) + H_2O(\ell) \rightleftharpoons C_6H_5CO_2H \ (aq) + OH^-(aq)$

$[C_6H_5CO_2^-] = \dfrac{0.00192 \text{ mol}}{0.118 \text{ L}} = 0.0163 \text{ M}$

$K_b = \dfrac{K_w}{K_a} = 1.6 \times 10^{-10} = \dfrac{[C_6H_5CO_2H][OH^-]}{[C_6H_5CO_2^-]} = \dfrac{x^2}{0.0163 - x} \approx \dfrac{x^2}{0.0163}$

$x = 1.6 \times 10^{-6} \text{ M} = [OH^-]$ $\qquad\qquad$ $[H_3O^+] = \dfrac{K_w}{[OH^-]} = 6.2 \times 10^{-9} \text{ M}$

$[Na^+] = [C_6H_5CO_2^-] = 0.0163 \text{ M}$

(c) $pH = -\log[H_3O^+] = 8.21$

18.40   (a) $NH_3(aq) + H_3O^+(aq) \rightarrow NH_4^+(aq) + H_2O(\ell)$

$[NH_3] = \dfrac{0.0105 \text{ mol HCl}}{1.00 \text{ L}} \cdot 0.03678 \text{ L} \cdot \dfrac{1 \text{ mol } NH_3}{1 \text{ mol HCl}} \cdot \dfrac{1}{0.0250 \text{ L}} = 0.0154 \text{ M}$

(b) $NH_4^+(aq) + H_2O(\ell) \rightleftharpoons H_3O^+(aq) + NH_3(aq)$

Total volume = 0.03678 L + 0.0250 L = 0.0618 L

$[NH_4^+] = \dfrac{0.0105 \text{ mol HCl}}{1.00 \text{ L}} \cdot 0.03678 \text{ L} \cdot \dfrac{1 \text{ mol } NH_4^+}{1 \text{ mol HCl}} \cdot \dfrac{1}{0.0618 \text{ L}} = 0.00625 \text{ M}$

$K_a = 5.6 \times 10^{-10} = \dfrac{[H_3O^+][NH_3]}{[NH_4^+]} = \dfrac{x^2}{0.00625 - x} \approx \dfrac{x^2}{0.00625}$

$x = 1.9 \times 10^{-6} \text{ M} = [H_3O^+]$ $\quad$ $[OH^-] = \dfrac{K_w}{[H_3O^+]} = 5.3 \times 10^{-9} \text{ M}$ $\quad$ $[NH_4^+] = 0.00625 \text{ M}$

(c) $pH = -\log[H_3O^+] = 5.73$

18.41   (a) $[C_6H_5NH_2] = \dfrac{0.175 \text{ mol HCl}}{1.00 \text{ L}} \cdot 0.02567 \text{ L} \cdot \dfrac{1 \text{ mol } C_6H_5NH_2}{1 \text{ mol HCl}} \cdot \dfrac{1}{0.0250 \text{ L}} = 0.180 \text{ M}$

(b) $C_6H_5NH_3^+(aq) + H_2O(\ell) \rightleftharpoons H_3O^+(aq) + C_6H_5NH_2(aq)$

Total volume = 0.02567 L + 0.0250 L = 0.0507 L

$[C_6H_5NH_3^+] = \dfrac{0.175 \text{ mol HCl}}{1.00 \text{ L}} \cdot 0.02567 \text{ L} \cdot \dfrac{1 \text{ mol } C_6H_5NH_3^+}{1 \text{ mol HCl}} \cdot \dfrac{1}{0.0507 \text{ L}} = 0.0887 \text{ M}$

$$K_a = \frac{K_w}{K_b} = 2.5 \times 10^{-5} = \frac{[H_3O^+][C_6H_5NH_2]}{[C_6H_5NH_3^+]} = \frac{x^2}{0.0887 - x} \approx \frac{x^2}{0.0887}$$

$$x = 0.0015 \text{ M} = [H_3O^+] \qquad [OH^-] = \frac{K_w}{[H_3O^+]} = 6.7 \times 10^{-12} \text{ M} \qquad [C_6H_5NH_3^+] \approx 0.0887 \text{ M}$$

(c) pH = $-\log[H_3O^+]$ = 2.83

18.42   Initial pH = 13, pH at equivalence point = 7, total volume at equivalence point = 30 + 30 = 60.0 mL

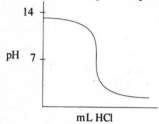

18.43   Initial pH ≈ 9, pH at equivalence point ≈ 3, total volume at equivalence point = 50 + 25 = 75 mL.

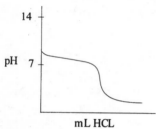

18.44   (a) $K_b = 1.8 \times 10^{-5} = \frac{[OH^-][NH_4^+]}{[NH_3]} = \frac{x^2}{0.10 - x} \approx \frac{x^2}{0.10}$

$x = [OH^-] = 0.0013 \text{ M} \qquad pOH = 2.87 \qquad pH = 11.13$

(b) $NH_3(aq) + H_3O^+(aq) \rightarrow NH_4^+(aq) + H_2O(\ell)$ Total volume = 0.0250 + 0.0250 = 0.0500 L

$$[NH_4^+] = \frac{0.10 \text{ mol } NH_3}{1.0 \text{ L}} \cdot 0.0250 \text{ L} \cdot \frac{1 \text{ mol } NH_4^+}{1 \text{ mol } NH_3} \cdot \frac{1}{0.0500 \text{ L}} = 0.050 \text{ M}$$

$NH_4^+(aq) + H_2O(\ell) \rightleftharpoons H_3O^+(aq) + NH_3(aq)$

$$K_a = 5.6 \times 10^{-10} = \frac{[H_3O^+][NH_3]}{[NH_4^+]} = \frac{x^2}{0.050 - x} \approx \frac{x^2}{0.050}$$

$x = [H_3O^+] = 5.3 \times 10^{-6} \text{ M} \qquad pH = -\log[H_3O^+] = 5.28$

(c) At titration midpoint, $[NH_3] = [NH_4^+]$ and pH = pK_a = $-\log(5.6 \times 10^{-10})$ = 9.25

(d) Methyl red would detect the equivalence point.

(e)

mL HCl added	mol H_3O^+ added	mol NH_4^+ produced	mol NH_3 remaining	pH
5.00	0.00050	0.00050	0.0020	9.85
15.00	0.0015	0.0015	0.0010	9.08
20.00	0.0020	0.0020	0.0005	8.65
22.00	0.0022	0.0022	0.0003	8.39
30.00	0.0030			2.04

When 30.00 mL HCl is added, pH depends only on the excess H_3O^+

$[H_3O^+] = (0.0030 \text{ mol} - 0.0025 \text{ mol})/0.0550 \text{ L} = 0.009 \text{ M}$

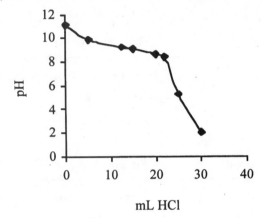

18.45   Rough plot of pH versus volume of base:

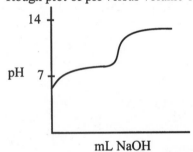

(a) $K_a = 4.0 \times 10^{-10} = \dfrac{[CN^-][H_3O^+]}{[HCN]} = \dfrac{x^2}{0.050 - x} \approx \dfrac{x^2}{0.050}$

$x = [H_3O^+] = 4.5 \times 10^{-6} \text{ M}$ $pH = -\log[H_3O^+] = 5.35$

(b)   At the half-neutralization point, $[HCN] = [CN^-]$, and $pH = pK_a = 9.40$

(c)   When 95% of NaOH has been added

mol $CN^- = 0.95(\text{mol HCN})_{initial} = 0.95(0.0250 \text{ L})(0.050 \text{ mol/L}) = 0.0012 \text{ mol } CN^-$

mol $HCN = 0.05(\text{mol HCN})_{initial} = 0.05(0.0250 \text{ L})(0.050 \text{ mol/L}) = 6 \times 10^{-5} \text{ mol HCN}$

$pH = pK_a + \log\dfrac{[CN^-]}{[HCN]} = -\log(4.0 \times 10^{-10}) + \log\left(\dfrac{0.0012 \text{ mol}}{6 \times 10^{-5} \text{ mol}}\right) = 10.7$

(d) $\dfrac{0.050 \text{ mol HCN}}{1.0 \text{ L}} \cdot 0.0250 \text{ L} \cdot \dfrac{1 \text{ mol NaOH}}{1 \text{ mol HCN}} \cdot \dfrac{1 \text{ L}}{0.075 \text{ mol NaOH}} = 0.017 \text{ L} = 17 \text{ mL}$

(e) $CN^-(aq) + H_2O(\ell) \rightleftarrows HCN(aq) + OH^-(aq)$

$$[CN^-] = \frac{0.050 \text{ mol HCN}}{1.0 \text{ L}} \cdot 0.025 \text{ L} \cdot \frac{1 \text{ mol } CN^-}{1 \text{ mol HCN}} \cdot \frac{1}{0.042 \text{ L}} = 0.030 \text{ M}$$

$$K_b = \frac{K_w}{K_a} = 2.5 \times 10^{-5} = \frac{[HCN][OH^-]}{[CN^-]} = \frac{x^2}{0.030 - x} \approx \frac{x^2}{0.030}$$

$$x = [OH^-] = 8.7 \times 10^{-4} \text{ M} \qquad pOH = -\log[OH^-] = 3.06 \qquad pH = 14.00 - pOH = 10.94$$

(f) Alizarin yellow GG would be a reasonable choice for an indicator.

(g) When 105% of NaOH has been added, pH depends only on the excess OH^-

excess $OH^- = = 0.05(0.017 \text{ L NaOH})(0.075 \text{ mol/L}) = 6 \times 10^{-5} \text{ mol } OH^-$

$$[OH^-] = \frac{6 \times 10^{-5} \text{ mol}}{0.042 \text{ L}} = 0.0015 \text{ M} \qquad pOH = 2.83 \qquad pH = 11.17$$

18.46

Titration	pH at Equivalence Point	Possible Indicator
(a) C_5H_5N titrated with HCl	<7 (about 3-4)	thymol blue or bromphenol blue
(b) HCO_2H with NaOH	>7 (about 8-10)	phenolphthalein
(c) H_2NNH_2 with HCl	<7 (about 4-5)	bromcresol green

18.47

Titration	pH at Equiv. Point	Possible Indicator
HCO_3^- titrated with HCl	<7 (about 3-4)	bromcresol green
HClO with NaOH	>7 (about 10-11)	thymolphthalein
$(CH_3)_3N$ with HCl	<7 (about 5-6)	methyl red

18.48 (a) AgCl and $PbCl_2$

(b) $Zn(OH)_2$ and $ZnCO_3$

(c) $Fe(OH)_2$ and FeS

18.49 (a) $BaSO_4$ and $PbSO_4$

(b) $Ni(OH)_2$ and $NiCO_3$

(c) $PbBr_2$ and AgBr

18.50 (a) soluble (most ammonium salts are soluble)

(b) soluble (most sulfate salts are soluble)

(c) insoluble (most sulfide salts are insoluble)

(d) insoluble (most sulfate salts are soluble, barium sulfate is an exception)

18.51 (a) soluble (most nitrate salts are soluble).

(b) insoluble (most hydroxide salts are insoluble).

(c) soluble (most chloride salts are soluble).

(d) insoluble (most sulfide salts are insoluble).

18.52 (a) $AgCN(s) \rightleftharpoons Ag^+(aq) + CN^-(aq)$ $K_{sp} = [Ag^+][CN^-]$

(b) $NiCO_3(s) \rightleftharpoons Ni^{2+}(aq) + CO_3^{2-}(aq)$ $K_{sp} = [Ni^{2+}][CO_3^{2-}]$

(c) $AuBr_3(s) \rightleftharpoons Au^{3+}(aq) + 3\ Br^-(aq)$ $K_{sp} = [Au^{3+}][Br^-]^3$

18.53 (a) $PbSO_4(s) \rightleftharpoons Pb^{2+}(aq) + SO_4^{2-}(aq)$ $K_{sp} = [Pb^{2+}][SO_4^{2-}]$

(b) $BaF_2(s) \rightleftharpoons Ba^{2+}(aq) + 2\ F^-(aq)$ $K_{sp} = [Ba^{2+}][F^-]^2$

(c) $Ag_3PO_4(s) \rightleftharpoons 3\ Ag^+(aq) + PO_4^{3-}(aq)$ $K_{sp} = [Ag^+]^3[PO_4^{3-}]$

18.54 $K_{sp} = [Tl^+][Br^-] = (1.9 \times 10^{-3})(1.9 \times 10^{-3}) = 3.6 \times 10^{-6}$

18.55 $[Ag^+] = [CH_3CO_2^-] = \dfrac{1.0\ g}{0.1000\ L} \cdot \dfrac{1\ mol\ AgCH_3CO_2}{167\ g} = 0.060\ M$

$K_{sp} = [Ag^+][CH_3CO_2^-] = (0.060)(0.060) = 0.0036$

18.56 $[F^-] = 2 \times [Sr^{2+}] = 2.06 \times 10^{-3}\ M$ $K_{sp} = [Sr^{2+}][F^-]^2 = (1.03 \times 10^{-3})(2.06 \times 10^{-3})^2 = 4.37 \times 10^{-9}$

18.57 $[Ca^{2+}] = \dfrac{1.04\ g\ Ca(OH)_2}{1\ L} \cdot \dfrac{1\ mol}{74.09\ g} = 0.0140\ M$

$K_{sp} = [Ca^{2+}][OH^-]^2 = (0.0140)(2 \times 0.0140)^2 = 1.11 \times 10^{-5}$

18.58 $pOH = 14.00 - pH = 4.85$ $[OH^-] = 10^{-pOH} = 1.4 \times 10^{-5}\ M$ $[Pb^{2+}] = \frac{1}{2} \times [OH^-] = 7.1 \times 10^{-6}\ M$

$K_{sp} = [Pb^{2+}][OH^-]^2 = (7.1 \times 10^{-6})(1.4 \times 10^{-5})^2 = 1.4 \times 10^{-15}$

18.59 $pOH = 14.00 - pH = 1.32$ $[OH^-] = 10^{-pOH} = 0.048\ M$ $[Ca^{2+}] = \frac{1}{2} \times [OH^-] = 0.024$

$K_{sp} = [Ca^{2+}][OH^-]^2 = (0.024)(0.048)^2 = 5.5 \times 10^{-5}$

18.60 $AgI(s) \rightleftharpoons Ag^+(aq) + I^-(aq)$ $K_{sp} = [Ag^+][I^-] = (x)(x) = x^2$

	Ag^+	I^-
Initial (M)	0	0
Change (M)	$+x$	$+x$
Equilibrium (M)	x	x

(a) $x = \sqrt{K_{sp}} = \sqrt{8.5 \times 10^{-17}} = 9.2 \times 10^{-9}\ mol/L$

(b) $\dfrac{9.2 \times 10^{-9}\ mol}{1\ L} \cdot \dfrac{235\ g}{1\ mol\ AgI} = 2.2 \times 10^{-6}\ g/L$

18.61
$$\text{AuCl(s)} \rightleftharpoons \text{Au}^+(\text{aq}) + \text{Cl}^-(\text{aq}) \qquad K_{sp} = [\text{Au}^+][\text{Cl}^-] = (x)(x) = x^2$$

	Au$^+$	Cl$^-$
Initial (M)	0	0
Change (M)	$+x$	$+x$
Equilibrium (M)	x	x

$$x = [\text{Au}^+] = \sqrt{K_{sp}} = \sqrt{2.0 \times 10^{-13}} = 4.5 \times 10^{-7} \text{ mol/L}$$

18.62
$$\text{MgF}_2(\text{s}) \rightleftharpoons \text{Mg}^{2+}(\text{aq}) + 2\,\text{F}^-(\text{aq}) \qquad K_{sp} = [\text{Mg}^{2+}][\text{F}^-]^2 = (x)(2x)^2 = 4x^3$$

	Mg^{2+}	F$^-$
Initial (M)	0	0
Change (M)	$+x$	$+2x$
Equilibrium (M)	x	$2x$

(a) $\quad x = \sqrt[3]{\dfrac{K_{sp}}{4}} = \sqrt[3]{\dfrac{5.2 \times 10^{-11}}{4}} = 2.4 \times 10^{-4} \text{ mol/L}$

(b) $\quad \dfrac{2.4 \times 10^{-4} \text{ mol}}{1 \text{ L}} \cdot \dfrac{62.3 \text{ g}}{1 \text{ mol MgF}_2} = 0.015 \text{ g/L}$

18.63
$$\text{PbBr}_2(\text{s}) \rightleftharpoons \text{Pb}^{2+}(\text{aq}) + 2\,\text{Br}^-(\text{aq}) \qquad K_{sp} = [\text{Pb}^{2+}][\text{Br}^-]^2 = (x)(2x)^2 = 4x^3$$

	Pb^{2+}	Br$^-$
Initial (M)	0	0
Change (M)	$+x$	$+2x$
Equilibrium (M)	x	$2x$

(a) $\quad x = \sqrt[3]{\dfrac{K_{sp}}{4}} = \sqrt[3]{\dfrac{6.6 \times 10^{-6}}{4}} = 0.012 \text{ mol/L}$

(b) $\quad \dfrac{0.012 \text{ mol}}{1 \text{ L}} \cdot \dfrac{367 \text{ g}}{1 \text{ mol PbBr}_2} = 4.3 \text{ g/L}$

18.64
$$\text{RaSO}_4(\text{s}) \rightleftharpoons \text{Ra}^{2+}(\text{aq}) + \text{SO}_4^{2-}(\text{aq}) \qquad K_{sp} = [\text{Ra}^{2+}][\text{SO}_4^{2-}] = (x)(x) = x^2$$

	Ra^{2+}	SO$_4^{2-}$
Initial (M)	0	0
Change (M)	$+x$	$+x$
Equilibrium (M)	x	x

$$x = \sqrt{K_{sp}} = \sqrt{3.7 \times 10^{-11}} = 6.1 \times 10^{-6} \text{ mol/L}$$

$$\dfrac{6.1 \times 10^{-6} \text{ mol}}{1 \text{ L}} \cdot 0.100 \text{ L} \cdot \dfrac{322 \text{ g}}{1 \text{ mol RaSO}_4} \cdot \dfrac{10^3 \text{ mg}}{1 \text{ g}} = 0.20 \text{ mg RaSO}_4 \text{ dissolves}$$

18.65 $\qquad$ $PbSO_4(s) \rightleftharpoons Pb^{2+}(aq) + SO_4^{2-}(aq)$ $\qquad$ $K_{sp} = [Pb^{2+}][SO_4^{2-}] = (x)(x) = x^2$

Initial (M)	0	0
Change (M)	+x	+x
Equilibrium (M)	x	x

$x = \sqrt{K_{sp}} = \sqrt{2.5 \times 10^{-8}} = 1.6 \times 10^{-4}$ mol/L

$\dfrac{1.6 \times 10^{-4} \text{ mol}}{1 \text{ L}} \cdot 0.250 \text{ L} \cdot \dfrac{303 \text{ g}}{1 \text{ mol PbSO}_4} \cdot \dfrac{10^3 \text{ mg}}{1 \text{ g}} = 12$ mg PbSO$_4$ dissolves

18.66 (a) PbCl$_2$

(b) FeS

(c) Fe(OH)$_2$

18.67 (a) AgSCN

(b) SrSO$_4$

(c) PbI$_2$ (Caution! Solubility must be calculated.)

(d) CaF$_2$

18.68 $K_{sp} = 1.0 \times 10^{-12} = [Ag^+][SCN^-] = (x)(x) = x^2$

x = solubility of AgSCN in pure water = 1.0×10^{-6} mol/L

In water containing 0.010 M SCN$^-$ $\qquad$ $K_{sp} = 1.0 \times 10^{-12} = (x)(0.010 + x) \approx x(0.010)$

x = solubility of AgSCN in water containing 0.010 M SCN$^-$ = 1.0×10^{-10} mol/L

18.69 $K_{sp} = 5.4 \times 10^{-13} = [Ag^+][Br^-] = (x)(x) = x^2$

x = solubility of AgBr in pure water = 7.3×10^{-7} mol/L

$[Br^-] = \dfrac{0.15 \text{ g NaBr}}{0.225 \text{ L}} \cdot \dfrac{1 \text{ mol}}{103 \text{ g}} = 0.0065$ M

In water containing 0.0065 M Br$^-$ $\qquad$ $K_{sp} = 5.4 \times 10^{-13} = (x)(0.0065 + x) \approx x(0.0065)$

x = solubility of AgBr in water containing 0.0065 M Br$^-$ = 8.3×10^{-11} mol/L

18.70 (a) $K_{sp} = 8.5 \times 10^{-17} = [Ag^+][I^-] = (x)(x) = x^2$ $\qquad$ $x = \sqrt{K_{sp}} = \sqrt{8.5 \times 10^{-17}} = 9.2 \times 10^{-9}$ mol/L

$\dfrac{9.2 \times 10^{-9} \text{ mol}}{1 \text{ L}} \cdot \dfrac{235 \text{ g}}{1 \text{ mol AgI}} \cdot \dfrac{10^3 \text{ mg}}{1 \text{ g}} \cdot \dfrac{1 \text{ L}}{10^3 \text{ mL}} = 2.2 \times 10^{-6}$ mg/mL in pure water

(b) $K_{sp} = 8.5 \times 10^{-17} = [Ag^+][I^-] = (x)(0.020 + x) \approx x(0.020)$ $\qquad$ $x = 4.3 \times 10^{-15}$ mol/L

$\dfrac{4.3 \times 10^{-15} \text{ mol}}{1 \text{ L}} \cdot \dfrac{235 \text{ g}}{1 \text{ mol AgI}} \cdot \dfrac{10^3 \text{ mg}}{1 \text{ g}} \cdot \dfrac{1 \text{ L}}{10^3 \text{ mL}} = 1.0 \times 10^{-12}$ mg/mL in 0.020 M AgNO$_3$

18.71   (a) $K_{sp} = 1.8 \times 10^{-7} = [Ba^{2+}][F^-]^2 = (x)(2x)^2 = 4x^3$ $x = \sqrt[3]{\dfrac{K_{sp}}{4}} = \sqrt[3]{\dfrac{1.8 \times 10^{-7}}{4}} = 0.0036$ mol/L

$$\dfrac{0.0036 \text{ mol}}{1 \text{ L}} \cdot \dfrac{175 \text{ g}}{1 \text{ mol BaF}_2} \cdot \dfrac{10^3 \text{ mg}}{1 \text{ g}} \cdot \dfrac{1 \text{ L}}{10^3 \text{ mL}} = 0.62 \text{ mg/mL in pure water}$$

    (b) $[F^-] = \dfrac{0.0050 \text{ g KF}}{0.001 \text{ L}} \cdot \dfrac{1 \text{ mol}}{58.1 \text{ g}} = 0.086$ M

$K_{sp} = 1.8 \times 10^{-7} = [Ba^{2+}][F^-]^2 = (x)(0.086 + 2x)^2 \approx (x)(0.086)^2$ $x = 2.4 \times 10^{-5}$ mol/L

$$\dfrac{2.4 \times 10^{-5} \text{ mol}}{1 \text{ L}} \cdot \dfrac{175 \text{ g}}{1 \text{ mol BaF}_2} \cdot \dfrac{10^3 \text{ mg}}{1 \text{ g}} \cdot \dfrac{1 \text{ L}}{10^3 \text{ mL}} = 4.3 \times 10^{-3} \text{ mg/mL in 5.0 mg/mL KF}$$

18.72   (a)   PbS

    (b) Ag_2CO_3

    (c) $Al(OH)_3$

18.73   (a) Ag_2CO_3

    (b) $PbCO_3$

    (c)   AgCN

18.74 $Q = [Pb^{2+}][Cl^-]^2 = (0.0012)(0.010)^2 = 1.2 \times 10^{-7}$ $Q < K_{sp}$ $PbCl_2$ will not precipitate

18.75   (a) $Q = [Ni^{2+}][CO_3^{2-}] = (0.0024)(1.0 \times 10^{-6}) = 2.4 \times 10^{-9}$ $Q < K_{sp}$ $NiCO_3$ will not precipitate

    (b) $Q = [Ni^{2+}][CO_3^{2-}] = (0.0024)(1.0 \times 10^{-4}) = 2.4 \times 10^{-7}$ $Q > K_{sp}$ $NiCO_3$ will precipitate

18.76 $[OH^-] = \dfrac{0.0040 \text{ g}}{0.010 \text{ L}} \cdot \dfrac{1 \text{ mol}}{40.0 \text{ g}} = 0.010$ M

$Q = [Zn^{2+}][OH^-]^2 = (1.6 \times 10^{-4})(0.010)^2 = 1.6 \times 10^{-8}$ $Q > K_{sp}$ $Zn(OH)_2$ will precipitate

18.77 $[Cl^-] = \dfrac{1.20 \text{ g}}{0.095 \text{ L}} \cdot \dfrac{1 \text{ mol}}{58.44 \text{ g}} = 0.216$ M

$Q = [Pb^{2+}][Cl^-]^2 = (0.0012)(0.216)^2 = 5.6 \times 10^{-5}$ $Q > K_{sp}$ $PbCl_2$ will precipitate

18.78 $[Mg^+] = \dfrac{1.350 \text{ g Mg}^{2+}}{1 \text{ L}} \cdot \dfrac{1 \text{ mol Mg}^{2+}}{24.305 \text{ g}} = 0.0555$ M

For $Mg(OH)_2$ to precipitate, Q must exceed K_{sp} (5.6×10^{-12})

$K_{sp} = [Mg^{2+}][OH^-]^2 = 5.6 \times 10^{-12} = (0.0555)[OH^-]^2$

$[OH^-]$ must be greater than 1.0×10^{-5} M

18.79 $[OH^-] = \dfrac{(0.0250 \text{ L})(0.010 \text{ mol/L})}{0.100 \text{ L}} = 0.0025$ M $[Mg^{2+}] = \dfrac{(0.0750 \text{ L})(0.10 \text{ mol/L})}{0.100 \text{ L}} = 0.075$ M

$Q = [Mg^{2+}][OH^-]^2 = (0.075)(0.0025)^2 = 4.7 \times 10^{-7}$ $Q > K_{sp}$ $Mg(OH)_2$ will precipitate

18.80 $AuCl(s) \rightleftharpoons Au^+(aq) + Cl^-(aq)$ $K_{sp} = 2.0 \times 10^{-13}$

   $Au^+(aq) + 2\ CN^-(aq) \rightleftharpoons Au(CN)_2^-(aq)$ $K_{form} = 2.0 \times 10^{38}$

   $AuCl(s) + 2\ CN^-(aq) \rightleftharpoons Au(CN)_2^-(aq) + Cl^-(aq)$ $K_{net} = K_{sp} \cdot K_{form} = 4.0 \times 10^{25}$

18.81 $AgI(s) \rightleftharpoons Ag^+(aq) + I^-(aq)$ $K_{sp} = 8.5 \times 10^{-17}$

   $Ag^+(aq) + 2\ CN^-(aq) \rightleftharpoons Ag(CN)_2^-(aq)$ $K_{form} = 5.6 \times 10^{18}$

   $AgI(s) + 2\ CN^-(aq) \rightleftharpoons Ag(CN)_2^-(aq) + I^-(aq)$ $K_{net} = K_{sp} \cdot K_{form} = 480$

18.82   (a) Add H_2SO_4, precipitating $BaSO_4$ and leaving $Na^+(aq)$ in solution.

   (b) Add HCl or another source of chloride ion. $PbCl_2$ will precipitate, but $NiCl_2$ is water-soluble.

18.83   (a) Add HCl to precipitate the Ag^+ as AgCl and leave $Cu^{2+}(aq)$ in solution.

   (b) Add $(NH_4)_2S$ to precipitate the Fe^{3+} as Fe_2S_3.

18.84 $[Ba^{2+}] = \dfrac{(0.048\ L)(0.0.0012\ mol/L)}{0.072\ L} = 8.0 \times 10^{-4}\ M$

   $[SO_4^{2-}] = \dfrac{(0.024\ L)(1.0 \times 10^{-6}\ mol/L)}{0.072\ L} = 3.3 \times 10^{-7}\ M$

   $Q = [Ba^{2+}][SO_4^{2-}] = (8.0 \times 10^{-4})(3.3 \times 10^{-7}) = 2.6 \times 10^{-10}$ $Q > K_{sp}$ $BaSO_4$ will precipitate

18.85 $CH_3CO_2H(aq) + OH^-(aq) \rightarrow CH_3CO_2^-(aq) + H_2O(\ell)$

   $(0.0100\ L\ NaOH)(0.15\ mol/L) = 0.0015\ mol\ NaOH = mol\ CH_3CO_2H\ consumed = mol\ CH_3CO_2^-\ produced$

   $(0.0200\ L\ CH_3CO_2H)(0.15\ mol/L) = 0.0030\ mol\ CH_3CO_2H$

   $0.0030\ mol\ CH_3CO_2H - 0.0015\ mol\ consumed = 0.0015\ mol\ CH_3CO_2H\ remaining$

   $pH = pK_a + \log\dfrac{[CH_3CO_2^-]}{[CH_3CO_2H]} = -\log(1.8 \times 10^{-5}) + \log\left(\dfrac{0.0015\ mol}{0.0015\ mol}\right) = 4.74$

18.86 $NH_3(aq) + H_3O^+(aq) \rightarrow NH_4^+(aq) + H_2O(\ell)$

   $(0.0500\ L\ NH_3)(0.40\ mol/L) = 0.020\ mol\ NH_3$

   $(0.0500\ L\ HCl)(0.40\ mol/L) = 0.020\ mol\ HCl = mol\ NH_3\ consumed = mol\ NH_4^+\ produced$

   $[NH_4^+] = \dfrac{0.020\ mol}{0.1000\ L} = 0.20\ M$

   $NH_4^+(aq) + H_2O(\ell) \rightleftharpoons H_3O^+(aq) + NH_3(aq)$

   $K_a = 5.6 \times 10^{-10} = \dfrac{[NH_3][H_3O^+]}{[NH_4^+]} = \dfrac{x^2}{0.20 - x} \approx \dfrac{x^2}{0.20}$

   $x = [H_3O^+] = 1.1 \times 10^{-5}\ M$ $pH = -\log[H_3O^+] = 4.98$

18.87   (a) pH > 7 The solution will contain the conjugate base of the weak acid.

(b) pH > 7 The solution will contain the NH_3/NH_4^+ buffer

(c) pH = 7 The solution will contain neutral ions

(d) pH = 7 The solution will contain neutral ions

18.88 $BaCO_3 < Ag_2CO_3 < NaCO_3$

18.89   For CaF_2 to precipitate, Q must exceed K_{sp} (5.3×10^{-11})

$K_{sp} = [Ca^{2+}][F^-]^2 = 5.3 \times 10^{-11} = (2.0 \times 10^{-3})[F^-]^2$

$[F^-]$ must be greater than 1.6×10^{-4} M

18.90 $[NH_4^+] = \dfrac{5.15 \text{ g}}{0.10 \text{ L}} \cdot \dfrac{1 \text{ mol } NH_4NO_3}{80.04 \text{ g}} = 0.64$ M

$pH = pK_a + \log\dfrac{[NH_3]}{[NH_4^+]} = -\log(5.6 \times 10^{-10}) + \log\left(\dfrac{0.15}{0.64}\right) = 8.62$

Diluting a buffer solution will not change the pH.

18.91   (a) $K_b = 3.2 \times 10^{-5} = \dfrac{[OH^-][HOCH_2CH_2NH_3^+]}{[HOCH_2CH_2NH_2]} = \dfrac{x^2}{0.010 - x} \approx \dfrac{x^2}{0.010}$

$x = [OH^-] = 5.7 \times 10^{-4}$ M   pOH = 3.25   pH = 10.75

(b) (0.0250 L ethanolamine)(0.010 mol/L) = 2.5×10^{-4} mol ethanolamine

Total volume = 0.025 L + (2.5×10^{-4} mol)(1 L/0.0095 mol) = 0.0513 L

$[HOCH_2CH_2NH_3^+] = \dfrac{0.010 \text{ mol}}{1.0 \text{ L}} \cdot 0.0250 \text{ L} \cdot \dfrac{1}{0.0513 \text{ L}} = 0.0049$ M

$K_a = \dfrac{K_w}{K_b} = 3.1 \times 10^{-10} = \dfrac{[H_3O^+][HOCH_2CH_2NH_2]}{[HOCH_2CH_2NH_3^+]} = \dfrac{x^2}{0.0049 - x} \approx \dfrac{x^2}{0.0049}$

$x = [H_3O^+] = 1.2 \times 10^{-6}$ M   pH = $-\log[H_3O^+]$ = 5.91

(c) At titration midpoint $[HOCH_2CH_2NH_2] = [HOCH_2CH_2NH_3^+]$ and pH = $pK_a = -\log(3.1 \times 10^{-10}) = 9.51$

(d) Methyl red would detect the equivalence point.

(e)

mL HCl added	mol H_3O^+ added	mol conjugate acid produced	mol base remaining	pH
5.00	4.8×10^{-5}	4.8×10^{-5}	2.0×10^{-4}	10.13
10.00	9.5×10^{-5}	9.5×10^{-5}	1.6×10^{-4}	9.72
20.00	1.9×10^{-4}	1.9×10^{-4}	6×10^{-5}	9.00
30.00	2.9×10^{-4}			3.20

When 30.00 mL HCl is added, pH depends only on the excess H_3O^+

$$[H_3O^+] = (2.9 \times 10^{-4} \text{ mol} - 2.5 \times 10^{-4} \text{ mol})/0.0550 \text{ L} = 6.4 \times 10^{-4} \text{ M}$$

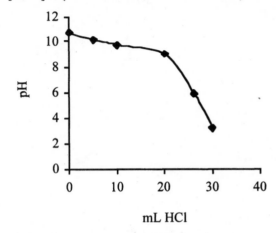

18.92   (a) $K_a = 2.4 \times 10^{-5} = \dfrac{[H_3O^+][C_6H_5NH_3^+]}{[C_6H_5NH_2]} = \dfrac{x^2}{0.100 - x} \approx \dfrac{x^2}{0.100}$

$x = [H_3O^+] = 0.00155 \text{ M}$ pH = 2.81

(b) $(0.0500 \text{ L } C_6H_5NH_3Cl)(0.100 \text{ mol/L}) = 0.00500 \text{ mol } C_6H_5NH_3^+$

Total volume = 0.0500 L + (0.00500 mol)(1 L/0.185 mol) = 0.0770 L

$[C_6H_5NH_2] = \dfrac{0.100 \text{ mol}}{1 \text{ L}} \cdot 0.0500 \cdot \dfrac{1}{0.0770 \text{ L}} = 0.0649 \text{ M}$

$K_b = \dfrac{K_w}{K_a} = 4.2 \times 10^{-10} = \dfrac{[C_6H_5NH_3^+][OH^-]}{[C_6H_5NH_2]} = \dfrac{x^2}{0.0649 - x} \approx \dfrac{x^2}{0.0649}$

$x = [OH^-] = 5.2 \times 10^{-6} \text{ M}$ pOH = 5.28   pH = 8.72

(c) At the midpoint of the titration, $[C_6H_5NH_3^+] = [C_6H_5NH_2]$, and pH = pK_a = 4.62.

(d) o-Cresolphthalein or phenolphthalein would be reasonable choices for an indicator.

(e)

mL NaOH added	mol OH⁻ added	mol conjugate base produced	mol acid remaining	pH
10.00	0.00185	0.00185	0.00315	4.39
20.00	0.00370	0.00370	0.00130	5.07
30.00	0.00555			11.84

When 30.00 mL NaOH is added, pH depends only on the excess OH⁻

$[OH^-] = (0.00555 \text{ mol} - 0.00500 \text{ mol})/0.0800 \text{ L} = 0.00688 \text{ M}$

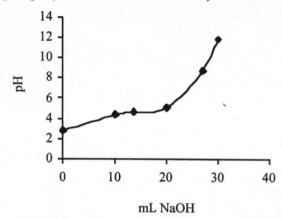

18.93 $K_{sp} = [Sr^{2+}][CO_3^{2-}] = (x)(x) = x^2$ $x = \sqrt{K_{sp}} = \sqrt{5.6 \times 10^{-10}} = 2.4 \times 10^{-5} \text{ mol/L}$

$\dfrac{2.4 \times 10^{-5} \text{ mol}}{1 \text{ L}} \cdot 1.0 \text{ L} \cdot \dfrac{148 \text{ g}}{1 \text{ mol SrCO}_3} \cdot \dfrac{10^3 \text{ mg}}{1 \text{ g}} = 3.5 \text{ mg SrCO}_3 \text{ dissolves}$

18.94 $pH = 2.50 = -\log(7.5 \times 10^{-3}) + \log\dfrac{[H_2PO_4^-]}{[H_3PO_4]}$

$\dfrac{[H_2PO_4^-]}{[H_3PO_4]} = \dfrac{\text{mol H}_2\text{PO}_4^-}{\text{mol H}_3\text{PO}_4} = 2.4$ $(0.100 \text{ L H}_3\text{PO}_4)(0.230 \text{ mol/L}) = 0.0230 \text{ mol H}_3\text{PO}_4$

One mole of $H_2PO_4^-$ is formed for each mole of H_3PO_4 consumed by reaction with NaOH

$\dfrac{x}{0.0230 - x} = 2.4$ $x = \text{mol H}_2\text{PO}_4^- = \text{mol OH}^- = 0.016 \text{ mol}$

$(0.016 \text{ mol OH}^-)(1 \text{ L}/0.150 \text{ mol}) = 0.11 \text{ L}$

18.95 $pH = 7.75 = -\log(6.2 \times 10^{-8}) + \log\dfrac{[HPO_4^{2-}]}{[H_2PO_4^-]}$

$\dfrac{[HPO_4^{2-}]}{[H_2PO_4^-]} = \dfrac{\text{mol HPO}_4^{2-}}{\text{mol H}_2\text{PO}_4^-} = 3.5$ $(0.0800 \text{ L HCl})(0.200 \text{ mol/L}) = 0.0160 \text{ mol H}_3\text{O}^+$

The total H_3O^+ available can be used to produce HPO_4^- (1 H_3O^+/PO_4^{3-}) and $H_2PO_4^-$ (2 H_3O^+/PO_4^{3-})

$0.0160 \text{ mol H}_3\text{O}^+ = (\text{mol HPO}_4^{2-}) + 2 \times (\text{mol H}_2\text{PO}_4^-) = (\text{mol H}_2\text{PO}_4^-)(3.5) + 2 \times (\text{mol H}_2\text{PO}_4^-)$

total mol PO_4^{3-} needed = mol HPO_4^{2-} + mol $H_2PO_4^-$ = 0.0029 mol + 0.010 mol = 0.013 mol PO_4^{3-}

$0.013 \text{ mol Na}_3\text{PO}_4 \cdot \dfrac{164 \text{ g}}{1 \text{ mol}} = 2.1 \text{ g Na}_3\text{PO}_4$

18.96 (a) $K_b = 4.27 \times 10^{-4} = \dfrac{[OH^-][C_2H_5NH_3^+]}{[C_2H_5NH_2]} = \dfrac{x^2}{0.150 - x}$

The approximation $x \ll 0.150$ is not valid. Solve using the quadratic equation.

$x = [OH^-] = 0.00779 \text{ M} \qquad pOH = 2.11 \qquad\qquad pH = 11.89$

(b) At the halfway point $[C_2H_5NH_2] = [C_2H_5NH_3^+]$ and $pH = pK_a = -\log(2.3 \times 10^{-11}) = 10.63$

(c) $(0.0500 \text{ L } C_2H_5NH_2)(0.150 \text{ mol/L}) = 0.00750 \text{ mol } C_2H_5NH_2$

When 75% of required acid has been added

$(0.75)(0.00750 \text{ mol } C_2H_5NH_2) = 0.00563 \text{ mol } C_2H_5NH_2 \text{ consumed} = \text{mol } C_2H_5NH_3^+ \text{ produced}$

$(0.25)(0.00750 \text{ mol } C_2H_5NH_2) = 0.00188 \text{ mol } C_2H_5NH_2 \text{ remains}$

$pH = pK_a + \log\dfrac{[C_2H_5NH_2]}{[C_2H_5NH_3^+]} = 10.63 + \log\left(\dfrac{0.00188 \text{ mol}}{0.00563 \text{ mol}}\right) = 10.15$

(d) Total volume $= 0.0500 \text{ L} + (0.00750 \text{ mol})(1 \text{ L}/0.100 \text{ mol}) = 0.125 \text{ L}$

$[C_2H_5NH_3^+] = \dfrac{0.00750 \text{ mol}}{0.125 \text{ L}} = 0.0600 \text{ M}$

$K_a = 2.3 \times 10^{-11} = \dfrac{[H_3O^+][C_2H_5NH_2]}{[C_2H_5NH_3^+]} = \dfrac{x^2}{0.0600 - x} \approx \dfrac{x^2}{0.0600}$

$x = [H_3O^+] = 1.2 \times 10^{-6} \text{ M} \qquad\qquad pH = -\log[H_3O^+] = 5.93$

(e) pH depends only on the excess H_3O^+

$[H_3O^+] = \dfrac{(0.0100 \text{ L})(0.100 \text{ mol/L})}{0.135 \text{ L}} = 0.00741 \text{ M} \qquad pH = 2.13$

(f)

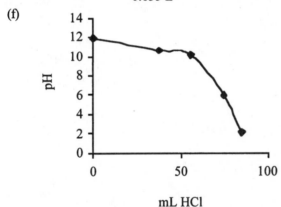

mL HCl

(d) Alizarin or bromcresol purple would detect the equivalence point.

18.97 $pH = 4.70 = -\log(6.4 \times 10^{-5}) + \log\dfrac{[C_2O_4^{2-}]}{[HC_2O_4^-]}$

$\dfrac{[C_2O_4^{2-}]}{[HC_2O_4^-]} = \dfrac{\text{mol } C_2O_4^{2-}}{\text{mol } HC_2O_4^-} = 3.2 \qquad\qquad (0.100 \text{ L } HC_2O_4^-)(0.100 \text{ mol/L}) = 0.0100 \text{ mol } HC_2O_4^-$

One mole of $C_2O_4^{2-}$ is formed for each mole of $HC_2O_4^-$ consumed by reaction with NaOH

$\dfrac{x}{0.0100 - x} = 3.2 \qquad\qquad x = \text{mol } C_2O_4^{2-} = \text{mol } OH^- = 0.0076 \text{ mol}$

$(0.0076 \text{ mol } OH^-)(1 \text{ L}/0.120 \text{ mol}) = 0.064 \text{ L}$

18.98   (a) pH will increase

        (b) pH will not change

        (c) The effects are not the same because the acetate ion is a weak base (it is the conjugate base of a weak acid) while both ions in $NaNO_3$ are neutral and do not affect the pH of a solution.

18.99   (a) $1.50 \text{ g} \cdot \dfrac{1 \text{ mol } C_6H_5CO_2H}{122.1 \text{ g}} = 0.0123 \text{ mol}$ $\qquad\qquad$ $1.50 \text{ g} \cdot \dfrac{1 \text{ mol } NaC_6H_5CO_2}{144.1} = 0.0104 \text{ mol}$

        $pH = pK_a + \log\dfrac{[C_6H_5CO_2^-]}{[C_6H_5CO_2H]} = -\log(6.3 \times 10^{-5}) + \log\left(\dfrac{0.0104 \text{ mol}}{0.0123 \text{ mol}}\right) = 4.13$

        (b) Additional acid ($C_6H_5CO_2H$) must be added to lower the pH to 4.00

             $4.00 = -\log(6.3 \times 10^{-5}) + \log\dfrac{0.0104 \text{ mol}}{x}$ $\qquad\qquad$ $x = 0.017 \text{ mol } C_6H_5CO_2H$

             $(0.017 \text{ mol} - 0.0123 \text{ mol})\dfrac{122.1 \text{ g}}{1 \text{ mol } C_6H_5CO_2H} = 0.5 \text{ g } C_6H_5CO_2H$ should be added

        (c) $4.00 = -\log(6.3 \times 10^{-5}) + \log\dfrac{[C_6H_5CO_2^-]}{[C_6H_5CO_2H]}$

             $\dfrac{[C_6H_5CO_2^-]}{[C_6H_5CO_2H]} = \dfrac{\text{mol } C_6H_5CO_2^-}{\text{mol } C_6H_5CO_2H} = 0.63 = \dfrac{0.0104 - x}{0.0123 + x}$

             $x = 0.0016 \text{ mol } H_3O^+$

             $(0.0016 \text{ mol})(1 \text{ L}/2.0 \text{ mol}) = 8.2 \times 10^{-4}$ L or 8.2 mL of 2.0 M HCl should be added

18.100 (a) $pH = 12.00 = -\log(3.6 \times 10^{-13}) + \log\dfrac{[PO_4^{3-}]}{[HPO_4^{2-}]}$

             $\dfrac{[PO_4^{3-}]}{[HPO_4^{2-}]} = 0.36$ $\qquad$ HPO_4^{2-} is present in a larger amount

        (b) $\dfrac{0.400}{[HPO_4^{2-}]} = 0.36$ $\qquad$ $[HPO_4^{2-}] = 1.1 \text{ mol/L}$

             $\dfrac{1.1 \text{ mol}}{1 \text{ L}} \cdot 0.2000 \text{ L} \cdot \dfrac{142.0 \text{ g}}{1 \text{ mol } Na_2HPO_4} = 32 \text{ g } Na_2HPO_4$

        (c) Additional base (PO_4^{3-}) must be added to raise the pH to 12.25.

             $12.25 = -\log(3.6 \times 10^{-13}) + \log\dfrac{x}{1.1}$

             $x = [PO_4^{3-}] = 0.70 \text{ mol/L}$

             $(0.70 \text{ mol/L})(0.2000 \text{ L}) - (0.400 \text{ mol/L})(0.2000 \text{ L}) = 0.061 \text{ mol } Na_3PO_4$

             $0.061 \text{ mol} \cdot \dfrac{163.9 \text{ g}}{1 \text{ mol } Na_3PO_4} = 10. \text{ g } Na_3PO_4$ should be added

18.101 $pH = 9.00 = -\log(5.6 \times 10^{-10}) + \log\dfrac{[NH_3]}{[NH_4^+]}$ $\qquad\qquad$ $\dfrac{[NH_3]}{[NH_4^+]} = 0.56$

        $(0.5000 \text{ L } NH_3)(0.250 \text{ mol/L}) = 0.125 \text{ mol } NH_3$

        $\dfrac{[NH_3]}{[NH_4^+]} = \dfrac{0.125 - x}{x} = 0.56$ $\qquad\qquad$ $x = 0.080 \text{ mol } H_3O^+$ to be added

        $(0.080 \text{ mol } H_3O^+)(1 \text{ L}/0.200 \text{ mol}) = 0.40 \text{ L of } 0.200 \text{ M HCl}$ should be added

18.102 $K_{sp}(BaSO_4) < K_{sp}(SrSO_4)$ $BaSO_4$ will precipitate first

18.103 $K_{sp} = 4.9 \times 10^{-17} = [Fe^{2+}][OH^-]^2 = (0.1)[OH^-]^2$ [OH^-] required to precipitate $Fe(OH)_2 = 2.2 \times 10^{-8}$ M

$K_{sp} = 1.4 \times 10^{-15} = [Pb^{2+}][OH^-]^2 = (0.1)[OH^-]^2$ [OH^-] required to precipitate $Pb(OH)_2 = 1.2 \times 10^{-7}$ M

$K_{sp} = 1.3 \times 10^{-33} = [Al^{3+}][OH^-]^3 = (0.1)[OH^-]^3$ [OH^-] required to precipitate $Al(OH)_3 = 2.4 \times 10^{-11}$ M

$Al(OH)_3$ will precipitate first, followed by $Fe(OH)_2$ and then $Pb(OH)_2$

18.104 $AgCl(s) \rightleftharpoons Ag^+(aq) + Cl^-(aq)$ $K_{sp} = 1.8 \times 10^{-10}$

$Ag^+(aq) + I^-(aq) \rightleftharpoons AgI(s)$ $K = 1/K_{sp} = 1.2 \times 10^{16}$

$AgCl(s) + I^-(aq) \rightleftharpoons AgI(s) + Cl^-(aq)$ $K_{net} = (1.8 \times 10^{-10})(1.2 \times 10^{16}) = 2.1 \times 10^6$

The equilibrium lies predominantly to the right. AgI will form if I^- is added to a saturated solution of AgCl.

18.105 $Zn(OH)_2(s) \rightleftharpoons Zn^{2+}(aq) + 2\ OH^-(aq)$ $K_{sp} = 3 \times 10^{-17}$

$Zn^{2+}(aq) + 2\ CN^-(aq) \rightleftharpoons Zn(CN)_2(s)$ $K = 1/K_{sp} = 1.3 \times 10^{11}$

$Zn(OH)_2(s) + 2\ CN^-(aq) \rightleftharpoons Zn(CN)_2(s) + 2\ OH^-(aq)$ $K_{net} = (3 \times 10^{-17})(1.3 \times 10^{11}) = 4 \times 10^{-6}$

The equilibrium lies predominantly to the left. The transformation of zinc hydroxide into zinc cyanide will not occur to a large extent because of the unfavorable equilibrium constant.

18.106   (a) $K_{sp} = 1.8 \times 10^{-7} = [Ba^{2+}][F^-]^2 = (0.10\ M)[F^-]^2$

$[F^-] = 1.3 \times 10^{-3}$ M

When [F^-] reaches this concentration, the maximum amount of CaF_2 will have precipitated without precipitating BaF_2.

(b) $K_{sp} = 5.3 \times 10^{-11} = [Ca^{2+}][F^-]^2 = [Ca^{2+}](1.3 \times 10^{-3})^2$

$[Ca^{2+}] = 2.9 \times 10^{-5}$ M

18.107   (a) $K_{sp} = 9.8 \times 10^{-9} = [Pb^{2+}][I^-]^2 = [Pb^{2+}](0.10)^2$ $[Pb^{2+}] = 9.8 \times 10^{-7}$ mol/L

$K_{sp} = 7.4 \times 10^{-14} = [Pb^{2+}][CO_3^{2-}] = [Pb^{2+}](0.10)$ $[Pb^{2+}] = 7.4 \times 10^{-13}$ mol/L

$PbCO_3$ will precipitate first

(b) $K_{sp} = 7.4 \times 10^{-14} = [Pb^{2+}][CO_3^{2-}] = (9.8 \times 10^{-7})[CO_3^{2-}]$ $[CO_3^{2-}] = 7.6 \times 10^{-8}$ mol/L

18.108   (a) $K_{sp} = 4.9 \times 10^{-5} = [Ca^{2+}][SO_4^{2-}] = (0.010)[SO_4^{2-}]$ $[SO_4^{2-}] = 4.9 \times 10^{-3}$ mol/L

$K_{sp} = 2.5 \times 10^{-8} = [Pb^{2+}][SO_4^{2-}] = (0.010)[SO_4^{2-}]$ $[SO_4^{2-}] = 2.5 \times 10^{-8}$ mol/L

$PbSO_4$ will precipitate first

(b) $K_{sp} = 2.5 \times 10^{-8} = [Pb^{2+}][SO_4^{2-}] = [Pb^{2+}](4.9 \times 10^{-3})$ $[Pb^{2+}] = 5.1 \times 10^{-6}$ mol/L

18.109 $Ba(OH)_2$ and $BaCO_3$

18.110   CuS has a K_{spa} value of 6×10^{-37} (see Appendix J), so it is not expected to be readily soluble in strong acid. Addition of strong acid to the mixture of CuS and $Cu(OH)_2$ will dissolve the hydroxide salt but not CuS.

18.111   (a)   fraction ionized = (0.0291 M)/(0.10 M) = 0.291

           (b)   The fraction ionized decreases

18.112   Increasing $[NH_4Cl]$ decreases the pH. Increasing $[NH_3]$ increases pH

18.113 $[NaHCO_3] = 0.21$ M and $[Na_2CO_3] = 0.10$ M

18.114   (a)   15.0 mL

           (b)   pH = 9.01   The principle species in solution is the weak base, $CH_3CO_2^-$

           (c)   either phenolphthalein or thymolphthalein

18.115   (a) $[Cl^-]$ is equal to $2 \times [Pb^{2+}]$ when the only source of these ions is $PbCl_2$.

           (b)   Watch the video on this screen for a description of how the instrument works.

18.116   The solubility of $BaSO_4$ would increase.

18.117   (a) 1.0×10^{-5} M

           (b)   Silver ions and chloride ions form larger and larger ion clusters in the solution.

18.118   Adding Cl^- to the test tube shifts the equilibrium to the left, forming more $PbCl_2$ and decreasing $[Pb^{2+}]$

18.119   (a)   Add $Cl^-(aq)$ to precipitate silver and lead ions, leaving copper ions in solution

           (b)   Lead chloride is soluble in hot water, and silver chloride is not.

           (c)   Adding chromate ions will precipitate the lead ions as the insoluble salt $PbCrO_4(s)$.

18.120   (a) $PbCl_2(s) \rightleftharpoons Pb^{2+}(aq) + 2\ Cl^-(aq)$ $Pb^{2+}(aq) + CrO_4^{2-}(aq) \rightleftharpoons PbCrO_4(s)$

           (b)   If the lead chloride equilibrium were static, only a small amount of lead chromate would precipitate and the lead chloride would not dissolve in a solution containing $CrO_4^{2-}(aq)$.

18.121   (a)   Adding acid to the solid decreases $[OH^-]$, shifting the equilibrium to the right.

           (b)   The solubility would increase as pH decreases.

           (c)   Decreasing pH by 1.0 is equivalent to increasing $[H_3O^+]$ by a factor of 10, which decreases $[OH^-]$ by a factor of 10. The hydroxide ion concentration is squared in the equilibrium constant expression, so decreasing $[OH^-]$ by factor of 10 results in the solubility increasing by a factor of 10^2, or 100.

18.122   See the description of floor wax application and removal on the sidebar to Screen 18.17.

Chapter 19
Principles of Reactivity: Entropy and Free Energy

INSTRUCTOR'S NOTES

This subject is treated, in an admittedly superficial way, in 2-3 lectures. However, at the introductory level our goal is relatively limited: to convey the idea of reaction spontaneity and to differentiate this from reaction speed.

Although we usually cover thermodynamics following our discussion of equilibria, we have sometimes reversed these topics and find no particular problems in doing so. When thermodynamics is discussed before equilibrium we make the connection between ΔG and K very early in the lectures on general equilibria.

This chapter has been somewhat modified from the previous edition to give a probability introduction to entropy. The discussion of entropy is further expanded to include considerations and calculations of the entropy of the surroundings. Consequently, Gibb's Free Energy is then presented.

SUGGESTED DEMONSTRATIONS

1.   Spontaneous Reactions and Speed: Thermodynamics versus Kinetics

-   We usually begin these lectures with a series of reactions designed to show that some product-favored reactions ($Na + H_2O$, $Mg + O_2$) proceed with the evolution of heat, while others proceed while requiring heat (the melting of ice, the evaporation of liquid nitrogen, or the dissolution of some solids).

-   There are many suitable demonstrations in Volume 1 of Shakhashiri's *Chemical Demonstrations*.

Solutions to Study Questions

19.1   First law: The total energy of the universe is constant.

Second law: In spontaneous process the entropy of the universe increases.

Third law: There is no disorder in a perfect crystal at 0 K.

19.2   A spontaneous change is one that occurs without outside intervention. It does not say anything about the rate of the change, only that a spontaneous change is one that is naturally occurring and leads inexorably to equilibrium. The reverse is true for a non-spontaneous process.

Spontaneous chemical process: a strong acid reacts with a strong base to form water and an ionic salt

Non-spontaneous chemical process: water reacts with NaCl to form HCl and NaOH

Spontaneous physical process: at room temperature, ice melts to form liquid water

Non-spontaneous physical process: at room temperature, liquid water forms ice

19.3   See Problem-Solving Tip 19.1, page 791

19.4   (a) Reactant-favored (mercury is a liquid under standard conditions)

(b) Product-favored (water vapor will condense to liquid)

(c) Reactant-favored (a continuous supply of energy is required)

(d) Product-favored (carbon will burn)

(e) Product-favored (salt will dissolve in water)

(f) Reactant-favored (calcium carbonate is insoluble)

19.5   (a) The entropy of the universe increases in all product-favored reactions.

(b) Product-favored reactions can occur at any rate, not necessarily a fast rate.

(c) While many spontaneous processes are exothermic, endothermic processes can be spontaneous at high temperatures.

(d) Endothermic processes can be spontaneous at high temperatures.

19.6   (a) True

(b) False Whether an exothermic reaction is product- or reactant- favored also depends on the entropy change of the system.

(c) False Reactions with $+\Delta H^{\circ}_{rxn}$ and $+\Delta S^{\circ}_{rxn}$ are product-favored at higher temperatures.

(d) True

19.7   The entropy of a pure crystal is zero at 0 K. A substance cannot have $S = 0$ J/K·mol at standard conditions (25 °C, 1 bar). All substances have positive entropy values at temperatures above 0 K. Based on the third law of thermodynamics, negative values of entropy cannot occur. The only exception to this is the entropy of the solvation process. When water molecules are constrained to a more ordered arrangement in a solution than in pure water, a higher degree of order results and entropy is negative.

19.8 $2 C_2H_6(g) + 7 O_2(g) \rightarrow 4 CO_2(g) + 6 H_2O(g)$

$\Delta S^\circ_{sys} > 0$ (the number of moles of gases increases from 9 to 10)

$\Delta S^\circ_{surr} > 0$ (burning a hydrocarbon is an exothermic process)

$\Delta S^\circ_{univ} > 0$ ($= \Delta S^\circ_{sys} + \Delta S^\circ_{surr}$)

19.9 $\Delta H^\circ < 0$ (exothermic process)

$\Delta G^\circ < 0$ ($= - T\Delta S^\circ_{univ}$)

19.10 $\Delta G^\circ < 0$ so K should be greater than 1 (very large)

The reaction is exothermic. Raising the temperature will shift the equilibrium to the left, decreasing K_p

19.11   In a solid the particles have fixed positions in the solid lattice. When a solid is dissolved in water the ions are dispersed throughout the solution.

19.12   (a)   The CO_2 vapor at 0 °C has a higher entropy than the sample of solid CO_2

        (b)   Liquid water at the higher temperature (50 °C) has a higher entropy

        (c)   Ruby has a higher entropy than pure alumina

        (d)   The sample of $N_2(g)$ at the lower pressure (1 bar) has a higher entropy

19.13   (a)   The sample of silicon containing trace impurities has a higher entropy

        (b)   The sample of $O_2(g)$ at the higher temperature (0 °C) has a higher entropy

        (c) $I_2(g)$ has a higher entropy than $I_2(s)$

        (d)   The sample of $O_2(g)$ at the lower pressure (0.01 bar) has a higher entropy

19.14   (a) $CH_3OH(g)$ has a higher entropy than $O_2(g)$

        (b) $HBr(g)$ has a higher entropy than $HCl(g)$ or $HF(g)$

        (c) $NH_4Cl(aq)$ has a higher entropy than $NH_4Cl(s)$

        (d) $HNO_3(g)$ has a higher entropy than $HNO_3(\ell)$ or $HNO_3(aq)$

19.15   (a) $NaCl(g)$ has a higher entropy than $NaCl(s)$ or $NaCl(aq)$

        (b) $H_2S(g)$ has a higher entropy than $H_2O(g)$

        (c) $C_2H_4(g)$ has a higher entropy than $N_2(g)$

        (d) $H_2SO_4(aq)$ has a higher entropy than $H_2SO_4(\ell)$

317

19.16 (a) $\Delta S^\circ = S^\circ[KOH(aq)] - \Delta S^\circ[KOH(s)]$

$\Delta S^\circ = 1$ mol (91.6 J/K·mol) $- 1$ mol (78.9 J/K·mol) $= 12.7$ J/K

A positive ΔS° indicates an increase in entropy

(b) $\Delta S^\circ = S^\circ[Na(s)] - \Delta S^\circ[Na(g)]$

$\Delta S^\circ = 1$ mol (51.21 J/K·mol) $- 1$ mol (153.765 J/K·mol) $= -102.56$ J/K

A negative ΔS° indicates a decrease in entropy

(c) $\Delta S^\circ = S^\circ[Br_2(g)] - \Delta S^\circ[Br_2(\ell)]$

$\Delta S^\circ = 1$ mol (245.42 J/K·mol) $- 1$ mol (152.2 J/K·mol) $= 93.2$ J/K

A positive ΔS° indicates an increase in entropy

(d) $\Delta S^\circ = S^\circ[HCl(g)] - \Delta S^\circ[HCl(aq)]$

$\Delta S^\circ = 1$ mol (186.2 J/K·mol) $- 1$ mol (56.5 J/K·mol) $= 129.7$ J/K

A positive ΔS° indicates an increase in entropy

19.17 (a) $\Delta S^\circ = S^\circ[NH_4Cl(aq)] - S^\circ[NH_4Cl(s)]$

$\Delta S^\circ = 1$ mol (169.9 J/K·mol) $- 1$ mol (94.85 J/K·mol) $= 75.1$ J/K

A positive ΔS° indicates an increase in entropy

(b) $\Delta S^\circ = S^\circ[C_2H_5OH(g)] - S^\circ[C_2H_5OH(\ell)]$

$\Delta S^\circ = 1$ mol (282.70 J/K·mol) $- 1$ mol (160.7 J/K·mol) $= 122.0$ J/K

A positive ΔS° indicates an increase in entropy

(c) $\Delta S^\circ = S^\circ[CCl_4(\ell)] - S^\circ[CCl_4(g)]$

$\Delta S^\circ = 1$ mol (214.39 J/K·mol) $- 1$ mol (309.65 J/K·mol) $= -95.26$ J/K

A negative ΔS° indicates a decrease in entropy

(d) $\Delta S^\circ = S^\circ[NaCl(g)] - \Delta S^\circ[NaCl(s)]$

$\Delta S^\circ = 1$ mol (229.79 J/K·mol) $- 1$ mol (72.11 J/K·mol) $= 157.68$ J/K

A positive ΔS° indicates an increase in entropy

19.18 $\Delta S^\circ = S^\circ[C_2H_6(g)] - \{2\ S^\circ[C(graphite)] + 3\ S^\circ[H_2(g)]\}$

$\Delta S^\circ = 1$ mol (229.2 J/K·mol) $- [2$ mol (5.6 J/K·mol) $+ 3$ mol (130.7 J/K·mol)]

$\Delta S^\circ = -174.1$ J/K

19.19 $\Delta S^\circ = S^\circ[NH_3(g)] - \{^1/_2\ S^\circ[N_2(g)] + ^3/_2\ S^\circ[H_2(g)]\}$

$\Delta S^\circ = 1$ mol (192.77 J/K·mol) $- [^1/_2$ mol (191.56 J/K·mol) $+ ^3/_2$ mol (130.7 J/K·mol)]

$\Delta S^\circ = -99.1$ J/K

19.20   (a) $\frac{1}{2}$ H$_2$(g) + $\frac{1}{2}$ Cl$_2$(g) → HCl(g)

$\Delta S° = S°[HCl(g)] - \{\frac{1}{2} S°[H_2(g)] + \frac{1}{2} S°[Cl_2(g)]\}$

$\Delta S° = 1$ mol (186.2 J/K·mol) $- [\frac{1}{2}$ mol (130.7 J/K·mol) $+ \frac{1}{2}$ mol (223.08 J/K·mol)]

$\Delta S° = 9.3$ J/K

(b)   Ca(s) + O$_2$(g) + H$_2$(g) → Ca(OH)$_2$(s)

$\Delta S° = S°[Ca(OH)_2(s)] - \{S°[Ca(s)] + S°[O_2(g)] + S°[H_2(g)]\}$

$\Delta S° = 1$ mol (83.39 J/K·mol) $- [1$ mol (41.59 J/K·mol) $+ 1$ mol (205.07 J/K·mol)

$+ 1$ mol (130.7 J/K·mol]

$\Delta S° = -294.0$ J/K

19.21   (a)   H$_2$(g) + S(s) → H$_2$S(g)

$\Delta S° = S°[H_2S(g)] - \{S°[H_2(g)] + S°[S(s)]\}$

$\Delta S° = 1$ mol (205.79 J/K·mol) $- [1$ mol (130.7 J/K·mol) $+ 1$ mol (32.1 J/K·mol)]

$\Delta S° = 43.0$ J/K

(b)   Mg(s) + C(graphite) + $\frac{3}{2}$ O$_2$(g) → MgCO$_3$(s)

$\Delta S° = S°[MgCO_3(s)] - \{S°[Mg(s)] + S°[C(graphite)] + \frac{3}{2} S°[O_2(g)]\}$

$\Delta S° = 1$ mol (65.84 J/K·mol) $- [1$ mol (32.67 J/K·mol) $+ 1$ mol (5.6 J/K·mol) $+ \frac{3}{2}$ (205.07 J/K·mol)]

$\Delta S° = -208.0$ J/K

19.22   (a) $\Delta S° = 2 S°[AlCl_3(s)] - \{2 S°[Al(s)] + 3 S°[Cl_2(g)]\}$

$\Delta S° = 2$ mol (109.29 J/K·mol) $- [2$ mol (28.3 J/K·mol) $+ 3$ mol (223.08 J/K·mol)]

$\Delta S° = -507.3$ J/K   A negative $\Delta S°$ indicates a decrease in entropy

(b) $\Delta S° = \{2 S°[CO_2(g)] + 4 S°[H_2O(g)]\} - \{2 S°[CH_3OH(\ell)] + 3 S°[O_2(g)]\}$

$\Delta S° = 2$ mol (213.74 J/K·mol) $+ 4$ mol (188.84 J/K·mol) $- [2$ mol (127.19 J/K·mol)

$+ 3$ mol (205.07 J/K·mol)]

$\Delta S° = 313.25$ J/K   A positive $\Delta S°$ indicates an increase in entropy

19.23   (a) $\Delta S° = 2 S°[NaOH(aq)] + S°[H_2(g)] - \{2 S°[Na(s)] + 2 S°[H_2O(\ell)]\}$

$\Delta S° = 2$ mol (48.1 J/K·mol) $+ 1$ mol (130.7 J/K·mol) $- [2$ mol (51.21 J/K·mol)

$+ 2$ mol (69.96 J/K·mol)]

$\Delta S° = -15.4$ J/K   A negative $\Delta S°$ indicates a decrease in entropy

(b) $\Delta S° = 2 S°[NaCl(aq)] + S°[H_2O(\ell)] + S°[CO_2(g)] - \{S°[Na_2CO_3(s)] + 2 S°[HCl(aq)]\}$

$\Delta S° = 2$ mol (115.5 J/K·mol) $+ 1$ mol (69.95 J/K·mol) $+ 1$ mol (213.74 J/K·mol)

$- [1$ mol (134.79 J/K·mol) $+ 2$ mol (56.5 J/K·mol)]

$\Delta S° = 266.9$ J/K A positive $\Delta S°$ indicates an increase in entropy

19.24 $\Delta S^{\circ}_{sys} = S^{\circ}[SiCl_4(g)] - \{S^{\circ}[Si(s)] + 2\ S^{\circ}[Cl_2(g)]\}$

$\Delta S^{\circ}_{sys} = 1\ mol\ (330.86\ J/K \cdot mol) - [1\ mol\ (18.82\ J/K \cdot mol) + 2\ mol\ (223.08\ J/K \cdot mol)]$

$\Delta S^{\circ}_{sys} = -134.12\ J/K$

$\Delta S^{\circ}_{surr} = -\Delta H^{\circ}_{sys}/T = -\Delta H_f^{\circ}[SiCl_4(g)]/(298.15\ K) = -[1\ mol\ (-662.75\ kJ/mol)/(298.15\ K)] = 2.2240\ kJ/K$

$\Delta S^{\circ}_{univ} = \Delta S^{\circ}_{sys} + \Delta S^{\circ}_{surr} = -134.12\ J/K + (2.2240\ kJ/K)(1\ J/1000\ kJ) = 2089.9\ J/K$

The reaction is spontaneous

19.25 $\Delta S^{\circ}_{sys} = S^{\circ}[SiH_4(g)] - \{S^{\circ}[Si(s)] + 2\ S^{\circ}[H_2(g)]\}$

$\Delta S^{\circ}_{sys} = 1\ mol\ (204.65\ J/K \cdot mol) - [1\ mol\ (18.82\ J/K \cdot mol) + 2\ mol\ (130.7\ J/K \cdot mol)]$

$\Delta S^{\circ}_{sys} = -75.6\ J/K$

$\Delta S^{\circ}_{surr} = -\Delta H^{\circ}_{sys}/T = -\Delta H_f^{\circ}[SiH_4(g)]/(298.15\ K) = -[1\ mol\ (34.31\ kJ/mol)/(298.15\ K)] = -0.1151\ kJ/K$

$\Delta S^{\circ}_{univ} = \Delta S^{\circ}_{sys} + \Delta S^{\circ}_{surr} = -75.6\ J/K + (-0.01151\ kJ/K)(10^3\ J/1\ kJ) = -190.7\ J/K$

The reaction is not spontaneous

19.26 $H_2O(\ell) \rightarrow H_2(g) + {}^1\!/_2\ O_2(g)$

$\Delta H^{\circ} = -\Delta H_f^{\circ}[H_2O(\ell)] = -[1\ mol\ (-285.83\ kJ/mol)] = 285.83\ kJ$

$\Delta S^{\circ} = S^{\circ}[H_2(g)] + {}^1\!/_2\ S^{\circ}[O_2(g)] - S^{\circ}[H_2O(\ell)]$

$\Delta S^{\circ} = 1\ mol\ (130.7\ J/K \cdot mol) + {}^1\!/_2\ mol\ (205.07\ J/K \cdot mol) - 1\ mol\ (69.95\ J/K \cdot mol) = 163.3\ J/K$

$\Delta S^{\circ}_{univ} = \Delta S^{\circ}_{sys} + \Delta S^{\circ}_{surr} = (163.3\ J/K) + -[(285.83\ kJ)(10^3\ J/1\ kJ)/298.15\ K)] = -795.4\ J/K$

The reaction is not spontaneous as ΔS°_{univ} is negative. The reaction is disfavored by energy dispersal.

19.27 ${}^1\!/_2\ H_2(g) + {}^1\!/_2\ Cl_2(g) \rightarrow HCl(g)$

$\Delta H^{\circ} = \Delta H_f^{\circ}[HCl(g)] = 1\ mol\ (-92.31\ kJ/mol) = -92.31\ kJ$

$\Delta S^{\circ} = S^{\circ}[HCl(g)] - \{{}^1\!/_2\ S^{\circ}[H_2(g)] + {}^1\!/_2\ S^{\circ}[Cl_2(g)]\}$

$\Delta S^{\circ} = 1\ mol\ (186.2\ J/K \cdot mol) - [{}^1\!/_2\ mol\ (130.7\ J/K \cdot mol) + {}^1\!/_2\ mol\ (223.08\ J/K \cdot mol)] = 9.3\ J/K$

$\Delta S^{\circ}_{univ} = \Delta S^{\circ}_{sys} + \Delta S^{\circ}_{surr} = (9.3\ J/K) + -[(-92.31\ kJ)(10^3\ J/1\ kJ)/298.15\ K)] = 318.9\ J/K$

The reaction is spontaneous as ΔS°_{univ} is positive.

19.28   (a) $\Delta H^{\circ} < 0$, $\Delta S^{\circ} < 0$; depends on T and relative magnitudes of ΔH and ΔS, more favorable at lower T.

(b) $\Delta H^{\circ} > 0$, $\Delta S^{\circ} < 0$; not spontaneous under all conditions

19.29   (a) $\Delta H^{\circ} < 0$, $\Delta S^{\circ} > 0$; spontaneous under all conditions

(b) $\Delta H^{\circ} > 0$, $\Delta S^{\circ} > 0$; depends on T and relative magnitudes of ΔH and ΔS, more favorable at higher T.

19.30   (a) $\Delta H^\circ = \Delta H_f^\circ[MgO(s)] + \Delta H_f^\circ[CO_2(g)] - \Delta H_f^\circ[MgCO_3(s)]$

$\Delta H^\circ = 1 \text{ mol } (-601.24 \text{ kJ/mol}) + 1 \text{ mol } (-393.509 \text{ kJ/mol}) - 1 \text{ mol } (-1111.69 \text{ kJ/mol})$

$\Delta H^\circ = 116.94 \text{ kJ}$

$\Delta S^\circ = S^\circ[MgO(s)] + S^\circ[CO_2(g)] - S^\circ[MgCO_3(s)]$

$\Delta S^\circ = 1 \text{ mol } (26.85 \text{ J/K·mol}) + 1 \text{ mol } (213.74 \text{ J/K·mol}) - 1 \text{ mol } (65.84 \text{ J/K·mol})$

$\Delta S^\circ = 174.75 \text{ J/K}$

(b) $\Delta G^\circ = \Delta H^\circ - T\Delta S^\circ = 116.94 \text{ kJ} - (298 \text{ K})(174.75 \text{ J/K})(1 \text{ kJ}/10^3 \text{ J}) = 64.9 \text{ kJ}$

The reaction is predicted to be non-spontaneous at 298 K ($\Delta G^\circ > 0$)

(c)   The reaction is predicted to be spontaneous at higher temperatures.

19.31   (a) $\Delta H^\circ = \Delta H_f^\circ[CO_2(g)] - \Delta H_f^\circ[SnO_2(s)]$

$\Delta H^\circ = 1 \text{ mol } (-393.509 \text{ kJ/mol}) - 1 \text{ mol } (-577.63 \text{ kJ/mol}) = 184.12 \text{ kJ}$

$\Delta S^\circ = S^\circ[Sn(s, \text{white})] + S^\circ[CO_2(g)] - \{S^\circ[SnO_2(s)] + S^\circ[C(\text{graphite})]\}$

$\Delta S^\circ = 1 \text{ mol } (51.08 \text{ J/K·mol}) + 1 \text{ mol } (213.74 \text{ J/K·mol}) - [1 \text{ mol } (49.04 \text{ J/K·mol})$

$- 1 \text{ mol } (5.6 \text{ J/K·mol})]$

$\Delta S^\circ = 210.2 \text{ J/K}$

(b) $\Delta G^\circ = \Delta H^\circ - T\Delta S^\circ = 184.12 \text{ kJ} - (298 \text{ K})(210.2 \text{ J/K})(1 \text{ kJ}/10^3 \text{ J}) = 121.5 \text{ kJ}$

The reaction is predicted to be non-spontaneous at 298 K ($\Delta G^\circ > 0$)

(c)   The reaction is predicted to be spontaneous at higher temperatures.

19.32   (a) $\Delta H^\circ = 2 \Delta H_f^\circ[PbO(s)] = 2 \text{ mol } (-219 \text{ kJ/mol}) = -438 \text{ kJ}$

$\Delta S^\circ = 2 S^\circ[(PbO(s)] - \{2 S^\circ[Pb(s)] + S^\circ[O_2(g)]\}$

$\Delta S^\circ = 2 \text{ mol } (66.5 \text{ J/K·mol}) - [2 \text{ mol } (64.81 \text{ J/K·mol}) + 1 \text{ mol } (205.07 \text{ J/K·mol})] = -201.7 \text{ J/K}$

$\Delta G^\circ = \Delta H^\circ - T\Delta S^\circ = -438 \text{ kJ} - (298 \text{ K})(-201.7 \text{ J/K})(1 \text{ kJ}/10^3 \text{ J}) = -378 \text{ kJ}$

The reaction is product-favored and enthalpy-driven.

(b) $\Delta H^\circ = \Delta H_f^\circ[NH_4NO_3(aq)] - \{\Delta H_f^\circ[NH_3(g)] + \Delta H_f^\circ[HNO_3(aq)]\}$

$\Delta H^\circ = 1 \text{ mol } (-339.87 \text{ kJ/mol}) - [1 \text{ mol } (-45.90 \text{ kJ/mol}) + 1 \text{ mol } (-207.36 \text{ kJ/mol})] = -86.61 \text{ kJ}$

$\Delta S^\circ = S^\circ[NH_4NO_3(aq)] - \{S^\circ[NH_3(g)] + S^\circ[HNO_3(aq)]\}$

$\Delta S^\circ = 1 \text{ mol } (259.8 \text{ J/K·mol}) - [1 \text{ mol } (192.77 \text{ J/K·mol}) + 1 \text{ mol } (146.4 \text{ J/K·mol})] = -79.4 \text{ J/K}$

$\Delta G^\circ = \Delta H^\circ - T\Delta S^\circ = -86.61 \text{ kJ} - (298 \text{ K})(-79.4 \text{ J/K})(1 \text{ kJ}/10^3 \text{ J}) = -62.9 \text{ kJ}$

The reaction is product-favored and enthalpy-driven.

19.33   (a) $\Delta H^\circ = \Delta H_f^\circ[\text{Ca(OH)}_2(\text{aq})] - 2\, \Delta H_f^\circ[\text{H}_2\text{O}(\ell)]$

$\Delta H^\circ = 1\ \text{mol}\ (-1002.82\ \text{kJ/mol}) - 2\ \text{mol}\ (-285.83\ \text{kJ/mol}) = -431.16\ \text{kJ}$

$\Delta S^\circ = S^\circ[\text{Ca(OH)}_2(\text{aq})] + S^\circ[\text{H}_2(\text{g})] - \{S^\circ[\text{Ca(s)}] + 2\, S^\circ[\text{H}_2\text{O}(\ell)]\}$

$\Delta S^\circ = 1\ \text{mol}\ (-74.5\ \text{J/K·mol}) + 1\ \text{mol}\ (130.7\ \text{J/K·mol}) - [1\ \text{mol}\ (41.59\ \text{J/K·mol})$

$+\ 2\ \text{mol}\ (69.95\ \text{J/K·mol})]$

$\Delta S^\circ = -125.3\ \text{J/K}$

$\Delta G^\circ = \Delta H^\circ - T\Delta S^\circ = -431.16\ \text{kJ} - (298\ \text{K})(-125.3\ \text{J/K})(1\ \text{kJ}/10^3\ \text{J}) = -393.8\ \text{kJ}$

(b) $\Delta H^\circ = \Delta H_f^\circ[\text{C}_6\text{H}_6(\ell)] = 1\ \text{mol}\ (49.03\ \text{kJ/mol}) = 49.03\ \text{kJ}$

$\Delta S^\circ = S^\circ[\text{C}_6\text{H}_6(\ell)] - \{6\, S^\circ[\text{C(graphite)}] + 3\, S^\circ[\text{H}_2(\text{g})]\}$

$\Delta S^\circ = 1\ \text{mol}\ (173.26\ \text{J/K·mol}) - [6\ \text{mol}\ (5.6\ \text{J/K·mol}) + 3\ \text{mol}\ (130.7\ \text{J/K·mol})] = -252.4\ \text{J/K}$

$\Delta G^\circ = \Delta H^\circ - T\Delta S^\circ = 49.03\ \text{kJ} - (298\ \text{K})(-252.4\ \text{J/K})(1\ \text{kJ}/10^3\ \text{J}) = 124.3\ \text{kJ}$

Reaction (a) is product-favored and is enthalpy-driven.

Reaction (b) is enthalpy-driven.

19.34   (a) $\text{C(graphite)} + 2\ \text{S(s)} \rightarrow \text{CS}_2(\text{g})$

$\Delta H^\circ = \Delta H_f^\circ[\text{CS}_2(\text{g})] = 1\ \text{mol}\ (116.7\ \text{kJ/mol}) = 116.7\ \text{kJ}$

$\Delta S^\circ = S^\circ[\text{CS}_2(\text{g})] - \{S^\circ[\text{C(graphite)}] + 2\, S^\circ[\text{S(s)}]\}$

$\Delta S^\circ = 1\ \text{mol}\ (237.8\ \text{J/K·mol}) - [1\ \text{mol}\ (5.6\ \text{J/K·mol}) + 2\ \text{mol}\ (32.1\ \text{J/K·mol})] = 168.0\ \text{J/K}$

$\Delta G_f^\circ = \Delta H^\circ - T\Delta S^\circ = 116.7\ \text{kJ} - (298\ \text{K})(168.0\ \text{J/K})(1\ \text{kJ}/10^3\ \text{J}) = 66.6\ \text{kJ}$

Appendix L value 66.61 kJ

(b) $\text{Na(s)} + \frac{1}{2}\ \text{O}_2(\text{g}) + \frac{1}{2}\ \text{H}_2(\text{g}) \rightarrow \text{NaOH(s)}$

$\Delta H^\circ = \Delta H_f^\circ[\text{NaOH(s)}] = 1\ \text{mol}\ (-425.93\ \text{kJ/mol}) = -425.93\ \text{kJ}$

$\Delta S^\circ = S^\circ[\text{NaOH(s)}] - \{S^\circ[\text{Na(s)}] + \frac{1}{2}\, S^\circ[\text{O}_2(\text{g})] + \frac{1}{2}\, S^\circ[\text{H}_2(\text{g})]\}$

$\Delta S^\circ = 1\ \text{mol}\ (64.46\ \text{J/K·mol}) - [1\ \text{mol}\ (51.21\ \text{J/K·mol}) + \frac{1}{2}\ \text{mol}\ (205.087\ \text{J/K·mol})$

$+\ \frac{1}{2}\ \text{mol}\ (130.7\ \text{J/K·mol})$

$\Delta S^\circ = -154.6\ \text{kJ}$

$\Delta G_f^\circ = \Delta H^\circ - T\Delta S^\circ = -425.93\ \text{kJ} - (298\ \text{K})(-154.6\ \text{J/K})(1\ \text{kJ}/10^3\ \text{J}) = -379.9\ \text{kJ}$

Appendix L value −379.75 kJ

(c) $\frac{1}{2}\ \text{I}_2(\text{s}) + \frac{1}{2}\ \text{Cl}_2(\text{g}) \rightarrow \text{ICl(g)}$

$\Delta H^\circ = \Delta H_f^\circ[\text{ICl(g)}] = 1\ \text{mol}\ (17.51\ \text{kJ/mol}) = 17.51\ \text{kJ}$

$\Delta S^\circ = S^\circ[\text{ICl(g)}] - \{\frac{1}{2}\, S^\circ[\text{I}_2(\text{s})] + \frac{1}{2}\, S^\circ[\text{Cl}_2(\text{g})]\}$

$\Delta S^\circ = 1\ \text{mol}\ (247.56\ \text{J/K·mol}) - [\frac{1}{2}\ \text{mol}\ (116.135\ \text{J/K·mol}) + \frac{1}{2}\ \text{mol}\ (223.08\ \text{J/K·mol})] = 77.95\ \text{J/K}$

$\Delta G_f^\circ = \Delta H^\circ - T\Delta S^\circ = 17.51\ \text{kJ} - (298\ \text{K})(77.95\ \text{J/K})(1\ \text{kJ}/10^3\ \text{J}) = -5.72\ \text{kJ}$

Appendix L value −5.73 kJ

19.35　(a)　$Ca(s) + O_2(g) + H_2(g) \rightarrow Ca(OH)_2(s)$

$\Delta H° = \Delta H_f°[Ca(OH)_2(s)] = 1$ mol $(-986.09$ kJ/mol$) = -986.09$ kJ

$\Delta S° = S°[Ca(OH)_2(s)] - \{S°[Ca(s)] + S°[O_2(g)] + S°[H_2(g)]\}$

$\Delta S° = 1$ mol $(83.39$ J/K·mol$) - [1$ mol $(41.59$ J/K·mol$) + 1$ mol $(205.07$ J/K·mol$)$

$+ 1$ mol $(130.7$ J/K·mol$)]$

$\Delta S° = -294.0$ J/K

$\Delta G_f° = \Delta H° - T\Delta S° = -986.09$ kJ $- (298$ K$)(-294.0$ J/K$)(1$ kJ/10^3 J$) = -898.5$ kJ

Appendix L value -898.43 kJ

(b)　$^1/_2$ $Cl_2(g) \rightarrow Cl(g)$

$\Delta H° = \Delta H_f°[Cl(g)] = 1$ mol $(121.3$ kJ/mol$) = 121.3$ kJ

$\Delta S° = S°[Cl(g)] - {}^1/_2 S°[Cl_2(g)]$

$\Delta S° = 1$ mol $(165.19$ J/K·mol$) - {}^1/_2$ mol $(223.08$ J/K·mol$) = 53.65$ J/K

$\Delta G_f° = \Delta H° - T\Delta S° = 121.3$ kJ $- (298$ K$)(53.65$ J/K$)(1$ kJ/10^3 J$) = 105.3$ kJ

Appendix L value 105.3 kJ

(c)　2 $Na(s) + C(graphite) + {}^3/_2 O_2(g) \rightarrow Na_2CO_3(s)$

$\Delta H° = \Delta H_f°[Na_2CO_3(s)] = 1$ mol $(-1130.77$ kJ/mol$) = -1130.77$ kJ

$\Delta S° = S°[Na_2CO_3(s)] - \{2 S°[Na(s)] + S°[C(graphite)] + {}^3/_2 S°[O_2(g)]\}$

$\Delta S° = 1$ mol $(134.79$ J/K·mol$) - [2$ mol $(51.21$ J/K·mol$) + 1$ mol $(5.6$ J/K·mol$)$

$+ {}^3/_2$ mol $(205.07$ J/K·mol$)]$

$\Delta S° = -280.84$ J/K

$\Delta G_f° = \Delta H° - T\Delta S° = -1130.77$ kJ $- (298$ K$)(-280.84$ J/K$)(1$ kJ/10^3 J$) = -1047.08$ kJ

Appendix L value -1048.08 kJ

19.36　(a)　$\Delta G°_{rxn} = 2 \Delta G_f°[KCl(s)] = 2$ mol $(-408.77$ kJ/mol$) = -817.54$ kJ

product-favored

(b)　$\Delta G°_{rxn} = -(2 \Delta G_f°[CuO(s)]) = -[2$ mol $(-128.3$ kJ/mol$)] = 256.6$ kJ

reactant-favored

(c)　$\Delta G°_{rxn} = 4 \Delta G_f°[NO_2(g)] + 6 \Delta G_f°[H_2O(g)] - 4 \Delta G_f°[NH_3(g)]$

$\Delta G°_{rxn} = 4$ mol $(51.23$ kJ/mol$) + 6$ mol $(-228.59$ kJ/mol$) - 4$ mol $(-16.37$ kJ/mol$) = -1101.14$ kJ

product-favored

19.37　(a)　$\Delta G°_{rxn} = \Delta G_f°[SO_2(g)] - \Delta G_f°[HgS(s)]$

$\Delta G°_{rxn} = 1$ mol $(-300.13$ kJ/mol$) - 1$ mol $(-50.6$ kJ/mol$) = -249.5$ kJ

Product-favored

(b)　$\Delta G°_{rxn} = 2 \Delta G_f°[H_2O(g)] + 2 \Delta G_f°[SO_2(g)] - 2 \Delta G_f°[H_2S(g)]$

$\Delta G°_{rxn} = 2$ mol $(-228.59$ kJ/mol$) + 2$ mol $(-300.13$ kJ/mol$) - 2$ mol $(-33.56$ kJ/mol$) = -990.32$ kJ

Product-favored

(c) $\Delta G^{\circ}_{rxn} = 2 \Delta G_f^{\circ}[MgCl_2(s)] - \Delta G_f^{\circ}[SiCl_4(g)]$

ΔG°_{rxn} = 2 mol (−592.09 kJ/mol) − 1 mol (−622.76 kJ/mol) = −561.42 kJ

Product favored

19.38 $\Delta G^{\circ}_{rxn} = \Delta G_f^{\circ}[BaO(s)] + \Delta G_f^{\circ}[CO_2(g)] - \Delta G_f^{\circ}[BaCO_3(s)]$

219.7 kJ = 1 mol (−520.38 kJ/mol) + 1 mol (−394.359 kJ/mol) − 1 mol $\Delta G_f^{\circ}[BaCO_3(s)]$

$\Delta G_f^{\circ}[BaCO_3(s)]$ = −1134.4 kJ/mol

19.39 $\Delta G^{\circ}_{rxn} = \Delta G_f^{\circ}[TiCl_4(\ell)] - \Delta G_f^{\circ}[TiCl_2(s)]$

−272.8 kJ = 1 mol (−737.2 kJ/mol) − 1 mol $\Delta G_f^{\circ}[TiCl_2(s)]$

$\Delta G_f^{\circ}[TiCl_2(s)]$ = −464.4 kJ/mol

19.40   (a) $\Delta S^{\circ} = 2 S^{\circ}[NO_2(g)] - \{S^{\circ}[N_2(g)] + 2 S^{\circ}[O_2(g)]\}$

ΔS° = 2 mol (240.04 J/K·mol) − [1 mol (191.56 J/K·mol) + 2 mol (205.07 J/K·mol)] = −121.62 J/K

Entropy-disfavored. Increasing the temperature will make the reaction more reactant-favored

(b) $\Delta S^{\circ} = 2 S^{\circ}[CO(g)] - \{2 S^{\circ}[C(graphite)] + S^{\circ}[O_2(g)]\}$

ΔS° = 2 mol (197.674 J/K·mol) − [2 mol (5.6 J/K·mol) + 1 mol (205.07 J/K·mol)] = 179.1 J/K

Entropy-favored. Increasing the temperature will make the reaction more product-favored

(c) $\Delta S^{\circ} = S^{\circ}[CaCO_3(s)] - \{S^{\circ}[CaO(s)] + S^{\circ}[CO_2(g)]\}$

ΔS° = 1 mol (91.7 J/K·mol) − [1 mol (38.2 J/K·mol) + 1 mol (213.74 J/K·mol)] = −160.2 J/K

Entropy-disfavored. Increasing the temperature will make the reaction more reactant-favored

(d) $\Delta S^{\circ} = 2 S^{\circ}[Na(s)] + S^{\circ}[Cl_2(g)] - 2 S^{\circ}[NaCl(s)]$

ΔS° = 2 mol (51.21 J/K·mol) + 1 mol (223.08 J/K·mol) − 2 mol (72.11 J/K·mol) = 181.28 J/K

Entropy-favored. Increasing the temperature will make the reaction more product-favored

19.41   (a) $\Delta S^{\circ} = 2 S^{\circ}[I(g)] - S^{\circ}[I_2(g)]$

ΔS° = 2 mol (180.791) − 1 mol (260.69) = 100.89 J/K

Entropy-favored. Increasing the temperature will make the reaction more product-favored

(b) $\Delta S^{\circ} = 2 S^{\circ}[SO_3(g)] - \{2 S^{\circ}[SO_2(g)] + S^{\circ}[O_2(g)]\}$

ΔS° = 2 mol (256.77 J/K·mol) − [2 mol (248.21 J/K·mol) + 1 mol (205.07 J/K·mol)] = −187.95 J/K

Entropy-disfavored. Increasing the temperature will make the reaction more reactant-favored

(c)   **NOTE:** Physical state of $SiCl_4$ should be (g) not (ℓ)

$\Delta S^{\circ} = S^{\circ}[SiO_2(s)] + 4 S^{\circ}[HCl(g)] - \{S^{\circ}[SiCl_4(g)] + 2 S^{\circ}[H_2O(\ell)]\}$

ΔS° = 1 mol (41.46 J/K·mol) + 4 mol (186.2 J/K·mol) − [1 mol (330.86 J/K·mol)

+ 2 mol (69.95 J/K·mol)]

ΔS° = 315.5 J/K

Entropy-favored. Increasing the temperature will make the reaction more product-favored

(d) $\Delta S° = 4\ S°[PH_3(g)] - \{S°[P_4(s,\ white)] + 6\ S°[H_2(g)]\}$

$\Delta S° = 4$ mol (210.24 J/K·mol) – [1 mol (41.1 J/K·mol) + 6 mol (130.7 J/K·mol)] = 15.7 J/K

Entropy-favored. Increasing the temperature will make the reaction more product-favored

19.42 $HgS(s) \rightarrow Hg(\ell) + S(g)$

$\Delta H° = \Delta H_f°[S(g) - \Delta H_f°[HgS(s)] = 1$ mol (278.98 kJ/mol) – 1 mol (–58.2 kJ/mol) = 337.2 kJ

$\Delta S° = S°[Hg(\ell)] + S°[S(g)] - S°[HgS(s)]$

$\Delta S° = 1$ mol (76.02 J/K·mol) + 1 mol (167.83 J/K·mol) – 1 mol (82.4 J/K·mol) = 161.5 J/K

$\Delta G° = 0 = \Delta H° - T\Delta S° = 337.2$ kJ – T(161.5 J/K)(1 kJ/10^3 J)

$T = 2088$ K or greater

19.43 $CaSO_4(s) \rightarrow CaO(s) + SO_3(g)$

$\Delta H° = \Delta H_f°[CaO(s)] + \Delta H_f°[SO_3(g)] - \Delta H_f°[CaSO_4(s)]$

$\Delta H° = 1$ mol (–635.09 kJ/mol) + 1 mol (–395.77 kJ/mol) – 1 mol (–1434.52 kJ/mol) = 403.66 kJ

$\Delta S° = S°[CaO(s)] + S°[SO_3(g)] - S°[CaSO_4(s)]$

$\Delta S° = 1$ mol (38.2 J/K·mol) + 1 mol (256.77 J/K·mol) – 1 mol (106.5 J/K·mol) = 188.5 J/K

$\Delta G° = 0 = \Delta H° - T\Delta S° = 403.66$ kJ – T(188.5 J/K)(1 kJ/10^3 J)

$T = 2141$ K or greater

19.44 $\Delta G° = -RT \ln K_p$

86.58 kJ/mol = –(8.3145 × 10^{-3} kJ/K·mol)(298 K) ln K_p

ln K_p = –34.94

$K_p = 6.7 × 10^{-16}$

The large, positive $\Delta G°$ value results in a K_p value much less than 1

19.45 $\Delta G° = -RT \ln K_p$

163.2 kJ/mol = –(8.3145 × 10^{-3} kJ/K·mol)(298 K) ln K_p

ln K_p = –65.87

$K_p = 2.5 × 10^{-29}$

The large, positive $\Delta G°$ value results in a K_p value much less than 1

19.46 $\Delta G° = \Delta G_f°[C_2H_6(g)] - \Delta G_f°[C_2H_4(g)]$

$\Delta G° = 1$ mol (–31.89 kJ/mol) – 1 mol (68.35 kJ/mol) = –100.24 kJ

$\Delta G° = -RT \ln K_p$

–100.24 kJ/mol = –(8.3145 × 10^{-3} kJ/K·mol)(298 K) ln K_p

ln K_p = 40.46

$K_p = 3.7 × 10^{17}$

Both the negative $\Delta G°$ value and the large K value indicate a product-favored reaction

19.47 $\Delta G° = 2 \Delta G_f°[HCl(g)] - 2 \Delta G_f°[HBr(g)]$

$\Delta G° = 2 \text{ mol} (-95.09 \text{ kJ/mol}) - 2 \text{ mol} (-53.45 \text{ kJ/mol}) = -83.28 \text{ kJ}$

$\Delta G° = -RT \ln K_p$

$-83.28 \text{ kJ/mol} = -(8.3145 \times 10^{-3} \text{ kJ/K·mol})(298 \text{ K}) \ln K_p$

$\ln K_p = 33.61$

$K_p = 4.0 \times 10^{14}$

Both the negative $\Delta G°$ value and the large K value indicate a product-favored reaction

19.48 $\Delta S°(1) = S°[CH_4(g)] - \{S°[C(graphite)] + 2 S°[H_2(g)]\}$

$\Delta S°(1) = 1 \text{ mol} (186.26 \text{ J/K·mol}) - [1 \text{ mol} (5.6 \text{ J/K·mol}) + 2 \text{ mol} (130.7 \text{ J/K·mol})]$

$\Delta S°(1) = -80.74 \text{ J/K}$

$\Delta S°(2) = S°[CH_3OH(\ell)] - \{S°[CH_4(g)] + \tfrac{1}{2} S°[O_2(g)]\}$

$\Delta S°(2) = 1 \text{ mol} (127.19 \text{ J/K·mol}) - [1 \text{ mol} (186.26 \text{ J/K·mol}) + \tfrac{1}{2} \text{ mol} (205.07 \text{ J/K·mol})]$

$\Delta S°(2) = -161.61 \text{ J/K}$

$\Delta S°(3) = S°[CH_3OH(\ell) - \{S°[C(graphite)] + 2 S°[H_2(g)] + \tfrac{1}{2} S°[O_2(g)]\}$

$\Delta S°(3) = 1 \text{ mol} (127.19 \text{ J/K·mol}) - [1 \text{ mol} (5.6 \text{ J/K·mol}) + 2 \text{ mol} (130.7 \text{ J/K·mol})$

$+ \tfrac{1}{2} \text{ mol} (205.07 \text{ J/K·mol})]$

$\Delta S°(3) = -242.35$

$\Delta S°(3) = \Delta S°(1) + \Delta S°(2)$ Entropy is a state function

19.49 $\Delta H° = \Delta H_f°[C_8H_{18}(g)] - \Delta H_f°[C_8H_{16}(g)] = 1 \text{ mol} (-208.45 \text{ kJ/mol}) - 1 \text{ mol} (-82.93 \text{ kJ/mol}) = -125.52 \text{ kJ}$

$\Delta S° = S°[C_8H_{18}(g)] - \{S°[C_8H_{16}(g)] + S°[H_2(g)]\}$

$\Delta S° = 1 \text{ mol} (463.6 \text{ J/K·mol}) - [1 \text{ mol} (462.8 \text{ J/K·mol}) + 1 \text{ mol} (130.7 \text{ J/K·mol})] = -129.9 \text{ J/K}$

$\Delta G° = \Delta H° - T\Delta S° = -125.52 \text{ kJ} - (298 \text{ K})(-129.9 \text{ J/K})(1 \text{ kJ}/10^3 \text{ J}) = -86.81 \text{ kJ}$

The reaction is product-favored under standard conditions

19.50 $\Delta H° = 2 \Delta H_f°[CO_2(g)] + 3 \Delta H_f°[H_2O(g)] - \Delta H_f°[C_2H_6(g)]$

$\Delta H° = 2 \text{ mol} (-393.509 \text{ kJ/mol}) + 3 \text{ mol} (-241.83 \text{ kJ/mol}) - 1 \text{ mol} (-83.85 \text{ kJ/mol}) = -1428.66 \text{ kJ}$

$\Delta S°_{sys} = 2 S°[CO_2(g)] + 3 S°[H_2O(g)] - \{S°[C_2H_6(g)] + \tfrac{7}{2} S°[O_2(g)]\}$

$\Delta S°_{sys} = 2 \text{ mol} (213.74 \text{ J/K·mol}) + 3 \text{ mol} (188.84 \text{ J/K·mol}) - [1 \text{ mol} (229.2 \text{ J/K·mol})$

$+ \tfrac{7}{2} \text{ mol} (205.07 \text{ J/K·mol})]$

$\Delta S°_{sys} = 47.1 \text{ J/K}$

$\Delta S°_{univ} = \Delta S°_{sys} + \Delta S°_{surr} = 47.1 \text{ J/K} + -[(-1428.66 \text{ kJ})(10^3 \text{ J/1 kJ})/298 \text{ K}] = 4840 \text{ J/K}$

The reaction is spontaneous

19.51 $\Delta H^\circ = \Delta H_f^\circ[\text{Mg(OH)}_2(s)] - 2\,\Delta H_f^\circ[\text{H}_2\text{O}(\ell)]$

$\Delta H^\circ = 1\text{ mol }(-924.54\text{ kJ/mol}) - 2\text{ mol }(-285.83\text{ kJ/mol})$

$\Delta H^\circ = -352.88\text{ kJ}$

$\Delta S^\circ_{sys} = S^\circ[\text{Mg(OH)}_2(s)] + S^\circ[\text{H}_2(g)] - \{S^\circ[\text{Mg}(s)] + 2\,S^\circ[\text{H}_2\text{O}(\ell)]\}$

$\Delta S^\circ_{sys} = 1\text{ mol }(63.18\text{ J/K·mol}) + 1\text{ mol }(130.7\text{ J/K·mol}) - [1\text{ mol }(32.67\text{ J/K·mol})$

$+\ 2\text{ mol }(69.95\text{ J/K·mol})]$

$\Delta S^\circ_{sys} = 21.31\text{ J/K}$

$\Delta S_{univ} = \Delta S^\circ_{sys} + \Delta S^\circ_{surr} = 21.31\text{ J/K} + -[(-352.88\text{ kJ})(10^3\text{ J/1 kJ})/298\text{ K}] = 1205\text{ J/K}$

The reaction is spontaneous

19.52 $2\text{ Fe}(s) + {}^3/_2\text{ O}_2(g) \rightarrow \text{Fe}_2\text{O}_3(s)$

from Appendix L, $\Delta G_f^\circ[\text{Fe}_2\text{O}_3(s)] = -742.2\text{ kJ/mol}$

$454\text{ g Fe}_2\text{O}_3 \cdot \dfrac{1\text{ mol}}{159.7\text{ g}} \cdot \dfrac{-742.2\text{ kJ}}{\text{mol}} = -2110\text{ kJ}$

19.53   (a) The reaction is endothermic and reactant-favored. Therefore, $\Delta H^\circ > 0$, $\Delta S^\circ_{surr} < 0$, $\Delta S^\circ_{univ} < 0$, and

$\Delta G > 0$. $\Delta S^\circ_{sys} > 0$ because one mol of gas and two mol of liquid are produced from two mol solid

$\Delta S^\circ_{sys} = 2\,S^\circ[\text{Hg}(\ell)] + S^\circ[\text{O}_2(g)] - 2\,S^\circ[\text{HgO}(s)]$

$\Delta S^\circ_{sys} = 2\text{ mol }(76.02\text{ J/K·mol}) + 1\text{ mol }(205.07\text{ J/K·mol}) - 2\text{ mol }(70.29\text{ J/K·mol}) = 216.53\text{ J/K}$

$\Delta H^\circ = -(2\,\Delta H_f^\circ[\text{HgO}(s)]) = -[2\text{ mol }(-90.83\text{ kJ/mol})] = 181.66\text{ kJ}$

$\Delta S^\circ_{surr} = -\Delta H^\circ/T = -[(181.66\text{ kJ})(10^3\text{ J/1 kJ})/298\text{ K}] = -609.6\text{ J/K}$

$\Delta S_{univ} = \Delta S^\circ_{sys} + \Delta S^\circ_{surr} = 216.53\text{ J/K} + (-609.6\text{ J/K}) = -393.1\text{ J/K}$

$\Delta G^\circ = \Delta H^\circ - T\Delta S^\circ = 181.66\text{ kJ} - (298\text{ K})(216.53\text{ J/K})(1\text{ kJ}/10^3\text{ J}) = 117\text{ kJ}$

(b) $\Delta G^\circ = -RT\ln K_p$

$117\text{ kJ/mol} = -(8.3145 \times 10^{-3}\text{ kJ/K·mol})(298\text{ K})\ln K_p$

$\ln K_p = -47.22$

$K_p = 3.1 \times 10^{-21}$

The reaction is reactant-favored

19.54   (a)   The reaction occurs spontaneously and is product-favored. Therefore $\Delta S^\circ_{univ} > 0$ and $\Delta G^\circ_{rxn} < 0$. The reaction is likely to be exothermic, so $\Delta H^\circ_{rxn} < 0$ and $\Delta S^\circ_{surr} > 0$. $\Delta S^\circ_{sys} < 0$ because two moles of gas form one mol of solid.

$\Delta S^\circ_{sys} = S^\circ[NH_4Cl(s)] - \{S^\circ[HCl(g)] + S^\circ[NH_3(g)]\}$

$\Delta S^\circ_{sys} = 1 \text{ mol } (94.85 \text{ J/K·mol}) - [1 \text{ mol } (186.2 \text{ J/K·mol}) + 1 \text{ mol } (192.77 \text{ J/K·mol})] = -284.1 \text{ J/K}$

$\Delta H^\circ = \Delta H_f^\circ[NH_4Cl(s)] - \{\Delta H_f^\circ[HCl(g)] + \Delta H_f^\circ[NH_3(g)]\}$

$\Delta H^\circ = 1 \text{ mol } (-314.55 \text{ kJ/mol}) - [1 \text{ mol } (-92.31 \text{ kJ/mol}) + 1 \text{ mol } (-45.90 \text{ kJ/mol}] = -176.34 \text{ kJ}$

$\Delta S^\circ_{surr} = -\Delta H^\circ/T = -[(-176.34 \text{ kJ})(10^3 \text{ J/1 kJ})/298 \text{ K}] = 591.7 \text{ J/K}$

$\Delta S_{univ} = \Delta S^\circ_{sys} + \Delta S^\circ_{surr} = -284.1 \text{ J/K} + 591.7 \text{ J/K} = 307.6 \text{ J/K}$

$\Delta G^\circ = \Delta H^\circ - T\Delta S^\circ = -176.34 \text{ kJ} - (298 \text{ K})(-284.1 \text{ J/K})(1 \text{ kJ}/10^3 \text{ J}) = -91.68 \text{ kJ}$

  (b) $\Delta G^\circ = -RT \ln K_p$

$-91.68 \text{ kJ/mol} = -(8.3145 \times 10^{-3} \text{ kJ/K·mol})(298 \text{ K}) \ln K_p$

$\ln K_p = 37.00$

$K_p = 1.2 \times 10^{16}$

19.55   C(graphite) $\rightarrow$ C(diamond)

  (a) $\Delta S^\circ_{sys} = S^\circ[C(diamond)] - S^\circ[C(graphite)]$

$\Delta S^\circ_{sys} = 1 \text{ mol } (2.377 \text{ J/K·mol}) - 1 \text{ mol } (5.6 \text{ J/K·mol}) = -3.2 \text{ J/K}$

$\Delta H^\circ = \Delta H_f^\circ[C(diamond)] = 1 \text{ mol } (1.8 \text{ kJ/mol}) = 1.8 \text{ kJ}$

$\Delta S^\circ_{surr} = -\Delta H^\circ/T = -[(1.8 \text{ kJ})(10^3 \text{ J/1 kJ})/298 \text{ K}] = -6.0 \text{ J/K}$

$\Delta S_{univ} = \Delta S^\circ_{sys} + \Delta S^\circ_{surr} = -3.2 \text{ J/K} + (-6.0 \text{ J/K}) = -9.2 \text{ J/K}$

$\Delta G^\circ = \Delta H^\circ - T\Delta S^\circ = 1.8 \text{ kJ} - (298 \text{ K})(-3.2 \text{ J/K})(1 \text{ kJ}/10^3 \text{ J}) = 2.8 \text{ kJ}$

  (b)   Nonstandard conditions of extremely high pressure and temperature must be used to "force" the carbon atoms are close to one another, overcoming the unfavorable thermodynamics and allowing the conversion of graphite to diamond.

19.56   (a) $\Delta S^\circ_{sys} = S^\circ[NaCl(aq)] - S^\circ[NaCl(s)]$

$\Delta S^\circ_{sys} = 1 \text{ mol } (115.5 \text{ J/K·mol}) - 1 \text{ mol } (72.11 \text{ J/K·mol}) = 43.4 \text{ J/K}$

$\Delta H^\circ = \Delta H_f^\circ[NaCl(aq)] - \Delta H_f^\circ[NaCl(s)]$

$\Delta H^\circ = 1 \text{ mol } (-407.27 \text{ kJ/mol}) - 1 \text{ mol } (-411.12 \text{ kJ/mol}) = 3.85 \text{ kJ}$

$\Delta S^\circ_{surr} = -\Delta H^\circ/T = -[(3.85 \text{ kJ})(10^3 \text{ J/1 kJ})/298 \text{ K}] = -12.9 \text{ J/K}$

$\Delta S_{univ} = \Delta S^\circ_{sys} + \Delta S^\circ_{surr} = 43.4 \text{ J/K} + (-12.9 \text{ J/K}) = 30.5 \text{ J/K}$

(b) $\Delta S°_{sys} = S°[NaOH(aq)] - S°[NaOH(s)]$

$\Delta S°_{sys} = 1 \text{ mol } (48.1 \text{ J/K·mol}) - 1 \text{ mol } (64.46 \text{ J/K·mol}) = -16.4 \text{ J/K}$

$\Delta H° = \Delta H_f°[NaOH(aq)] - \Delta H_f°[NaOH(s)]$

$\Delta H° = 1 \text{ mol } (-469.15 \text{ kJ/mol}) - 1 \text{ mol } (-425.93 \text{ kJ/mol}) = -43.22 \text{ kJ}$

$\Delta S°_{surr} = -\Delta H°/T = -[(-43.22 \text{ kJ})(10^3 \text{ J/1 kJ})/298 \text{ K}] = 145.0 \text{ J/K}$

$\Delta S_{univ} = \Delta S°_{sys} + \Delta S°_{surr} = -16.4 \text{ J/K} + 145.0 \text{ J/K} = 128.6 \text{ J/K}$

Both systems are product-favored, but the NaCl system is entropy-driven while the NaOH system is enthalpy-driven.

19.57 $\Delta S° = S°[LiOH(aq)] - S°[LiOH(s)] = 1 \text{ mol } (2.80 \text{ J/K·mol}) - 1 \text{ mol } (42.81 \text{ J/K·mol}) = -40.01 \text{ J/K}$

$\Delta H° = \Delta H_f°[LiOH(aq)] - \Delta H_f°[LiOH(s)] = 1 \text{ mol } (-508.48 \text{ kJ/mol}) - 1 \text{ mol } (-484.93 \text{ kJ/mol}) = -23.55 \text{ kJ}$

$\Delta G° = \Delta H° - T\Delta H° = -23.55 \text{ kJ} - (298 \text{ K})(-40.01 \text{ J/K})(1 \text{ kJ}/10^3 \text{ J}) = -11.63 \text{ kJ}$

$\Delta G° = \Delta G_f°[LiOH(aq)] - \Delta G_f°[LiOH(s)] = 1 \text{ mol } (-450.58 \text{ kJ/mol}) - 1 \text{ mol } (-438.96 \text{ kJ/mol}) = -11.62 \text{ kJ}$

19.58 $\Delta G° = \Delta G_f°[CH_3OH(\ell)] = -166.27 \text{ kJ}$

$-166.27 \text{ kJ} = -RT \ln K = -(8.3145 \times 10^{-3} \text{ kJ/K·mol})(298 \text{ K}) \ln K$

$\ln K = 67.1$

$K = 1.3 \times 10^{29}$

The large, negative $\Delta G°$ value results in a K value much greater than 1. The reaction has a negative $\Delta S°$ value (-242.3 J/K) so a higher temperature would make the reaction less product-favored but a lower temperature would make the reaction more product-favored, increasing K_p.

19.59   (a) $(C_2H_5)_2O(\ell) \rightleftharpoons (C_2H_5)_2O(g)$ At equilibrium, $\Delta G° = 0$

$\Delta S° = \dfrac{\Delta H°_{vap}}{T} = \dfrac{26.0 \times 10^3 \text{ J/mol}}{308.2 \text{ K}} = 84.4 \text{ J/K·mol}$

(b) $(C_2H_5)_2O(g) \rightleftharpoons (C_2H_5)_2O(\ell)$ $\Delta S° = -84.4 \text{ J/K·mol}$

19.60 $C_2H_5OH(\ell) \rightleftharpoons C_2H_5OH(g)$ At equilibrium, $\Delta G° = 0$

$\Delta S° = \dfrac{\Delta H°_{vap}}{T} = \dfrac{39.3 \times 10^3 \text{ J/mol}}{351.2 \text{ K}} = 112 \text{ J/K·mol}$

19.61 $\Delta S° = S°[CH_4(g)] + S°[H_2O(g)] - \{3 \, S°[H_2(g)] + S°[CO(g)]\}$

$\Delta S° = 1 \text{ mol } (186.26 \text{ J/K·mol}) + 1 \text{ mol } (188.84 \text{ J/K·mol}) - [3 \text{ mol } (130.7 \text{ J/K·mol})$

$+ 1 \text{ mol } (197.674 \text{ J/K·mol})]$

$\Delta S° = -214.7 \text{ J/K}$

$\Delta H° = \Delta H_f°[CH_4(g)] + \Delta H_f°[H_2O(g)] - \Delta H_f°[CO(g)]$

$\Delta H° = 1 \text{ mol } (-74.87 \text{ kJ/mol}) + 1 \text{ mol } (-241.83 \text{ kJ/mol}) - 1 \text{ mol } (-110.525 \text{ kJ/mol}) = -206.18 \text{ kJ}$

$\Delta G° = \Delta H° - T\Delta H° = -206.18 \text{ kJ} - (298 \text{ K})(-214.7 \text{ J/K})(1 \text{ kJ}/10^3 \text{ J}) = -142.2 \text{ kJ}$

The reaction is predicted to be product-favored.

19.62 $C_2H_5OH(\ell) \rightleftarrows C_2H_5OH(g)$

$\Delta S° = S°[C_2H_5OH(g)] - S°[C_2H_5OH(\ell)] = 1 \text{ mol } (282.70 \text{ J/K·mol}) - 1 \text{ mol } (160.7 \text{ J/K·mol}) = 122.0 \text{ J/K}$

$\Delta H° = \Delta H_f°[C_2H_5OH(g)] - \Delta H_f°[C_2H_5OH(\ell)] = 1 \text{ mol } (-235.3 \text{ kJ/mol}) - 1 \text{ mol } (-277.0 \text{ J/K·mol})$

$\Delta H° = 41.7 \text{ kJ}$

At equilibrium, $\Delta G° = 0$ and $\Delta S° = \dfrac{\Delta H°}{T}$

$T = \dfrac{\Delta H°}{\Delta S°} = \dfrac{41.7 \times 10^3 \text{ J/mol}}{122.0 \text{ J/K·mol}} = 342 \text{ K} = 69 \text{ °C}$

The calculated value is somewhat lower than the actual value (78 °C).

19.63   At the normal boiling point of ethanol, 78 °C, the vapor pressure of ethanol is 1.0 atm. From Study

Question 19.60, $\Delta H_{vap} = 39.3 \text{ kJ/mol}$

$\ln\left(\dfrac{P_2}{P_1}\right) = \dfrac{\Delta H_{vap}}{R}\left(\dfrac{1}{T_1} - \dfrac{1}{T_2}\right)$

$\ln\left(\dfrac{P_2}{760 \text{ mm Hg}}\right) = \dfrac{39.3 \text{ kJ/mol}}{0.0083145 \text{ kJ/K·mol}}\left(\dfrac{1}{351 \text{ K}} - \dfrac{1}{310. \text{ K}}\right)$

$P_2 = 128 \text{ mm Hg}$

19.64 $\Delta S°$ for this reaction is positive (+137.2 J/K, one mole of gaseous reactant forms two moles of gaseous products). This means that raising the temperature will increase the product-favorability of the reaction (because $T\Delta S°$ will become more negative).

19.65   **NOTE:** Problem should read "Estimate the value of $\Delta S°$ at 897 °C for the reaction."

At 897 °C the system is at equilibrium

$\Delta G° = -RT \ln K_p = -RT \ln (1.00) = 0$

Assuming $\Delta H°$ values are relatively constant as the temperature changes,

$\Delta S° = \dfrac{\Delta H°}{T} = \dfrac{179.1 \times 10^3 \text{ J/mol}}{1170 \text{ K}} = 153.1 \text{ J/K·mol}$

19.66   (a) positive (endothermic process)

(b) positive (solid → liquid)

(c) zero (equilibrium)

(d) positive (reactant-favored)

(e) negative (product-favored)

19.67 $H_2O(\ell) \rightleftharpoons H_2O(g)$

$\Delta H° = \Delta H_f°[H_2O(g)] - \Delta H_f°[H_2O(\ell)] = 1 \text{ mol } (-241.83 \text{ kJ/mol}) - 1 \text{ mol } (-285.83 \text{ kJ/mol}) = 44.00 \text{ kJ}$

$\ln\left(\dfrac{P_2}{P_1}\right) = \dfrac{\Delta H_{vap}}{R}\left(\dfrac{1}{T_1} - \dfrac{1}{T_2}\right)$

$\ln\left(\dfrac{630 \text{ mm Hg}}{760 \text{ mm Hg}}\right) = \dfrac{44.00 \text{ kJ/mol}}{0.0083145 \text{ kJ/K·mol}}\left(\dfrac{1}{373 \text{ K}} - \dfrac{1}{T_2}\right)$

$T_2 = 368 \text{ K} = 95 \text{ °C}$

19.68 $\Delta H°$ is negative (exothermic) and $\Delta S°$ is positive (solid and liquid converted to aqueous solution and gas)

$\Delta H° = \Delta H_f°[NaOH(aq)] - \Delta H_f°[H_2O(\ell)] = 1 \text{ mol } (-469.15 \text{ kJ/mol}) - 1 \text{ mol } (-285.83 \text{ kJ/mol}) = -183.32 \text{ kJ}$

$\Delta S° = S°[NaOH(aq)] + \tfrac{1}{2} S°[H_2(g)] - \{S°[Na(s)] + S°[H_2O(\ell)]\}$

$\Delta S° = 1 \text{ mol } (48.1 \text{ J/K·mol}) + \tfrac{1}{2} \text{ mol } (130.7 \text{ J/K·mol}) - [1 \text{ mol } (51.21 \text{ J/K·mol}) + 1 \text{ mol } (69.95 \text{ J/K·mol})]$

$\Delta S° = -7.7 \text{ J/K}$

The entropy change is slightly negative, not positive as predicted. The reason for this is the negative entropy change for dissolving NaOH.

19.69

	$\Delta H°$	$\Delta S°$	$\Delta G°$
(a)	+	+	+
(b)	−	+	−
(c)	−	+	−

19.70 $\Delta H° = 2 \Delta H_f°[C_2H_5OH(\ell)] + 2 \Delta H_f°[CO_2(g)] - \Delta H_f°[C_6H_{12}O_6(aq)]$

$\Delta H° = 2 \text{ mol } (-277.0 \text{ kJ/mol}) + 2 \text{ mol } (-393.509 \text{ kJ/mol}) - 1 \text{ mol } (-1260.0 \text{ kJ/mol}) = -81.2 \text{ kJ}$

$\Delta S° = 2 S°[C_2H_5OH(\ell)] + 2 S°[CO_2(g)] - S°[C_6H_{12}O_6(aq)]$

$\Delta S° = 2 \text{ mol } (160.7 \text{ J/K·mol}) + 2 \text{ mol } (213.74 \text{ J/K·mol}) - 1 \text{ mol } (289 \text{ J/K·mol}) = 460. \text{ J/K}$

$\Delta G° = \Delta H° - T\Delta S° = -81.2 \text{ kJ} - (298 \text{ K})(460. \text{ J/K})(1 \text{ kJ/}10^3 \text{ J}) = -218.1 \text{ kJ}$

The reaction is spontaneous as written.

19.71 $\Delta H° = 3 \Delta H_f°[HCl(g)] - \Delta H_f°[BCl_3(g)] = 3 \text{ mol } (-92.31 \text{ kJ/mol}) - 1 \text{ mol } (-402.96 \text{ kJ/mol}) = 126.03 \text{ kJ}$

$\Delta S° = S°[B(s)] + 3 S°[HCl(g)] - \{S°[BCl_3(g)] + \tfrac{3}{2} S°[H_2(g)]\}$

$\Delta S° = 1 \text{ mol } (5.86 \text{ J/K·mol}) + 3 \text{ mol } (186.2 \text{ J/K·mol}) - [1 \text{ mol } (290.17 \text{ J/K·mol})$

$+ \tfrac{3}{2} \text{ mol } (130.7 \text{ J/K·mol})]$

$\Delta S° = 78.2 \text{ J/K}$

$\Delta G° = \Delta H° - T\Delta S° = 126.03 \text{ kJ} - (298 \text{ K})(78.2 \text{ J/K})(1 \text{ kJ/}10^3 \text{ J}) = 103 \text{ kJ}$

The reaction is not predicted to be product-favored under standard conditions.

19.72 $\Delta G° = -RT \ln K = -(8.3145 \times 10^{-3} \text{ kJ/K·mol})(298 \text{ K}) \ln(0.14) = 4.87 \text{ kJ/mol}$

$\Delta G° = 2 \Delta G_f°[NO_2(g)] - \Delta G_f°[N_2O_4(g)] = 2 \text{ mol } (51.23 \text{ kJ/mol}) - 1 \text{ mol } (97.73 \text{ kJ/mol}) = 4.73 \text{ kJ}$

19.73 $\Delta G°_{rxn} = -RT \ln K = -(8.3145 \times 10^{-3} \text{ kJ/K·mol})(973 \text{ K}) \ln(0.422) = 6.98 \text{ kJ/mol}$

19.74 $\Delta G°_{rxn} = -RT \ln K = -(8.3145 \times 10^{-3} \text{ kJ/K·mol})(298 \text{ K}) \ln(2.5) = -2.27 \text{ kJ/mol}$

19.75 $\Delta G° = \Delta H° - T\Delta S° = -206.7 \text{ kJ} - (298 \text{ K})(-361.5 \text{ J/K})(1 \text{ kJ}/10^3 \text{ J}) = -99.0 \text{ kJ}$

The reaction is spontaneous under standard conditions and is enthalpy-driven.

19.76   Iodine dissolves readily so the process is favorable and $\Delta G°$ must be less than zero. Because $\Delta H° = 0$, the process is entropy-driven.

19.77   (a) $\Delta G°_{rxn} = \Delta G_f°[CO(g)] - \Delta G_f°[H_2O(g)] = 1 \text{ mol } (-137.168 \text{ kJ/mol}) - 1 \text{ mol } (-228.59 \text{ kJ/mol})$

   $\Delta G°_{rxn} = 91.42 \text{ kJ}$

(b) $91.4 \text{ kJ} = -RT \ln K = -(8.3145 \times 10^{-3} \text{ kJ/K·mol})(298 \text{ K}) \ln K$

   $\ln K = -36.9$

   $K = 9.5 \times 10^{-17}$

(c) The reaction is not product-favored at 25 °C

   $\Delta H°_{rxn} = \Delta H_f°[CO(g)] - \Delta H_f°[H_2O(g)] = 1 \text{ mol } (-110.525 \text{ kJ/mol}) - 1 \text{ mol } (-241.83 \text{ kJ/mol})$

   $\Delta H°_{rxn} = 131.31 \text{ kJ}$

   $\Delta S°_{rxn} = S°[CO(g)] + S°[H_2(g)] - \{S°[C(s)] + S°[H_2O(g)]\}$

   $\Delta S° = 1 \text{ mol } (197.674 \text{ J/K·mol}) + 1 \text{ mol } (130.7 \text{ J/K·mol}) - [1 \text{ mol } (5.6 \text{ J/K·mol})$

$+ 1 \text{ mol } (188.84 \text{ J/K·mol})]$

   $\Delta S° = 133.9 \text{ J/K}$

   $T = \dfrac{\Delta H°}{\Delta S°} = \dfrac{131.31 \times 10^3 \text{ J/mol}}{133.9 \text{ J/K}} = 980.4 \text{ K} = 707.3 °C$

19.78 $\Delta G°_{rxn} = 2 \Delta G_f°[SO_2(g)] - 2 \Delta G_f°[SO_3(g)] = 2 \text{ mol } (-300.13 \text{ kJ/mol}) - 2 \text{ mol } (-371.04 \text{ kJ/mol}) = 141.82 \text{ kJ}$

(a) The reaction is not product-favored under standard conditions.

(b) $\Delta H°_{rxn} = 2 \Delta H_f°[SO_2(g)] - 2 \Delta H_f°[SO_3(g)] = 2 \text{ mol } (-296.84 \text{ kJ/mol}) - 2 \text{ mol } (-395.77 \text{ kJ/mol})$

   $\Delta H°_{rxn} = 197.86 \text{ kJ}$

   $\Delta S° = 2 S°[SO_2(g)] + S°[O_2(g)] - 2 S°[SO_3(g)]$

   $\Delta S° = 2 \text{ mol } (248.21 \text{ J/K·mol}) + 1 \text{ mol } (205.07 \text{ J/K·mol}) - 2 \text{ mol } (256.77 \text{ J/K·mol}) = 187.95 \text{ J/K}$

   $T = \dfrac{\Delta H°}{\Delta S°} = \dfrac{197.86 \times 10^3 \text{ J/mol}}{187.95 \text{ J/K}} = 1052.7 \text{ K} = 779.6 °C$

(c) $\Delta G°_{rxn} = \Delta H°_{rxn} - T\Delta S°_{rxn} = 197.86 \text{ kJ} - (1773 \text{ K})(187.95 \text{ J/K})(1 \text{ kJ}/10^3 \text{ J}) = -135 \text{ kJ}$

   $-135 \text{ kJ} = -RT \ln K = -(8.3145 \times 10^{-3} \text{ kJ/K·mol})(1773 \text{ K}) \ln K$

   $\ln K = 9.2$

   $K = 1 \times 10^4$

19.79   (a) $\Delta S^\circ = S^\circ[CH_4(g)] + \frac{1}{2} S^\circ[O_2(g)] - S^\circ[CH_3OH(\ell)]$

$\Delta S^\circ = 1 \text{ mol } (186.26 \text{ J/K·mol}) + \frac{1}{2} \text{ mol } (205.07 \text{ J/K·mol}) - 1 \text{ mol } (127.19 \text{ J/K·mol}) = 161.61 \text{ J/K}$

The sign of ΔS° agrees with the predicted sign because a liquid is being converted to two gases.

(b) $\Delta H^\circ = \Delta H_f^\circ[CH_4(g)] - \Delta H_f^\circ[CH_3OH(\ell)] = 1 \text{ mol } (-74.87 \text{ kJ/mol}) - 1 \text{ mol } (-238.4 \text{ kJ/mol}) = 163.5 \text{ kJ}$

$\Delta G^\circ = \Delta H^\circ - T\Delta S^\circ = 163.5 \text{ kJ} - (298 \text{ K})(161.61 \text{ J/K})(1 \text{ kJ}/10^3 \text{ J}) = 115.3 \text{ kJ}$

The reaction is not spontaneous at 25 °C

(c) $T = \dfrac{\Delta H^\circ}{\Delta S^\circ} = \dfrac{163.5 \times 10^3 \text{ J/mol}}{161.61 \text{ J/K}} = 1012 \text{ K} = 739 \text{ °C}$

19.80 $\Delta H^\circ = \Delta H_f^\circ[H_2SO_4(\ell)] - \Delta H_f^\circ[H_2S(g)] = 1 \text{ mol } (-814 \text{ kJ/mol}) - 1 \text{ mol } (-20.63 \text{ kJ/mol}) = -793 \text{ kJ}$

$\Delta S^\circ = S^\circ[H_2SO_4(\ell)] - \{S^\circ[H_2S(g)] + 2 S^\circ[O_2(g)]\}$

$\Delta S^\circ = 1 \text{ mol } (156.9 \text{ J/K·mol}) - [1 \text{ mol } (205.79 \text{ J/K·mol}) + 2 \text{ mol } (205.07 \text{ J/K·mol})] = -459.0 \text{ J/K}$

$\Delta G^\circ = \Delta H^\circ - T\Delta S^\circ = -793 \text{ kJ} - (298 \text{ K})(-459.0 \text{ J/K})(1 \text{ kJ}/10^3 \text{ J}) = -657 \text{ kJ}$

The reaction is product-favored and enthalpy-driven.

19.81 $CaCO_3(s) + SO_2(g) + \frac{1}{2} H_2O(\ell) \rightarrow CaSO_3 \cdot \frac{1}{2} H_2O(s) + CO_2(g)$

$\Delta H^\circ = \Delta H_f^\circ[CaSO_3 \cdot \frac{1}{2} H_2O(s)] + \Delta H_f^\circ[CO_2(g)] - \{\Delta H_f^\circ[CaCO_3(s)] + \Delta H_f^\circ[SO_2(g)] + \frac{1}{2} \Delta H_f^\circ[H_2O(\ell)]\}$

$\Delta H^\circ = 1 \text{ mol } (-1311.7 \text{ kJ/mol}) + 1 \text{ mol } (-393.509 \text{ kJ/mol})$

$- [1 \text{ mol } (-1207.6 \text{ kJ/mol}) + 1 \text{ mol } (-296.84 \text{ kJ/mol}) + \frac{1}{2} \text{ mol } (-285.83 \text{ kJ/mol})]$

$\Delta H^\circ = -57.9 \text{ kJ}$

$\Delta S^\circ = S^\circ[CaSO_3 \cdot \frac{1}{2} H_2O(s)] + S^\circ[CO_2(g)] - \{S^\circ[CaCO_3(s)] + S^\circ[SO_2(g)] + \frac{1}{2} S^\circ[H_2O(\ell)]\}$

$\Delta S^\circ = 1 \text{ mol } (121.3 \text{ J/K·mol}) + 1 \text{ mol } (213.74 \text{ J/K·mol})$

$- [1 \text{ mol } (91.7 \text{ J/K·mol}) + 1 \text{ mol } (248.21 \text{ J/K·mol}) + \frac{1}{2} \text{ mol } (69.95 \text{ J/K·mol})]$

$\Delta S^\circ = -39.8 \text{ J/K}$

$\Delta G^\circ = \Delta H^\circ - T\Delta S^\circ = -57.9 \text{ kJ} - (298 \text{ K})(-39.8 \text{ J/K})(1 \text{ kJ}/10^3 \text{ J}) = -46.0 \text{ kJ}$

$CaCO_3(s) + SO_2(g) + \frac{1}{2} H_2O(\ell) + \frac{1}{2} O_2(g) \rightarrow CaSO_4 \cdot \frac{1}{2} H_2O(s) + CO_2(g)$

$\Delta H^\circ = \Delta H_f^\circ[CaSO_4 \cdot \frac{1}{2} H_2O(s)] + \Delta H_f^\circ[CO_2(g)] - \{\Delta H_f^\circ[CaCO_3(s)] + \Delta H_f^\circ[SO_2(g)] + \frac{1}{2} \Delta H_f^\circ[H_2O(\ell)]\}$

$\Delta H^\circ = 1 \text{ mol } (-1574.65 \text{ kJ/mol}) + 1 \text{ mol } (-393.509 \text{ kJ/mol})$

$- [1 \text{ mol } (-1207.6 \text{ kJ/mol}) + 1 \text{ mol } (-296.84 \text{ kJ/mol}) + \frac{1}{2} \text{ mol } (-285.83 \text{ kJ/mol})]$

$\Delta H^\circ = -320.8 \text{ kJ}$

$\Delta S^\circ = S^\circ[CaSO_4 \cdot \frac{1}{2} H_2O(s)] + S^\circ[CO_2(g)] - \{S^\circ[CaCO_3(s)] + S^\circ[SO_2(g)] + \frac{1}{2} S^\circ[H_2O(\ell)] + \frac{1}{2} S^\circ[O_2(g)]\}$

$\Delta S^\circ = 1 \text{ mol } (134.8 \text{ J/K·mol}) + 1 \text{ mol } (213.74 \text{ J/K·mol}) - [1 \text{ mol } (91.7 \text{ J/K·mol})$

$+ 1 \text{ mol } (248.21 \text{ J/K·mol}) + \frac{1}{2} \text{ mol } (69.95 \text{ J/K·mol}) + \frac{1}{2} \text{ mol } (205.07 \text{ J/K·mol})]$

$\Delta S^\circ = -128.9 \text{ J/K}$

$\Delta G^\circ = \Delta H^\circ - T\Delta S^\circ = -320.8 \text{ kJ} - (298 \text{ K})(-128.9 \text{ J/K})(1 \text{ kJ}/10^3 \text{ J}) = -282.4 \text{ kJ}$

The second reaction is more product-favored.

19.82 $\Delta H^\circ = - (2\ \Delta H_f^\circ[Ag_2O(s)]) = -[2\ mol\ (-31.1\ kJ/mol)] = 62.2\ kJ/mol$

      $\Delta S^\circ = 4\ S^\circ[Ag(s)] + S^\circ[O_2(g)] - 2\ S^\circ[Ag_2O(s)]$

      $\Delta S^\circ = 4\ mol\ (42.55\ J/K{\cdot}mol) + 1\ mol\ (205.07\ J/K{\cdot}mol) - 2\ mol\ (121.3\ J/K{\cdot}mol) = 132.7\ J/K$

      $\Delta G^\circ = - (2\ \Delta G_f^\circ[Ag_2O(s)]) = -[2\ mol\ (-11.32\ kJ/mol)] = 22.64\ kJ/mol$

      The decomposition is not product-favored at 25 °C

$$T = \frac{\Delta H^\circ}{\Delta S^\circ} = \frac{62.2 \times 10^3\ J/mol}{132.7\ J/K} = 469\ K = 196\ °C$$

19.83 $HCl(g) \rightarrow HCl(aq)$

      $\Delta S^\circ = S^\circ[HCl(aq)] - S^\circ[HCl(g)] = 1\ mol\ (56.5\ J/K{\cdot}mol) - 1\ mol\ (186.2\ J/K{\cdot}mol) = -129.7\ J/K$

      Yes, the negative value indicates a decrease in entropy, which is expected when going from a gaseous phase to a solvated phase.

19.84   (a) $\Delta G^\circ(80.0\ °C) = 3.213\ kJ - (353.2\ K)(8.7\ J/K)(1\ kJ/10^3\ J) = 0.14\ kJ$

          $\Delta G^\circ(110.0\ °C) = 3.213\ kJ - (383.2\ K)(8.7\ J/K)(1\ kJ/10^3\ J) = -0.12\ kJ$

          Rhombic sulfur is more stable than monoclinic sulfur at 80 °C, but the reverse is true at 110 °C.

      (b) $T = \dfrac{\Delta H^\circ}{\Delta S^\circ} = \dfrac{3.213 \times 10^3\ J/mol}{8.7\ J/K} = 370\ K = 96\ °C$

          This is the temperature at which the transition takes place.

19.85 $\Delta G^\circ = \Delta G_f^\circ[H_2O(g)] - \Delta G_f^\circ[CuO(s)] = 1\ mol\ (-228.59\ kJ/mol) - 1\ mol\ (-128.3\ kJ/mol) = -100.3\ kJ$

      The reaction is product-favored

19.86   Abba's refrigerator has liquid water on the cloth covering the pots and moistened sand in between the pots. The evaporation process is spontaneous at "room temperature," so $\Delta G < 0$. But we also know that $\Delta H^\circ > 0$ (evaporation absorbs heat), and $\Delta S^\circ > 0$ (evaporation increases disorder). This means at "room temperature" the process is entropy driven. Eventually, however, as the system approaches equilibrium ($\Delta G = 0$), the temperature must drop in order that $\Delta H^\circ = T\Delta S^\circ$.

19.87   (a) $N_2H_4(\ell) + O_2(g) \rightarrow 2\ H_2O(\ell) + N_2(g)$

          O_2 is the oxidizing agent and N_2H_4 is the reducing agent

      (b) $\Delta H^\circ = 2\ \Delta H_f^\circ[H_2O(\ell)] - \Delta H_f^\circ[N_2H_4(\ell)] = 2\ mol\ (-285.83\ kJ/mol) - 1\ mol\ (50.63\ kJ/mol)$

          $\Delta H^\circ = -622.29\ kJ$

          $\Delta S^\circ = 2\ S^\circ[H_2O(\ell)] + S^\circ[N_2(g)] - \{S^\circ[N_2H_4(\ell)] + S^\circ[O_2(g)]\}$

          $\Delta S^\circ = 2\ mol\ (69.95\ J/K{\cdot}mol) + 1\ mol\ (191.56\ J/K{\cdot}mol) - [1\ mol\ (121.52\ J/K{\cdot}mol)$

                                       $+ 1\ mol\ (205.07\ J/K{\cdot}mol)]$

          $\Delta S^\circ = 4.87\ J/K$

          $\Delta G^\circ = -622.29\ kJ - (298\ K)(4.87\ J/K)(1\ kJ/10^3\ J) = -623.77\ kJ$

19.88   (a) $\Delta H° = 2 \Delta H_f°[NO(g)] = 2$ mol (90.29 kJ/mol) = 180.58 kJ

$\Delta S° = 2 S°[NO(g)] - \{S°[N_2(g)] + S°[O_2(g)]\}$

$\Delta S° = 2$ mol (210.76 J/K·mol) - [1 mol (191.56 J/K·mol) + 1 mol (205.07 J/K·mol)] = 24.89 J/K

$\Delta G° = \Delta H° - T\Delta S° = 180.58$ kJ - (298 K)(24.89 J/K)(1 kJ/10^3 J) = 173.16 kJ

173.16 kJ = $-(8.3145 \times 10^{-3}$ kJ/K·mol)(298 K) ln K_p

$K_p = 4.4 \times 10^{-31}$ The reaction is not product-favored at this temperature

(b) $\Delta G° = 180.58$ kJ - (973 K)(24.89 J/K)(1 kJ/10^3 J) = 156.4 kJ

156.4 kJ = $-(8.3145 \times 10^{-3}$ kJ/K·mol)(973 K) ln K_p

$K_p = 4 \times 10^{-9}$ The reaction is not product-favored at this temperature

(c) $K_p = 4 \times 10^{-9} = \dfrac{P_{NO}^2}{P_{N_2}P_{O_2}} = \dfrac{(2x)^2}{(1.00 - x)(1.00 - x)} \approx \dfrac{(2x)^2}{(1.00)^2}$

$x = 3 \times 10^{-5}$ bar

$P_{NO} = 2x = 6 \times 10^{-5}$ bar

$P_{N_2} = P_{O_2} = 1.00$ bar

19.89 $K_p = \dfrac{P_{HI}}{P_{H_2}^{1/2} P_{I_2}^{1/2}} = \dfrac{1.61}{(0.132)^{1/2}(0.295)^{1/2}} = 8.16$

$\Delta G° = -RT$ ln $K = -(8.3145 \times 10^{-3}$ kJ/K·mol)(623 K) ln(8.16) = -10.9 kJ/mol

19.90   (a) $\Delta H°_{rxn} = 2 \Delta H_f°[Ag_2O(s)] = 2$ mol (-31.1 kJ/mol) = -62.2 kJ/mol

$\Delta S°_{rxn} = 2 S°[Ag_2O(s)] - \{4 S°[Ag(s)] + S°[O_2(g)]\}$

$\Delta S°_{rxn} = 2$ mol (121.3 J/K·mol) - [4 mol (42.55 J/K·mol) + 1 mol (205.07 J/K·mol)] = -132.7 J/K

$\Delta G°_{rxn} = 2 \Delta G_f°[Ag_2O(s)] = 2$ mol (-11.32 kJ/mol) = -22.64 kJ/mol

(b)   -22.64 = $-(8.3145 \times 10^{-3}$ kJ/K·mol)(298 K) ln K_p

$K_p = 9.3 \times 10^3 = 1/P_{O_2}$

$P_{O_2} = 1.1 \times 10^4$ atm

(c) $T = \dfrac{\Delta H°}{\Delta S°} = \dfrac{-62.2 \times 10^3 \text{ J/mol}}{-132.7 \text{ J/K}} = 469$ K = 196 °C

19.91

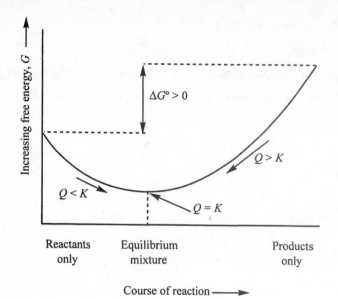

19.92   Dissolving a solid such as NaCl in water is a spontaneous process. Thus, $\Delta G° < 0$. If $\Delta H°$ is zero, then the only way the free energy change can be negative is if $\Delta S°$ is positive. Generally the entropy change is the driving force in forming a solution.

19.93   First, calculate $\Delta S°_{rxn}$, $\Delta H°_{rxn}$, and $\Delta G°_{rxn}$

$\Delta S°_{rxn} = S°[Hg(g)] - S°[Hg(\ell)] = 1\ mol\ (174.97\ J/K \cdot mol) - 1\ mol\ (76.02\ J/K \cdot mol) = 98.95\ J/K$

$\Delta H°_{rxn} = \Delta H_f°[Hg(g)] = 61.38\ kJ$

$\Delta G°_{rxn} = \Delta G_f°[Hg(g)] = 31.88\ kJ$

(a) $K_p = P_{Hg(g)}$

      When $K_p = 1$, $\Delta G°_{rxn} = 0$ and $T = \Delta H°/\Delta S°$. Therefore,

$$T = \frac{61.38 \times 10^3\ J}{98.95\ J/K} = 620.3\ K = 347.2\ °C$$

(b)   Use the Clausius-Clapeyron equation and the temperature for $P = 1.00$ atm to calculate the temperature at which $P_{Hg(g)} = 1$ mm Hg:

$$\ln\left(\frac{P_2}{P_1}\right) = \frac{\Delta H_{vap}}{R}\left(\frac{1}{T_1} - \frac{1}{T_2}\right)$$

$$\ln\left(\frac{1\ mm\ Hg}{760\ mm\ Hg}\right) = \frac{61.38\ kJ/mol}{0.0083145\ kJ/K \cdot mol}\left(\frac{1}{620.3\ K} - \frac{1}{T_2}\right)$$

$T_2 = 398.3\ K = 125.2\ °C$

Since $K_p = P_{Hg(g)}$

347.2 °C: $P_{Hg(g)} = 1$ bar = 0.987 atm   125.2 °C: $P_{Hg(g)} = (1/760)$ bar = 0.987 mm Hg

19.94   Kinetics

19.95   (a) Energy dispersal

        (b) No, the process is endothermic.

19.96   (a) Matter dispersal

        (b) Entropy for a substance is directly related to the substances molecular motions, which increase in rate
             and magnitude with increasing temperature.

19.97   The entropy change for the surroundings (energy dispersal) is greater than the entropy change for the system
        (matter dispersal). Overall, the entropy of the universe increases.

19.98   (a) –60.49 J/K

        (b) no

        (c) yes

        (d) yes

        (e) No. $\Delta S°_{sys}$ is equal to $\Delta S°_{rxn}$; it is not related to $\Delta H°_{rxn}$.

        (f) The reaction is spontaneous at 400 K but not at 700 K.

        (g) The spontaneity decreases as temperature increases. There is no temperature between 400 K and
             1000 K at which the decomposition is spontaneous.

19.99   (a) $\Delta G°$ decreases as temperature increases.

        (b) No, this reaction is always spontaneous.

        (c) The spontaneity of a reaction is dependent on temperature, and it is related to the sign of $\Delta H°_{rxn}$.

19.100 (a) There will not be an appreciable concentration of B. Species C will predominate because the
             activation energies are relatively small and the overall free energy change is negative.

        (b) There is not an appreciable concentration of B. Species A and C are present in equal amounts. The
             activation energies remain relatively small, but now the overal free energy change is zero.

Chapter 20
Principles of Reactivity: Electron Transfer Reactions

INSTRUCTOR'S NOTES

About 4-5 lecture hours are reserved for a discussion of oxidation-reduction reactions. These lectures are usually placed after those on equilibrium and thermodynamics. However, there is no particular reason why it is not possible to place electrochemistry before these other subjects. In any event, electrochemistry should be covered before beginning any systematic descriptive chemistry.

SUGGESTED DEMONSTRATIONS

1.   Oxidation–Reduction Reactions

*   This subject lends itself well to demonstrations, particularly to show the practical importance of redox reactions. A variety of redox reactions were described as demonstrations for Chapters 4 and 5, and the *Periodic Table Videodisc* and the *Redox Videodisc* contain many examples of such reactions and demonstrations.

*   Volume 4 of Shakhashiri's *Chemical Demonstrations* contains many useful electrochemistry demonstrations.

*   To illustrate redox reactions in general we suggest the following possibilities:

    (a)   The reaction of Al foil with concentrated $CuCl_2$ solution:

    $$3\ Cu^{2+}(aq) + 2\ Al(s) \rightarrow 2\ Al^{3+}(aq) + 3\ Cu(s) + heat$$

    This reaction is interesting because it does not occur with other copper salts such as $Cu(NO_3)_2$ or $CuSO_4$. Apparently the reason is that the Cl^- ion is able to diffuse through the layer of Al_2O_3 on the foil and open a pathway for electron transfer between Cu^{2+} and Al. This is, in itself, a very useful point to make, since this shows the importance of Cl^- in corroding systems; for example, one can note that aluminum objects are particularly sensitive to corrosion near the ocean.

    (b)   A copper screen is placed in a silver nitrate solution in a petri dish on an overhead projector.

    $$2\ Ag^+(aq) + Cu(s) \rightarrow 2\ Ag(s) + Cu^{2+}(aq)$$

    In a short time silver needles are clearly seen growing off of the copper wire, and the solution visibly takes on a blue color from aqueous copper(II) ion.

2.   Chemical Change Leading to Electric Current

*   Contrast the reaction of zinc foil in a copper solution with a true electrochemical cell setup, where current is obtained.

*   Contrast the reactivity of Zn metal in 1 M HCl with that of Cu metal in the same acid.

- See Scharlin, P. "The Human Salt Bridge," *Journal of Chemical Education* **1990**, *67*, 156; and Schearer, E. C. "The Construction and Use of Commercial Cell Displays in Freshman Chemistry," *ibid.* **1990**, *67*, 158.

3.   Corrosion: Redox Reactions in the Environment

- See Ward, C. R.; Greenbowe, T. J. "Cathodic Protection: An Overhead Projector Demonstration," *Journal of Chemical Education* **1981**, *58*, 505.

4.   Electrolysis: Chemical Change from Electrical Energy

- The electrolytic process in Figure 20.15 can be done in a cell such as that shown there or in a petri dish on the overhead projector. Fill the dish with dilute KI and place platinum electrodes in the dish; add a few drops of phenolphthalein. When the cell is attached to a battery, I_2 is clearly seen at the anode and H_2 gas (as well as a red color from OH^- ions) at the cathode.

- H_2 and O_2 can be obtained by the electrolysis of aqueous sulfuric acid (see Heidemen, S. "Electrolysis of Water," *Journal of Chemical Education* **1986**, *63*, 809).

- Manjkow, J.; Levine, D. "Electrodeposition of Ni on Cu," *Journal of Chemical Education* **1986**, *63*, 809

5.   Additional suggestions:

- There are *ChemMatters* issues about electrochemistry (February 1990) and batteries (April 1993).

Solutions to Study Questions

20.1   (a)   Zn is oxidized and is the reducing agent. HNO_3 is reduced and is the oxidizing agent.

        (b)   Not a redox reaction

        (c)   Cu is oxidized and is the reducing agent. NO_3^- is reduced and is the oxidizing agent.

        (d)   HOCl is reduced and is the oxidizing agent. Cl^- is oxidized and is the reducing agent.

20.2   (a)   The electrode at the right is a magnesium anode; magnesium metal supplies electrons and is oxidized to Mg^{2+} ions. Electrons pass through the wire to the silver cathode where Ag^+ ions are reduced to silver. Nitrate ions in the salt bridge move from the $AgNO_3$ solution to the $Mg(NO_3)_2$ solution (and Na^+ ions move in the opposite direction).

        (b)   Anode: $Mg(s) \rightarrow Mg^{2+}(aq) + 2\ e^-$

             Cathode: $Ag^+(aq) + e^- \rightarrow Ag(s)$

             Net reaction: $Mg(s) + 2\ Ag^+(aq) \rightarrow Mg^{2+}(aq) + 2\ Ag(s)$

20.3   See 20.2(a). The salt bridge is necessary to maintain charge balance in the cell.

20.4   Anode: lead(IV) oxide is reduced to lead metal

        $PbO_2(s) + 4\ H^+(aq) + SO_4^{2-}(aq) + 2\ e^- \rightarrow PbSO_4(s) + 2\ H_2O(\ell)$

        Cathode: lead is oxidized to lead(II) ions

        $Pb(s) + SO_4^{2-}(aq) \rightarrow PbSO_4(s) + 2\ e^-$

        The battery can be recharged because the reaction products are attached to the electrode surface.

20.5   The standard reduction potential of zinc is determined using a standard hydrogen electrode (SHE). See pages 848-849.

20.6   Concentrations of reactants and products are the primary factors that affect the cell voltage in a voltaic cell.

20.7   (a)   Ease of oxidation (equivalent to declining ability to act as a reducing agent): $K > Zn > H_2 > Cu > Cl^-$

        (b)   Ease of reduction: $Ag^+ > I_2 > H^+ > H_2O > Na^+$

20.8   (a)   product-favored (I_2 is a stronger oxidizing agent than Zn^{2+})

        (b)   reactant-favored (Cl_2 is a stronger oxidizing agent than I_2)

        (c)   reactant-favored (Cl_2 is a stronger oxidizing agent than Na^+)

        (d)   product-favored (H_2O is a stronger oxidizing agent than K^+)

20.9   A product-favored reaction has $E°$ positive and $\Delta G°$ negative.

20.10   The apparatus consists of a cathode and anode separated by a semi-permeable membrane. An external
         battery supplies an electric current. Electrons flow from the battery to the negatively charged cathode where
         H_2O is reduced to H_2 and OH^-. Chloride ions are attracted to the positively charged anode where they are
         oxidized to Cl_2, producing electrons that pass through the wire to the battery.

         Anode: $2\ Cl^-(aq) \rightarrow Cl_2(g) + 2\ e^-$

         Cathode: $2\ H_2O(\ell) + 2\ e^- \rightarrow H_2(g) + 2\ OH^-$

20.11   Current (A) = Charge (C)/time (s). Each mole of electrons carries a charge of 96,500 C. To produce 1.00
         mol of Ag requires 1.00 mol of electrons or 96,500 C. If the current is 1.00 A, the time is 96,500 s.

20.12   (a) $Cr(s) \rightarrow Cr^{3+}(aq) + 3\ e^-$ oxidation

         (b) $AsH_3(g) \rightarrow As(s) + 3\ H^+(aq) + 3\ e^-$ oxidation

         (c) $VO_3^-(aq) + 6\ H^+(aq) + 4\ e^- \rightarrow V^{2+}(aq) + 3\ H_2O(\ell)$ reduction

         (d) $2\ Ag(s) + 2\ OH^-(aq) \rightarrow Ag_2O(s) + H_2O(\ell) + 2\ e^-$ oxidation

20.13   (a) $H_2O_2(aq) \rightarrow O_2(g) + 2\ H^+(aq) + 2\ e^-$ oxidation

         (b) $H_2C_2O_4(aq) \rightarrow 2\ CO_2(g) + 2\ H^+(aq) + 2\ e^-$ oxidation

         (c) $NO_3^-(aq) + 4\ H^+(aq) + 3\ e^- \rightarrow NO(g) + 2\ H_2O(\ell)$ reduction

         (d) $MnO_4^-(aq) + 2\ H_2O(\ell) + 3\ e^- \rightarrow MnO_2(s) + 4\ OH^-(aq)$ reduction

20.14   (a) $Ag(s) \rightarrow Ag^+(aq) + e^-$

              $NO_3^-(aq) + 2\ H^+(aq) + e^- \rightarrow NO_2(g) + H_2O(\ell)$
              _____
              $Ag(s) + NO_3^-(aq) + 2\ H^+(aq) \rightarrow Ag^+(aq) + NO_2(g) + H_2O(\ell)$

         (b) $2[MnO_4^-(aq) + 8\ H^+(aq) + 5\ e^- \rightarrow Mn^{2+}(aq) + 4\ H_2O(\ell)]$

              $5[HSO_3^-(aq) + H_2O(\ell) \rightarrow SO_4^{2-}(aq) + 3\ H^+(aq) + 2\ e^-]$
              _____
              $2\ MnO_4^-(aq) + H^+(aq) + 5\ HSO_3^-(aq) \rightarrow 2\ Mn^{2+}(aq) + 3\ H_2O(\ell) + 5\ SO_4^{2-}(aq)$

         (c) $4[Zn(s) \rightarrow Zn^{2+}(aq) + 2\ e^-]$

              $2\ NO_3^-(aq) + 8\ e^- + 10\ H^+(aq) \rightarrow 5\ H_2O(\ell) + N_2O(g)$
              _____
              $4\ Zn(s) + 2\ NO_3^-(aq) + 10\ H^+(aq) \rightarrow 5\ H_2O(\ell) + 4\ Zn^{2+}(aq) + N_2O(g)$

         (d) $Cr(s) \rightarrow Cr^{3+}(aq) + 3\ e^-$

              $NO_3^-(aq) + 4\ H^+(aq) + 3\ e^- \rightarrow NO(g) + 2\ H_2O(\ell)$
              _____
              $Cr(s) + NO_3^-(aq) + 4\ H^+(aq) \rightarrow Cr^{3+}(aq) + NO(g) + 2\ H_2O(\ell)$

20.15   (a) $Sn(s) \rightarrow Sn^{2+}(aq) + 2\ e^-$

              $2\ H^+(aq) + 2\ e^- \rightarrow H_2(g)$
              _____
              $Sn(s) + 2\ H^+(aq) \rightarrow Sn^{2+}(aq) + H_2(g)$

(b) $Cr_2O_7^{2-}(aq) + 14\ H^+(aq) + 6\ e^- \rightarrow 2\ Cr^{3+}(aq) + 7\ H_2O(\ell)$

$6[Fe^{2+}(aq) \rightarrow Fe^{3+}(aq) + e^-]$

$\overline{\qquad\qquad\qquad\qquad\qquad\qquad\qquad\qquad\qquad\qquad\qquad\qquad}$

$Cr_2O_7^{2-}(aq) + 14\ H^+(aq) + 6\ Fe^{2+}(aq) \rightarrow\ 2\ Cr^{3+}(aq) + 7\ H_2O(\ell) + 6\ Fe^{3+}(aq)$

(c) $MnO_2(s) + 4\ H^+(aq) + 2\ e^- \rightarrow Mn^{2+}(aq) + 2\ H_2O(\ell)$

$2\ Cl^-(aq) \rightarrow Cl_2(g) + 2\ e^-$

$\overline{\qquad\qquad\qquad\qquad\qquad\qquad\qquad\qquad\qquad\qquad\qquad\qquad}$

$MnO_2(s) + 4\ H^+(aq) + 2\ Cl^-(aq) \rightarrow Mn^{2+}(aq) + 2\ H_2O(\ell) + Cl_2(g)$

(d) $CH_2O(aq) + H_2O(\ell) \rightarrow HCO_2H(aq) + 2\ H^+(aq) + 2\ e^-$

$2[Ag^+(aq) + e^- \rightarrow Ag(s)]$

$\overline{\qquad\qquad\qquad\qquad\qquad\qquad\qquad\qquad\qquad\qquad\qquad\qquad}$

$CH_2O(aq) + H_2O(\ell) + 2\ Ag^+(aq) \rightarrow HCO_2H(aq) + 2\ H^+(aq) + 2\ Ag(s)$

20.16 (a) $2[Al(s) + 4\ OH^-(aq) \rightarrow 3\ e^- + Al(OH)_4^-(aq)]$

$3[OH^-(aq) + 2\ H_2O(\ell) + 2\ e^- \rightarrow 3\ OH^-(aq) + H_2(g)]$

$\overline{\qquad\qquad\qquad\qquad\qquad\qquad\qquad\qquad\qquad\qquad\qquad\qquad}$

$2\ Al(s) + 6\ H_2O(\ell) + 2\ OH^-(aq) \rightarrow 2\ Al(OH)_4^-(aq) + 3\ H_2(g)$

(b) $2[CrO_4^-(aq) + 4\ H_2O(\ell) + 3\ e^- \rightarrow Cr(OH)_3(s) + 5\ OH^-(aq)]$

$3[SO_3^{2-}(aq) + 2\ OH^-(aq) \rightarrow SO_4^{2-}(aq) + H_2O(\ell) + 2\ e^-]$

$\overline{\qquad\qquad\qquad\qquad\qquad\qquad\qquad\qquad\qquad\qquad\qquad\qquad}$

$2\ CrO_4^-(aq) + 5\ H_2O(\ell) + 3\ SO_3^{2-}(aq) \rightarrow 2\ Cr(OH)_3(s) + 4\ OH^-(aq) + 3\ SO_4^{2-}(aq)$

(c) $Zn(s) + 4\ OH^-(aq) \rightarrow Zn(OH)_4^{2-}(aq) + 2\ e^-$

$Cu(OH)_2(s) + 2\ e^- \rightarrow Cu(s) + 2\ OH^-(aq)$

$\overline{\qquad\qquad\qquad\qquad\qquad\qquad\qquad\qquad\qquad\qquad\qquad\qquad}$

$Zn(s) + 2\ OH^-(aq) + Cu(OH)_2(s) \rightarrow Zn(OH)_4^{2-}(aq) + Cu(s)$

(d) $3[HS^-(aq) + OH^-(aq) \rightarrow S(s) + H_2O(\ell) + 2\ e^-]$

$ClO_3^-(aq) + 3\ H_2O(\ell) + 6\ e^- \rightarrow Cl^-(aq) + 6\ OH^-(aq)$

$\overline{\qquad\qquad\qquad\qquad\qquad\qquad\qquad\qquad\qquad\qquad\qquad\qquad}$

$3\ HS^-(aq) + ClO_3^-(aq) \rightarrow 3\ S(s) + Cl^-(aq) + 3\ OH^-(aq)$

20.17 (a) $3[Fe(OH)_3(s) + e^- \rightarrow Fe(OH)_2(s) + OH^-(aq)]$

$Cr(s) + 3\ OH^-(aq) \rightarrow Cr(OH)_3(s) + 3\ e^-$

$\overline{\qquad\qquad\qquad\qquad\qquad\qquad\qquad\qquad\qquad\qquad\qquad\qquad}$

$3\ Fe(OH)_3(s) + Cr(s) \rightarrow 3\ Fe(OH)_2(s) + Cr(OH)_3(s)$

(b) $NiO_2(s) + 2\ H_2O(\ell) + 2\ e^- \rightarrow Ni(OH)_2(s) + 2\ OH^-(aq)$

$Zn(s) + 2\ OH^-(aq) \rightarrow Zn(OH)_2(s) + 2\ e^-$

$\overline{\qquad\qquad\qquad\qquad\qquad\qquad\qquad\qquad\qquad\qquad\qquad\qquad}$

$NiO_2(s) + 2\ H_2O(\ell) + Zn(s) \rightarrow Ni(OH)_2(s) + Zn(OH)_2(s)$

(c) $3[Fe(OH)_2(s) + OH^-(aq) \rightarrow Fe(OH)_3(s) + e^-]$

$CrO_4^{2-}(aq) + 3\ e^- + 4\ H_2O(\ell) \rightarrow Cr(OH)_4^-(aq) + 4\ OH^-(aq)$

$\overline{\qquad\qquad\qquad\qquad\qquad\qquad\qquad\qquad\qquad\qquad\qquad\qquad}$

$3\ Fe(OH)_2(s) + CrO_4^{2-}(aq) + 4\ H_2O(\ell) \rightarrow 3\ Fe(OH)_3(s) + Cr(OH)_4^-(aq) + OH^-(aq)$

(d) $N_2H_4(aq) + 4\ OH^-(aq) \rightarrow N_2(g) + 4\ H_2O(\ell) + 4\ e^-$

$2[Ag_2O(s) + H_2O(\ell) + 2\ e^- \rightarrow 2\ Ag(s) + 2\ OH^-(aq)]$

$N_2H_4(aq) + 2\ Ag_2O(s) \rightarrow N_2(g) + 2\ H_2O(\ell) + 4\ Ag(s)$

20.18   Electrons flow from the Cr electrode to the Fe electrode. Negative ions move in the salt bridge from the Fe/Fe^{2+} half-cell to the Cr/Cr^{3+} half-cell.

Anode (oxidation): $Cr(s) \rightarrow Cr^{3+}(aq) + 3\ e^-$

Cathode (reduction): $Fe^{2+}(aq) + 2\ e^- \rightarrow Fe(s)$

20.19   (a) Oxidation (anode): $Mg(s) \rightarrow Mg^{2+}(aq) + 2\ e^-$

Reduction (cathode): $2\ H^+(aq) + 2\ e^- \rightarrow H_2(g)$

(b) Oxidation occurs in the Mg/Mg^{2+} compartment and reduction occurs in the H$^+$/H$_2$ compartment.

(c) Electrons in the external circuit flow from the Mg electrode to the positive (site of H$^+$ reduction) electrode. Negative ions move in the salt bridge from the H$^+$/H$_2$ half-cell to the Mg/Mg^{2+} half-cell. The half-reaction at the anode and the cathode are shown in (a).

20.20   (a) Oxidation: $Fe(s) \rightarrow Fe^{2+}(aq) + 2\ e^-$

Reduction: $O_2(g) + 4\ H^+(aq) + 4\ e^- \rightarrow 2\ H_2O(\ell)$

Overall: $2\ Fe(s) + O_2(g) + 4\ H^+(aq) \rightarrow 2\ H_2O(\ell) + 2\ Fe^{2+}(aq)$

(b) Oxidation occurs in the anode compartment and reduction occurs in the cathode compartment.

(c) Electrons in the external circuit flow from the Fe electrode to the positive (site of O$_2$ reduction) electrode. Negative ions move in the salt bridge from the O$_2$/H$_2$O half-cell to the Fe/Fe^{2+} half-cell.

20.21   (a) Oxidation: $Ag(s) \rightarrow Ag^+(aq) + e^-$

Reduction: $Cl_2(g) + 2\ e^- \rightarrow 2\ Cl^-(aq)$

Overall: $2\ Ag(s) + Cl_2(g) \rightarrow 2\ Ag^+(aq) + 2\ Cl^-(aq)$

(b) Oxidation occurs in the anode compartment and reduction occurs in the cathode compartment.

(c) Electrons in the external circuit flow from the Ag electrode to the positive (site of Cl$_2$ reduction) electrode. Negative ions move in the salt bridge from the Cl$_2$/Cl$^-$ half-cell to the Ag/Ag$^+$ half-cell.

20.22   See pages 840-843.

(a) All are primary batteries, not rechargeable.

(b) All have Zn as the anode.

(c) Dry cells have an acidic environment, whereas the environment is alkaline for alkaline and mercury cells.

20.23   Lead(II) sulfate is oxidized to lead(IV) oxide and reduced to elemental lead.

20.24　(a)　$E°_{cell} = E°_{cathode} - E°_{anode} = (-0.763\ V) - (+0.535\ V) = -1.298\ V$　　　not product-favored

　　　　(b)　$E°_{cell} = E°_{cathode} - E°_{anode} = (-0.763\ V) - (-0.25\ V) = -0.51\ V$　　　not product-favored

　　　　(c)　$E°_{cell} = E°_{cathode} - E°_{anode} = (+0.337\ V) - (+1.360\ V) = -1.023\ V$　　　not product-favored

　　　　(d)　$E°_{cell} = E°_{cathode} - E°_{anode} = (+0.80\ V) - (+0.771\ V) = +0.03\ V$　　　product-favored

20.25　(a)　$E°_{cell} = E°_{cathode} - E°_{anode} = (+1.08\ V) - (-2.37\ V) = +3.45\ V$　　　product-favored

　　　　(b)　$E°_{cell} = E°_{cathode} - E°_{anode} = (-0.763\ V) - (-2.37\ V) = +1.61\ V$　　　product-favored

　　　　(c)　$E°_{cell} = E°_{cathode} - E°_{anode} = (+0.80\ V) - (+0.15\ V) = +0.65\ V$　　　product-favored

　　　　(d)　$E°_{cell} = E°_{cathode} - E°_{anode} = (+0.40\ V) - (-1.22\ V) = +1.62\ V$　　　product-favored

20.26　(a)　$Sn^{2+}(aq) + 2\ e^- \rightarrow Sn(s)$

　　　　　　$2[Ag(s) \rightarrow Ag^+(aq) + e^-]$

　　　　　　—————————————————————

　　　　　　$Sn^{2+}(aq) + 2\ Ag(s) \rightarrow Sn(s) + 2\ Ag^+(aq)$

　　　　　　$E°_{cell} = E°_{cathode} - E°_{anode} = (-0.14\ V) - (+0.80\ V) = -0.94\ V$　　　not product-favored

　　　　(b)　$2[Al(s) \rightarrow Al^{3+}(aq) + 3\ e^-]$

　　　　　　$3[Sn^{4+}(aq) + 2\ e^- \rightarrow Sn^{2+}(aq)]$

　　　　　　—————————————————————

　　　　　　$2\ Al(s) + 3\ Sn^{4+}(aq) \rightarrow 2\ Al^{3+}(aq) + 3\ Sn^{2+}(aq)$

　　　　　　$E°_{cell} = E°_{cathode} - E°_{anode} = (+0.15\ V) - (-1.66\ V) = +1.81\ V$　　　product-favored

　　　　(c)　$ClO_3^-(aq) + 6\ H^+(aq) + 6\ e^- \rightarrow Cl^-(aq) + 3\ H_2O(\ell)$

　　　　　　$6[Ce^{3+}(aq) \rightarrow Ce^{4+}(aq) + e^-]$

　　　　　　—————————————————————

　　　　　　$ClO_3^-(aq) + 6\ H^+(aq) + 6\ Ce^{3+}(aq) \rightarrow Cl^-(aq) + 3\ H_2O(\ell) + Ce^{4+}(aq)$

　　　　　　$E°_{cell} = E°_{cathode} - E°_{anode} = (+0.62\ V) - (+1.61\ V) = -0.99\ V$　　　not product-favored

　　　　(d)　$3[Cu(s) \rightarrow Cu^{2+}(aq) + 2\ e^-]$

　　　　　　$2[NO_3^-(aq) + 4\ H^+(aq) + 3\ e^- \rightarrow NO(g) + 2\ H_2O(\ell)]$

　　　　　　—————————————————————

　　　　　　$3\ Cu(s) + 2\ NO_3^-(aq) + 8\ H^+(aq) \rightarrow 2\ NO(g) + 3\ Cu^{2+}(aq) + 4\ H_2O(\ell)$

　　　　　　$E°_{cell} = E°_{cathode} - E°_{anode} = (+0.96\ V) - (+0.337\ V) = +0.62\ V$　　　product-favored

20.27　(a)　$I_2(s) + 2\ e^- \rightarrow 2\ I^-(aq)$

　　　　　　$2\ Br^-(aq) \rightarrow Br_2(\ell) + 2\ e^-$

　　　　　　—————————————————————

　　　　　　$I_2(s) + 2\ Br^-(aq) \rightarrow 2\ I^-(aq) + Br_2(\ell)$

　　　　　　$E°_{cell} = E°_{cathode} - E°_{anode} = (+0.535\ V) - (+1.08\ V) = -0.55\ V$　　　not product-favored

(b) $2[Fe^{2+}(aq) \rightarrow Fe^{3+}(aq) + e^-]$

$Cu^{2+}(aq) + 2 e^- \rightarrow Cu(s)$

$2 Fe^{2+}(aq) + Cu^{2+}(aq) \rightarrow Fe^{3+}(aq) + Cu(s)$

$E^\circ_{cell} = E^\circ_{cathode} - E^\circ_{anode} = (+0.337 \text{ V}) - (+0.771 \text{ V}) = -0.434 \text{ V}$ not product-favored

(c) $6[Fe^{2+}(aq) \rightarrow Fe^{3+}(aq) + e^-]$

$Cr_2O_7^{2-}(aq) + 14 H^+(aq) + 6 e^- \rightarrow 2 Cr^{3+}(aq) + 7 H_2O(\ell)$

$6 Fe^{2+}(aq) + Cr_2O_7^{2-}(aq) + 14 H^+(aq) \rightarrow 6 Fe^{3+}(aq) + 7 H_2O(\ell) + 2 Cr^{3+}(aq)$

$E^\circ_{cell} = E^\circ_{cathode} - E^\circ_{anode} = (+1.33 \text{ V}) - (+.0771 \text{ V}) = +0.56 \text{ V}$ product-favored

(d) $2[MnO_4^-(aq) + 8 H^+(aq) + 5 e^- \rightarrow Mn^{2+}(aq) + 4 H_2O(\ell)]$

$5[HNO_2(aq) + H_2O(\ell) \rightarrow NO_3^-(aq) + 3 H^+(aq) + 2 e^-]$

$2 MnO_4^-(aq) + H^+(aq) + 5 HNO_2(aq) \rightarrow 2 Mn^{2+}(aq) + 5 NO_3^-(aq) + 3 H_2O(\ell)$

$E^\circ_{cell} = E^\circ_{cathode} - E^\circ_{anode} = (+1.52 \text{ V}) - (+0.94 \text{ V}) = +0.58 \text{ V}$ product-favored

20.28 (a) Al(s)

(b) Zn(s) and Al(s)

(c) $Fe^{2+}(aq) + Sn(s) \rightarrow Fe(s) + Sn^{2+}(aq)$

$E^\circ_{cell} = E^\circ_{cathode} - E^\circ_{anode} = (-0.44 \text{ V}) - (-0.14 \text{ V}) = -0.30 \text{ V}$ reactant-favored

(d) $Zn^{2+}(aq) + Sn(s) \rightarrow Zn(s) + Sn^{2+}(aq)$

$E^\circ_{cell} = E^\circ_{cathode} - E^\circ_{anode} = (-0.76 \text{ V}) - (-0.14 \text{ V}) = -0.62 \text{ V}$ reactant-favored

20.29 (a) MnO_4^- is the strongest oxidizing agent and SO_4^{2-} is the weakest oxidizing agent

(b) MnO_4^-

(c) $Cr_2O_7^{2-}(aq) + 14 H^+(aq) + 6 e^- \rightarrow 2 Cr^{3+}(aq) + 7 H_2O(\ell)$

$3[SO_2(g) + 2 H_2O(\ell) \rightarrow SO_4^{2-}(aq) + 4 H^+(aq) + 2 e^-]$

$Cr_2O_7^{2-}(aq) + 2 H^+(aq) + 3 SO_2(g) \rightarrow 2 Cr^{3+}(aq) + H_2O(\ell) + 3 SO_4^{2-}(aq)$

$E^\circ_{cell} = E^\circ_{cathode} - E^\circ_{anode} = (+1.33 \text{ V}) - (+0.20 \text{ V}) = +1.13 \text{ V}$ reactant-favored

(d) $5[Cr_2O_7^{2-}(aq) + 14 H^+(aq) + 6 e^- \rightarrow 2 Cr^{3+}(aq) + 7 H_2O(\ell)]$

$6[Mn^{2+}(aq) + 4 H_2O(\ell) \rightarrow MnO_4^-(aq) + 8 H^+(aq) + 5 e^-]$

$5 Cr_2O_7^{2-}(aq) + 22 H^+(aq) + 6 Mn^{2+}(aq) \rightarrow 10 Cr^{3+}(aq) + 11 H_2O(\ell) + 6 MnO_4^-(aq)$

$E^\circ_{cell} = E^\circ_{cathode} - E^\circ_{anode} = (+1.33 \text{ V}) - (+1.51 \text{ V}) = -0.18 \text{ V}$ reactant-favored

20.30 (b) Zn

20.31 (b) Zn, (c) Fe, and (e) Cr

20.32 (d) $Ag^+(aq)$

20.33   (a) $Cu^{2+}(aq)$ and (d) $Ag^+(aq)$

20.34   (a) F_2

(b) Cl_2 and F_2

20.35   (a) $I^-(aq)$

(b) $Br^-(aq)$ and $I^-(aq)$

20.36   Assume $P_{H_2} = 1.0$ atm

$Zn(s) + 4\ OH^-(aq) \rightarrow Zn(OH)_4^{2-}(aq) + 2\ e^-$

$2\ H_2O(\ell) + 2\ e^- \rightarrow H_2(g) + 2\ OH^-(aq)$

$E^\circ_{cell} = E^\circ_{cathode} - E^\circ_{anode} = (-0.8277\ V) - (-1.22\ V) = +0.39\ V$

$E_{cell} = E^\circ_{cell} - \dfrac{0.0257}{n}\ \ln \dfrac{[Zn(OH)_4^{2-}]P_{H_2}}{[OH^-]^2} = +0.39\ V - \dfrac{0.0257}{2}\ \ln\dfrac{(0.025)(1.00)}{(0.025)^2} = 0.34\ V$

20.37 $2[Fe^{2+}(aq) \rightarrow Fe^{3+}(aq) + e^-]$

$H_2O_2(aq) + 2\ H^+(aq) + 2\ e^- \rightarrow 2\ H_2O(\ell)$

$E^\circ_{cell} = E^\circ_{cathode} - E^\circ_{anode} = (1.77\ V) - (0.771\ V) = +1.00\ V$

$E_{cell} = E^\circ_{cell} - \dfrac{0.0257}{n}\ \ln \dfrac{[Fe^{3+}]^2}{[Fe^{2+}]^2[H_2O_2][H^+]^2} = +1.00\ V - \dfrac{0.0257}{2}\ \ln\dfrac{(0.015)^2}{(0.015)^2(0.015)(0.015)^2}$

$E_{cell} = 0.84\ V$

20.38 $Zn(s) \rightarrow Zn^{2+}(aq) + 2\ e^-$

$2[Ag^+(aq) + e^- \rightarrow Ag(s)]$

$Zn(s) + 2\ Ag^+(aq) \rightarrow Zn^{2+}(aq) + 2\ Ag(s)$

$E^\circ_{cell} = E^\circ_{cathode} - E^\circ_{anode} = (0.80\ V) - (-0.763\ V) = +1.56\ V$

$E_{cell} = E^\circ_{cell} - \dfrac{0.0257}{n}\ \ln \dfrac{[Zn^{2+}]}{[Ag^+]^2} = +1.56\ V - \dfrac{0.0257}{2}\ \ln\dfrac{0.010}{(0.25)^2} = 1.59\ V$

20.39 $Zn(s) + Cu^{2+}(aq) \rightarrow Zn^{2+}(aq) + Cu(s)$

$E^\circ_{cell} = E^\circ_{cathode} - E^\circ_{anode} = (0.337\ V) - (-0.763\ V) = +1.100\ V$

$E_{cell} = E^\circ_{cell} - \dfrac{0.0257}{n}\ \ln \dfrac{[Zn^{2+}]}{[Cu^{2+}]} = +1.100\ V - \dfrac{0.0257}{2}\ \ln\dfrac{0.40}{4.8 \times 10^{-3}} = 1.043\ V$

20.40 $Zn(s) + 2\ Ag^+(aq) \rightarrow Zn^{2+}(aq) + 2\ Ag(s)$

$E^\circ_{cell} = E^\circ_{cathode} - E^\circ_{anode} = (0.80\ V) - (-0.763\ V) = +1.56\ V$

$E_{cell} = 1.48\ V = 1.56\ V - \dfrac{0.0257}{2}\ \ln\dfrac{1.0}{[Ag^+]^2}$

$[Ag^+] = 0.040\ M$

20.41 $Fe(s) + 2 H^+(aq) \rightarrow Fe^{2+}(aq) + H_2(g)$

$E^\circ_{cell} = E^\circ_{cathode} - E^\circ_{anode} = (0.00 \text{ V}) - (-0.44 \text{ V}) = +0.44 \text{ V}$

$E_{cell} = 0.49 \text{ V} = 0.44 \text{ V} - \dfrac{0.0257}{2} \ln \dfrac{[Fe^{2+}]1.0}{(1.0)^2}$

$[Fe^{2+}] = 0.020 \text{ M}$

20.42   (a) $2[Fe^{3+}(aq) + e^- \rightarrow Fe^{2+}(aq)]$

$2 I^-(aq) \rightarrow I_2(s) + 2 e^-$

$E^\circ_{cell} = E^\circ_{cathode} - E^\circ_{anode} = (0.771 \text{ V}) - (0.535 \text{ V}) = +0.236 \text{ V}$

$\Delta G^\circ = -nFE^\circ = -(2 \text{ mol } e^-)(96,500 \text{ C/mol } e^-)(0.236 \text{ V})(1 \text{ J/1 C·V})(1 \text{ kJ}/10^3 \text{ J}) = -45.5 \text{ kJ}$

$\ln K = \dfrac{nE^\circ}{0.0257 \text{ V}} = \dfrac{(2)(0.236 \text{ V})}{0.0257 \text{ V}} = 18.4 \qquad K = 9 \times 10^7$

(b) $I_2(s) + 2 e^- \rightarrow 2 I^-(aq)$

$2 Br^-(aq) \rightarrow Br_2(\ell) + 2 e^-$

$E^\circ_{cell} = E^\circ_{cathode} - E^\circ_{anode} = (0.535 \text{ V}) - (1.08 \text{ V}) = -0.55 \text{ V}$

$\Delta G^\circ = -nFE^\circ = -(2 \text{ mol } e^-)(96,500 \text{ C/mol } e^-)(-0.55 \text{ V})(1 \text{ J/1 C·V})(1 \text{ kJ}/10^3 \text{ J}) = 110 \text{ kJ}$

$\ln K = \dfrac{nE^\circ}{0.0257 \text{ V}} = \dfrac{(2)(-0.55 \text{ V})}{0.0257 \text{ V}} = -42 \qquad K = 4 \times 10^{-19}$

20.43   (a) $Zn^{2+}(aq) + 2 e^- \rightarrow Zn(s)$

$Ni(s) \rightarrow Ni^{2+}(aq) + 2 e^-$

$E^\circ_{cell} = E^\circ_{cathode} - E^\circ_{anode} = (-0.763 \text{ V}) - (-0.25 \text{ V}) = -0.51 \text{ V}$

$\Delta G^\circ = -nFE^\circ = -(2 \text{ mol } e^-)(96,500 \text{ C/mol } e^-)(-0.51 \text{ V})(1 \text{ J/1 C·V})(1 \text{ kJ}/10^3 \text{ J}) = 99 \text{ kJ}$

$\ln K = \dfrac{nE^\circ}{0.0257 \text{ V}} = \dfrac{(2)(-0.51 \text{ V})}{0.0257 \text{ V}} = -40. \qquad K = 5 \times 10^{-18}$

(b) $Cu(s) \rightarrow Cu^{2+}(aq) + 2 e^-$

$2[Ag^+(aq) + e^- \rightarrow Ag(s)]$

$E^\circ_{cell} = E^\circ_{cathode} - E^\circ_{anode} = (0.80 \text{ V}) - (0.337 \text{ V}) = 0.46 \text{ V}$

$\Delta G^\circ = -nFE^\circ = -(2 \text{ mol } e^-)(96,500 \text{ C/mol } e^-)(0.46 \text{ V})(1 \text{ J/1 C·V})(1 \text{ kJ}/10^3 \text{ J}) = -89 \text{ kJ}$

$\ln K = \dfrac{nE^\circ}{0.0257 \text{ V}} = \dfrac{(2)(0.46 \text{ V})}{0.0257 \text{ V}} = 36 \qquad K = 4 \times 10^{15}$

20.44 $AgBr(s) + e^- \rightarrow Ag(s) + Br^-(aq)$

$Ag(s) \rightarrow Ag^+(aq) + e^-$

$AgBr(s) \rightarrow Ag^+(aq) + Br^-(aq)$

$E^\circ_{cell} = E^\circ_{cathode} - E^\circ_{anode} = (0.0713 \text{ V}) - (0.7994 \text{ V}) = -0.7281 \text{ V}$

$\ln K = \dfrac{nE^\circ}{0.0257 \text{ V}} = \dfrac{(1)(-0.7281 \text{ V})}{0.0257 \text{ V}} = -28.33 \qquad K = 5.0 \times 10^{-12}$

20.45 $Hg_2Cl_2(s) + 2\ e^- \rightarrow 2\ Hg(\ell) + 2\ Cl^-(aq)$

$\underline{2\ Hg(\ell) \rightarrow Hg_2^{2+}(aq) + 2\ e^-}$

$Hg_2Cl_2(s) \rightarrow Hg_2^{2+}(aq) + 2\ Cl^-(aq)$

$E^\circ_{cell} = E^\circ_{cathode} - E^\circ_{anode} = (0.27\ V) - (0.789\ V) = -0.52\ V$

$\ln K = \dfrac{nE^\circ}{0.0257\ V} = \dfrac{(2)(-0.52\ V)}{0.0257\ V} = -40.$ $K = 3 \times 10^{-18}$

20.46 $Au(s) + 4\ Cl^-(aq) \rightarrow AuCl_4^-(aq) + 3\ e^-$

$\underline{Au^{3+}(aq) + 3\ e^- \rightarrow Au(s)}$

$Au^{3+}(aq) + 4\ Cl^-(aq) \rightarrow AuCl_4^-(aq)$

$E^\circ_{cell} = E^\circ_{cathode} - E^\circ_{anode} = (1.50\ V) - (1.00\ V) = 0.50\ V$

$\ln K = \dfrac{nE^\circ}{0.0257\ V} = \dfrac{(3)(0.50\ V)}{0.0257\ V} = 58$ $K = 2 \times 10^{25}$

20.47 $Zn(s) + 4\ OH^-(aq) \rightarrow Zn(OH)_4^{2-}(aq) + 2\ e^-$

$\underline{Zn^{2+}(aq) + 2\ e^- \rightarrow Zn(s)}$

$Zn^{2+}(aq) + 4\ OH^-(aq) \rightarrow Zn(OH)_4^{2-}(aq)$

$E^\circ_{cell} = E^\circ_{cathode} - E^\circ_{anode} = (-0.763\ V) - (-1.22\ V) = 0.46\ V$

$\ln K = \dfrac{nE^\circ}{0.0257\ V} = \dfrac{(2)(0.46\ V)}{0.0257\ V} = 36$ $K = 3 \times 10^{15}$

20.48   (a) $Fe^{2+}(aq) + 2\ e^- \rightarrow Fe(s)$

$2[Fe^{2+}(aq) \rightarrow Fe^{3+}(aq) + e^-]$

(b) $E^\circ_{cell} = E^\circ_{cathode} - E^\circ_{anode} = (-0.44\ V) - (0.771\ V) = -1.21\ V$ not product-favored

(c) $\ln K = \dfrac{nE^\circ}{0.0257\ V} = \dfrac{(2)(-1.21\ V)}{0.0257\ V} = -94.2$ $K = 1 \times 10^{-41}$

20.49   (a) $Cu^+(aq) + e^- \rightarrow Cu(s)$

$Cu^+(aq) \rightarrow Cu^{2+}(aq) + e^-$

(b) $E^\circ_{cell} = E^\circ_{cathode} - E^\circ_{anode} = (0.521\ V) - (0.153\ V) = 0.368\ V$ product-favored

(c) $\ln K = \dfrac{nE^\circ}{0.0257\ V} = \dfrac{(1)(0.368\ V)}{0.0257\ V} = 14.3$ $K = 2 \times 10^6$

20.50

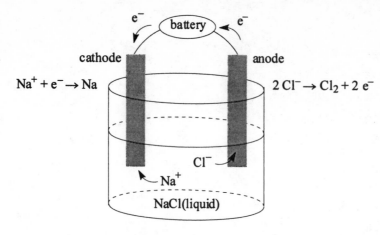

20.51

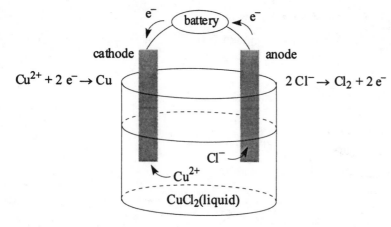

20.52 F^- is much more difficult to oxidize than water, so O_2 is more likely to be formed at the anode.

20.53 Ca^{2+} is much more difficult to reduce than water, so H_2 is more likely to be formed at the cathode.

20.54   (a) $2\,H_2O(\ell) + 2\,e^- \rightarrow H_2(g) + 2\,OH^-(aq)$

          (b) $2\,Br^-(aq) \rightarrow Br_2(\ell) + 2\,e^-$

20.55   (a) $2\,H_2O(\ell) + 2\,e^- \rightarrow H_2(g) + 2\,OH^-(aq)$

          (b) $S^{2-}(aq) \rightarrow S(s) + 2\,e^-$

20.56   Charge = current $\times$ time = (0.150 A)(12.2 min)(60.0 s/min) = 110. C

          $\text{mol } e^- = (110.\ \text{C})\left(\dfrac{1 \text{ mol } e^-}{96{,}500 \text{ C}}\right) = 0.00114 \text{ mol } e^-$

          $\text{mass of Ni} = (0.00114\,\text{mol } e^-)\left(\dfrac{1 \text{ mol Ni}}{2 \text{ mol } e^-}\right)\left(\dfrac{58.69 \text{ g}}{1 \text{ mol Ni}}\right) = 0.0334 \text{ g Ni}$

20.57   Charge = current × time = (1.12 A)(2.40 h)(60.0 min/h)(60.0 s/min) = 9.68×10^3 C

mol e⁻ = $(9.68 \times 10^3$ C$)\left(\dfrac{1 \text{ mol e}^-}{96,500 \text{ C}}\right)$ = 0.100 mol e⁻

mass of Ag = $(0.100 \text{ mol e}^-)\left(\dfrac{1 \text{ mol Ag}}{1 \text{ mol e}^-}\right)\left(\dfrac{107.9 \text{ g}}{1 \text{ mol Ni}}\right)$ = 10.8 g Ag

20.58   mol e⁻ = $(0.50 \text{ g Cu})\left(\dfrac{1 \text{ mol Cu}}{63.55 \text{ g}}\right)\left(\dfrac{2 \text{ mol e}^-}{1 \text{ mol Cu}}\right)$ = 0.016 mol e⁻

Charge = $(0.016 \text{ mol e}^-)\left(\dfrac{96,500 \text{ C}}{1 \text{ mol e}^-}\right)$ = 1.5×10^3 C

Time = 1.5×10^3 C/0.66 A = 2300 s (or 38 min)

20.59   mol e⁻ = $(2.5 \text{ g Zn})\left(\dfrac{1 \text{ mol Zn}}{65.39 \text{ g}}\right)\left(\dfrac{2 \text{ mol e}^-}{1 \text{ mol Zn}}\right)$ = 0.076 mol e⁻

Charge = $(0.076 \text{ mol e}^-)\left(\dfrac{96,500 \text{ C}}{1 \text{ mol e}^-}\right)$ = 7.4×10^3 C

Time = 7.4×10^3 C/2.12 A = 3500 s (or 58 min)

20.60   Al(s) → Al^{3+}(aq) + 3 e⁻

$(84 \text{ g Al})\left(\dfrac{1 \text{ mol Al}}{27.0 \text{ g}}\right)\left(\dfrac{3 \text{ mol e}^-}{1 \text{ mol Al}}\right)\left(\dfrac{96,500 \text{ C}}{1 \text{ mol e}^-}\right)$ = 9.0×10^5 C

$(9.0 \times 10^5$ C/1.0 A$)$(1 min/60.0 s)(1 h/60.0 min) = 250 h

20.61   Charge = current × time = (0.25 A)(1.00 h)(60.0 min/h)(60.0 s/min) = 9.0×10^2 C

mass of Cd = $(9.0 \times 10^2$ C$)\left(\dfrac{1 \text{ mol e}^-}{96,500 \text{ C}}\right)\left(\dfrac{1 \text{ mol Cd}}{2 \text{ mol e}^-}\right)\left(\dfrac{112.4 \text{ g}}{1 \text{ mol Cd}}\right)$ = 0.52 g Cd

20.62   (a) UO_2^+(aq) + 4 H^+(aq) + e⁻ → U^{4+}(aq) + 2 H_2O(ℓ)

(b) ClO_3^-(aq) + 6 H^+(aq) + 6 e⁻ → Cl^-(aq) + 3 H_2O(ℓ)

(c) N_2H_4(aq) + 4 OH⁻(aq) → N_2(g) + 4 H_2O(ℓ) + 4 e⁻

(d)   OCl⁻(aq) H_2O(ℓ) + 2 e⁻ → Cl⁻(aq) + 2 OH⁻(aq)

20.63   (a)   Zn(s) → Zn^{2+}(aq) + 2 e⁻

2[VO^{2+}(aq) + 2 H^+(aq) + e⁻ → V^{3+}(aq) + H_2O(ℓ)]

──

Zn(s) + 2 VO^{2+}(aq) + 4 H^+(aq) → Zn^{2+}(aq) + 2 V^{3+}(aq) + 2 H_2O(ℓ)

(b)   3[Zn(s) → Zn^{2+}(aq) + 2 e⁻]

2[VO_3^-(aq) + 6 H^+(aq) + 3 e⁻ → V^{2+}(aq) + 3 H_2O(ℓ)]

──

3 Zn(s) + 2 VO_3^-(aq) + 12 H^+(aq) → 3 Zn^{2+}(aq) + 2 V^{3+}(aq) + 6 H_2O(ℓ)

(c) $Zn(s) + 2\ OH^-(aq) \rightarrow Zn(OH)_2(s) + 2\ e^-$

$ClO^-(aq) + H_2O(\ell) + 2\ e^- \rightarrow Cl^-(aq) + 2\ OH^-(aq)$

$Zn(s) + OCl^-(aq) + H_2O(\ell) \rightarrow Zn(OH)_2(s) + Cl^-(aq)$

(d) $3[ClO^-(aq) + H_2O(\ell) + 2\ e^- \rightarrow Cl^-(aq) + 2\ OH^-(aq)]$

$2[Cr(OH)_4^-(aq) + 4\ OH^-(aq) \rightarrow CrO_4^{2-}(aq) + 4\ H_2O(\ell) + 3\ e^-]$

$3\ ClO^-(aq) + 2\ Cr(OH)_4^-(aq) + 2\ OH^-(aq) \rightarrow 3\ Cl^-(aq) + 2\ CrO_4^{2-}(aq) + 5\ H_2O(\ell)$

20.64 $Zn^{2+}(aq) + 2\ e^- \rightarrow Zn(s)$ $E°_{cathode} = -0.763\ V$ $Zn(s) \rightarrow Zn^{2+}(aq) + 2\ e^-$ $E°_{anode} = -0.763\ V$

$E°_{cell} = E°_{cathode} - E°_{anode}$

(a) $E°_{anode} = E°_{cathode} - E°_{cell} = -0.763\ V - (1.1\ V) = -1.86\ V$

Aluminum (−1.66 V) would be an appropriate choice

$E°_{cathode} = E°_{cell} + E°_{anode} = 1.1\ V + (-0.763\ V) = 0.34\ V$

Copper (0.337 V) would be an appropriate choice

(b) $E°_{anode} = E°_{cathode} - E°_{cell} = -0.763\ V - (0.5\ V) = -1.26\ V$

Vanadium (−1.18 V) or manganese (−1.18 V) would be appropriate choices

$E°_{cathode} = E°_{cell} + E°_{anode} = 0.5\ V + (-0.763\ V) = -0.26\ V$

Nickel (−0.25 V) or cobalt (−0.28 V) would be appropriate choices

20.65 $Ag^+(aq) + e^- \rightarrow Ag(s)$ $E°_{cathode} = 0.7994\ V$ $Ag(s) \rightarrow Ag^+(aq) + e^-$ $E°_{anode} = 0.7994\ V$

$E°_{cell} = E°_{cathode} - E°_{anode}$

(a) $E°_{anode} = E°_{cathode} - E°_{cell} = 0.7994\ V - (1.7\ V) = -0.90\ V$

Chromium (−0.91 V) would be an appropriate choice

$E°_{cathode} = E°_{cell} + E°_{anode} = 1.7\ V + (0.7994\ V) = 2.5\ V$

Fluorine (2.87 V) would be an appropriate choice

(b) $E°_{anode} = E°_{cathode} - E°_{cell} = 0.7994\ V - (0.5\ V) = 0.30\ V$

Copper (0.337 V) would be an appropriate choice

$E°_{cathode} = E°_{cell} + E°_{anode} = 0.5\ V + (0.7994\ V) = 1.3\ V$

Chlorine (1.36 V) would be an appropriate choice

20.66 (a) $Zn^{2+}(aq)$ (e) Yes

(b) $Au^+(aq)$ (f) No

(c) $Zn(s)$ (g) $Cu^{2+}(aq),\ Ag^+(aq),\ Au^+(aq)$

(d) $Au(s)$ (h) $Cu(s),\ Sn(s),\ Co(s),\ Zn(s)$

20.67 (a) Se(s)   (e) Yes

          (b) F^-(aq)   (f) No

          (c) Cl_2(g), F_2(g)   (g) No

          (d) F_2(g), Cl_2(g), O_2(g), $Br_2(\ell)$, I_2(s)   (h) Yes

20.68 (a) The combination of a negative E°_{anode} half-cell with a SHE cathode (0 V) will result in a positive E°_{cell}

$$Cr^{3+}(aq) + 3\ e^- \rightarrow Cr(s) \qquad E^\circ_{anode} = -0.74\ V$$

$$Fe^{2+}(aq) + 2\ e^- \rightarrow Fe(s) \qquad E^\circ_{anode} = -0.44\ V$$

$$Mg^{2+}(aq) + 2\ e^- \rightarrow Mg(s) \qquad E^\circ_{anode} = -2.37\ V$$

          (b) Highest voltage (Mg): $E^\circ_{cell} = (0.00\ V) - (2.37\ V) = 2.37\ V$

                 Lowest voltage (Cu): $E^\circ_{cell} = (0.337\ V) - (0.00\ V) = 0.337\ V$

20.69 (a) Cu-Zn and Cu-Co

                 Cu-Co and Ag-Co

          (b) Ag-Zn: $E^\circ_{cell} = (0.7994\ V) - (-0.763\ V) = 1.562\ V$

                 Ag-Cu: $E^\circ_{cell} = (0.7994\ V) - (0.337\ V) = 0.462\ V$

20.70 (a)

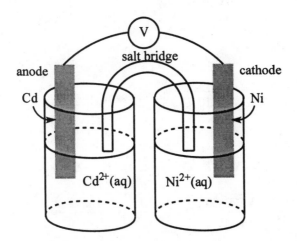

          (b) $Ni^{2+}(aq) + Cd(s) \rightarrow Ni(s) + Cd^{2+}(aq)$

          (c) The anode is negative and the cathode is positive

          (d) $E^\circ_{cell} = (-0.25\ V) - (-0.40V) = 0.15\ V$

          (e) Electrons flow from the anode to the cathode

          (f) Na^+ ions move from the Cd/Cd^{2+} half-cell to the Ni/Ni^{2+} half-cell. NO_3^- ions move in the opposite direction, from the Ni/Ni^{2+} half-cell to the Cd/Cd^{2+} half-cell.

          (g) $\ln K = \dfrac{nE^\circ}{0.0257\ V} = \dfrac{(2)(0.15\ V)}{0.0257\ V} = 12$

              $K = 1 \times 10^5$

(h) $E_{cell} = E^{\circ}_{cell} - \dfrac{0.0257}{n} \ln \dfrac{[Cd^{2+}]}{[Ni^{2+}]} = 0.15 \text{ V} - \dfrac{0.0257}{2} \ln\left(\dfrac{0.010}{1.0}\right) = 0.21 \text{ V}$

The reaction is still the one written in part (b).

(i) Determine which reactant is consumed first:

$(1.0 \text{ L Ni}^{2+})(1.0 \text{ mol/L}) = 1.0 \text{ mol Ni}^{2+}$ $50.0 \text{ g Cd} \cdot \dfrac{1 \text{ mol Cd}}{112.4 \text{ g}} = 0.445 \text{ mol Cd (limiting reactant)}$

$(0.445 \text{ mol Cd})\left(\dfrac{2 \text{ mol e}^-}{1 \text{ mol Cd}}\right)\left(\dfrac{96,500 \text{ C}}{1 \text{ mol e}^-}\right) = 8.59 \times 10^4 \text{ C}$

$(8.59 \times 10^4 \text{ C}/0.050 \text{ A}) = 1.7 \times 10^6 \text{ s (or 480 h)}$

20.71 $(24 \text{ h})(60 \text{ min/1 h})(60 \text{ s/1 min})(1.0 \times 10^5 \text{ A}) = 8.6 \times 10^9 \text{ C}$

$(8.6 \times 10^9 \text{ C})\left(\dfrac{1 \text{ mol e}^-}{96,500 \text{ C}}\right)\left(\dfrac{1 \text{ mol Al}}{3 \text{ mol e}^-}\right)\left(\dfrac{27.0 \text{ g}}{1 \text{ mol Al}}\right) = 8.1 \times 10^5 \text{ g Al}$

20.72   (a) $E^{\circ}_{cathode} = E^{\circ}_{cell} + E^{\circ}_{anode} = -0.146 \text{ V} + (0.7994 \text{ V}) = 0.653 \text{ V}$

(b) $\ln K = \dfrac{nE^{\circ}}{0.0257 \text{ V}} = \dfrac{(2)(-0.146 \text{ V})}{0.0257 \text{ V}} = -11.4$ $K = 1 \times 10^{-5}$

20.73   (a) $E^{\circ}_{anode} = E^{\circ}_{cathode} - E^{\circ}_{cell} = -0.126 \text{ V} - (-0.142 \text{ V}) = 0.016 \text{ V}$

(b) $\ln K = \dfrac{nE^{\circ}}{0.0257 \text{ V}} = \dfrac{(2)(-0.142 \text{ V})}{0.0257 \text{ V}} = -11.1$ $K = 2 \times 10^{-5}$

20.74 $Cl_2(g) + Zn(s) \rightarrow Zn^{2+}(aq) + 2 \text{ Cl}^-(aq)$

$\Delta G^{\circ} = nFE^{\circ} = -(2 \text{ mol e}^-)(96,500 \text{ C/mol e}^-)(2.12 \text{ V})(1 \text{ J/1 C}\cdot\text{V})(1 \text{ kJ/10}^3 \text{ J}) = -409 \text{ kJ}$

20.75 $Mg(s) + I_2(s) \rightarrow 2 \text{ I}^-(aq) + Mg^{2+}(aq)$

$\Delta G^{\circ} = nFE^{\circ} = -(2 \text{ mol e}^-)(96,500 \text{ C/mol e}^-)(2.91 \text{ V})(1 \text{ J/1 C}\cdot\text{V})(1 \text{ kJ/10}^3 \text{ J}) = -562 \text{ kJ}$

20.76 $(1.0 \times 10^3 \text{ kg})\left(\dfrac{10^3 \text{ g}}{1 \text{ kg}}\right)\left(\dfrac{1 \text{ mol Al}}{27.0 \text{ g}}\right)\left(\dfrac{3 \text{ mol e}^-}{1 \text{ mol Al}}\right)\left(\dfrac{96,500 \text{ C}}{1 \text{ mol e}^-}\right)(5.0 \text{ V})\left(\dfrac{1 \text{ J}}{1 \text{ C}\cdot\text{V}}\right)\left(\dfrac{1 \text{ kwh}}{3.6 \times 10^6 \text{ J}}\right) = 1.5 \times 10^4 \text{ kwh}$

20.77 $2 \text{ NaCl}(\ell) \rightarrow 2 \text{ Na}(s) + Cl_2(g)$

$(24 \text{ h})(60 \text{ min/1 h})(60 \text{ s/1 min})(4.0 \times 10^4 \text{ A}) = 3.5 \times 10^9 \text{ C}$

$(3.5 \times 10^9 \text{ C})\left(\dfrac{1 \text{ mol e}^-}{96,500 \text{ C}}\right)\left(\dfrac{2 \text{ mol Na}}{2 \text{ mol e}^-}\right)\left(\dfrac{23.0 \text{ g}}{1 \text{ mol Na}}\right) = 8.2 \times 10^5 \text{ g Na}$

$(3.5 \times 10^9 \text{ C})\left(\dfrac{1 \text{ mol e}^-}{96,500 \text{ C}}\right)\left(\dfrac{1 \text{ mol Cl}_2}{2 \text{ mol e}^-}\right)\left(\dfrac{70.9 \text{ g}}{1 \text{ mol Cl}_2}\right) = 1.3 \times 10^6 \text{ g Cl}_2$

$(3.5 \times 10^9 \text{ C})(7.0 \text{ V})(1 \text{ J/1 C}\cdot\text{V})(1 \text{ kwh/3.6} \times 10^6 \text{ J}) = 6700 \text{ kwh}$

20.78 $0.038 \text{ g} \cdot \dfrac{1 \text{ mol Rh}}{102.9 \text{ g}} = 3.7 \times 10^{-4} \text{ mol Rh}$

(3.00 h)(60.0 min/1 h)(60.0 s/1 min)(0.0100 A) = 108 C

$(108 \text{ C})\left(\dfrac{1 \text{ mol e}^-}{96,500 \text{ C}}\right) = 0.00112 \text{ mol e}^-$

$\dfrac{0.00112 \text{ mol e}^-}{3.7 \times 10^{-4} \text{ mol Rh}} = 3 \text{ mol e}^-/\text{mol Rh} \qquad \text{Rh}^{3+} \qquad \text{Rh}_2(\text{SO}_4)_3$

20.79 $0.345 \text{ g} \cdot \dfrac{1 \text{ mol Ru}}{101.1 \text{ g}} = 0.00341 \text{ mol Ru}$ \qquad (25.0 min)(60.0 s/1 min)(0.44 A) = 660 C

$(660 \text{ C})\left(\dfrac{1 \text{ mol e}^-}{96,500 \text{ C}}\right) = 0.0068 \text{ mol e}^-$

$\dfrac{0.0068 \text{ mol e}^-}{0.00341 \text{ mol Ru}} = 2 \text{ mol e}^-/\text{mol Ru} \qquad \text{Ru}^{2+} \qquad \text{Ru(NO}_3)_2$

20.80 $35 \text{ A-h} = \dfrac{35 \text{ C-h}}{1 \text{ sec}} \cdot \dfrac{3600 \text{ sec}}{1 \text{ h}} \cdot \dfrac{1 \text{ mol e}^-}{96,500 \text{ C}} \cdot \dfrac{1 \text{ mol Zn}}{2 \text{ mol e}^-} \cdot \dfrac{65.39 \text{ g}}{1 \text{ mol Zn}} = 43 \text{ g Zn}$

20.81 $(24 \text{ h})(60.0 \text{ min}/1 \text{ h})(60.0 \text{ s}/1 \text{ min})(3.0 \times 10^5 \text{ A}) = 2.4 \times 10^{11} \text{ C}$

$(2.4 \times 10^{11} \text{ C})\left(\dfrac{1 \text{ mol e}^-}{96,500 \text{ C}}\right)\left(\dfrac{1 \text{ mol Cl}_2}{2 \text{ mol e}^-}\right)\left(\dfrac{70.9 \text{ g}}{1 \text{ mol Cl}_2}\right) = 8.9 \times 10^7 \text{ g Cl}_2$

20.82 $0.052 \text{ g Ag}\left(\dfrac{1 \text{ mol Ag}}{107.9 \text{ g}}\right)\left(\dfrac{1 \text{ mol e}^-}{1 \text{ mol Ag}}\right)\left(\dfrac{96,500 \text{ C}}{1 \text{ mol e}^-}\right) = 47 \text{ C}$

Current = charge/time = (46 C)/(450 s) = 0.10 A

20.83 $0.089 \text{ g}\left(\dfrac{1 \text{ mol Ag}}{107.9 \text{ g}}\right)\left(\dfrac{1 \text{ mol e}^-}{1 \text{ mol Ag}}\right)\left(\dfrac{1 \text{ mol Au}}{3 \text{ mol e}^-}\right)\left(\dfrac{197.0 \text{ g}}{1 \text{ mol Au}}\right) = 0.054 \text{ g Au}$

20.84   (a) $\text{HCO}_2\text{H(aq)} + 2 \text{ H}^+\text{(aq)} + 2 \text{ e}^- \rightarrow \text{HCHO(aq)} + \text{H}_2\text{O}(\ell)$

(b) $\text{C}_6\text{H}_5\text{CO}_2\text{H(aq)} + 6 \text{ H}^+\text{(aq)} + 6 \text{ e}^- \rightarrow \text{C}_6\text{H}_5\text{CH}_3\text{(aq)} + 2 \text{ H}_2\text{O}(\ell)$

(c) $\text{CH}_3\text{CH}_2\text{CHO(aq)} + 2 \text{ H}^+\text{(aq)} + 2 \text{ e}^- \rightarrow \text{CH}_3\text{CH}_2\text{CH}_2\text{OH(aq)}$

(d) $\text{CH}_3\text{OH(aq)} + 2 \text{ H}^+\text{(aq)} + 2 \text{ e}^- \rightarrow \text{CH}_4\text{(aq)} + \text{H}_2\text{O}(\ell)$

20.85   (a) $2[\text{Ag}^+\text{(aq)} + \text{e}^- \rightarrow \text{Ag(s)}]$

$\text{C}_6\text{H}_5\text{CHO(aq)} + \text{H}_2\text{O}(\ell) \rightarrow \text{C}_6\text{H}_5\text{CO}_2\text{H(aq)} + 2 \text{ H}^+\text{(aq)} + 2 \text{ e}^-$

$\overline{}$

$2 \text{ Ag}^+\text{(aq)} + \text{C}_6\text{H}_5\text{CHO(aq)} + \text{H}_2\text{O}(\ell) \rightarrow \text{C}_6\text{H}_5\text{CO}_2\text{H(aq)} + 2 \text{ H}^+\text{(aq)} + \text{Ag(s)}$

(b) $3[\text{CH}_3\text{CH}_2\text{OH(aq)} + \text{H}_2\text{O}(\ell) \rightarrow \text{CH}_3\text{CO}_2\text{H(aq)} + 4 \text{ H}^+\text{(aq)} + 4 \text{ e}^-]$

$2[\text{Cr}_2\text{O}_7{}^{2-}\text{(aq)} + 14 \text{ H}^+\text{(aq)} + 6 \text{ e}^- \rightarrow 2 \text{ Cr}^{3+}\text{(aq)} + 7 \text{ H}_2\text{O}(\ell)]$

$\overline{}$

$3 \text{ CH}_3\text{CH}_2\text{OH(aq)} + 2 \text{ Cr}_2\text{O}_7{}^{2-}\text{(aq)} + 16 \text{ H}^+\text{(aq)} \rightarrow 3 \text{ CH}_3\text{CO}_2\text{H(aq)} + 4 \text{ Cr}^{3+}\text{(aq)} + 11 \text{ H}_2\text{O}(\ell)$

20.86   (a) $E°_{cell} = E°_{cathode} - E°_{anode} = (0.7994 \text{ V}) - (0.771 \text{ V}) = 0.028 \text{ V}$

(b) $Ag^+(aq) + Fe^{2+}(aq) \rightarrow Ag(s) + Fe^{3+}(aq)$

(c) Reduction takes place at the silver cathode and oxidation occurs at the platinum electrode in the Fe^{2+}/Fe^{3+} solution.

(d) $E_{cell} = E°_{cell} - \dfrac{0.0257}{n} \ln \dfrac{[Fe^{3+}]}{[Ag^+][Fe^{2+}]} = 0.028 \text{ V} - \dfrac{0.0257}{1} \ln \dfrac{1.0}{(0.10)(1.0)} = -0.031 \text{ V}$

The net cell reaction is now the reverse, $Ag(s) + Fe^{3+}(aq) \rightarrow Ag^+(aq) + Fe^{2+}(aq)$

20.87   (a) $\left(\dfrac{1 \text{ mol reactants}}{231.7 \text{ g} + 65.39 \text{ g} + 18.02 \text{ g}}\right)\left(\dfrac{2 \text{ mol e}^-}{1 \text{ mol reactants}}\right)\left(\dfrac{96,500 \text{ C}}{1 \text{ mol e}^-}\right)(1.59 \text{ V})\left(\dfrac{1 \text{ J}}{1 \text{ C·V}}\right)\left(\dfrac{1 \text{ kJ}}{10^3 \text{ J}}\right) = 0.974 \text{ kJ/g}$

(b) $Pb(s) + PbO_2(s) + 2 H_2SO_4(aq) \rightarrow 2 PbSO_4(s) + 2 H_2O(\ell)$

$\left(\dfrac{1 \text{ mol reactants}}{207.2 \text{ g} + 239.2 \text{ g} + 2(98.08 \text{ g})}\right)\left(\dfrac{2 \text{ mol e}^-}{1 \text{ mol reactants}}\right)\left(\dfrac{96,500 \text{ C}}{1 \text{ mol e}^-}\right)(2.0 \text{ V})\left(\dfrac{1 \text{ J}}{1 \text{ C·V}}\right)\left(\dfrac{1 \text{ kJ}}{10^3 \text{ J}}\right) = 0.60 \text{ kJ/g}$

(c) The silver-zinc battery produces more energy per gram of reactants

20.88   pH = 7: $E_{cell} = E°_{cell} - \dfrac{0.0257}{n} \ln [OH^-]^2 P_{H_2} = -0.83 \text{ V} - \dfrac{0.0257}{2} \ln(1.0 \times 10^{-7})^2(1) = -0.42 \text{ V}$

pH = 0: $E_{cell} = -0.83 \text{ V} - \dfrac{0.0257}{2} \ln(1.0 \times 10^{-14})^2(1) = 0 \text{ V}$

pH = 1: $E_{cell} = -0.83 \text{ V} - \dfrac{0.0257}{2} \ln(1.0 \times 10^{-13})^2(1) = -0.06 \text{ V}$

It is much more advantageous to reduce water in an acidic solution.

20.89 I^- is the strongest reducing agent of the three halide ions. It reduces Cu^{2+} to Cu^+, forming insoluble CuI(s).

$2 Cu^{2+}(aq) + 4 I^-(aq) \rightarrow 2 CuI(s) + I_2(aq)$

20.90   (a) Reducing agent strength: $H_2 <$ A and C

(b) C is stronger than B, D, and A

(c) D is stronger than B

$B < D < H_2 < A < C$

20.91   (a) $(15 \text{ h})(60.0 \text{ min}/1 \text{ h})(60.0 \text{ s}/1 \text{ min})(1.5 \text{ A}) = 8.1 \times 10^4 \text{ C}$

$(8.1 \times 10^4 \text{ C})\left(\dfrac{1 \text{ mol e}^-}{96,500 \text{ C}}\right)\left(\dfrac{1 \text{ mol Pb}}{2 \text{ mol e}^-}\right)\left(\dfrac{207.2 \text{ g}}{1 \text{ mol Pb}}\right) = 87 \text{ g Pb}$

(b) $(8.1 \times 10^4 \text{ C})\left(\dfrac{1 \text{ mol e}^-}{96,500 \text{ C}}\right)\left(\dfrac{1 \text{ mol PbO}_2}{2 \text{ mol e}^-}\right)\left(\dfrac{239.2 \text{ g}}{1 \text{ mol PbO}_2}\right) = 100. \text{ g PbO}_2$

(c) $(8.1 \times 10^4 \text{ C})\left(\dfrac{1 \text{ mol e}^-}{96,500 \text{ C}}\right)\left(\dfrac{2 \text{ mol H}_2SO_4}{2 \text{ mol e}^-}\right)\left(\dfrac{1}{0.50 \text{ L}}\right) = 1.7 \text{ M}$

20.92 (a) $150 \text{ g} \cdot \dfrac{1 \text{ mol } CH_3SO_2F}{98.1 \text{ g}} \cdot \dfrac{3 \text{ mol } HF}{1 \text{ mol } CH_3SO_2F} \cdot \dfrac{20.0 \text{ g}}{1 \text{ mol } HF} = 92 \text{ g } HF$

$150 \text{ g} \cdot \dfrac{1 \text{ mol } CH_3SO_2F}{98.1 \text{ g}} \cdot \dfrac{1 \text{ mol } CF_3SO_2F}{1 \text{ mol } CH_3SO_2F} \cdot \dfrac{152 \text{ g}}{1 \text{ mol } CF_3SO_2F} = 230 \text{ g } CF_3SO_2F$

$150 \text{ g} \cdot \dfrac{1 \text{ mol } CH_3SO_2F}{98.1 \text{ g}} \cdot \dfrac{3 \text{ mol } H_2}{1 \text{ mol } CH_3SO_2F} \cdot \dfrac{2.02 \text{ g}}{1 \text{ mol } H_2} = 9.3 \text{ g } H_2$

(b) H_2 is produced at the cathode.

(c) $(24 \text{ h})\left(\dfrac{3600 \text{ sec}}{1 \text{ h}}\right)\left(\dfrac{250 \text{ C}}{1 \text{ sec}}\right)(8.0 \text{ V})\left(\dfrac{1 \text{ J}}{1 \text{ V} \cdot \text{C}}\right)\left(\dfrac{1 \text{ kwh}}{3.6 \times 10^6 \text{ J}}\right) = 48 \text{ kwh}$

20.93 (a) $\text{Efficiency} = \dfrac{\Delta G_f°[H_2O(\ell)]}{\Delta H_f°[H_2O(\ell)]} \cdot 100\% = \dfrac{-237.15 \text{ kJ/mol}}{-285.83 \text{ kJ/mol}} \cdot 100\% = 82.969\%$

(b) $\text{Efficiency} = \dfrac{\Delta G_f°[H_2O(g)]}{\Delta H_f°[H_2O(g)]} \cdot 100\% = \dfrac{-228.59 \text{ kJ/mol}}{-241.83 \text{ kJ/mol}} \cdot 100\% = 94.525\%$

(c) The efficiency is greater for the gaseous product, possibly due to energy loss when converting gaseous water to the liquid phase.

20.94 $n_{H_2} = \dfrac{PV}{RT} = \dfrac{(200. \text{ atm})(1.0 \text{ L})}{(0.082057 \text{ L} \cdot \text{atm/K} \cdot \text{mol})(298 \text{ K})} = 8.2 \text{ mol } H_2$

$(8.2 \text{ mol } H_2)\left(\dfrac{2 \text{ mol } e^-}{1 \text{ mol } H_2}\right)\left(\dfrac{96,500 \text{ C}}{1 \text{ mol } e^-}\right) = 1.6 \times 10^6 \text{ C}$

Time $= (1.6 \times 10^6 \text{ C})/(1.5 \text{ A}) = 1.1 \times 10^6 \text{ s (or 290 h)}$

20.95 (a) $2.4 \times 10^3 \text{ kcal} \cdot \dfrac{4.184 \text{ kJ}}{1 \text{ kcal}} \cdot \dfrac{1 \text{ mol glucose}}{2800 \text{ kJ}} = 3.6 \text{ mol glucose}$

$3.6 \text{ mol glucose} \cdot \dfrac{6 \text{ mol } O_2}{1 \text{ mol glucose}} = 22 \text{ mol } O_2$

(b) $O_2(g) + 4 H^+(aq) + 4 e^- \rightarrow 2 H_2O(\ell)$

$22 \text{ mol } O_2 \cdot \dfrac{4 \text{ mol } e^-}{1 \text{ mol } O_2} = 86 \text{ mol } e^-$

(c) $\dfrac{3.6 \text{ mol glucose}}{24 \text{ h}} \cdot \dfrac{1 \text{ h}}{3600 \text{ sec}} \cdot \dfrac{86 \text{ mol } e^-}{3.6 \text{ mol glucose}} \cdot \dfrac{96,500 \text{ C}}{1 \text{ mol } e^-} = 96 \text{ amps}$

(d) $\dfrac{96 \text{ C}}{1 \text{ sec}} \cdot 1.0 \text{ V} \cdot \dfrac{1 \text{ J}}{1 \text{ V} \cdot \text{C}} \cdot \dfrac{1 \text{ watt}}{1 \text{ J/s}} = 96 \text{ watts}$

20.97 In direct redox reactions the oxidizing and reducing agents are in direct contact. In indirect redox reactions, they are separated and current flows through a wire.

20.98   (a) Different metals have greater or less tendency to release electrons.

     (b) $Zn > Cu > Ag$

     (c) $Ag^+ > Cu^{2+} > Zn^{2+}$

     (d) The two are inversely related. If a metal has a strong tendency to give up electrons, the metal ion will have a weak tendency to accept electrons.

20.99   (a) $Au^{3+}, Br_2, Hg^{2+}, Ag^+, Hg_2^{2+}$

     (b) Al, Mg, Li

20.100 (a) All have a zinc anode

     (b) Cd

20.101 (a) $2\ Fe(s) \rightarrow 2\ Fe^{2+}(aq) + 4\ e^-$

         $O_2(g) + 2\ H_2O(\ell) + 4\ e^- \rightarrow 4\ OH^-(aq)$

     (b) kinetics

Chapter 21
The Chemistry of the Main Group Elements

INSTRUCTOR'S NOTES

Because main group elements and their compounds are of such great economic importance, and have an interesting chemistry, this chapter is a brief introduction to these elements. Beginning with this chapter, the material in the remainder of the book is covered to the extent that time is available at the end of the course. We have, regrettably, little time at the end of the course for a discussion of descriptive chemistry. Indeed, this was one motivating factor in placing as much chemistry as possible early in the text.

Normally we hope to have at least six to nine lectures on descriptive chemistry at the end of the second term. This enables us to discuss a few aspects of the chemistry of the following elements: H; Li and Na; Mg and Ca; B and Al; C and Si; N and P; O and S; and F and Cl.

SUGGESTED DEMONSTRATIONS

1.   The Periodic Table—A Guide to the Elements

   • *The Periodic Table Videodisc* and the *Periodic Table Live!* CD-ROM have excellent images of the reactions of the elements with air, water, and acids and bases. The advantage in using the videodisc is that one can quickly scan through the various types of reactions and illustrate the periodic trends of the elements. In addition, the videodisc contains images of the uses of the elements. Many of the demonstrations described in this chapter can also be found on the *Redox Videodisc*.

2.   Hydrogen

   • An excellent demonstration to use at the beginning of the discussion of hydrogen chemistry is to blow up a hydrogen-filled balloon. This can be made more interesting by filling a balloon with He and contrasting their behavior. The students can readily figure out which balloon contains H_2 gas.

   • One can demonstrate the various ways of making H_2, such as electrolysis, a metal + acid, Al + base, or a metal hydride + water. For more information on hydrogen, you will find it interesting and useful to read the book *Hydrogen Power* by L. O. Williams, Pergamon, 1980. Also useful are chapters in *The Modern Inorganic Chemicals Industry* (R. Thompson, ed., Royal Society, 1977) and *Industrial Inorganic Chemistry* by W. Büchner, R. Schliebs, G. Winter, and K. H. Büchel (VCH, 1989). A very interesting article on the "hydrogen economy" was done by G. Graff in *High Technology* magazine, May, 1983. Finally, *ChemMatters* for October, 1985 was devoted to hydrogen and helium chemistry.

3.   Sodium and Potassium

•   Demonstrate the flame colors of Na- and K-containing salts.

•   Show the reactions of the alkali metals with water. Caution! The reaction of K with water should be done behind a shield. In both cases, place an indicator in the water to show the formation of metal hydroxide.

•   Show the ease with which Na and K can be cut with a knife.

4.   Calcium and Magnesium

•   Minerals containing alkaline earth metals are readily available: calcite, marble, shells, and fluorite, among others.

•   Show the flame colors of the alkaline earth elements.

•   The reactions of Mg and Ca can be compared with Group 1 A elements. Magnesium will not react with water at room temperature, whereas Ca will react readily.

•   Calcium carbide is an important chemical. Its hydrolysis to give acetylene is readily illustrated.

5.   Aluminum

•   Demonstrate the formation of $Al(OH)_3$ and its amphoterism.

•   Illustrate the absorption of dyes by aluminum hydroxide and alumina.

•   Show the non reactivity of aluminum with an oxidizing acid. This can be contrasted with the reaction of Al with $CuCl_2$.

•   The thermite reaction is an impressive classroom demonstration. Directions for this reaction are given in Shakhashiri, Volume 1. We do the reaction by piling a small quantity of the reactants on a bed of sand on the demonstration table. The students are kept back about 20 feet.

•   Aluminum chloride is a very important industrial chemical; almost 25000 tons are produced annually in the United States. It is very useful to show that this halide is unstable toward water, in contrast with Group 1A and 2A halides. Use $AlCl_3$ from a newly opened bottle of $AlCl_3$ and add a spatula-full to 10-20 mL of water.

•   The reaction of Al with Br_2 is spectacular. However, it can only be done in a lecture room that has an excellent hood.

6.   Silicon

•   Silicon and silicon-based minerals are extremely important in our economy. It would be well to exhibit as many examples as possible. These include quartz, amethyst, various clays (including "kitty litter), zeolites, mica, talc, vermiculite, and (with proper precautions) asbestos.

•   Other silicon-containing materials are silicon carbide, glass, and cement.

7.   Nitrogen and Phosphorus

•   Demonstrations involving nitrogen and phosphorus that can be found in B. Z. Shakhashiri's *Chemical*

Demonstrations: A Handbook for Teachers of Chemistry:

Reaction of Zn with NH_4NO_3 and NH_4Cl
Reaction of white P_4 and Cl_2
Reaction of red P_4 and Br_2
Combustion of white P_4
Decomposition of $(NH_4)_2Cr_2O_7$
Preparation and properties of NO
NO_2/N_2O_4 equilibrium

8.   Oxygen and Sulfur

•   Demonstrations involving sulfur and oxygen that can be found in B. Z. Shakhashiri's *Chemical*

Demonstrations: A Handbook for Teachers of Chemistry:

Heat of Dilution of H_2SO_4
Reaction of Zn and S_8
Reaction of Fe and S_8
Dehydration of sugar by H_2SO_4
Preparation and properties of O_2
Preparation and properties of liquid O_2

9.   Chlorine

•   Demonstrations involving chlorine that can be found in B. Z. Shakhashiri's *Chemical Demonstrations: A*

Handbook for Teachers of Chemistry:

Reaction of Na and Cl_2
Reaction of Fe and Cl_2

Solutions to Study Questions

21.1   The name, atomic number, symbol, and atomic mass of an element.

The position of an element in the periodic table provides information about its reactivity and the types of compounds the element forms.

Whether an element is a metal, a nonmetal, or a metalloid.

21.2

Acid	Formula	Oxidation number	Periodic group number
Nitric acid	HNO_3	+5	5A
Sulfuric acid	H_2SO_4	+6	6A
Hydrobromic acid	HBr	−1	7A (= 8 − 1)
Perchloric acid	$HClO_4$	+7	7A
Carbonic acid	H_2CO_3	+4	4A

21.3   An amphoteric substance can act either as an acid or a base in chemical reactions.

Lewis acid: $Al(OH)_3(s) + OH^-(aq) \rightarrow Al(OH)_4^-(aq)$

Brønsted base: $Al(OH)_3(s) + 3\ H^+(aq) \rightarrow Al^{3+}(aq) + 3\ H_2O(\ell)$

21.4 $4\ Li(s) + O_2(g) \rightarrow 2\ Li_2O(s)$ $Li_2O(s) + H_2O(\ell) \rightarrow 2\ LiOH(aq)$

$2\ Ca(s) + O_2(g) \rightarrow 2\ CaO(s)$ $CaO(s) + H_2O(\ell) \rightarrow Ca(OH)_2(aq)$

21.5 $N_2(g) + 2\ O_2(g) \rightarrow 2\ NO_2(g)$ $2\ NO_2(g) + H_2O(\ell) \rightarrow HNO_3(aq) + HNO_2(aq)$

$2\ S(s) + 3\ O_2(g) \rightarrow 2\ SO_3(g)$ $SO_3(g) + H_2O(\ell) \rightarrow H_2SO_4(aq)$

21.6   The number of valence electrons for the second-period elements is equal to the group number.

Li (1), Be (2), B (3), C (4), N (5), O (6), F (7), Ne (8)

21.7   The elements in Group 4A have the general electron configuration [noble gas]ns^2np^2 CH_4, SiO_2

Group 4A elements typically share four electrons from other elements to achieve a noble gas configuration.

21.8   These are the elements of Group 3A: Boron, B; Aluminum, Al; Gallium, Ga; Indium, In; Thallium, Tl

21.9 S^{2-}, sulfide ion; Cl^-, chloride ion; K^+, potassium ion; Ca^{2+}, calcium ion

21.10   NaCl consists of a face-centered array of chloride anions with sodium cations in octahedral holes. The ions are held together by electrostatic attractive forces.

21.11 $2\ Na(s) + Cl_2(g) \rightarrow 2\ NaCl(s)$

The reaction is likely to be exothermic and the product is ionic.

21.12 $2 Mg(s) + O_2(g) \rightarrow 2 MgO(s)$

The reaction is likely to be exothermic and the product is ionic.

21.13   NaCl is colorless, a solid, and soluble in water.

21.14   MgO is white, a solid, and insoluble in water.

21.15
Element	Main Group element?	Chemical species
Oxygen	yes	H_2O, $CaCO_3$
Silicon	yes	SiO_2, silicate minerals
Aluminum	yes	Al_2O_3
Iron	no	
Calcium	yes	$CaCO_3$
Sodium	yes	NaCl
Potassium	yes	KCl
Magnesium	yes	$MgCl_2$
Hydrogen	yes	H_2O
Titanium	no	

21.16   No, calcium is a reactive metal and would not be found as a free element.

21.17   Only C is found as the free element in Earth's crust. H, Li, Be, B, N, O, and F are found in compounds.

21.18 $CO_2 < SiO_2 < SnO_2$

—increasing basicity→

21.19 $SO_3 < SiO_2 < Al_2O_3 < Na_2O$

—increasing basicity→

21.20   (a) $2 Na(s) + Br_2(\ell) \rightarrow 2 NaBr(s)$

(b) $2 Mg(s) + O_2(g) \rightarrow 2 MgO(s)$

(c) $2 Al(s) + 3 F_2(g) \rightarrow 2 AlF_3(g)$

(d) $C(s) + O_2(g) \rightarrow CO_2(g)$

21.21   (a) $2 K(s) + I_2(s) \rightarrow 2 KI(s)$

(b) $2 Ba(s) + O_2(g) \rightarrow 2 BaO(s)$

(c) $16 Al(s) + 3 S_8(s) \rightarrow 8 Al_2S_3(s)$

(d) $Si(s) + 2 Cl_2(g) \rightarrow SiCl_4(\ell)$

21.22 $2 H_2(g) + O_2(g) \rightarrow 2 H_2O(g)$

$H_2(g) + Cl_2(g) \rightarrow 2 HCl(g)$

$3 H_2(g) + N_2(g) \rightarrow 2 NH_3(g)$

21.23 $2 K(s) + H_2(g) \rightarrow 2 KH(s)$ potassium hydride

The compound is ionic, a solid, and has a high melting point, and reacts vigorously with water.

21.24   (a) $2 SO_2(g) + 4 H_2O(\ell) + 2 I_2(s) \rightarrow 2 H_2SO_4(\ell) + 4 HI(g)$

(b) $2 H_2SO_4(\ell) \rightarrow 2 H_2O(\ell) + 2 SO_2(g) + O_2(g)$

(c) $4 HI(g) \rightarrow 2 H_2(g) + 2 I_2(g)$

_____

$2 H_2O(\ell) \rightarrow 2 H_2(g) + O_2(g)$

21.25 $CH_4(g) + 2 H_2O(g) \rightarrow 4 H_2(g) + CO_2(g)$

$\Delta H^\circ = \Delta H_f^\circ[CO_2(g)] - \{\Delta H_f^\circ[CH_4(g)] + 2 \Delta H_f^\circ[H_2O(g)]\}$

$\Delta H^\circ = 1 \text{ mol } (-393.509 \text{ kJ/mol}) - [1 \text{ mol } (-74.87 \text{ kJ/mol}) + 2 \text{ mol } (-241.83 \text{ kJ/mol})] = 165.02 \text{ kJ}$

$\Delta S^\circ = 4 S^\circ[H_2(g)] + S^\circ[CO_2(g)] - \{S^\circ[CH_4(g)] + 2 S^\circ[H_2O(g)]\}$

$\Delta S^\circ = 4 \text{ mol } (130.7 \text{ J/K·mol}) + 1 \text{ mol } (213.74 \text{ J/K·mol}) - [1 \text{ mol } (186.26 \text{ J/K·mol})$

$+ 2 \text{ mol } (188.84 \text{ J/K·mol})]$

$\Delta S^\circ = 172.6 \text{ J/K}$

$\Delta G^\circ = \Delta H^\circ - T\Delta S^\circ = 165.02 \text{ kJ} - (298 \text{ K})(172.6 \text{ J/K})(1 \text{ kJ}/10^3 \text{ J}) = 113.6 \text{ kJ}$

21.26 $C(s) + H_2O(g) \rightarrow CO(g) + H_2(g)$

$\Delta H^\circ = \Delta H_f^\circ[CO(g)] - \Delta H_f^\circ[H_2O(g)] = 1 \text{ mol } (-110.525 \text{ kJ/mol}) - 1 \text{ mol } (-241.83 \text{ kJ/mol}) = 131.31 \text{ kJ}$

$\Delta S^\circ = S^\circ[CO(g)] + S^\circ[H_2(g)] - \{S^\circ[C(s)] + S^\circ[H_2O(g)]\}$

$\Delta S^\circ = 1 \text{ mol } (197.674 \text{ J/K·mol}) + 1 \text{ mol } (130.7 \text{ J/K·mol}) - [1 \text{ mol } (5.6 \text{ J/K·mol})$

$+ 1 \text{ mol } (188.84 \text{ J/K·mol})]$

$\Delta S^\circ = 133.9 \text{ J/K}$

$\Delta G^\circ = \Delta H^\circ - T\Delta S^\circ = 131.31 \text{ kJ} - (298 \text{ K})(133.9 \text{ J/K})(1 \text{ kJ}/10^3 \text{ J}) = 91.4 \text{ kJ}$

21.27   Insert a glowing splint in to the gas. Hydrogen will ignite (burning in air). If the gas is oxygen, the splint will burst into flame. If it is nitrogen, the splint will cease to glow.

21.28 $Na(s) + F_2(g) \rightarrow 2 NaF(s)$

$Na(s) + Cl_2(g) \rightarrow 2 NaCl(s)$

$Na(s) + Br_2(\ell) \rightarrow 2 NaBr(s)$

$Na(s) + I_2(s) \rightarrow 2 NaI(s)$

The alkali metal halides are white, crystalline solids. They have high melting and boiling points, and are soluble in water.

21.29 $Na(s) + O_2(g) \rightarrow Na_2O_2(s)$ Na^+ and O_2^{2-}

21.30 $4\ Li(s) + O_2(g) \rightarrow 2\ Li_2O(s)$ lithium oxide

$2\ Na(s) + O_2(g) \rightarrow 2\ Na_2O_2(s)$ sodium peroxide

$K(s) + O_2(g) \rightarrow KO_2(s)$ potassium superoxide

21.31   Use an inert dry chemical fire extinguisher if available. The worst thing would be to throw water on this fire since sodium reacts with water to produce hydrogen, a flammable gas.

21.32   (a) $2\ NaCl(aq) + 2\ H_2O(\ell) \rightarrow Cl_2(g) + H_2(g) + 2\ NaOH(aq)$

(b) $\dfrac{2\ mol\ NaOH}{1\ mol\ Cl_2} \cdot \dfrac{1\ mol\ Cl_2}{70.91\ g} \cdot \dfrac{40.00\ g}{1\ mol\ NaOH} = \dfrac{1.13\ g\ NaOH}{1\ g\ Cl_2}$

$\dfrac{1.19 \times 10^{10}\ kg\ NaOH}{1.14 \times 10^{10}\ kg\ Cl_2} = \dfrac{1.04\ kg\ NaOH}{1\ kg\ Cl_2}$

More chlorine is produced than can be accounted for by the electrolysis of aqueous sodium chloride. Chlorine is most likely produced by additional methods industrially.

21.33   Electrolysis of an aqueous solution of KCl:

Anode: $2\ Cl^-(aq) \rightarrow Cl_2(g) + 2\ e^-$

Cathode: $2\ H_2O(\ell) + 2\ e^- \rightarrow 2\ OH^-(aq) + H_2(g)$

Chloride ion is oxidized and water is reduced.

21.34 $2\ Mg(s) + O_2(g) \rightarrow 2\ MgO(s)$

$3\ Mg(s) + N_2(g) \rightarrow Mg_3N_2(s)$

21.35   (a) $Ca(s) + H_2(g) \rightarrow CaH_2(s)$

(b) $CaH_2(s) + 2\ H_2O(\ell) \rightarrow Ca(OH)_2(s) + 2\ H_2(g)$

21.36 $CaCO_3$ is used in agriculture to neutralize acidic soil, to prepare CaO for use in mortar, and in steel production. $CaCO_3(s) + H_2O(\ell) + CO_2(g) \rightarrow Ca^{2+}(aq) + 2\ HCO_3^-(aq)$

21.37   Hard water contains metal ions such as Ca^{2+} and Mg^{2+}. Hard water occurs as ground water flows through mineral beds having slightly soluble salts such as carbonates. Hard water ions react with soap to form insoluble soap scum. The ions decrease the lathering ability of the soap. Hard water leads to deposits of boiler scale in hot water heaters.

21.38 $CaO(s) + SO_2(g) \rightarrow CaSO_3(s)$

$1.2 \times 10^3\ kg \cdot \dfrac{10^3\ g}{1\ kg} \cdot \dfrac{1\ mol\ CaO}{56.1\ g} \cdot \dfrac{1\ mol\ SO_2}{1\ mol\ CaO} \cdot \dfrac{64.1\ g}{1\ mol\ SO_2} = 1.4 \times 10^6\ g\ SO_2$

21.39 $Ca(OH)_2(s) \rightleftharpoons Ca^{2+}(aq) + 2\ OH^-(aq)$ $K_{sp} = 5.5 \times 10^{-5}$

$Mg^{2+}(aq) + 2\ OH^-(aq) \rightleftharpoons Mg(OH)_2(s)$ $1/K_{sp} = 1/(5.6 \times 10^{-12})$

$Ca(OH)_2(s) + Mg^{2+}(aq) \rightleftharpoons Mg(OH)_2(s) + Ca^{2+}(aq)$ $K = 9.8 \times 10^6$

Adding $Ca(OH)_2$ to sea water will lead to the precipitation of $Mg(OH)_2$ which can then be further processed to ultimately yield Mg metal.

21.40 $2\ Al(s) + 6\ HCl(aq) \rightarrow 2\ Al^{3+}(aq) + 6\ Cl^-(aq) + 3\ H_2(g)$

$2\ Al(s) + 3\ Cl_2(g) \rightarrow 2\ AlCl_3(s)$

$4\ Al(s) + 3\ O_2(g) \rightarrow 2\ Al_2O_3(s)$

21.41 $2\ Al(s) + 3\ H_2O(\ell) \rightarrow 3\ H_2(g) + Al_2O_3(s)$

$\Delta H^\circ = \Delta H_f^\circ[Al_2O_3(s)] - 3\ \Delta H_f^\circ[H_2O(\ell)] = 1\ mol\ (-1675.7\ kJ/mol) - 3\ mol\ (-285.83\ kJ/mol)$

$\Delta H^\circ = -818.2\ kJ$

$\Delta S^\circ = S^\circ[Al_2O_3(s)] + 3\ S^\circ[H_2(g)] - \{2\ S^\circ[Al(s)] + 3\ S^\circ[H_2O(\ell)]\}$

$\Delta S^\circ = 1\ mol\ (50.92\ J/K\cdot mol) + 3\ mol\ (130.7\ J/K\cdot mol) - [2\ mol\ (28.3\ J/K\cdot mol) + 3\ mol\ (69.95\ J/K\cdot mol)]$

$\Delta S^\circ = 176.6\ J/K$

$\Delta G^\circ = \Delta G_f^\circ[Al_2O_3(s)] - 3\ \Delta G_f^\circ[H_2O(\ell)] = 1\ mol\ (-1582.3\ kJ/mol) - 3\ mol\ (-237.15\ kJ/mol)$

$\Delta G^\circ = -870.9\ kJ$

The data suggest the reaction is product-favored. A thin film of Al_2O_3 on the surface of the metal is slow to react with water and other substances, preventing further reaction.

21.42 $2\ Al(s) + 2\ NaOH(aq) + 6\ H_2O(\ell) \rightarrow 2\ Na^+(aq) + 2\ Al(OH)_4^-(aq) + 3\ H_2(g)$

$n_{H_2} = 13.2\ g\ Al \cdot \dfrac{1\ mol\ Al}{26.98\ g} \cdot \dfrac{3\ mol\ H_2}{2\ mol\ Al} = 0.734\ mol\ H_2$

$V = \dfrac{nRT}{P} = \dfrac{(0.734\ mol)(0.082057\ L\cdot atm/\ K\cdot mol)(295.7\ K)}{735\ mm\ Hg \cdot \dfrac{1\ atm}{760\ mm\ Hg}} = 18.4\ L\ (or\ 1.84 \times 10^4\ mL)$

21.43 (a) $Al_2O_3(s) + 3\ SiO_2(s) \rightarrow Al_2(SiO_3)_3(s)$

(b) $Al_2O_3(s) + CaO(s) \rightarrow Ca(AlO_2)_2(s)$

21.44 $Al_2O_3(s) + 3\ H_2SO_4(aq) \rightarrow Al_2(SO_4)_3(aq) + 3\ H_2O(\ell)$

$1.00 \times 10^3\ g \cdot \dfrac{1\ mol\ Al_2(SO_4)_3}{342.15\ g} \cdot \dfrac{1\ mol\ Al_2O_3}{1\ mol\ Al_2(SO_4)_3} \cdot \dfrac{101.96\ g}{1\ mol\ Al_2O_3} \cdot \dfrac{1\ kg}{10^3\ g} = 0.298\ kg\ Al_2O_3$

$1.00 \times 10^3\ g \cdot \dfrac{1\ mol\ Al_2(SO_4)_3}{342.15\ g} \cdot \dfrac{3\ mol\ H_2SO_4}{1\ mol\ Al_2(SO_4)_3} \cdot \dfrac{98.08\ g}{1\ mol\ H_2SO_4} \cdot \dfrac{1\ kg}{10^3\ g} = 0.860\ kg\ H_2SO_4$

21.45 $Ga(OH)_3(s) + 3\ HCl(aq) \rightarrow GaCl_3(aq) + 3\ H_2O(\ell)$

$Ga(OH)_3(s) + NaOH(aq) \rightarrow Ga(OH)_4^-(aq) + Na^+(aq)$

$1.25\ g \cdot \dfrac{1\ mol\ Ga(OH)_3}{120.7\ g} \cdot \dfrac{3\ mol\ HCl}{1\ mol\ Ga(OH)_3} \cdot \dfrac{1\ L}{0.0112\ mol\ HCl} = 2.77\ L$

21.46
$$
\left[\ :\!\overset{\displaystyle ..}{\underset{\displaystyle ..}{Cl}}\!: \;\;\; :\!\overset{..}{\underset{..}{Cl}}\!-\!Al\!-\!\overset{..}{\underset{..}{Cl}}\!: \;\;\; :\!\overset{\displaystyle ..}{\underset{\displaystyle ..}{Cl}}\!:\ \right]^-
$$
The ion has a tetrahedral geometry. The Al atom is sp^3 hybridized.

21.47 $0.56\ g\ Al \cdot \dfrac{1\ mol\ Al}{27.0\ g} \cdot \dfrac{3\ mol\ H_2}{2\ mol\ Al} = 0.031\ mol\ H_2$

$V = \dfrac{nRT}{P} = \dfrac{(0.031\ mol\ H_2)(0.082057\ L \cdot atm/K \cdot mol)(299\ K)}{745\ mm\ Hg \cdot \dfrac{1\ atm}{760\ mm\ Hg}} = 0.78\ L$

21.48 SiO_2 is a network solid, with tetrahedral silicon atoms covalently bonded to four oxygens in an infinite array; CO_2 consists of individual molecules, with oxygen atoms double bonded to carbon. Melting SiO_2 requires breaking very stable Si—O bonds. Weak intermolecular forces of attraction between CO_2 molecules result in this substance being a gas at ambient conditions.

21.49   Sand (SiO_2) is reduced to Si by reaction with coke (C) in an electric furnace at 3000 °C. The Si obtained this way is reacted with chlorine to form $SiCl_4(\ell)$, which is purified by distillation. The $SiCl_4(\ell)$ is reduced to Si by reaction with very pure magnesium or zinc. This "pure" silicon is made ultrapure by a process known as zone refining.

21.50   (a) $Si(s) + 2\ CH_3Cl(g) \rightarrow (CH_3)_2SiCl_2(\ell)$

(b) $n_{CH_3Cl} = 2.65\ g \cdot \dfrac{1\ mol\ Si}{28.09\ g} \cdot \dfrac{2\ mol\ CH_3Cl}{1\ mol\ Si} = 0.189\ mol\ CH_3Cl$

$P = \dfrac{nRT}{V} = \dfrac{(0.189\ mol\ CH_3Cl)(0.082057\ L \cdot atm/K \cdot mol)(297.7\ K)}{5.60\ L} = 0.823\ atm$

(c) $2.65\ g \cdot \dfrac{1\ mol\ Si}{28.09\ g} \cdot \dfrac{1\ mol\ (CH_3)_2SiCl_2}{1\ mol\ Si} \cdot \dfrac{129.1\ g}{1\ mol\ (CH_3)_2SiCl_2} = 12.2\ (CH_3)_2SiCl_2$

21.51   Pyroxenes have as their basic structural unit an extended chain of linked SiO_4 tetrahedra. The ratio of Si to O is 1:3.

21.52   None of the nitrogen oxides are stable with respect to decomposition to the elements. All have negative ΔG_f° values, so the general reaction $N_xO_y(g) \rightarrow {}^x\!/_2\ N_2(g) + {}^y\!/_2\ O_2(g)$ will have a positive ΔG° value.

21.53 $\Delta H^{\circ} = \Delta H_f^{\circ}[N_2O_4(g)] - 2\,\Delta H_f^{\circ}[NO_2(g)] = 1\text{ mol }(9.08\text{ kJ/mol}) - 2\text{ mol }(33.1\text{ kJ/mol}) = -57.1\text{ kJ}$

The reaction is exothermic

21.54 $\Delta H^{\circ} = 2\,\Delta H_f^{\circ}[NO_2(g)] - 2\,\Delta H_f^{\circ}[NO(g)] = 2\text{ mol }(33.1\text{ kJ/mol}) - 2\text{ mol }(90.29\text{ kJ/mol}) = -114.4\text{ kJ}$

The reaction is exothermic

21.55 $\Delta G^{\circ} = \Delta G_f^{\circ}[HNO_3(aq)] + \Delta G_f^{\circ}[H_2O(\ell)] - \Delta G_f^{\circ}[NH_3(g)]$

$\Delta G^{\circ} = 1\text{ mol }(-111.25\text{ kJ/mol}) + 1\text{ mol }(-237.15\text{ kJ/mol}) - 1\text{ mol }(-16.37\text{ kJ/mol}) = -332.03\text{ kJ}$

$\Delta G^{\circ} = -332.03\text{ kJ} = -RT\ln K = -(8.3145 \times 10^{-3}\text{ kJ/K·mol})(298\text{ K})\ln K$

$K = 2 \times 10^{58}$

21.56   (a) $N_2H_4(aq) + O_2(g) \rightarrow N_2(g) + 2\,H_2O(\ell)$

(b) $3.00 \times 10^4\text{ L }H_2O \cdot \dfrac{3.08\text{ mL }O_2}{100.\text{ mL }H_2O} \cdot \dfrac{1\text{ mol }O_2}{22.414\,L} \cdot \dfrac{1\text{ mol }N_2H_4}{1\text{ mol }O_2} \cdot \dfrac{32.05\text{ g}}{1\text{ mol }N_2H_4} = 1320\text{ g }N_2H_4$

21.57 $3.00 \times 10^4\text{ L }H_2O \cdot \dfrac{3.08\text{ mL }O_2}{100.\text{ mL }H_2O} \cdot \dfrac{1\text{ mol }O_2}{22.414\,L} \cdot \dfrac{2\text{ mol }Na_2SO_3}{1\text{ mol }O_2} \cdot \dfrac{126.0\text{ g}}{1\text{ mol }Na_2SO_3} = 1.04 \times 10^4\text{ g }Na_2SO_3$

21.58 $5[N_2H_5^{+}(aq) \rightarrow N_2(g) + 5\,H^{+}(aq) + 4\text{ e}^-]$

$4[IO_3^{-}(aq) + 6\,H^{+}(aq) + 5\text{ e}^- \rightarrow \tfrac{1}{2}\,I_2(aq) + 3\,H_2O(\ell)]$

$\overline{}$

$5\,N_2H_5^{+}(aq) + 4\,IO_3^{-}(aq) \rightarrow 5\,N_2(g) + H^{+}(aq) + 2\,I_2(aq) + 12\,H_2O(\ell)$

$E^{\circ} = E^{\circ}_{\text{cathode}} - E^{\circ}_{\text{anode}} = (1.195\text{ V}) - (-0.23\text{ V}) = 1.43\text{ V}$

21.59   (a) N_2O_4 is the oxidizing agent and $H_2NN(CH_3)_2$ is the reducing agent.

(b) $H_2NN(CH_3)_2(\ell) + 2\,N_2O_4(\ell) \rightarrow 3\,N_2(g) + 4\,H_2O(g) + 2\,CO_2(g)$

$4100\text{ kg} \cdot \dfrac{1\text{ mol }H_2NN(CH_3)_2}{60.1\text{ g}} \cdot \dfrac{2\text{ mol }N_2O_4}{1\text{ mol }H_2NN(CH_3)_2} \cdot \dfrac{92.0\text{ g}}{1\text{ mol }N_2O_4} = 13000\text{ kg }N_2O_4$

$4100\text{ kg} \cdot \dfrac{1\text{ mol }H_2NN(CH_3)_2}{60.1\text{ g}} \cdot \dfrac{3\text{ mol }N_2}{1\text{ mol }H_2NN(CH_3)_2} \cdot \dfrac{28.0\text{ g}}{1\text{ mol }N_2} = 5700\text{ kg }N_2$

$4100\text{ kg} \cdot \dfrac{1\text{ mol }H_2NN(CH_3)_2}{60.1\text{ g}} \cdot \dfrac{4\text{ mol }H_2O}{1\text{ mol }H_2NN(CH_3)_2} \cdot \dfrac{18.0\text{ g}}{1\text{ mol }H_2O} = 4900\text{ kg }H_2O$

$4100\text{ kg} \cdot \dfrac{1\text{ mol }H_2NN(CH_3)_2}{60.1\text{ g}} \cdot \dfrac{2\text{ mol }CO_2}{1\text{ mol }H_2NN(CH_3)_2} \cdot \dfrac{44.0\text{ g}}{1\text{ mol }CO_2} = 6.0 \times 10^3\text{ kg }CO_2$

21.60   The azide ion has three resonance structures:

$$\left[\,:N\!\equiv\!N\!-\!\ddot{\underset{\cdot\cdot}{N}}:\,\right]^{-} \longleftrightarrow \left[\,\ddot{\underset{\cdot\cdot}{N}}\!=\!N\!=\!\ddot{\underset{\cdot\cdot}{N}}\,\right]^{-} \longleftrightarrow \left[\,:\ddot{\underset{\cdot\cdot}{N}}\!-\!N\!\equiv\!N:\,\right]^{-}$$

21.61 $CaO(s) + H_3PO_4(aq) \rightarrow CaHPO_4(s) + H_2O(\ell)$

21.62   (a) 1.80×10^6 kg $\cdot \dfrac{1 \text{ mol H}_2\text{SO}_4}{98.08 \text{ g}} \cdot \dfrac{1 \text{ mol SO}_2}{1 \text{ mol H}_2\text{SO}_4} \cdot \dfrac{64.06 \text{ g}}{1 \text{ mol SO}_2} \cdot \dfrac{0.0030 \text{ kg SO}_2 \text{ released}}{1.00 \text{ kg SO}_2 \text{ produced}}$

$$= 3.5 \times 10^3 \text{ kg SO}_2$$

(b) 3.5×10^3 kg $\cdot \dfrac{1 \text{ mol SO}_2}{64.06 \text{ g}} \cdot \dfrac{1 \text{ mol Ca(OH)}_2}{1 \text{ mol SO}_2} \cdot \dfrac{74.09 \text{ g}}{1 \text{ mol Ca(OH)}_2} = 4.1 \times 10^3 \text{ kg Ca(OH)}_2$

21.63   (1) $S + O_2 \rightarrow SO_2$ $\qquad\qquad \Delta H^\circ = \Delta H_f^\circ[SO_2] = -296.84$ kJ

(2) $SO_2 + {}^1/_2\,O_2 \rightarrow SO_3$ $\qquad \Delta H^\circ = \Delta H_f^\circ[SO_3] - \Delta H_f^\circ[SO_2] = -98.93$ kJ

(3) $SO_3 + H_2O \rightarrow H_2SO_4$ $\qquad \Delta H^\circ = -130$ kJ

$S + {}^3/_2\,O_2 + H_2O \rightarrow H_2SO_4$ $\qquad \Delta H^\circ_{rxn} = \Delta H^\circ(1) + \Delta H^\circ(2) + \Delta H^\circ(3) = -530$ kJ

907×10^3 g $\cdot \dfrac{1 \text{ mol H}_2\text{SO}_4}{98.08 \text{ g}} \cdot \dfrac{530 \text{ kJ}}{1 \text{ mol H}_2\text{SO}_4} = 4.9 \times 10^6$ kJ

21.64 $\left[:\!\ddot{\text{S}}\!-\!\ddot{\text{S}}\!: \right]^{2-}$

21.65 S_2F_2 $\qquad :\!\ddot{\text{F}}\!-\!\ddot{\text{S}}\!-\!\ddot{\text{S}}\!-\!\ddot{\text{F}}\!:$ $\qquad$ S oxidation number is +1.

SF_2 $\qquad :\!\ddot{\text{F}}\!-\!\ddot{\text{S}}\!-\!\ddot{\text{F}}\!:$ $\qquad$ S oxidation number is +2

SF_4 $\qquad$ S oxidation number is +4 (lone pairs on F not shown)

SF_6 $\qquad$ S oxidation number is +6 (lone pairs on F not shown)

S_2F_{10} $\qquad$ S oxidation number is +5 (lone pairs on F not shown)

21.66 $2[Mn^{2+}(aq) + 4 H_2O(\ell) \rightarrow MnO_4^-(aq) + 8 H^+(aq) + 5 e^-]$

$2 BrO_3^-(aq) + 12 H^+(aq) + 10 e^- \rightarrow Br_2(aq) + 6 H_2O(\ell)$

$2 Mn^{2+}(aq) + 2 H_2O(\ell) + 2 BrO_3^-(aq) \rightarrow 2 MnO_4^-(aq) + 4 H^+(aq) + Br_2(aq)$

$E^\circ_{cell} = E^\circ_{cathode} - E^\circ_{anode} = (1.44 \text{ V}) - (1.51 \text{ V}) = -0.07$ V $\qquad$ The reaction is not product-favored

21.67 $OCl^-(aq) + H_2O(\ell) \rightleftharpoons HClO(aq) + OH^-(aq)$

$K_b = \dfrac{K_w}{K_a} = 2.9 \times 10^{-7} = \dfrac{[HClO][OH^-]}{[OCl^-]} = \dfrac{(x)(x)}{0.10 - x} \approx \dfrac{x^2}{0.10}$

$x = [OH^-] = 1.7 \times 10^{-4}$ M $\qquad$ pOH = 3.77 $\qquad$ pH = 10.23

21.68 $Cl_2(g) + 2 Br^-(aq) \rightarrow 2 Cl^-(aq) + Br_2(\ell)$ Cl_2 is the oxidizing agent and Br^- is the reducing agent

$E^{\circ}_{cell} = E^{\circ}_{cathode} - E^{\circ}_{anode} = (1.36 \text{ V}) - (1.08 \text{ V}) = 0.28 \text{ V}$ The reaction is product-favored

21.69 BrO_3^-: $BrO_3^-(aq) + 6 H^+(aq) + 6 Cl^-(aq) \rightarrow Br^-(aq) + 3 H_2O(\ell) + 3 Cl_2(g)$

   MnO_4^-: $2 MnO_4^-(aq) + 10 Cl^-(aq) + 16 H^+(aq) \rightarrow 2 Mn^{2+}(aq) + 5 Cl_2(g) + 8 H_2O(\ell)$

   Ce^{4+}: $2 Ce^{4+}(aq) + 2 Cl^-(aq) \rightarrow 2 Ce^{3+}(aq) + Cl_2(g)$

21.70

Element	(a)	(b)	(c)
Na	metal	silvery gray	solid
Mg	metal	silvery gray	solid
Al	metal	silvery gray	solid
Si	nonmetal	gray	solid
P	nonmetal	white or red	solid
S	nonmetal	yellow	solid
Cl	nonmetal	pale yellow	gas
Ar	nonmetal	colorless	gas

21.71

Element	(a)	(b)	(c)
Li	metal	silvery gray	solid
Be	metal	silvery gray	solid
B	metalloid	gray	solid
C	nonmetal	gray/black	solid
N	nonmetal	colorless	gas
O	nonmetal	colorless	gas
F	nonmetal	pale yellow/green	gas
Ne	nonmetal	colorless	gas

21.72

Element	(a)	(b)
Na	$2 Na(s) + Cl_2(g) \rightarrow 2 NaCl(s)$	ionic
Mg	$Mg(s) + Cl_2(g) \rightarrow MgCl_2(s)$	ionic
Al	$2 Al(s) + 3 Cl_2(g) \rightarrow 2 AlCl_3(s)$	covalent
Si	$Si(s) + 2 Cl_2(g) \rightarrow SiCl_4(\ell)$	covalent
P	$P_4(s) + 10 Cl_2(g) \rightarrow 4 PCl_5(s)$	covalent
S	$S_8(s) + 16 Cl_2(g) \rightarrow 8 SCl_2(s)$	covalent

(c)

electron pair geometry	tetrahedral	trigonal bipyramidal
molecular geometry	tetrahedral	trigonal bipyramidal

21.73   Element   (a)   (b)

C $C(s) + 2\ Cl_2(g) \rightarrow CCl_4(\ell)$ covalent

Si $Si(s) + 2\ Cl_2(g) \rightarrow SiCl_4(\ell)$ covalent

Ge $Ge(s) + 2\ Cl_2(g) \rightarrow GeCl_4(s)$ covalent

Sn $Sn(s) + Cl_2(g) \rightarrow SnCl_2(s)$ ionic

                       $Sn(s) + 2\ Cl_2(g) \rightarrow SnCl_4(s)$ covalent

Pb $Pb(s) + Cl_2(g) \rightarrow PbCl_2(s)$ ionic

21.74   Cathode: $Li^+ + e^- \rightarrow Li$ Anode: $2\ H^- \rightarrow H_2 + 2\ e^-$

21.75 $1.0 \times 10^3\ g\ H_2 \cdot \dfrac{1\ mol\ H_2}{2.02\ g} = 5.0 \times 10^2\ mol\ H_2$

$V = \dfrac{nRT}{P} = \dfrac{(5.0 \times 10^2\ mol)(0.082057\ L \cdot atm/K \cdot mol)(298\ K)}{1.0\ atm} = 1.2 \times 10^4\ L$

21.76 $MCO_3(s) \rightarrow MO(s) + CO_2(g)$ $\Delta G° = \Delta G_f°[MO(s)] + \Delta G_f°[CO_2(g)] - \Delta G_f°[MCO_3(s)]$

Mg: $\Delta G° = 1\ mol\ (-568.93\ kJ/mol) + 1\ mol\ (-394.359\ kJ/mol) - 1\ mol\ (-1028.2\ kJ/mol) = 64.9\ kJ$

Ca: $\Delta G° = 1\ mol\ (-603.42\ kJ/mol) + 1\ mol\ (-394.359\ kJ/mol) - 1\ mol\ (-1129.16\ kJ/mol) = 131.38\ kJ$

Ba: $\Delta G° = 1\ mol\ (-520.38\ kJ/mol) + 1\ mol\ (-394.359\ kJ/mol) - 1\ mol\ (-1134.41\ kJ/mol) = 219.67\ kJ$

Relative tendency to decompose: $MgCO_3 > CaCO_3 > BaCO_3$

21.77 $2\ NH_4ClO_4(s) \rightarrow N_2(g) + Cl_2(g) + 2\ O_2(g) + 4\ H_2O(g)$

$6.35 \times 10^5\ kg \cdot \dfrac{1\ mol\ NH_4ClO_4}{117.5\ g} \cdot \dfrac{4\ mol\ H_2O}{2\ mol\ NH_4ClO_4} \cdot \dfrac{18.02\ g}{1\ mol\ H_2O} = 1.95 \times 10^5\ kg\ H_2O$

$6.35 \times 10^5\ kg \cdot \dfrac{1\ mol\ NH_4ClO_4}{117.5\ g} \cdot \dfrac{2\ mol\ O_2}{2\ mol\ NH_4ClO_4} \cdot \dfrac{32.00\ g}{1\ mol\ O_2} = 1.73 \times 10^5\ kg\ O_2$

$4\ Al(s) + 3\ O_2(g) \rightarrow 2\ Al_2O_3(s)$

$1.73 \times 10^5\ kg \cdot \dfrac{1\ mol\ O_2}{32.00\ g} \cdot \dfrac{4\ mol\ Al}{3\ mol\ O_2} \cdot \dfrac{26.98\ g}{1\ mol\ Al} = 1.94 \times 10^5\ kg\ Al$

$1.73 \times 10^5\ kg \cdot \dfrac{1\ mol\ O_2}{32.00\ g} \cdot \dfrac{2\ mol\ Al_2O_3}{3\ mol\ O_2} \cdot \dfrac{102.0\ g}{1\ mol\ Al_2O_3} = 3.67 \times 10^5\ kg\ Al_2O_3$

21.78   (a) $\Delta G°$ must be < 0 for the reaction to be product-favored. Calculate $\Delta G_f°[MX_n]$ when $\Delta G° = 0$

$\Delta G_f^{\circ}[MX_n(s)] = n\Delta G_f^{\circ}[HCl(g)] = n(-95.1 \text{ kJ/mol})$ when $\Delta G^{\circ} = 0$

If $[MX_n(s)] < n(-95.1 \text{ kJ/mol})$ then ΔG° will be negative

(b)

Metal	Ba	Pb	Hg	Ti
$\Delta G_f^{\circ}[MX_n(s)]$	−810.4	−310.10	−178.6	−737.2
n	2	2	2	4
$n(-95.1 \text{ kJ/mol})$	−190.2	−190.2	−190.2	−380.4

Ba, Pb, and Ti will react with HCl

21.79   (a)

(b)   B is sp^2 hybridized.

(c)

(d)   Reaction is possible because boron has an empty, unhybridized p orbital that can accept a pair of electrons from a Lewis base such as water. Boric acid acts as a Lewis acid in this reaction.

21.80   (a)   We rationalize the equivalence of the two N—O bond lengths by writing two resonance structures for this molecule. The greater bond order (1.5) explains the shorter bond length when compared to a NO single bond.

(b)   The central atom, nitrogen, has three sets of bonding electrons in its valence shell; VSEPR predicts that this atom is trigonal-planar. Oxygen, in the —OH group, has four electron pairs in its valence shell, arranged tetrahedrally. Two are bonding pairs, defining the bent molecular geometry.

(c) sp^2. There is an empty p orbital on N that is perpendicular to the plane of the molecule; this can overlap with p orbitals on the two terminal oxygens to form a delocalized π bond.

21.81   (a)   The hybridization of Al in Al_2Br_6 is sp^3.

(b)

(c)   The Br atom can act as a Lewis base, donating a lone pair of electrons into an empty, unhybridized p orbital on Al. In Al_2Br_6, each Al and Br atom is sp^3 hybridized. The Al—Br sigma bonds result from overlap of two sp^3 hybrid orbitals, each containing a single electron. The bridging Al—Br bonds result from overlap of a filled sp^3 orbital on bromine overlapping an empty sp^3 orbital on aluminum.

21.82   A is $BaCO_3$; B is BaO; C is $CaCO_3$; D is $BaCl_2$; E is $BaSO_4$

21.83   Since the flask contains a fixed number of moles of gas at the given pressure and temperature, one could determine the total mass of gas present and solve for the mass of H_2 in the mixture.

21.84 $\Delta H° = 4 \, \Delta H_f°[HNO_3(aq)] - 2 \, \Delta H_f°[H_2O(\ell)] = 4$ mol (−207.36 kJ/mol) − 2 mol (−285.83 kJ/mol)

$\Delta H° = -257.78$ kJ This reaction is entropy-disfavored, however, with $\Delta S° = -963$ J/K because of the decrease in the number of moles of gases. Combining these values gives $\Delta G° = 29.34$ kJ, indicating that under standard conditions at 298 K the reaction is not favorable. (The reaction has a favorable $\Delta G°$ below 268 K, indicating that further research on this system might be worthwhile. Note, however, that at that temperature water is a solid.)

21.85   Starting materials:

Produce $H_2(g)$ by the electrolysis of water.

Liquefy air and separate $N_2(\ell)$.

Use the Haber process to produce $NH_3(g)$ from $H_2(g)$ and $N_2(g)$.

React ammonia with water to produce $NH_4OH(aq)$.

Use Ostwald process to produce $HNO_3(aq)$ from $NH_3(g)$, $O_2(g)$, and $H_2O(\ell)$.

Combine $NH_4OH(aq)$ and $HNO_3(aq)$ to produce $NH_4NO_3(aq)$ and $H_2O(\ell)$.

Evaporate the water to isolate $NH_4NO_3(s)$.

21.86   (a) $1.00 \times 10^3 \, g \cdot \dfrac{1 \, mol \, Mg}{24.31 \, g} \cdot \dfrac{1 \, L}{0.050 \, mol \, Mg^{2+}} = 820$ L seawater

$CaO(s) + H_2O(\ell) + Mg^{2+}(aq) \rightarrow Mg(OH)_2(s) + Ca^{2+}(aq)$

$1.00 \times 10^3 \, g \cdot \dfrac{1 \, mol \, Mg}{24.31 \, g} \cdot \dfrac{1 \, mol \, CaO}{1 \, mol \, Mg^{2+}} \cdot \dfrac{56.08 \, g}{1 \, mol \, CaO} \cdot \dfrac{1 \, kg}{10^3 \, g} = 2.31$ kg CaO

(b) $MgCl_2(\ell) \rightarrow Mg(s) + Cl_2(g)$

$1.2 \times 10^3 \, kg \cdot \dfrac{1 \, mol \, MgCl_2}{95.2 \, g} \cdot \dfrac{1 \, mol \, Mg}{1 \, mol \, MgCl_2} \cdot \dfrac{24.3 \, g}{1 \, mol \, Mg} = 310$ kg Mg

Cl_2 gas is produced at the anode

$1.2 \times 10^3 \, kg \cdot \dfrac{1 \, mol \, MgCl_2}{95.2 \, g} \cdot \dfrac{1 \, mol \, Cl_2}{1 \, mol \, MgCl_2} \cdot \dfrac{70.9 \, g}{1 \, mol \, Cl_2} = 890$ kg Cl_2

$1.2 \times 10^3 \, kg \cdot \dfrac{10^3 \, g}{1 \, kg} \cdot \dfrac{1 \, mol \, MgCl_2}{95.2 \, g} \cdot \dfrac{2 \, mol \, e^-}{1 \, mol \, MgCl_2} \cdot \dfrac{1 \, F}{1 \, mol \, e^-} = 2.5 \times 10^4$ F

(c) $\dfrac{18.5 \, kwh}{1 \times 10^3 \, g \, Mg} \cdot \dfrac{3.6 \times 10^6 \, J}{1 \, kwh} \cdot \dfrac{24.31 \, g}{1 \, mol \, Mg} \cdot \dfrac{1 \, kJ}{10^3 \, J} = 1600$ kJ/mol

$-(\Delta H_f°[MgCl_2(s)]) = -(641.62 \, kJ/mol) = 641.62$ kJ/mol

The electrolysis process requires more energy because the $MgCl_2$ must be melted.

21.87 $2 \text{ Cl}^-(aq) \rightarrow \text{Cl}_2(g) + 2 \text{ e}^-$

$$1.00 \times 10^3 \text{ g} \cdot \frac{1 \text{ mol Cl}_2}{70.91 \text{ g}} \cdot \frac{2 \text{ mol e}^-}{1 \text{ mol Cl}_2} \cdot \frac{96,500 \text{ C}}{1 \text{ mol e}^-} = 2.72 \times 10^6 \text{ C}$$

$$(2.72 \times 10^6 \text{ C})(4.6 \text{ V})\left(\frac{1 \text{ J}}{1 \text{ C·V}}\right)\left(\frac{1 \text{ kwh}}{3.6 \times 10^6 \text{ J}}\right) = 3.5 \text{ kwh}$$

21.88 $2 \text{ NaCl}(\ell) \rightarrow 2 \text{ Na}(s) + \text{Cl}_2(g)$

(a) $\left(\dfrac{23 \text{ g Na}}{1 \text{ mol Na}}\right)\left(\dfrac{2 \text{ mol Na}}{2 \text{ mole e}^-}\right)\left(\dfrac{1 \text{ mole e}^-}{96,500 \text{ C}}\right)\left(\dfrac{1 \text{ C}}{1 \text{ A· 1s}}\right)(25 \times 10^3 \text{ A})\left(\dfrac{3600 \text{ s}}{1 \text{ h}}\right)\left(\dfrac{1 \text{ kg}}{1000 \text{ g}}\right) = 2.1 \text{ kg/h}$

(b) $\left(\dfrac{1 \text{ kwh}}{3.6 \text{ x } 10^6 \text{ J}}\right)\left(\dfrac{1 \text{ J}}{1 \text{ V·C}}\right)(7.0 \text{ V})\left(\dfrac{96,500 \text{ C}}{1 \text{ mol e}^-}\right)\left(\dfrac{1 \text{ mol e}^-}{1 \text{ mol Na}}\right)\left(\dfrac{1 \text{ mol Na}}{23.0 \text{ g Na}}\right)(1.00 \times 10^3 \text{ g Na}) = 8.2 \text{ kwh}$

Chapter 22
The Transition Elements

INSTRUCTOR'S NOTES

As this material is usually covered at the end of the course, there is not usually enough time to cover all of the chapter. However, enough of the basic ideas of crystal field theory can be introduced so that the color of complexes may be understand.

SUGGESTED DEMONSTRATIONS

1.   Properties of the Transition Elements

   •   The photographs in this chapter suggest many demonstrations, particularly of colored complexes. One that we have used to show the different colors of chromium in its different oxidation states is Figure 22.4. (Also see Cornelius, R. *Journal of Chemical Education* **1980**, *57*, 316 for an experiment involving vanadium oxidation states.) The chemistry of nickel and iron can be illustrated using demonstrations outlined in Shakhashiri, Volume 1. In addition, there are several other demonstrations in Shakhashiri and in L. R. Summerlin, J. L. Ealy, Jr. *Chemical Demonstrations: A Sourcebook for Teachers, 2nd Edition*, Volumes 1 and 2 involving transition metal compounds and chemical equilibria.

   •   The *Periodic Table Videodisc* and the *Periodic Table Live!* CD-ROM have images of almost all of the transition elements, the uses of these elements, and their reactions with air, water, acids, and bases. The *Redox Videodisc* is also a video source of transition metals, their chemistry, and their industrial uses.

   •   Demonstrations of magnetism involving transition metals: Walker, N. "Paramagnetic Properties of Fe(II) and Fe(III)," *Journal of Chemical Education* **1977**, *54*, 431; Knox, K.; Strothkamp, R. "Ferrimagnetism," *ibid.* **1989**, *66*, 337.

2.   Coordination Compounds

   •   For demonstrations of coordination complexes, see Volume 1 of Shakhashiri's *Chemical Demonstrations*.

375

Solutions to Study Questions

22.1   These terms refer to the orbital(s) being filled for a given element. In the sixth period there are 2 elements
        in the s-block, 6 in the p-block, 10 in the d-block, and 14 in the f-block.

22.2   V: $[Ar]3d^34s^2$ Mn: $[Ar]3d^54s^2$

        Ni: $[Ar]3d^84s^2$ Cu: $[Ar]3d^{10}4s^2$

22.3 Cr^{2+}: $[Ar]3d^4$ Cr^{3+}: $[Ar]3d^3$

        Fe^{2+}: $[Ar]3d^6$ Fe^{3+}: $[Ar]3d^5$

        Co^{2+}: $[Ar]3d^7$ Co^{3+}: $[Ar]3d^6$

        Zn^{2+}: $[Ar]3d^{10}$

22.4   All transition metals are solids with high melting points and boiling points. They have a metallic sheen
        and are conductors of electricity and heat. They react with oxidizing agents such as O_2 and Cl_2 to produce
        ionic compounds and react with acids to form ionic compounds and hydrogen gas.

22.5   Ti: used in white pigments as TiO_2 Cr: used in glass as the oxide to give a green color

        Ni: used in nitinol, the memory metal   Cu: used in coins

22.6   Pyrometallurgy involves using high temperatures to separate the metal from other elements and impurities.
        Hydrometallurgy uses reactions in aqueous solution to enrich and isolate a metal from impurities in the
        ore.

22.7   In a coordinate covalent bond, the bonding pair of electrons originates on one of the bonded atoms. In the
        case of coordination complexes, the electron pair was originally on the ligand. The formation of a
        coordinate covalent bond is an example of a Lewis acid-base reaction. The metal ion is the Lewis acid, the
        lone pair acceptor, and the ligand is the Lewis base, the lone pair donor.

22.8   Coordination number is the number of ligands attached to the metal. Coordination geometry is the
        geometry described by the attached ligands.

22.9   Ligands must contain a lone pair of electrons. If a ligand has more than one donor atom (more than one
        atom with a lone pair of electrons), it can act as a bidentate ligand.

22.10   (a) Chelate: polydentate ligands, ligands that can coordinate to a metal using two or more donor atoms

        (b) Bidentate: "two-toothed," a ligand that can coordinate to a metal using two donor atoms

22.11   Diamagnetic: A species with no unpaired electrons (is repelled by a magnet). Paramagnetic: A species with one or more unpaired electrons (is attracted to a magnet).

22.12   (a) $[Co(en)_2Cl_2]^+$ can have *cis* and *trans* isomers (see Figure 22.17).

   cis-dichlorobis(ethylenediamine)cobalt(III) ion and *trans*-dichlorbis(ethylenediamine)cobalt(III) ion

   (b) $[Co(en)_3]^{3+}$ is a chiral complex (see Figure 22.19).

   tris(ethylenediamine)cobalt(III) ion

22.13   Repulsion between d electrons on the metal and the electron pairs of the ligands causes the splitting of the d orbitals into two sets.

22.14   The magnitude of Δ_o and the geometry of the complex determine whether a complex is high- or low-spin.

22.15   Magenta

22.16   (a) Cr^{3+} $[Ar]3d^3$ paramagnetic

   (b) V^{2+} $[Ar]3d^3$ paramagnetic

   (c) Ni^{2+} $[Ar]3d^8$ paramagnetic

   (d) Cu^+ $[Ar]3d^{10}$ diamagnetic

22.17   (a) Fe^{2+}, Co^{3+} (c) Mn^{2+}, Fe^{3+}

   (b) Cu^+, Zn^{2+} (d) Ni^{2+}, Co^+

22.18   (a) Mn^{2+} is isoelectronic with Fe^{3+}

   (b) Cu^+ is isoelectronic with Zn^{2+}

   (c) Co^{3+} is isoelectronic with Fe^{2+}

   (d) V^{2+} is isoelectronic with Cr^{3+}

22.19 Cu^+ and Zn^{2+}; Mn^{2+} and Fe^{3+}; Fe^{2+} and Co^{3+}; Ti^{2+} and V^{3+}

22.20   (a) $Cr_2O_3(s) + 2\ Al(s) \rightarrow Al_2O_3(s) + 2\ Cr(s)$

   (b) $TiCl_4(\ell) + 2\ Mg(s) \rightarrow Ti(s) + 2\ MgCl_2(s)$

   (c) $2\ [Ag(CN)_2]^-(aq) + Zn(s) \rightarrow 2\ Ag(s) + [Zn(CN)_4]^{2-}(aq)$

   (d) $3\ Mn_3O_4(s) + 8\ Al(s) \rightarrow 9\ Mn(s) + 4\ Al_2O_3(s)$

22.21   (a) $CuSO_4(aq) + Zn(s) \rightarrow Cu(s) + ZnSO_4(aq)$

   (b) $Zn(s) + 2\ HCl(aq) \rightarrow ZnCl_2(aq) + H_2(g)$

   (c) $2\ Fe(s) + 3\ Cl_2(g) \rightarrow 2\ FeCl_3(s)$

   (d) $4\ V(s) + 5\ O_2(g) \rightarrow 2\ V_2O_5(s)$

22.22   (a) monodentate   (d) bidentate

        (b) monodentate   (e) monodentate

        (c) monodentate   (f) bidentate

22.23 NH_4^+ is incapable of serving as a ligand because it does not have any unshared electron pairs.

22.24   (a) Mn^{2+} (c) Co^{3+}

        (b) Co^{3+} (d) Cr^{2+}

22.25   (a) Fe^{2+} (c) Co^{2+}

        (b) Zn^{2+} (d) Cu^{2+}

22.26 $[Ni(NH_3)_3(H_2O)(en)]^{2+}$ The complex has a +2 charge.

22.27 $[Cr(en)_2(NH_3)_2]^{3+}$ The complex has a +3 charge.

22.28   (a) $[NiCl_2(en)_2]$

        (b) $K_2[PtCl_4]$

        (c) $K[Cu(CN)_2]$

        (d) $[Fe(NH_3)_4(H_2O)_2]^{2+}$

22.29   (a) $[Cr(NH_3)_2(H_2O)_3(OH)]NO_3$

        (b) $[Fe(NH_3)_6](NO_3)_3$

        (c) $Fe(CO)_5$

        (d) $(NH_4)_2[CuCl_4]$

22.30   (a) diaquabis(oxalato)nickelate(II) ion

        (b) dibromobis(ethylenediamine)cobalt(II) ion

        (c) amminechlorobis(ethylenediamine)cobalt(III) ion

        (d) diammineoxalatoplatinum(II)

22.31   (a) tetraaquadichlorocobalt(III) ion

        (b) triaquatrifluorocobalt(III)

        (c) amminetribromoplatinate(II) ion

        (d) triamminechloroethylenediaminecobalt(III) ion

22.32   (a) $[Fe(H_2O)_5OH]^{2+}$

        (b) potassium tetracyanonickelate(II)

    (c)   potassium diaquabis(oxalato)chromate(III)

    (d) $(NH_4)_2[PtCl_4]$

22.33   (a) $[CrCl_2(H_2O)_4]Cl$

         (b)   pentaamminesulfatochromium(III) chloride

         (c) $Na_2[CoCl_4]$

         (d)   tris(oxalato)ferrate(III) ion

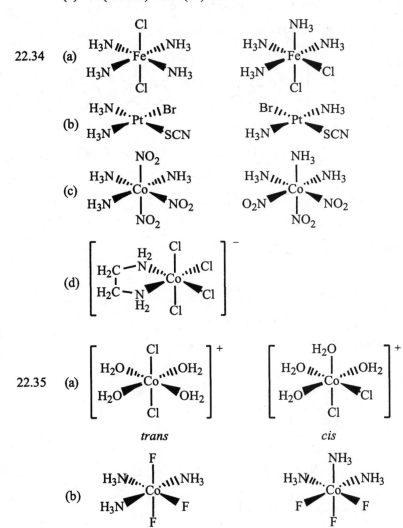

22.35   (a)

                trans   *cis*

        (b)

                mer   *fac*

        (c) No geometrical isomers possible.

        (d)

                trans   *cis*

22.36 (a) Yes. Mirror images of complexes of the stoichiometry $[M(\text{bidentate})_3]^{n+}$ do not superimpose

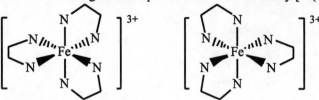

(b) Optical isomers are not possible. The mirror images are superimposable.

(c) Optical isomers are not possible. The mirror images are superimposable.

(d) Optical isomers are not possible. The mirror images are superimposable.

22.37

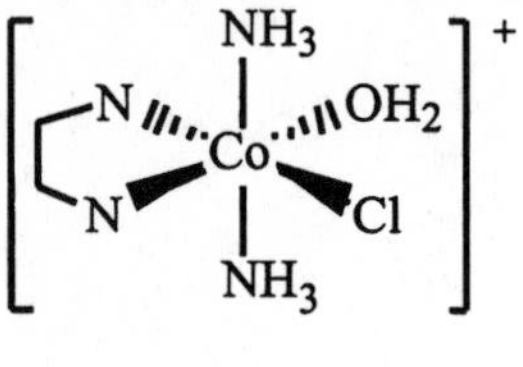

$$\begin{bmatrix} \overset{\displaystyle NH_3}{\underset{\displaystyle NH_3}{N\!\!\!\diagdown_{I\!I\!I_{\text{Co}}}\!\!\diagup^{\cdots\!\backslash\!\backslash OH_2}_{Cl}}} \end{bmatrix}^{+}$$

trans

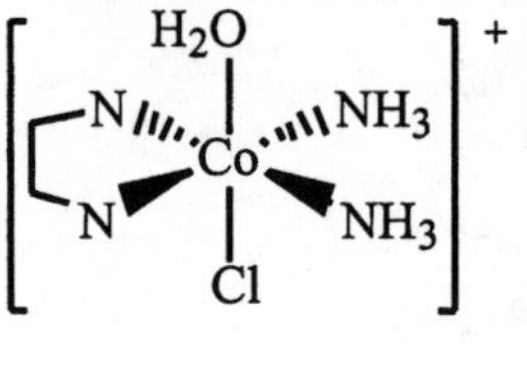

$$\begin{bmatrix} \overset{\displaystyle H_2O}{\underset{\displaystyle Cl}{N\!\!\!\diagdown_{I\!I\!I_{\text{Co}}}\!\!\diagup^{\cdots\!\backslash\!\backslash NH_3}_{NH_3}}} \end{bmatrix}^{+}$$

cis

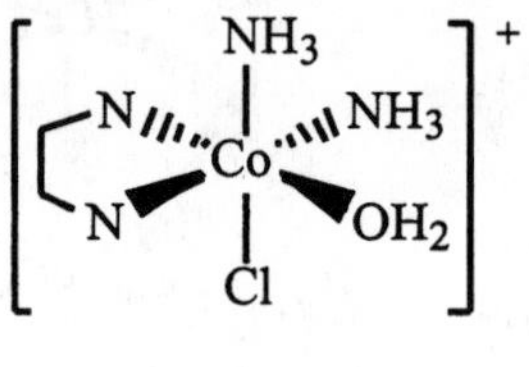

$$\begin{bmatrix} \overset{\displaystyle NH_3}{\underset{\displaystyle Cl}{N\!\!\!\diagdown_{I\!I\!I_{\text{Co}}}\!\!\diagup^{\cdots\!\backslash\!\backslash NH_3}_{OH_2}}} \end{bmatrix}^{+}$$

cis (chiral)

$$\begin{bmatrix} \overset{\displaystyle NH_3}{\underset{\displaystyle H_2O}{N\!\!\!\diagdown_{I\!I\!I_{\text{Co}}}\!\!\diagup^{\cdots\!\backslash\!\backslash NH_3}_{Cl}}} \end{bmatrix}^{+}$$

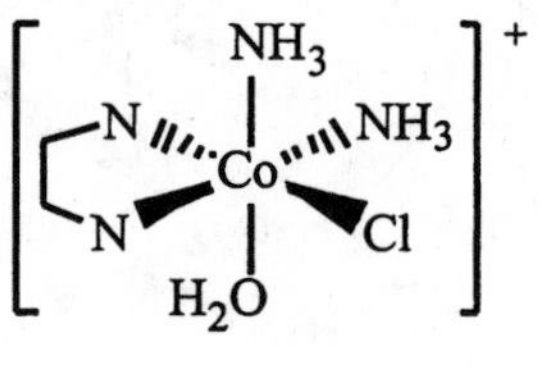

cis (chiral)

22.38 (a) Mn^{2+}, d^5 paramagnetic, 1 unpaired electron

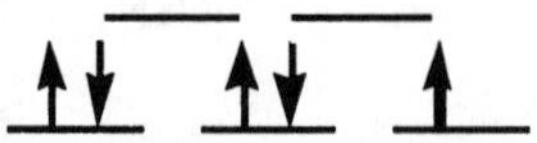

(b) Co^{3+}, d^6 diamagnetic

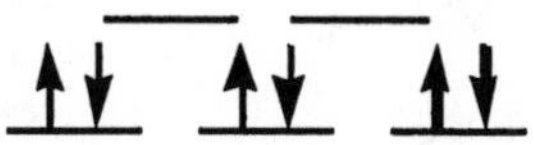

(c) Fe^{3+}, d^5 paramagnetic, 1 unpaired electron

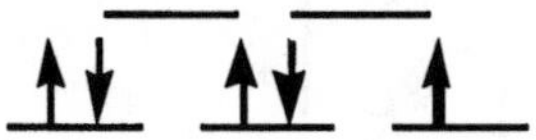

(d) Cr^{2+}, d^4 paramagnetic, 2 unpaired electrons

22.39 (a) Fe^{2+}, d^6 4 unpaired electrons

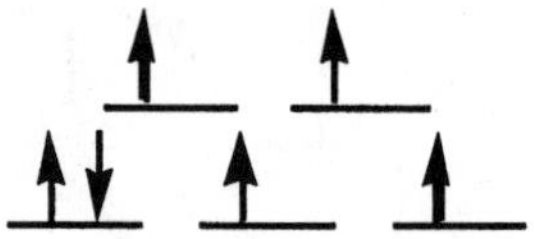

(b) Mn^{2+}, d^5 5 unpaired electrons

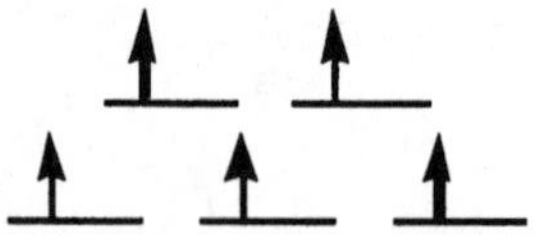

(c) Cr^{2+}, d^4 4 unpaired electrons

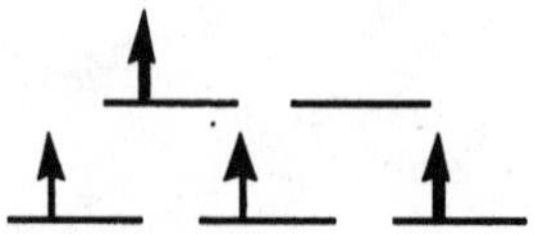

(d) Fe^{3+}, d^5 5 unpaired electrons

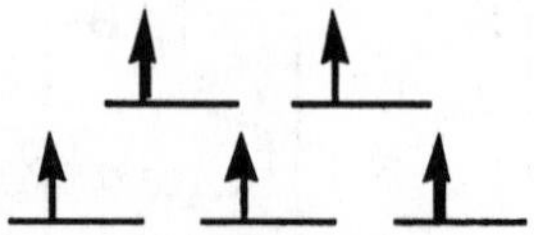

22.40   (a) Fe^{2+}, d^6 4 unpaired electrons

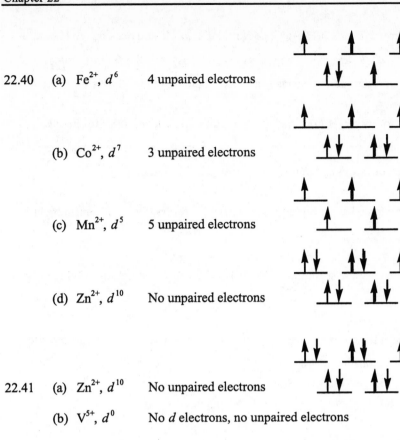

        (b) Co^{2+}, d^7 3 unpaired electrons

        (c) Mn^{2+}, d^5 5 unpaired electrons

        (d) Zn^{2+}, d^{10} No unpaired electrons

22.41   (a) Zn^{2+}, d^{10} No unpaired electrons

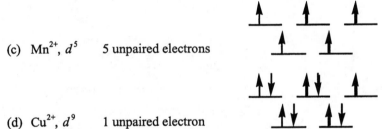

        (b) V^{5+}, d^0 No d electrons, no unpaired electrons

        (c) Mn^{2+}, d^5 5 unpaired electrons

        (d) Cu^{2+}, d^9 1 unpaired electron

22.42   (a) The coordination number of iron is 6

        (b) The coordination geometry is octahedral

        (c) Fe^{2+}

        (d) 4 unpaired electrons ([Ar]$3d^6$, high spin)

        (e) paramagnetic

22.43   (a) The coordination number of cobalt is 6

        (b) The coordination geometry is octahedral

        (c) Co^{3+}

        (d) No unpaired electrons ([Ar]$3d^6$, low spin).

        (e) diamagnetic

22.44   When $Co_2(SO_4)_3$ dissolves in water it forms $[Co(H_2O)_6]^{3+}$; addition of fluoride converts this to $[CoF_6]^{3-}$. The hexaaqua complex is low spin (d^6, diamagnetic, no unpaired electrons), and the fluoride complex is high spin (paramagnetic, 4 unpaired electrons). Fluoride is a weaker field ligand than water.

22.45   When $FeSO_4$ dissolves in water it forms $[Fe(H_2O)_6]^{2+}$; addition of ammonia converts this to $[Fe(NH_3)_6]^{2+}$. The hexaaqua complex is high spin (d^6, paramagnetic, 4 unpaired electrons), and the ammonia complex is low spin (diamagnetic, no unpaired electrons). Ammonia is a stronger field ligand than water.

22.46   The light absorbed is in the blue region of the spectrum (page 950). Therefore, the light transmitted (the color of the solution) is yellow.

22.47   The light absorbed is in the red region of the spectrum (page 950). Therefore, the light transmitted (the color of the solution) is blue-green.

22.48   Determine the magnetic properties of the complex. Square planar (Ni^{2+}, d^8) complexes are diamagnetic, whereas tetrahedral complexes are paramagnetic.

22.49   (a) Cr^{3+}, d^3 3 unpaired electrons   (c) Fe^{2+}, d^6 No unpaired electrons

        (b) Mn^{2+}, d^5 1 unpaired electron   (d) Ni^{2+}, d^8 2 unpaired electrons

22.50   high spin

4 unpaired electrons   low spin   No unpaired electrons

22.51   Only one chloride is not coordinated directly to the metal, so one mole of AgCl will precipitate.

22.52 d^8 complexes are commonly square planar. $Ni(CN)_4^{2-}$

22.53   Only (b) cis-$[Fe(C_2O_4)_2Cl_2]^{2-}$ has a nonsuperimposable mirror image.

22.54   Two geometric isomers are possible, with cis and $trans$ chloride ligands.

22.55   (c) The d_{xz}, d_{yz}, and d_{xy} orbitals are higher in energy than the $d_{x^2-y^2}$ and d_{z^2} orbitals.

22.56   The light absorbed is in the blue region of the spectrum (page 950). Therefore, the light transmitted (the color of the solution) is yellow.

22.57   (a) Fe^{3+}

    (b) The coordination number for iron is 6

    (c) The coordination geometry is octahedral

    (d) 1 unpaired electron ([Ar]$3d^5$, low spin)

    (e) Paramagnetic

    (f) Two possible geometric isomers, *cis* and *trans*

22.58   (a) Mn^{2+}

    (b) The coordination number for manganese is 6

    (c) The coordination geometry is octahedral

    (d) 5 unpaired electrons ([Ar]$3d^5$, high spin)

    (e) Paramagnetic

    (f) Two possible geometric isomers, *cis* and *trans*

22.59 $[Pt(NH_3)_4]^{2+}$ tetraammineplatinum(II) ion $[PtCl_4]^{2-}$ tetrachloroplatinate(II) ion

22.60 $[Co(NH_3)_4Cl_2]Cl$ tetraamminedichlorocobalt(III) chloride

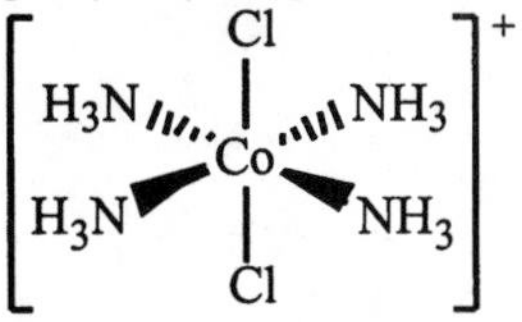

trans 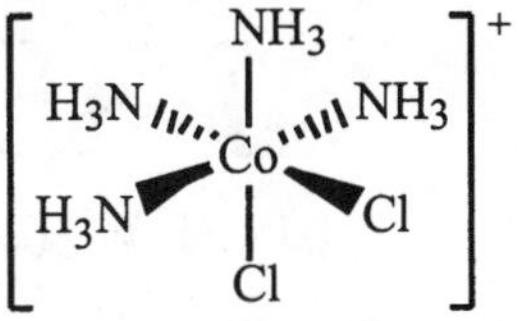   *cis*

22.61 $[Pt(NO_2)Cl(NH_3)_2]$ diamminechloronitroplatinum(II)

Two geometric isomers   *cis*   *trans*

22.62 $[Co(en)_2(H_2O)Cl]^+$ aquachlorobis(ethylenediamine)cobalt(III) ion   The complex has a +1 charge

22.63   Two geometric isomers of $[Cr(dmen)_3]^{3+}$ can exist

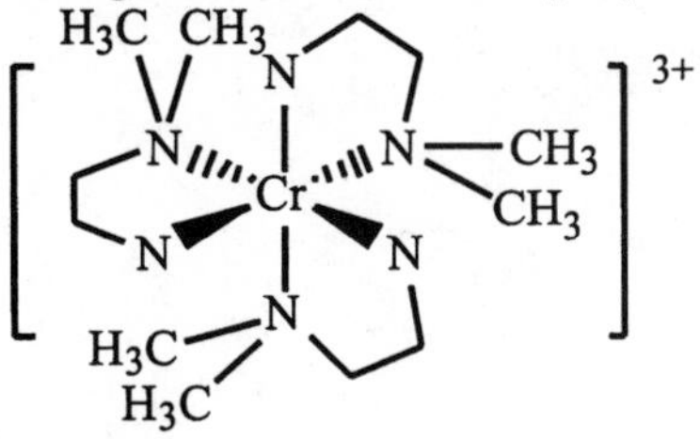

fac 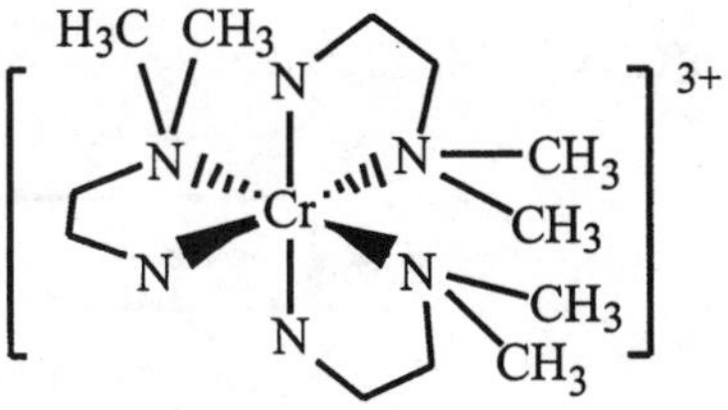   *mer*

22.64   (a)

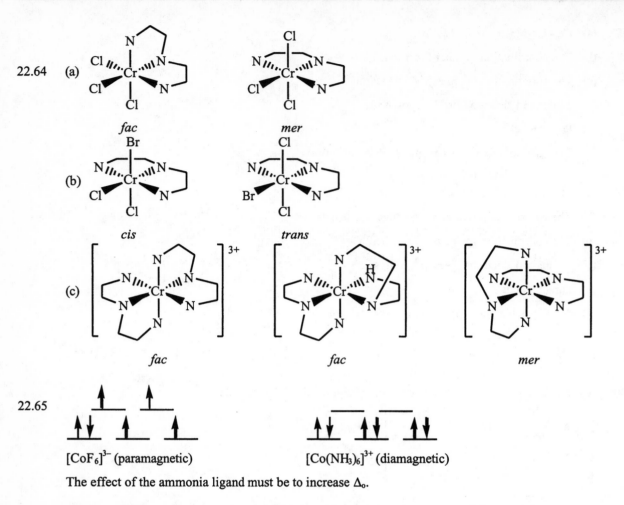

22.65

fac   *mer*

cis   *trans*

(c)

fac   *fac*   *mer*

$[CoF_6]^{3-}$ (paramagnetic) $[Co(NH_3)_6]^{3+}$ (diamagnetic)

The effect of the ammonia ligand must be to increase Δ_o.

22.66

cis-H_2O, *trans*-NH_3 *cis*-NH_3, *trans*-H_2O *cis*-H_2O, *cis*-NH_3 (chiral)

22.67   The bond angles and bond lengths are such that the nitrogen atoms cannot span the diagonal of the Pt complex and accomplish reasonable overlap with the Pt orbitals to form the bonds.

22.68   In $[Mn(H_2O)_6]^{2+}$ and $[Mn(CN)_6]^{4-}$, Mn has an oxidation number of +2 ([Ar]$3d^5$).

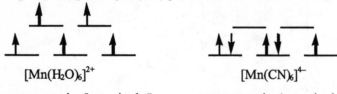

$[Mn(H_2O)_6]^{2+}$ $[Mn(CN)_6]^{4-}$

paramagnetic, 5 unpaired e^- paramagnetic, 1 unpaired e^-

The CN^- ligand results in an increased Δ_o.

22.69   In $K_4[Cr(CN)_6]$ and $K_4[Cr(SCN)_6]$, Cr has an oxidation number of +2 ($[Ar]3d^4$).

Cr^{2+} Cr^{2+}

paramagnetic, 2 unpaired e$^-$ paramagnetic, 4 unpaired e$^-$

The SCN$^-$ ligand is a weaker field ligand than the CN$^-$ ligand. The SCN$^-$ ligand occurs to the left (or lower) in the spectrochemical series relative to CN$^-$.

22.70   A: $[Co(NH_3)_5Br]SO_4$ B: $[Co(NH_3)_5SO_4]Br$

$[Co(NH_3)_5Br]SO_4(aq) + BaCl_2(aq) \rightarrow BaSO_4(s) + [Co(NH_3)_5Br]Cl_2(aq)$

22.71   (a)   The light absorbed is in the orange region of the spectrum (page 950). Therefore, the light transmitted (the color of the solution) is blue or cyan.

         (b)   According to Table 22.3, CO_3^{2-} belongs between F^- and $C_2O_4^{2-}$.

         (c) Δ_o should be small, so the complex should be high spin and paramagnetic.

22.72
ion	$K_{formation}$ (NH$_3$ complex)
Co^{2+}	7.7×10^4
Ni^{2+}	5.6×10^8
Cu^{2+}	6.8×10^{12}
Zn^{2+}	2.9×10^9

22.73   (a)   Cu^{2+}

         (b)   The coordination number of copper is 6

         (c) $[Ar]3d^9$ 1 unpaired electron

         (d)   Paramagnetic

22.74

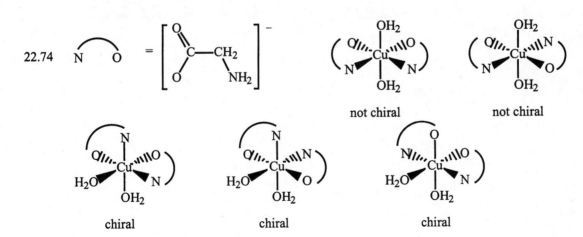

22.75   Determine the empirical formula:

$$19.51 \text{ g} \cdot \frac{1 \text{ mol Cr}}{51.996 \text{ g}} = 0.3752 \text{ mol Cr} = 1 \text{ mol Cr}$$

$$39.92 \text{ g} \cdot \frac{1 \text{ mol Cl}}{35.453 \text{ g}} = 1.126 \text{ mol Cl} = 3 \text{ mol Cl}$$

$$40.57 \text{ g} \cdot \frac{1 \text{ mol H}_2\text{O}}{18.015 \text{ g}} = 2.252 \text{ mol H}_2\text{O} = 6 \text{ mol H}_2\text{O}$$

$[Cr(H_2O)_6]Cl_3$ hexaaquachromium(III) chloride

$$Cl^-(aq) + Ag^+(aq) \rightarrow AgCl(s)$$

22.76   Substituting 10^8 and 10^{18} into the expression ($-RT \ln K$) produces ΔG values of -45.6 kJ (ammine) and -102.7 kJ (en). Since the differences in ΔH values are much less than this (~8 kJ), entropy must play a role. While there are fewer molecules in the second reaction, the change in entropy (as the much larger bidentate en ligands form the complex) is greater.

22.77 $1.00 \times 10^3 \text{ g} \cdot \dfrac{1 \text{ mol FeTiO}_3}{151.7 \text{ g}} \cdot \dfrac{3 \text{ mol H}_2\text{SO}_4}{1 \text{mol FeTiO}_3} \cdot \dfrac{1 \text{ L}}{18.0 \text{ mol H}_2\text{SO}_4} = 1.10 \text{ L}$

$1.00 \times 10^3 \text{ g} \cdot \dfrac{1 \text{ mol FeTiO}_3}{151.7 \text{ g}} \cdot \dfrac{1 \text{ mol TiO}_2}{1 \text{mol FeTiO}_3} \cdot \dfrac{79.87 \text{ g}}{1 \text{ mol TiO}_2} = 526 \text{ g TiO}_2$

22.78   (a) $FeTiO_3(s) + 2 HCl(aq) \rightarrow FeCl_2(aq) + TiO_2(s) + H_2O(\ell)$

(b) $2 FeTiO_3(s) + 4 HCl(aq) \rightarrow 2 FeCl_2(aq) + 2 TiO_2(s) + 2 H_2O(\ell)$

$2 FeCl_2(aq) + 2 H_2O(\ell) + \frac{1}{2} O_2(g) \rightarrow Fe_2O_3(s) + 4 HCl(aq)$

$2 FeTiO_3(s) + \frac{1}{2} O_2(g) \rightarrow Fe_2O_3(s) + 2 TiO_2(s)$

Yes, the HCl used in the first step is recovered in the second step.

(c) $908 \times 10^3 \text{ g} \cdot \dfrac{1 \text{ mol FeTiO}_3}{151.7 \text{ g/mol}} \cdot \dfrac{1 \text{ mol Fe}_2\text{O}_3}{2 \text{ mol FeTiO}_3} \cdot \dfrac{159.7 \text{ g}}{1 \text{ mol Fe}_2\text{O}_3} = 4.78 \times 10^5 \text{ g Fe}_2\text{O}_3$

Chapter 23
Nuclear Chemistry

INSTRUCTOR'S NOTES

For this edition of the text, the discussion of nuclear chemistry has again been placed as the final chapter. However, we believe the recent reactor accidents in the United States and the Soviet Union, and the ongoing debate in the United States concerning nuclear waste disposal, make it desirable to give this topic more prominence. In addition, its importance is indicated by the fact that about 20% of the papers abstracted in *Chemical Abstracts* annually in the general areas of physical, inorganic, and analytical chemistry concern nuclear chemistry. Nonetheless, it is our hope that the material will be discussed in class to some extent, or that students will read the chapter out of interest in the subject.

SUGGESTED DEMONSTRATIONS AND READINGS

1.   The Nature of Radioactivity

   • Fortman, J. J. "An Overhead Projector Demonstration of Nuclear Beta Emission," *Journal of Chemical Education* **1992**, *69*, 162.

   • Para, A. F.; Lazzarini, E. "Some Simple Classroom Experiments on the Monte Carlo Method," *ibid.* **1974**, *51*, 336.

   • Herber, R. H. "General Chemistry Demonstrations Based on Nuclear and Radiochemical Phenomena," *ibid.* **1969**, *46*, 665.

   • Smith, W. T.; Wood, J. H. "A Half-life Experiment for General Chemistry Students," (measurement of the half-life of bismuth-210), *ibid.* **1959**, *36*, 492.

2.   Radiation Effects and Units of Radiation

   • Since radon in homes is very much in the news, it might be interesting to have the class test some area of the chemistry building or dormitory for radon using a home testing kit available at most hardware stores .

Solutions to Study Questions

23.1   See sections 2.1, 23.5, and 23.6

23.2   The mass of a nucleus is not equal to the sum of the mass of the constituent particles. The mass difference, called the mass defect, is equated with the energy holding the nuclear particles together. For ^2H, the nuclear mass (2.01410 g/mol) is less than the sum of the mass of a proton (1.007825 g/mol) and a neutron (1.008665 g/mol).

23.3   Binding energy per nucleon is calculated by first calculating mass defect for an isotope, converting the mass defect to binding energy (using the equation $E = mc^2$), and then dividing binding energy by the number of nuclear particles for that isotope.

23.4   Isotopes that fall to the left of the band of stability (high n/p ratio) undergo beta emission, and isotopes that fall to the right of the band of stability (low n/p ratio) undergo positron emission or beta capture to become more stable. Isotopes beyond $Z = 83$ are unstable and undergo alpha emission.

23.5   See section 23.5

23.6   Radioactive decay follows first-order kinetics. A (activity) $= kN$ (number of atoms)

$\ln(N/N_0) = \ln(A/A_0) = -kt$

23.7   See the description of carbon-14 dating on page 977.

23.8   See section 23.4

23.9   Several naturally occurring radioactive isotopes are found to decay to form a product that is also radioactive. When this happens, the initial nuclear reaction is followed by a second nuclear reaction, and if the situation is repeated, a third and a fourth, and so on. Eventually, a nonradioactive isotope is formed to end the series. Uranium ore contains trace quantities of the radioactive elements formed in the radioactive decay series, including radium and polonium.

23.10   See sections 23.8 and 23.9

23.11   Curies (Ci) measure the number of decompositions per second; $1\ Ci = 3.7 \times 10^{10}$ dps. The amount of energy absorbed by living tissue is measured in rads. One rad represents 0.01 J of energy absorbed per kilogram of tissue. Biological damage is quantified in rems. A dose of radiation in rem is determined by multiplying the energy absorbed in rads by the quality factor for that kind of radiation.

23.12 (a) $^{56}_{28}\text{Ni}$ (d) $^{97}_{43}\text{Tc}$

     (b) $^{1}_{0}\text{n}$ (e) $^{0}_{-1}\beta$

     (c) $^{31}_{15}\text{P}$ (f) $^{0}_{+1}\beta$

23.13 (a) $^{1}_{1}\text{H}$ (d) $2\ ^{1}_{0}\text{n}$

     (b) $^{27}_{13}\text{Al}$ (e) $^{254}_{102}\text{No}$

     (c) $^{1}_{0}\text{n}$ (f) $^{16}_{8}\text{O}$

23.14 (a) $^{0}_{-1}\beta$ (d) $^{226}_{88}\text{Ra}$

     (b) $^{87}_{37}\text{Rb}$ (e) $^{0}_{-1}\beta$

     (c) $^{4}_{2}\text{He}$ (f) $^{24}_{11}\text{Na}$

23.15 (a) $^{19}_{9}\text{F}$ (d) $^{37}_{17}\text{Cl}$

     (b) $^{59}_{27}\text{Co}$ (e) $^{55}_{25}\text{Mn}$

     (c) $^{40}_{20}\text{Ca}$ (f) $^{1}_{1}\text{H}$

23.16 $^{235}_{92}\text{U} \rightarrow\ ^{231}_{90}\text{Th} +\ ^{4}_{2}\alpha$

$^{231}_{90}\text{Th} \rightarrow\ ^{231}_{91}\text{Pa} +\ ^{0}_{-1}\beta$

$^{231}_{91}\text{Pa} \rightarrow\ ^{227}_{89}\text{Ac} +\ ^{4}_{2}\alpha$

$^{227}_{89}\text{Ac} \rightarrow\ ^{227}_{90}\text{Th} +\ ^{0}_{-1}\beta$

$^{227}_{90}\text{Th} \rightarrow\ ^{223}_{88}\text{Ra} +\ ^{4}_{2}\alpha$

$^{223}_{88}\text{Ra} \rightarrow\ ^{219}_{86}\text{Rn} +\ ^{4}_{2}\alpha$

$^{219}_{86}\text{Rn} \rightarrow\ ^{215}_{84}\text{Po} +\ ^{4}_{2}\alpha$

$^{215}_{84}\text{Po} \rightarrow\ ^{211}_{82}\text{Pb} +\ ^{4}_{2}\alpha$

$^{211}_{82}\text{Pb} \rightarrow\ ^{211}_{83}\text{Bi} +\ ^{0}_{-1}\beta$

$^{211}_{83}\text{Bi} \rightarrow\ ^{211}_{84}\text{Po} +\ ^{0}_{-1}\beta$

$^{211}_{84}\text{Po} \rightarrow\ ^{207}_{82}\text{Pb} +\ ^{4}_{2}\alpha$

23.17 $^{232}_{90}\text{Th} \rightarrow\ ^{228}_{88}\text{Ra} +\ ^{4}_{2}\alpha$

$^{228}_{88}\text{Ra} \rightarrow\ ^{228}_{89}\text{Ac} +\ ^{0}_{-1}\beta$

$^{228}_{89}\text{Ac} \rightarrow\ ^{228}_{90}\text{Th} +\ ^{0}_{-1}\beta$

$^{228}_{90}\text{Th} \rightarrow\ ^{224}_{88}\text{Ra} +\ ^{4}_{2}\alpha$

$^{224}_{88}\text{Ra} \rightarrow\ ^{220}_{86}\text{Rn} +\ ^{4}_{2}\alpha$

$^{220}_{86}\text{Rn} \rightarrow\ ^{216}_{84}\text{Po} +\ ^{4}_{2}\alpha$

$^{216}_{84}\text{Po} \rightarrow\ ^{212}_{82}\text{Pb} +\ ^{4}_{2}\alpha$

$^{212}_{82}\text{Pb} \rightarrow\ ^{212}_{83}\text{Bi} +\ ^{0}_{-1}\beta$

$^{212}_{83}\text{Bi} \rightarrow\ ^{212}_{84}\text{Po} +\ ^{0}_{-1}\beta$

$^{212}_{84}\text{Po} \rightarrow\ ^{208}_{82}\text{Pb} +\ ^{4}_{2}\alpha$

23.18   (a) $^{198}_{79}\text{Au} \rightarrow \,^{198}_{80}\text{Hg} + \,^{0}_{-1}\beta$

(b) $^{222}_{86}\text{Rn} \rightarrow \,^{218}_{84}\text{Po} + \,^{4}_{2}\alpha$

(c) $^{137}_{55}\text{Cs} \rightarrow \,^{137}_{56}\text{Ba} + \,^{0}_{-1}\beta$

(d) $^{110}_{49}\text{In} \rightarrow \,^{110}_{48}\text{Cd} + \,^{0}_{+1}\beta$

23.19   (a) $^{67}_{31}\text{Ga} + \,^{0}_{-1}e \rightarrow \,^{67}_{30}\text{Zn}$

(b) $^{38}_{19}\text{K} \rightarrow \,^{38}_{18}\text{Ar} + \,^{0}_{+1}\beta$

(c) $^{99m}_{43}\text{Tc} \rightarrow \,^{99}_{43}\text{Tc} + \gamma$

(d) $^{56}_{25}\text{Mn} \rightarrow \,^{56}_{26}\text{Fe} + \,^{0}_{-1}\beta$

23.20   (a) $^{80m}_{35}\text{Br} \rightarrow \,^{80}_{35}\text{Br} + \gamma$

(b) $^{240}_{98}\text{Cf} \rightarrow \,^{4}_{2}\alpha + \,^{236}_{96}\text{Cm}$

(c) $^{61}_{27}\text{Co} \rightarrow \,^{0}_{-1}\beta + \,^{61}_{28}\text{Ni}$

(d) $^{11}_{6}\text{C} \rightarrow \,^{0}_{+1}\beta + \,^{11}_{5}\text{B}$

23.21   (a) $^{54}_{25}\text{Mn} \rightarrow \,^{0}_{+1}\beta + \,^{54}_{24}\text{Cr}$

(b) $^{241}_{95}\text{Am} \rightarrow \,^{4}_{2}\alpha + \,^{237}_{93}\text{Np}$

(c) $^{110}_{47}\text{Ag} \rightarrow \,^{0}_{-1}\beta + \,^{110}_{48}\text{Cd}$

(d) $^{197m}_{80}\text{Hg} \rightarrow \,^{197}_{80}\text{Hg} + \gamma$

23.22   (a) Both ^{3}H and ^{20}F have a high n/p ratio and will likely decay by beta emission

(b) ^{22}Na has a low n/p ratio and will likely decay by positron emission

23.23   (a) ^{32}P has a high n/p ratio and will likely decay by beta emission

(b) ^{38}K has a low n/p ratio and will likely decay by positron emission

23.24 $^{10}_{5}\text{B} \rightarrow 5\,^{1}_{1}\text{H} + 5\,^{1}_{0}\text{n}$

$\Delta m = [(5 \times 1.00783) + (5 \times 1.00867)] - 10.01294 = 0.06956$ g/mol nuclei

$E_b = (\Delta m)c^2 = (0.06956 \times 10^{-3}$ kg/mol$)(3.00 \times 10^8$ m/s$)^2 = 6.26 \times 10^{12}$ J/mol nuclei $(= 6.26 \times 10^9$ kJ/mol)

$\dfrac{E_b}{n} = \dfrac{6.26 \times 10^9 \text{ kJ/mol nuclei}}{10 \text{ mol nucleons/mol nuclei}} = 6.26 \times 10^8$ kJ/mol nucleons

$^{11}_{5}\text{B} \rightarrow 5\,^{1}_{1}\text{H} + 6\,^{1}_{0}\text{n}$

$\Delta m = [(5 \times 1.00783) + (6 \times 1.00867)] - 11.00931 = 0.08186$ g/mol nuclei

$E_b = (\Delta m)c^2 = (0.08186 \times 10^{-3}$ kg/mol$)(3.00 \times 10^8$ m/s$)^2 = 7.37 \times 10^{12}$ J/mol nuclei $(= 7.37 \times 10^9$ kJ/mol)

$\dfrac{E_b}{n} = \dfrac{7.37 \times 10^9 \text{ kJ/mol nuclei}}{11 \text{ mol nucleons/mol nuclei}} = 6.70 \times 10^8$ kJ/mol nucleons

23.25 $^{30}_{15}P \rightarrow 15\,^{1}_{1}H + 15\,^{1}_{0}n$

$\Delta m = [(15 \times 1.00783) + (15 \times 1.00867)] - 29.97832 = 0.26918$ g/mol nuclei

$E_b = (\Delta m)c^2 = (0.26918 \times 10^{-3}$ kg$)(3.00 \times 10^8$ m/s$)^2 = 2.42 \times 10^{13}$ J/mol nuclei (= 2.42×10^{10} kJ/mol)

$\dfrac{E_b}{n} = \dfrac{2.42 \times 10^{10} \text{ kJ/mol nuclei}}{30 \text{ mol nucleons/mol nuclei}} = 8.08 \times 10^8$ kJ/mol nucleons

$^{31}_{15}P \rightarrow 15\,^{1}_{1}H + 16\,^{1}_{0}n$

$\Delta m = [(15 \times 1.00783) + (16 \times 1.00867)] - 30.97376 = 0.28241$ g/mol

$E_b = (\Delta m)c^2 = (0.28241 \times 10^{-3}$ kg$)(3.00 \times 10^8$ m/s$)^2 = 2.54 \times 10^{13}$ J/mol nuclei (= 2.54×10^{10} kJ/mol)

$\dfrac{E_b}{n} = \dfrac{2.54 \times 10^{10} \text{ kJ/mol nuclei}}{31 \text{ mol nucleons/mol nuclei}} = 8.20 \times 10^8$ kJ/mol nucleons

23.26 $^{40}_{20}Ca \rightarrow 20\,^{1}_{1}H + 20\,^{1}_{0}n$

$\Delta m = [(20 \times 1.00783) + (20 \times 1.00867)] - 39.96259 = 0.36741$ g/mol nuclei

$E_b = (\Delta m)c^2 = (0.36741 \times 10^{-3}$ kg$)(3.00 \times 10^8$ m/s$)^2 = 3.31 \times 10^{13}$ J/mol nuclei (= 3.31×10^{10} kJ/mol)

$\dfrac{E_b}{n} = \dfrac{3.31 \times 10^{10} \text{ kJ/mol nuclei}}{40 \text{ mol nucleons/mol nuclei}} = 8.27 \times 10^8$ kJ/mol nucleons

23.27 $^{56}_{26}Fe \rightarrow 26\,^{1}_{1}H + 30\,^{1}_{0}n$

$\Delta m = [(26 \times 1.00783) + (30 \times 1.00867)] - 55.9349 = 0.5288$ g/mol nuclei

$E_b = (\Delta m)c^2 = (0.5288 \times 10^{-3}$ kg$)(3.00 \times 10^8$ m/s$)^2 = 4.76 \times 10^{13}$ J/mol nuclei (= 4.76×10^{10} kJ/mol)

$\dfrac{E_b}{n} = \dfrac{4.76 \times 10^{10} \text{ kJ/mol nuclei}}{56 \text{ mol nucleons/mol nuclei}} = 8.50 \times 10^8$ kJ/mol nucleons

23.28 $^{16}_{8}O \rightarrow 8\,^{1}_{1}H + 8\,^{1}_{0}n$

$\Delta m = [(8 \times 1.00783) + (8 \times 1.00867)] - 15.99492 = 0.13708$ g/mol nuclei

$E_b = (\Delta m)c^2 = (0.13708 \times 10^{-3}$ kg$)(3.00 \times 10^8$ m/s$)^2 = 1.23 \times 10^{13}$ J/mol nuclei (= 1.23×10^{10} kJ/mol)

$\dfrac{E_b}{n} = \dfrac{1.23 \times 10^{10} \text{ kJ/mol nuclei}}{16 \text{ mol nucleons/mol nuclei}} = 7.71 \times 10^8$ kJ/mol nucleons

23.29 $^{14}_{7}N \rightarrow 7\,^{1}_{1}H + 7\,^{1}_{0}n$

$\Delta m = [(7 \times 1.00783) + (7 \times 1.00867)] - 14.003074 = 0.11243$ g/mol nuclei

$E_b = (\Delta m)c^2 = (0.11243 \times 10^{-3}$ kg$)(3.00 \times 10^8$ m/s$)^2 = 1.01 \times 10^{13}$ J/mol nuclei (= 1.01×10^{10} kJ/mol)

$\dfrac{E_b}{n} = \dfrac{1.01 \times 10^{10} \text{ kJ/mol nuclei}}{14 \text{ mol nucleons/mol nuclei}} = 7.23 \times 10^8$ kJ/mol nucleons

23.30   64 h/12.7 h = 5 half-lives

Amount remaining = 25.0 μg $\times (^{1}/_{2})^5 = 0.781$ μg

23.31   10.8 d/2.69 d = 4 half-lives

Amount remaining = 2.8 μg $\times (^{1}/_{2})^4 = 0.18$ μg

23.32 (a) $^{131}_{53}I \rightarrow \, ^{0}_{-1}\beta + \, ^{131}_{54}Xe$

(b) 40.2 d/8.04 d = 5 half-lives

$2.4 \ \mu g \times (^1/_2)^5 = 0.075 \ \mu g$

23.33 (a) $^{32}_{15}P \rightarrow \, ^{0}_{-1}\beta + \, ^{32}_{16}S$

(b) 28.6 d/14.3 d = 2 half-lives

$4.8 \ \mu g \times (^1/_2)^2 = 1.2 \ \mu g$

23.34 $k = \dfrac{0.693}{t_{1/2}} = \dfrac{0.693}{78.25 \ h} = 0.008856 \ h^{-1}$

$\ln\dfrac{N}{N_0} = -kt$

$\ln\dfrac{x}{0.015} = -(0.008856 \ h^{-1})(13 \ d)(24 \ h/1 \ d)$ $x = 9.5 \times 10^{-4} \ mg$

23.35 (a) $^{131}_{53}I \rightarrow \, ^{0}_{-1}\beta + \, ^{131}_{54}Xe$

(b) $k = \dfrac{0.693}{t_{1/2}} = \dfrac{0.693}{8.04 \ d} = 0.0862 \ d^{-1}$

$\ln\dfrac{N}{N_0} = -kt$

$\ln\dfrac{35.0}{100.0} = -(0.0862 \ d^{-1})t$ $t = 12.2 \ days$

23.36 (a) $^{222}_{86}Rn \rightarrow \, ^{4}_{2}\alpha + \, ^{218}_{84}Po$

(b) $k = \dfrac{0.693}{t_{1/2}} = \dfrac{0.693}{3.82 \ d} = 0.181 \ d^{-1}$

$\ln\dfrac{N}{N_0} = -kt$

$\ln\dfrac{20.0}{100.0} = -(0.181 \ d^{-1})t$ $t = 8.87 \ days$

23.37 $k = \dfrac{0.693}{t_{1/2}} = \dfrac{0.693}{5.73 \times 10^3 \ y} = 1.21 \times 10^{-4} \ y^{-1}$

$\ln\left(\dfrac{11.2}{14.0}\right) = -(1.21 \times 10^{-4} \ y^{-1})t$ $t = 1850$ years old   Year made = 1998 − 1850 = 150 AD

23.38 $k = \dfrac{0.693}{t_{1/2}} = \dfrac{0.693}{5.73 \times 10^3 \ y} = 1.21 \times 10^{-4} \ y^{-1}$

$\ln\left(\dfrac{72}{100}\right) = -(1.21 \times 10^{-4} \ y^{-1})t$ $t = 2700$ years old

23.39   (a) $\ln\left(\dfrac{975}{1.0 \times 10^3}\right) = -k(1\ y)$ $k = 0.025\ y^{-1}$

$$t_{1/2} = \frac{0.693}{k} = \frac{0.693}{0.025\ y^{-1}} = 27\ y$$

(b) $\ln\left(\dfrac{1.0}{100.0}\right) = -(0.025\ y^{-1})t$ $t = 180\ \text{years}$

23.40   (a) $^1/_8 = (^1/_2)^3$ or three half-lives $(5.27\ y) \times 3 = 15.8\ y$

(b) $k = \dfrac{0.693}{t_{1/2}} = \dfrac{0.693}{5.27\ y} = 0.131\ y^{-1}$

$\ln\left(\dfrac{A}{A_0}\right) = -(0.131\ y^{-1})(1\ y)$ $\dfrac{A}{A_0}$ = fraction of activity = 0.88

23.41
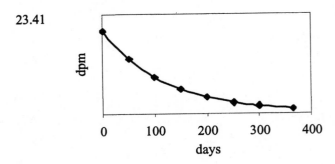

23.42
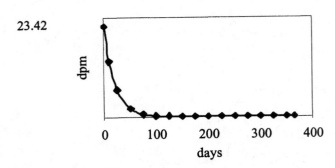

23.43   (a) $^{23}_{11}\text{Na} + {}^1_0\text{n} \rightarrow {}^{24}_{11}\text{Na}$

$^{24}_{11}\text{Na} \rightarrow {}^{\ 0}_{-1}\beta + {}^{24}_{12}\text{Mg}$

(b) $\ln\left(\dfrac{1.01 \times 10^4}{2.54 \times 10^4}\right) = -k(20\ h)$ $k = 0.046\ h^{-1}$

$$t_{1/2} = \frac{0.693}{k} = \frac{0.693}{0.046\ h^{-1}} = 15\ h$$

23.44 $\ln\left(\dfrac{5470}{7840}\right) = -k(72\ d)$ $k = 0.0050\ d^{-1}$

$$t_{1/2} = \frac{0.693}{k} = \frac{0.693}{0.0050\ d^{-1}} = 140\ \text{days}$$

23.45 $^{239}_{94}\text{Pu} + 2\,^{1}_{0}\text{n} \rightarrow\ ^{241}_{94}\text{Pu}$

       $^{241}_{94}\text{Pu} \rightarrow\ ^{0}_{-1}\beta +\ ^{241}_{95}\text{Am}$

23.46 $^{239}_{94}\text{Pu} +\ ^{4}_{2}\text{He} \rightarrow\ ^{240}_{95}\text{Am} +\ ^{1}_{1}\text{H} + 2\,^{1}_{0}\text{n}$

23.47 $^{238}_{92}\text{U} +\ ^{12}_{6}\text{C} \rightarrow\ ^{246}_{98}\text{Cf} + 4\,^{1}_{0}\text{n}$

23.48 $^{48}_{20}\text{Ca} +\ ^{242}_{94}\text{Pu} \rightarrow\ ^{287}_{114}114 + 3\,^{1}_{0}\text{n}$

23.49 $^{287}_{114}114 \rightarrow\ ^{4}_{2}\alpha +\ ^{283}_{112}112$

23.50   (a) $^{115}_{48}\text{Cd}$

         (b) $^{7}_{4}\text{Be}$

         (c) $^{4}_{2}\alpha$

         (d) $^{63}_{29}\text{Cu}$

23.51   (a) $^{1}_{1}\text{H}$

         (b) $^{12}_{6}\text{C}$

         (c) $^{27}_{13}\text{Al}$

         (d) $^{242}_{96}\text{Cm}$

23.52 $^{10}_{5}\text{B} +\ ^{1}_{0}\text{n} \rightarrow\ ^{4}_{2}\alpha +\ ^{7}_{3}\text{Li}$

23.53 $^{6}_{3}\text{Li} +\ ^{1}_{0}\text{n} \rightarrow\ ^{3}_{1}\text{H} +\ ^{4}_{2}\alpha$

23.54 $k = \dfrac{0.693}{t_{1/2}} = \dfrac{0.693}{4.8 \times 10^{10}\ \text{y}} = 1.4 \times 10^{-11}\ \text{y}^{-1}$

       $\ln\left(\dfrac{1.8}{1.6 + 1.8}\right) = -(1.4 \times 10^{-11}\ \text{y}^{-1})t \qquad\qquad t = 4.4 \times 10^{10}$ years old

23.55 $k = \dfrac{0.693}{t_{1/2}} = \dfrac{0.693}{4.8 \times 10^{10}\ \text{y}} = 1.4 \times 10^{-11}\ \text{y}^{-1}$

       $\ln(0.951) = -(1.4 \times 10^{-11}\ \text{y}^{-1})t \qquad\qquad t = 3.5 \times 10^{9}$ years old

23.56   When the ratio $^{206}\text{Pb}/^{238}\text{U} = 1/3$, $1/4$ of the ^{238}U has decayed to ^{206}Pb and $3/4$ remains as ^{238}U

       $k = \dfrac{0.693}{t_{1/2}} = \dfrac{0.693}{4.5 \times 10^{9}\ \text{y}} = 1.5 \times 10^{-10}\ \text{y}^{-1}$

       $\ln\left(\dfrac{3}{4}\right) = -(1.5 \times 10^{-10}\ \text{y}^{-1})t \qquad\qquad t = 1.9 \times 10^{9}$ years old

23.57 $k = \dfrac{0.693}{t_{1/2}} = \dfrac{0.693}{7.04 \times 10^8 \text{ y}} = 9.8 \times 10^{-10} \text{ y}^{-1}$

$\ln\left(\dfrac{0.72}{3.0}\right) = -(9.8 \times 10^{-10} \text{ y}^{-1})t \qquad\qquad t = 1.5 \times 10^9 \text{ years ago}$

23.58   (a) $^{238}_{92}\text{U} + ^{1}_{0}\text{n} \rightarrow ^{239}_{92}\text{U} + \gamma$

(b) $^{239}_{92}\text{U} \rightarrow ^{239}_{93}\text{Np} + ^{0}_{-1}\beta$

(c) $^{239}_{93}\text{Np} \rightarrow ^{239}_{94}\text{Pu} + ^{0}_{-1}\beta$

(d) $^{239}_{94}\text{Pu} + ^{1}_{0}\text{n} \rightarrow 2\,^{1}_{0}\text{n} + \text{energy} + \text{other nuclei}$

23.59   (a) $\Delta m = 7.01600 - [6.01512 + 1.00867] = -0.00779 \text{ g/mol}$

$\Delta E = (\Delta m)c^2 = (-0.00779 \times 10^{-3} \text{ kg/mol})(3.00 \times 10^8 \text{ m/s})^2 = -7.01 \times 10^{11} \text{ J/mol}$

$\dfrac{-7.01 \times 10^{11} \text{ J}}{1 \text{ mol}} \cdot \dfrac{1 \text{ mol}}{6.022 \times 10^{23} \text{ atoms}} = -1.16 \times 10^{-12} \text{ J/atom}$

(b) $\lambda = \dfrac{hc}{E} = \dfrac{(2.998 \times 10^8 \text{ m/s})(6.626 \times 10^{-34} \text{ J} \cdot \text{s})}{1.16 \times 10^{-12} \text{ J}} = 1.71 \times 10^{-13} \text{ m} = 0.171 \text{ pm}$

23.60 $1\text{lb} \cdot \dfrac{453.59 \text{ g}}{1 \text{ lb}} \cdot \dfrac{1 \text{ mol }^{235}\text{U}}{235 \text{ g}} \cdot \dfrac{2.1 \times 10^{10} \text{ kJ}}{1 \text{ mol }^{235}\text{U}} = 4.1 \times 10^{10} \text{ kJ}$

$\dfrac{4.1 \times 10^{10} \text{ kJ}}{2.6 \times 10^7 \text{ kJ/ton coal}} = 1600 \text{ tons of coal}$

23.61   (a) $^{0}_{-1}\text{e} + ^{0}_{+1}\beta \rightarrow 2\gamma \qquad\qquad$ mass of electron = mass of proton

$\Delta E = (\Delta m)c^2 = [2(9.109 \times 10^{-28} \text{ g})](1 \text{ kg}/10^3 \text{ g})(3.00 \times 10^8 \text{ m/s})^2 = 1.64 \times 10^{-13} \text{ J } (= 1.64 \times 10^{-16} \text{ kJ})$

(b) $\nu = \dfrac{E}{h} = \dfrac{1.64 \times 10^{-13} \text{ J/2 } \gamma\text{-rays}}{6.626 \times 10^{-34} \text{ J} \cdot \text{s}} = 1.24 \times 10^{17} \text{ s}^{-1}$

23.62 $(2.0 \times 10^6 \text{ dps})(1.0 \text{ mL}) = (1.5 \times 10^4 \text{ dps})(x)$

$x = \text{volume of circulatory system} = 130 \text{ mL}$

23.63   fraction separated = $(1200 \text{ dpm})/(3000 \text{ dpm}) = 0.40$

$(0.40)(3.00 \text{ mg}) = 1.2 \text{ mg threonine in sample}$

23.64 $\dfrac{27 \text{ tagged fish}}{5250 \text{ fish}} = \dfrac{1000 \text{ tagged fish}}{x} \qquad\qquad x = 1.9 \times 10^5 \text{ fish}$

23.65   Assume that the O atom of the alcohol is "tagged" with radioactive oxygen (^{15}O). If the O in the water comes from the —OH of the acid, the water is free of the radioactive ^{15}O isotope.

$$H_3C—\overset{\overset{\displaystyle O}{\|}}{C}—O—H \;+\; H—^{15}O—CH_3 \;\longrightarrow\; H_3C—\overset{\overset{\displaystyle O}{\|}}{C}—^{15}O—H \;+\; H—O—H$$

If the O in the water comes from the alcohol, however, then the water will contain radioactive oxygen.

$$H_3C—\overset{\overset{\displaystyle O}{\|}}{C}—O—H \;+\; H—^{15}O—CH_3 \;\longrightarrow\; H_3C—\overset{\overset{\displaystyle O}{\|}}{C}—O—H \;+\; H—^{15}O—H$$

23.66   (a)   The mass decreases by 4 units (with $^4_2\alpha$ emission) or is unchanged (with $^0_{-1}\beta$ emission) so the only masses possible are 4 units apart.

(b) ^{232}Th series, m = 4n; ^{235}U series, m = 4n + 3

(c)
Isotope	Series
^{226}Ra	^{238}U
^{215}At	^{235}U
^{228}Th	^{232}Th
^{210}Bi	^{238}U

(d)   Each series is headed by a long-lived isotope (in the order of 10^9 years, the age of the earth). The 4n + 1 series is missing because there is no long-lived isotope in this series. Over geologic time, all the members of this series have decayed completely.

23.67 $\dfrac{\Delta N}{\Delta t} = kN$ $\qquad N = \dfrac{1.0 \times 10^{-3}\ g}{238\ g/mol} \cdot \dfrac{6.02 \times 10^{23}\ nuclei}{1\ mol} = 2.5 \times 10^{18}\ nuclei$

12 dps = $k(2.5 \times 10^{18}\ nuclei)$ $\qquad\qquad k = 4.7 \times 10^{-18}\ s^{-1}$

$t_{1/2} = \dfrac{0.693}{k} = \dfrac{0.693}{4.7 \times 10^{-18}\ s^{-1}} \cdot \dfrac{1\ hr}{3600\ s} \cdot \dfrac{1\ day}{24\ hr} \cdot \dfrac{1\ year}{365\ day} = 4.7 \times 10^9\ years$

23.68   (a) ^{235}U series

(b) $^{235}_{92}U \rightarrow \,^{231}_{90}Th + \,^4_2\alpha$

$^{231}_{90}Th \rightarrow \,^{231}_{91}Pa + \,^0_{-1}\beta$

(c)   The concentration of ^{231}Pa in pitchblende is 1 ppm, or $1.0\ g/10^6\ g$. To isolate 1.0 g of ^{231}Pa you need 10^6 g of the ore.

(d) $^{231}_{91}Pa \rightarrow \,^{227}_{89}Ac + \,^4_2\alpha$